HANDBOOK: THE GUGGENHEIM MUSEUM COLLECTION 1900-1980

SELECTED BY THOMAS M. MESSER, DIRECTOR

Piet Mondrian, cat. no. 112, *Blue Chrysanthemum*. ca. early 1920s

HANDBOOK

The Guggenheim Museum Collection

1900-1980

BY VIVIAN ENDICOTT BARNETT

This volume is supported by grants from the
National Endowment for the Arts
in Washington, D.C., a Federal Agency

THE SOLOMON R. GUGGENHEIM MUSEUM, NEW YORK

THE SOLOMON R. GUGGENHEIM FOUNDATION

HONORARY TRUSTEES IN PERPETUITY

Solomon R. Guggenheim, Justin K. Thannhauser, Peggy Guggenheim

PRESIDENT | Peter O. Lawson-Johnston
VICE PRESIDENT | The Right Honorable Earl Castle Stewart

TRUSTEES | Anne L. Armstrong, Elaine Dannheisser, Michel David-Weill, Joseph W. Donner, Robin Chandler Duke, Robert M. Gardiner, John S. Hilson, Harold W. McGraw, Jr., Wendy L-J. McNeil, Thomas M. Messer, Seymour Slive, Michael F. Wettach, William T. Ylvisaker

ADVISORY BOARD | Barrie M. Damson, Susan Morse Hilles, Morton L. Janklow, Barbara Jonas, Denise Saul, Hannelore Schulhof, Stephen C. Swid

SECRETARY-TREASURER | Theodore G. Dunker
DIRECTOR | Thomas M. Messer

Library of Congress Cataloging in Publication Data

Barnett, Vivian Endicott.
  Handbook, the Guggenheim Museum collection, 1900-1980.

  Includes bibliographical references and index.
  1. Solomon R. Guggenheim Museum–Catalogs. 2. Art, Modern–20th century–Catalogs. 3. Art–New York (N.Y.)–Catalogs. I. Title.
N6487.N4S6386 1984   709'.04'007401471   84-5513
ISBN 0-89207-046-3

Published by The Solomon R. Guggenheim Foundation,

New York, 1984

© The Solomon R. Guggenheim Foundation, New York, 1984

CONTENTS

PREFACE

HANDBOOK: The Solomon R. Guggenheim Museum Collection 1900-1980 is the third catalogue in this institution's history to present a selective view of its entire collection. This new publication differs in various conspicuous ways from its immediate precursor published in 1970 and bears only titular resemblance to the first *Handbook* of 1959. The current version goes far beyond a mere revision of earlier texts even though it shares with these a common objective—the illumination of the collection as a whole through the description and illustration of outstanding examples in various media drawn from the Museum's chosen realm of modern art. Its appearance at this moment perpetuates the decennial rhythm that has prevailed in the periodic reevaluations of the Guggenheim's permanent holdings.

Unlike the Museum's Collection Catalogues, which convey about each work under consideration everything known and suggest unexplored directions of original inquiry, the *Handbook,* though it incorporates new research, primarily summarizes existing information. Concerned not only with isolated objects but also with their interrelationship, it tells less about each work and more about the collection as a whole. In numerical terms, the current volume is arbitrarily limited to 250 works by 141 artists as opposed to 252 works by 52 artists in the Collection volumes devoted to paintings from 1880 to 1945 and 75 works by 18 artists in the Thannhauser Collection catalogue.

To accentuate further the distinction between a primary orientation toward the separate object and the sequential implications of related works of art, the current *Handbook* has introduced a quasi-chronological organization to replace the arbitrary alphabetical ordering of past publications. We say "quasi-chronological" because a strictly chronological arrangement of individual works would destroy the unity of each artist's oeuvre, while a listing governed by the artists' birthdates would force us to disregard the more fundamental stylistic developments that underlie the creative production of each period. In adopting the sequential conventions of twentieth-century art history for our *Handbook,* we are, of course, accepting the imprecisions of this system in exchange for an outline that is suggestive rather than stylistically neutral. For the reader who wishes to consult the *Handbook* primarily as an abbreviated reference work for individual objects, we have provided a simple index.

* * *

The growth of art collections is obviously related to prevailing socio-economic conditions and it is well, therefore, to recall that the Guggenheim Museum has reached its present stage of development passing through three distinguishable phases—private, transitional and public—each recognizable by typical attributes.

The first, private phase, coinciding roughly with the founding administration of Hilla Rebay, was carried forward under the aegis of the Museum of Non-Objective Painting during the years 1937 to 1952. Collecting was then by far the most important activity of the Museum and followed patterns established from 1929 to 1937, when Hilla Rebay formed Solomon R. Guggenheim's private collection of abstract and non-objective art. Aided by ample means and an absence of bureaucratic impediments in an era of an authentic European avant-garde of which the American public was only partially aware, the results were superlative. It was a period marked by allegiance on the part of Miss Rebay to a dogmatic doctrine that saw in an art devoid of recognizable imagery the highest creative attainment. The collection today still derives its main strength from the purchases made in the era of the Museum of Non-Objective Painting, particularly since the dogma so strictly adhered to in theory was freely relaxed in practice, much to the Guggenheim's lasting benefit.

The second, transitional phase under James Johnson Sweeney's directorship (1952 to 1959) saw the abolition of the dogmatic premise of non-objectivism in favor of quality more or less unburdened by theoretical bias. The scope of the collection was extended beyond painting to sculpture and thus the present stylistically neutral appellation "The Solomon R. Guggenheim Museum" replaced "The Museum of Non-Objective Painting," as emphasis upon professional procedures, exhibitions and public education grew. The means available for the enrichment of the collection were still more than adequate, but Board deliberations and increased fiscal stringencies displaced the informal and wholly personal modus that prevailed during the time of Solomon R. Guggenheim and Hilla Rebay. The 1950s marked the ascendancy of the New American Painting and the Guggenheim's acquisition policies, in response to this development, began to swerve from their earlier, strongly European focus, to encompass the artistic achievements of both continents. The gap between advanced European art and American awareness thereof was closing, and Foundation purchases, for the first time modestly supplemented by gifts, engaged the interest of a functioning Board of Trustees in which Harry F. Guggenheim, the founder's nephew, took a strong and authoritative lead. During this transitional phase of the 1950s the Guggenheim became, at least embryonically, a general museum of modern art, whereas it had previously been, for all practical purposes, a private collection transferred to public quarters.

The full transformation of the Guggenheim into a major public modern art museum, however, had to await the completion of the Frank Lloyd Wright building on Fifth Avenue and the relocation of its operation from a small townhouse to a splendid museum palace. The present administration took charge shortly thereafter, at the outset of the 1960s, to develop a modified institutional premise during the two subsequent decades. In this evolution the new Frank Lloyd Wright edifice played no minor part. Its size, prominence and its initially provocative character attracted a public far exceeding that of earlier years. As a result, the need was felt to adjust internal procedures and public programs to the Museum's new potentialities, while preserving as far as possible the standards and accomplishments of the two preceding administrations. The Guggenheim's financial and administrative structures, which had served well enough during its initial phase and the years of transition, had to be altered to render them responsive to the needs of a museum operation that was no longer small. On the Board level, these changes were initiated by Harry F. Guggenheim and continued by Peter Lawson-Johnston, Solomon R. Guggenheim's grandson, acting first as Vice-President and eventually succeeding to the Foundation's Presidency. He soon began reconstituting the Board, and he established clear and workable relationships between the Museum's art and business functions, thereby setting the director free to build the curatorial and technical staffs upon which the institution's operational responsibilities rest today. The enlargement of the Guggenheim Museum's scope and the resulting concern with major exhibitions through which a sizeable public is addressed inevitably changed the character of the institution and diffused its former concentration upon the purchase of works of art. Funds, time and effort, formerly lavished solely upon the collection, were needed to satisfy the demands made on the Museum as it became one of the foremost exhibition centers in the world. Only when, in the 1970s, some of the newly inspired fervor had spent itself, did it become possible to focus again upon the Guggenheim Museum collection as the institution's principal responsibility and most important asset. It was then that the ambitious program of documentation of the collection now in progress was initiated.

But times had changed. Far-reaching and complex transformations deeply rooted in the altered character of the avant-garde made collecting a much different proposition than in the days of the Museum of Non-Objective Painting. More tangibly, the ability to collect was affected adversely by steep increases in the art market and by erosion of the economic bases of American cultural institutions, The Solomon R. Guggenheim Foundation among them. While a large endowment originally supported a small operation, the situation had gradually reversed: diminished funds were no longer adequate for major programs. Since acquisition funds were always drawn from operational surpluses, the decrease and eventual disappearance of these surpluses ultimately resulted in the total elimination of purchase monies. The Guggenheim thus was obliged first to collect with radically decreased funds and then, during the last decade, without any ready means whatsoever. Therefore, acquisition by gift has assumed increasing importance in the Museum's present financially handicapped phase of development. In addition to donations of single works, the Guggenheim collection has benefited in the last decade from three massive transfers: (1) Part of Hilla Rebay's private holdings were returned to the Museum by the executors of the Hilla Rebay Estate after the first Director's death (2) The Justin K. Thannhauser Collection, on loan here since 1965, was legally transferred in 1978 to The Solomon R. Guggenheim Foundation after Justin Thannhauser's death (3) The Peggy Guggenheim Collection, title to which was transferred to The Solomon R. Guggenheim Foundation before the donor's death, will remain in Venice and will be administered by the same Foundation. The last of these three major acquisitions is the subject of research presently in progress and therefore not further considered in this publication. The others contribute to the panorama of the Guggenheim collection for the first time in this *Handbook*. Although only a few key examples from these holdings are included, they nevertheless greatly strengthen the substance of the publication: the Thannhauser Collection because it provides a nineteenth-century preamble to our own collection of twentieth-century art while adding works by modern masters already in our possession; the Hilla

Rebay Collection because it reinforces areas of concentration in the Guggenheim's holdings, primarily in the abstract idiom of the first half of the twentieth century.

If, in addition to these donations of collections, we cite outstanding individual gifts of the works of such artists as Kupka, Gabo, Torres-García, Calder, Lindner, Gorky, Rothko, Nevelson, Martin and Warhol, to mention only the most conspicuous, we demonstrate thereby that the shift from emphasis on purchases by the Foundation to a growing reliance upon generous contributions is not without redeeming aspects. It must be conceded, nonetheless, that a radical diminution of acquisition funds cannot but exert a negative effect upon purposeful and methodical collecting, and that the restitution of an at least modest endowment, is therefore now among our highest priorities. A partial retention of buying initiative was fortunately secured through successive grants made to the Guggenheim by the National Endowment for the Arts under the Federal Agency's Museum Purchase Program. With matching private funds to bolster this government subsidy, key works by Frankenthaler, Diebenkorn, Tworkov, Krasner, Rickey and Andre among others, none formerly represented in the collection, were added.

While some of the gifts that have enriched our holdings in recent years were selected by the Museum and subsequently underwritten by generous friends, others were objects in private hands magnanimously donated to us to benefit the collection and, thereby, the public domain. Still other works acquired relatively recently were bought with what budgetary surpluses remained from more affluent times or with proceeds realized from sales from the Museum's collection. Various safeguards have been established to guard against abuses of this latter, inherently risky procedure. For example, none of the objects deemed worthy of inclusion in the *Handbook* of ten years ago has been eliminated from the collection even though they may not appear in the present publication. On the other hand, this catalogue reflects acquisitions made during the last decade of key works by artists of the greatest importance to the collection of a museum of modern art like our own.

* * *

Any selection from a museum's permanent collection is interpretative, and the choice for this new version of the *Handbook* is no exception. A fuller view of the collection would certainly have been desirable but it would have required the inclusion of more examples than can be compressed into a single portable volume meant to be carried into the galleries and consulted while the works themselves are viewed. In two areas the numerical limitations imposed by circumstances are cause for particular regret. In the first instance, we could not indicate the collection's rich concentrations in the era of an already historic modernism: of over one hundred Kandinskys and Klees and scores of Picassos, Légers and Gleizes, only a fraction could be presented; of many Marcs, Chagalls, Brancusis, Modiglianis, Mirós and Dubuffets, only a small number could be included. Although regrettable, these deletions were necessary if a certain balance between the Guggenheim's earlier and its contemporary holdings was to be preserved. Even so, sweeping cuts have been visited upon the highly valued contributions of younger artists, which the Guggenheim has consistently acquired and which are so much more fully represented in the collection than in this *Handbook*.

Such imbalances notwithstanding, *Handbook: The Solomon R. Guggenheim Museum Collection, 1900-1980* is intended, and we hope will be received, as a reference volume for works of particular interest as well as a projection of the Guggenheim Museum collection at this stage of our institutional development.

THOMAS M. MESSER, *Director*
The Solomon R. Guggenheim Foundation

9

ACKNOWLEDGEMENTS

The production of this *Handbook* was an encompassing task that engaged virtually every department of the Museum. But before giving credit to those directly involved in its preparation, it would seem appropriate to establish the contributions made by various individuals in the course of the process of collecting itself. The Guggenheim Museum's successive Directors who, throughout the institution's history, have assumed primary responsibility for the formation of the collection, were aided by advisors, artist friends, trustees and staffs, while their tasks were furthered by expertise, opinion and counsel from a variety of sources. Recent research based on correspondence of Hilla Rebay, for example, indicates the crucial role played by some of her painter friends, and analogous situations have certainly prevailed in subsequent administrations. The process eventually was formalized and the participation of trustees and staffs became increasingly frequent. Among trustees who served on the Guggenheim's Art and Museum Committee during various periods of my Directorship, H. Harvard Arnason, Carl Zigrosser and Daniel Catton Rich gave me much encouragement and support by contributing their own formidable knowledge in the Museum's interest. Exhibition curators affected eventual acquisition by assembling the shows from which purchases were made, and much that was bought, particularly in the contemporary field, reflects the recommendations and the initiative of members of past and present curatorial staffs. After 1961 Daniel

Robbins, Maurice Tuchman, Lawrence Alloway and Edward F. Fry expressed their opinions about possible acquisitions, while Dr. Louise A. Svendsen, Diane Waldman, Margit Rowell and Linda Shearer, among those presently active, have not infrequently located works that eventually found their way into the Guggenheim's permanent collection. In view of our dependence upon gifts to the collection, their efforts in persuading donors to direct their generosity toward the Guggenheim Museum should also be gratefully recorded here.

The donor's role is discussed in the preface to this publication and major benefactors have already been cited in that text. In addition, the following donors have enhanced the collection with works of outstanding importance, in some instances in great numbers: Katherine S. Dreier, Mary Reynolds through her brother Frank B. Hubachek, Mr. and Mrs. Werner Dannheisser, Mr. and Mrs. William C. Edwards, Jr., Mr. and Mrs. Andrew P. Fuller. The last three named have been elected to life membership in the Museum under the provisions established by the Board of The Solomon R. Guggenheim Foundation. The Museum's first benefactor, Solomon R. Guggenheim, whose original gifts remain the collection's richest reservoir, as well as Justin K. Thannhauser and Peggy Guggenheim, whose collections were subsequently transferred to the Guggenheim Foundation, were acknowledged with honorary trusteeships in perpetuity.

To return now to the *Handbook* itself, the Museum's foremost expression of gratitude is due to Vivian Barnett, the Guggenheim's Curator, who has spared no effort in documenting the 250 works reproduced here and whose advice on the selection and the organization of paintings, sculptures and works on paper has greatly influenced my own decisions. In writing her entries she depended upon many sources: among the most important of these are the immediate precursor of the present publication, the *Handbook* to works of 1900 to 1970, completed ten years ago, primarily through the efforts of Margit Rowell, as well as the two Collection Catalogues devoted to paintings from 1880 to 1945 and the Justin K. Thannhauser Collection, respectively authored by Angelica Zander Rudenstine and by Vivian Barnett herself. The major editorial task for the current volume was accomplished with the usual thoroughness and conscientiousness by Carol Fuerstein, the Guggenheim Museum's Editor.

Finally, it is a pleasure to acknowledge the generous financial support of the National Endowment for the Arts. The Federal Agency's aid to this and other projects has been of very great importance in this Museum's constant efforts to maintain high professional standards.

T.M.M.

INTRODUCTION

The chronological limits of *Handbook: The Guggenheim Museum Collection 1900-1980* restrict the selection to the twentieth century. From the first catalogue entries it is apparent that Cézanne, Rousseau and Munch belonged to the nineteenth century, although their careers continued into the twentieth and their works acted as catalysts to younger artists. Thus, the four Cézannes in the Museum's Thannhauser Collection, Rousseau's *Artillerymen* from about 1893-95 and Munch's *Sketch of the Model Posing* of 1893 have not been included in this book. It is our intention, however, to discuss selected late nineteenth-century works of art in this Introduction and to relate them to what follows in specific catalogue entries.

The scope of the Guggenheim Museum's collection extends as far back as the late 1860s, to Camille Pissarro's *The Hermitage at Pontoise* (fig. 1). In this large-scale canvas dating from about 1867 and thus preceding his Impressionist paintings, Pissarro represents an identifiable view in Pontoise. He has structured the composition in a traditional manner: an open foreground space functions as a repoussoir element, a winding road leads back to the houses in the middle distance and, finally, a hillside demarcates the background. The artist has positioned nine figures within the landscape to further define an orderly recession into the distance. Not only the conventional device of a road and the utilization of genre figures but, above all, the considerable dimensions—approximately five by six and a half feet—of this picture place it within the tradition of Salon painting. Although it is not possible to determine that *The Hermitage at Pontoise* was exhibited at the Salon of 1868, it certainly looks as if it were painted with that intention. Pissarro maintains clear distinctions between foreground and background, architectural and landscape elements, areas of light and shadow. He achieves a consistent pictorial space: clarity and solidity pervade his landscape.

12

fig. 1
Pissarro, *The Hermitage at Pontoise,* ca. 1867, Gift, Justin
K. Thannhauser, 1978

Paul Cézanne's *Still Life: Flask, Glass and Jug* of about 1877 (fig. 2) displays a traditional arrangement of objects. The earthenware jug, the flask and a glass as well as four apples and a knife are placed on a white tablecloth and are seen against a flat, minimally decorated background wall. The diagonal positioning of the knife is a device employed in the eighteenth century by Chardin and perpetuated by Manet in the nineteenth. Reinforced by the parallel drapery folds in the tablecloth, the knife projects beyond the plane of the tabletop: thus, it visually links the picture space with the viewer's space. The horizontal alignment of still-life objects is contained within a well-defined depth. Cézanne has emphasized the intervals between objects with foreground drapery and three lozenge shapes on the background wall. He frequently included subtly patterned backgrounds which function actively in his compositions.

The interrelationships within this early still life are readily intelligible; it has none of the spatial dislocations and ambiguities encountered in Cézanne's late paintings. Abrupt shifts in perspective, multiple vantage points, tipped planes, extensions and elisions commonly occur in his subsequent work. For example, in *Still Life: Plate of Peaches* of 1879-80 in the Thannhauser Collection, the position of the table legs is unclear and the left side of the white tablecloth possesses strangely buoyant, non-naturalistic drapery folds. And in *Man*

with Crossed Arms (cat. no. 1) the background moulding is discontinuous and the sitter's left hand seems disconnected from the sleeve of his jacket.

In *Still Life: Flask, Glass and Jug* the painted surface is quite heavily worked. The glass was once taller but Cézanne lowered the rim by approximately one and one-half inches to conform to the overall design. There is also evidence of reworking in the area of the flask and near the tipped-up mouth of the jug. The dark contour line of the jug accentuates its solidity as a shape. Likewise, the two apples in the center bear traces of black outlines and their rounded forms are modeled with red and green accents of color.

In the landscape of *Bibémus* (fig. 3), which dates from the mid-1890s, Cézanne has unified the picture surface with short, narrow, quite parallel brushstrokes. He achieved an overall consistency of surface by representing sky, rocks and foliage with similar touches of paint. The pigment has been thinly and uniformly applied and the canvas has been left bare in places. Definition of objects and passages between elements are provided by slight color gradations. Adjacent areas of foliage, earth and rock are rendered by patches of color. Within the green areas, for example, Cézanne has modulated the colored planes, thereby conveying contour, volume, light and shadow. In this landscape the artist chose to represent a light-filled, gentle aspect of Bibémus rather than the massive rocks and angular quarry excavations he depicted in other canvases. The warm ocher of the terrain is particularly characteristic of the Bibémus area near Aix-en-Provence in the south of France, where Cézanne worked from about 1895 until the early years of this century.

In *Mountains at Saint-Rémy* (fig. 4) Vincent van Gogh depicts another part of Provence. The Alpilles, a low, rugged mountain range, were visible from the Hospital of Saint-Paul-de-Mausole in Saint-Rémy where van Gogh was a patient in 1889. While Cézanne's line was implicit in his colored brushstrokes, van Gogh has concentrated on explicitly curving lines. His emphasis on the undulating and contorted line of the mountain peak is reinforced by repeated patterns of brushstrokes which delineate its slopes. The upper portion of this canvas displays heavily brushed blue pigment which functions as a visual equivalent for the sky and echoes the curvilinear shapes in the lower half. Van Gogh's powerful, thick strokes not only give contour and form but also provide directional movement and expressive energy. The intensity of van Gogh's painting derives primarily from the forms with their tumultuous, convoluted contours rather than from the colors. In this and other Saint-Rémy landscapes his colors (while still bold) have become noticeably more restrained than in previous

fig. 2
Cézanne, *Still Life: Flask, Glass and Jug*, ca. 1877, Gift, Justin K. Thannhauser, 1978

fig. 3
Cézanne, *Bibémus*, ca. 1894-95, Gift, Justin K. Thannhauser,
1978

fig. 4
Van Gogh, *Mountains at Saint-Rémy*, July 1889, Gift, Justin
K. Thannhauser, 1978

fig. 5
Gauguin, *In the Vanilla Grove, Man and Horse*, 1891, Gift,
Justin K. Thannhauser, 1978

fig. 6
Seurat, *Farm Women at Work*, ca. 1882, Gift, Solomon R.
Guggenheim, 1941

years. While Cézanne shifted from one area to another through gradual modulation of color, van Gogh has juxtaposed contrasting hues of blue, green and tan.

In addition to oils by van Gogh, the Thannhauser Collection includes several drawings he made around August 1, 1888, after recently completed paintings. Van Gogh sent these drawings with a letter to his friend, the Australian painter John Peter Russell. Thus, van Gogh quickly sketched *Boats at Saintes-Maries* in order to give Russell an idea of the oil of the same subject (now in the Pushkin Museum, Moscow). He used ink applied with reed pens of varying widths and a few pencil lines to represent the expanse of sea and boats: patterns of dots, commas, short lines, hatching and wavy strokes predominate. Pen lines correspond remarkably to the brushstrokes in the oil.

From van Gogh's letters to various friends and relatives, the circumstances surrounding the creation of specific pictures can be reconstructed. For example, around July 9, 1889, van Gogh mentioned *Mountains at Saint-Rémy* in a letter to his brother Theo: "The last canvas I have done is a view of mountains with a dark hut at the bottom among some olive trees." A month later he referred to our painting and associated it with a passage in a book he was reading, Edouard Rod's *Le Sens de la vie,* describing "a desolate country of somber mountains, among which are some dark goatherds' huts where sunflowers are blooming." Thus, the picture acquired points of reference far beyond the landscape the artist could see from the hospital at Saint-Rémy. Explicit copies of and borrowings from works by other artists, allusions to literary sources and the use of symbolic forms and colors multiply the levels of meaning in van Gogh's paintings. In these respects he was by no means unique in the late nineteenth century. Paul Gauguin also drew inspiration for his art from many sources and endowed his work with interpretive complexity.

Van Gogh and Gauguin were well acquainted with each other by late 1887 in Paris. From October to December 1888 Gauguin joined van Gogh in Arles. Earlier, in the mid-1870s, Gauguin had met Pissarro; in 1881 he had worked with Cézanne and Pissarro at Pontoise and during the winter of 1885-86 he was friendly with Seurat. From February 1888 until his death in July 1890, van Gogh lived in the south of France. From the late 1880s until his death in May 1903, Gauguin made many trips to Brittany and traveled to Martinique, the south of France, Tahiti and the Marquesas Islands. Two of Gauguin's landscapes painted during his first trip to Tahiti in 1891 entered the Museum collection through Justin K. Thannhauser's Bequest. *In the Vanilla Grove, Man and Horse* (fig. 5) contrasts two large foreground figures with a stylized landscape. Man and horse are presented in close proximity; their boldly outlined forms are derived from a similar pair from the West Frieze of the Parthenon. Gauguin turned to Greek, Egyptian, Indian, Javanese and primitive art for images and he is known to have used photographs for specific motifs. In this painting both the abstract color areas in the foreground and the tapestry-like foliage in the background compress space. Flat, colored shapes can be perceived as surface patterns. Like van Gogh, Gauguin sought bright light which tends to flatten volumes into areas of intense color. Both Gauguin and van Gogh developed their mature, individual styles by 1887-88.

Even earlier in the 1880s Georges Pierre Seurat (who was younger than both Gauguin and van Gogh) investigated the color theories of Charles Blanc, Michel-Eugène Chevreul and Ogden N. Rood; he explored the ways their theories could be incorporated into his pictures by breaking down different hues and systematically applying small dabs of paint to his canvases. Four of Seurat's early oils, ranging in date from 1882 to 1884, are in the Guggenheim Museum collection. In *Farm Women at Work* (fig. 6), the handling of color contrasts and divided color reveals Seurat's understanding of Rood's theories. The artist is known to have read the latter's *Modern Chromatics* in French translation in 1881. Within the green field orange and yellow brushstrokes indicating sunlight are juxtaposed with their opposites, blue and purple. Touches of gray, violet and white are added in certain places in order to intensify the color contrasts. Seurat's idiomatic treatment of foliage and shadows and his emphasis on horizontals can also be understood in terms of a dominant surface pattern of colored brushstrokes. The motif of two women bending over at work in the fields derives from Jean François Millet's *The Gleaners,* which he could have known through etchings. In the early 1880s Millet's influence is prevalent in the work of both Seurat and van Gogh.

Seurat's painting of a *Seated Woman,* which can be dated 1883, presents the figure in a strongly silhouetted profile view against a field. Seurat has omitted any indication of a horizon line or sky and has depicted the field with "broomswept" brushstrokes. The composition as well as the palette and brushwork demonstrate Camille Pissarro's influence on Seurat. In 1885 he met the elder painter and Seurat's innovative use of finely divided brushwork was subsequently adopted by Pissarro: a significant case of reciprocal influences. Pissarro, the mentor of Cézanne, Gauguin and Seurat, outlived the latter who died at the age of thirty-one. Within the span of a single decade Seurat's style evolved from the Barbizon art of Millet to Art Nouveau. Neither van Gogh nor Seurat lived into the 1890s. However, their work exerted a profound influence not only on the late nineteenth century but on the early twentieth century as well.

There is no definite break to mark the transition from the 1890s to the next century. During the last decade of the nineteenth century a multiplicity of styles co-existed. The Impressionist painters Degas, Monet and Renoir continued to produce work of importance. Edgar Degas' late work is included in the Thannhauser Collection: there are three sculptures and a pastel (fig. 7). *Dancers in Green and Yellow* is one of several very similar representations of a group of four dancers waiting in the wings which Degas executed around 1903. It was his practice to work in series, slightly modifying the same composition, repeating and refining the poses and changing the color schemes. Degas' pastels first appeared in the mid-1870s and over the decades his compositions in this medium became bolder and his technique increasingly experimental. In *Dancers in Green and Yellow,* the artist has used pastel not so much to draw as to paint, applying layer upon layer of brilliant color. He has adjusted the proportions by adding strips of paper at the top and bottom. As his eyesight deteriorated, Degas concentrated increasingly on modeling figures of dancers and bathers between 1896 and 1911. His sculptural production had originated in the seventies: the horses belong to that decade and the dancers predominate in the eighties and nineties. However, the pieces were cast in bronze only after the artist's death. Degas frequently translated the figures in his pastels and drawings into three-dimensional counterparts. The sculpture *Seated Woman Wiping Her Left Side,* which can be dated between 1896 and 1911, returns to the pose in a pastel from about 1886. The rather summary but expressive treatment of the bronze surface conveys a sense of its original modeling in wax.

fig. 7
Degas, *Dancers in Green and Yellow,* ca. 1903, Gift, Justin K. Thannhauser, 1978

While Degas' sculpture must be seen in relation to his paintings and drawings, Auguste Rodin was above all a sculptor. An almost exact contemporary of Degas, Rodin produced his mature work from the late 1870s into the second decade of the twentieth century. The Guggenheim's bronze, *Heroic Bust of Victor Hugo* of 1897, is over life-size and projects an imposing presence. The vigorous surface treatment results in dramatic contrasts of light and shadow. Rodin's influence as a sculptor extended well into this century: Matisse, Maillol and Brancusi all came into contact with him. In fact, Matisse's model for his first major bronze, *Le Serf* of 1900-3, and the many preliminary drawings (for example cat. no. 9) which preceded the final sculpture, was an Italian named Bevilaqua who had posed also for Rodin's *Walking Man* and *Saint John the Baptist.*

Both Rodin and Maillol were committed to the human figure as the basis for their sculpture and, although they carved in marble, both worked primarily with plaster which was then cast in bronze. Maillol's figures exemplify a traditional, classical aesthetic (see cat. no. 6). His earliest sculpture dates from the first decade of the twentieth century. However, his paintings and tapestries of the previous decade clearly reflect the stylistic influence of Gauguin and the *Nabis.*

Gauguin has already been discussed in connection with the Post-Impressionists. However, he played a crucial role in the evolution of the *Nabi* group and the development of the Symbolist movement. During the summer of 1888 Paul Sérusier executed the *Landscape of the Bois d'Amour* or *Le Talisman* (Private collection, France) under Gauguin's guidance at Pont-Aven. Upon his return to Paris that autumn, Sérusier showed this small panel to his friends Edouard Vuillard, Pierre Bonnard, Maurice Denis and Félix Vallotton at the Académie Julian. The primacy of the flat surface and the arrangement of colored areas upon it had an enormous effect upon their work. By 1891 these artists, who called themselves *Nabis,* exhibited as a group (see cat. nos. 4-6).

Both Gauguin and the *Nabis* were part of the larger Symbolist movement whose influence was pervasive in literature as well as the visual arts from the 1880s into the first decade of the following century. In 1888, through Emil Bernard, Gauguin became familiar with Symbolist ideas and painted his symbolic picture, *The Vision after the Sermon: Jacob Wrestling with the Angel* (Collection National Gallery of Scotland, Edinburgh). Through Bernard and G.-Albert Aurier, Gauguin came into contact with the Symbolist poets Stéphane Mallarmé, Paul Verlaine, Paul Fort, the group associated with the *Mercure de France* as well as Eugène Carrière, Rodin and other artists who frequented the Café Voltaire in Paris. Among the Symbolist artists in France, Carrière, Odilon Redon, Gustave Moreau and Pierre Puvis de Chavannes were most important. The latter's influence in particular is evident in the work of Gauguin, Seurat and Picasso. Elsewhere in Europe Symbolist tendencies appeared in the work of Ferdinand Hodler in Switzerland, Gustav Klimt in Austria, Jan Toorop in The Netherlands and Edvard Munch in Norway.

In addition to a late pastel by Munch (cat. no. 7), there is an earlier work of 1893 entitled *Sketch of the Model Posing* in the Museum collection (fig. 8). The woman's

fig. 8
Munch, *Sketch of the Model Posing,* 1893

fig. 9
Toulouse-Lautrec, *Au Salon,* 1893, Gift, Justin K. Thannhauser, 1978

fig. 10
Rousseau, *Artillerymen,* ca. 1893-95, Gift, Solomon R.
Guggenheim, 1938

face is averted, her head tipped back at a distinctive angle, the curves of her body are echoed and enclosed by linear patterns. This pastel is an evocative figure study which cannot be specifically related to a final work. Munch, who was fascinated with the stages of life, portrayed women as symbolic images: the youthful Virgin, Madonna, Vampire and an old, somber figure. The pictorial organization, the emphatic repetition of lines and stylized contours in our early work suggest the swirling, expressive shapes of Art Nouveau.

In the 1890s Art Nouveau was an international style which derived from the arts and crafts movement and encompassed decorative arts, architecture, sculpture, painting and the graphic arts. Art Nouveau was anticipated in the work of van Gogh, Gauguin and Seurat. In Munich, where it emerged as *Jugendstil*, it profoundly influenced Kandinsky's development and in Barcelona the style was manifest in Picasso's early work (cat. no. 13). Toulouse-Lautrec's work was an integral part of Art Nouveau: most apparent in the bold, decorative stylization of his posters and the synthesis of line and color in his lithographs. Lautrec was friends with van Gogh and Bernard and an admirer of Degas. He favored the Parisian world of the theater, dance hall, brothel, café and circus. There is an 1893 pastel, *Au Salon*, by Toulouse-Lautrec in the Thannhauser Collection (fig. 9). Like his other studies of brothels, *Au Salon* reveals the artist's acute observation of detail and his choice of scenes from the daily routine for subject matter. Through the attitudes of the three women and the discordant, rather oppressive colors, Lautrec projects an atmosphere heavy with boredom. The influence of his own work can readily be seen in Picasso's *Le Moulin de la Galette* (cat. no. 14), Picabia's *Portrait of Mistinguett* (cat. no. 33) and Kirchner's *Woman with Black Hat* (cat. no. 49).

The pastels by Toulouse-Lautrec and Munch are contemporary with Rousseau's *Artillerymen* of about 1893-95 (fig. 10) and Cézanne's *Bibémus* and only slightly later than Gauguin's Tahitian landscape. The juxtaposition of such dissimilar but coeval works underscores the diversity of artistic activity at the end of the nineteenth century. *Artillerymen* presents a group portrait within a landscape. Rousseau has schematically arranged fourteen soldiers around a cannon and has meticulously described the soft, delicate foliage. The rather formal placement of the figures has led to the assumption that the artist worked from a photograph. In his Paris pictures as well as his jungle scenes, Rousseau created a world of fantasy. The originality of Rousseau's work set him apart from the main artistic currents around the turn of the century. Like Cézanne, Rousseau belonged to an older generation; each arrived at a unique style of painting and each was a great source of inspiration to younger generations.

In the biographies of these artists, their friends are mentioned, their early and important exhibitions enumerated and their publications or theatrical productions listed. In the texts, whenever possible, connections are drawn between artists and references are made to closely related works of art. The brief, factual biographies are intended to situate the artists within their historical contexts.

Most of the biographies were written by Lucy Flint, Judith Tannenbaum, Carol Fuerstein, Susan Hirschfeld and Brian Wallis. I appreciate their assistance as well as the contributions made by the individuals already mentioned in the Acknowledgements. I would also like to thank Louise Averill Svendsen, Diane Waldman, Margit Rowell, Orrin Riley, Dana Cranmer, Saul Fuerstein, Robert E. Mates, Mary Donlon, Mary Joan Hall and Ward Jackson. Most of all, I am grateful to Thomas M. Messer who selected the works of art included in this *Handbook,* shared his insights and knowledge of the Museum collection and always gave me advice and encouragement.

VIVIAN ENDICOTT BARNETT, *Curator*
The Solomon R. Guggenheim Museum

EXPLANATORY NOTES

The *Handbook* has been organized according to essentially stylistic, art-historical designations. The arrangement is not strictly chronological, since all works by one artist have been kept together. Artists of the same generation and sometimes of the same nationality have been grouped together. The final sequence also takes into consideration the specific examples in the Guggenheim Museum's collection. A table of contents and an index are provided.

HEADINGS:

The heading provides the catalogue number, the title and the date. Whenever applicable, the title in its original language follows in parentheses. The year of acquisition and foundation number of each work are indicated on the next line.

MEASUREMENTS:

Dimensions are given in inches followed by centimeters. Height precedes width followed by depth, when relevant.

PROVENANCES:

The names of former owners are listed with their inclusive dates, when possible. The fact that the work of art was acquired directly from the artist is indicated by the phrase "from the artist." Gifts to the Guggenheim Museum are always cited with the proper credit line.

EXHIBITIONS AND REFERENCES:

Exhibitions and references are selective and limited to a maximum of twenty citations. If the exhibition was accompanied by a catalogue, it is noted in the exhibitions list and is not repeated as a reference. Certain major exhibitions at The Solomon R. Guggenheim Museum have been consistently included, but no attempt has been made to indicate every time a work has been on view at the Museum. An exhibition listing refers only to the places and dates a specific work of art was shown: if the work was removed before the conclusion of the exhibition or did not travel, the complete dates and institutions are not given. Nor is additional information, such as the organizer of the exhibition, usually provided.

ABBREVIATIONS:

Barnett, *Thannhauser Catalogue*, 1978
> V. E. Barnett, *The Guggenheim Museum: Justin K. Thannhauser Collection*, New York, 1978

Handbook, 1959
> *A Handbook to The Solomon R. Guggenheim Museum Collection*, New York, 1959

Handbook, 1970
> *Selections from The Solomon R. Guggenheim Museum Collection: 1900-1970*, ed. M. Rowell, New York, 1970

Rudenstine, *Collection Catalogue*, 1976
> A. Z. Rudenstine, *The Guggenheim Museum Collection: Paintings 1880-1945*, New York, 1976

I

Paul Cézanne 1839-1906

Paul Cézanne was born on January 19, 1839, in Aix-en-Provence. In 1854 he enrolled in the free drawing academy there, which he attended intermittently for several years. In 1858 he graduated from the Collège Bourbon, where he had become an intimate friend of his fellow-student Emile Zola. Cézanne entered the law school of the University of Aix in 1859 to placate his father, but abandoned his studies to join Zola in Paris in 1861. For the next twenty years Cézanne divided his time between the Midi and Paris. In the capital he briefly attended the Atelier Suisse with Pissarro, who later became an important influence on his art. In 1862 Cézanne began long friendships with Monet and Renoir. His paintings were included in the 1863 Salon des Refusés, which displayed works not accepted by the jury of the official Paris Salon. The Salon itself rejected Cézanne's submissions each year from 1864 to 1869.

In 1870, following the declaration of the Franco-Prussian War, Cézanne left Paris for Aix and then nearby L'Estaque, where he continued to paint. He made the first of several visits to Pontoise in 1872; there he worked alongside Pissarro. He participated in the first Impressionist exhibition of 1874. From 1876 to 1879 his works were again consistently rejected at the Salon. He showed again with the Impressionists in 1877 in their third exhibition. At this time Georges Rivière was one of the few critics to support Cézanne's art. In 1882 the Salon accepted his work for the first and only time. From 1883 Cézanne resided in the south of France, although he returned to Paris occasionally.

In 1890 Cézanne exhibited with the group *Les XX* in Brussels and spent five months in Switzerland. He traveled to Giverny in 1894 to visit Monet, who introduced him to Rodin and the critic Gustave Geffroy. Cézanne's first one-man show was held at Ambroise Vollard's gallery in Paris in 1895. From this time he received increasing recognition. In 1899 he participated in the Salon des Indépendants in Paris for the first time. The following year he took part in the Centennial Exhibition in Paris. In 1903 the Berlin and Vienna Secessions included Cézanne's work, and in 1904 he exhibited at the Paris Salon d'Automne. That same year he was given a solo exhibition at the Galerie Cassirer in Berlin. Cézanne died on October 22, 1906, in Aix-en-Provence.

1 **Man with Crossed Arms.** ca. 1899
(Homme aux bras croisés)

54.1387

Oil on canvas, 36¼ x 28⅝ in. (92 x 72.7 cm.)

Not signed or dated.

PROVENANCE:

Martha Reuther, Heidelberg, ca. 1906-52
Durand-Matthiesen Gallery, Geneva, 1952
M. Knoedler and Co., Inc., New York, 1953-54

A late portrait like *Man with Crossed Arms* follows
Cézanne's paintings of *Cardplayers* and *Smokers* from
earlier in the 1890s in his selection of a model whose
anonymity is preserved. Thus, the artist concentrates
upon the massive shape of the sitter as it dominates the
canvas, the acuteness and restlessness of his upward
gaze, the simplification of volumes into planes and the
realization of the whole through subdued, close-valued
brushstrokes. When the Guggenheim's painting is
compared with another version of *Man with Crossed
Arms* (Collection Mrs. Carleton Mitchell, Annapolis,
Maryland), subtle details unique to our canvas, such as
the way Cézanne presents the head at an angle, slants
the shoulders, broadens the span of the crossed arms,
emphasizes the discontinuity of the moulding behind
the sitter and includes the back of a stretcher and a
palette flat upon the picture plane at the lower left, are
immediately apparent. Cézanne endows the figure with
a presence which is not only physical but psychological
and spiritual.

EXHIBITIONS:

Paris, Grand Palais, *Salon d'Automne: Salle Paul Cézanne,*
Oct. 15-Nov. 15, 1904, no. 10

The Hague, Gemeentemuseum, *Paul Cézanne,* June-July
1956, no. 43, repr.

London, Tate Gallery, *An exhibition of paintings from The
Solomon R. Guggenheim Museum, New York,* Apr. 16-
May 26, 1957, no. 6, repr., traveled to The Hague, Gemeente-
museum, June 25-Sept. 1; Helsinki, Ateneumin Taidekokoel-
mat, Sept. 27-Oct. 20; Rome, Galleria Nazionale d'Arte
Moderna, Dec. 5, 1957-Jan. 8, 1958; Cologne, Wallraf-
Richartz-Museum, Jan. 26-Mar. 30; Paris, Musée des Arts
Décoratifs, Apr. 23-June 1

New York, The Solomon R. Guggenheim Museum,
Inaugural Selection, Oct. 21, 1959-June 19, 1960

New York, The Solomon R. Guggenheim Museum, *Cézanne
and Structure in Modern Painting,* June 6-Oct. 13, 1963,
color repr.

New York, The Museum of Modern Art, *Cézanne: The
Late Work,* Oct. 7, 1977-Jan. 3, 1978, no. 6, pl. 13

New York, The Solomon R. Guggenheim Museum, *Forty
Modern Masters: An Anniversary Show,* Jan. 5-Feb. 5,
1978, no. 16, repr.

REFERENCES:

A. Vollard, *Cézanne,* Paris, 1914, opp. p. 136, repr.

E. Bernard, "La Technique de Paul Cézanne," *L'Amour de
l'Art,* Iᵉ année, Dec. 1920, p. 271, repr.

L. Venturi, *Cézanne: son art, son oeuvre,* Paris, 1936,
vol. I, p. 213, no. 689, vol. II, pl. 224

K. Badt, *The Art of Cézanne,* Berkeley, 1965, p. 122

W. Andersen, *Cézanne's Portrait Drawings,* Cambridge,
Mass., 1970, pp. 37, 43, fn. 2

Handbook, 1970, pp. 64-65, color repr.

Rudenstine, *Collection Catalogue,* 1976, no. 24, color repr.

T. Reff, "Painting and Theory in the Final Decade,"
Cézanne: The Late Work, exh. cat., New York, 1977, p. 21

Henri Rousseau 1844-1910

Born on May 21, 1844, in Laval, France, Henri Julien Félix Rousseau attended the lycée there until 1860. While working for a lawyer in 1863, Rousseau was charged with petty larceny and joined the army to avoid scandal. He never saw combat and did not travel outside of France, but his colleagues' adventures in Mexico inspired him to create legends of his own foreign journeys. Upon his father's death in 1868, Rousseau left the army. The following year he entered the Paris municipal toll-collecting service as a second-class clerk; he was never promoted although he has traditionally been called "Le Douanier" (customs official). In 1884 Rousseau obtained a permit to sketch in the national museums. He sent two paintings to the Salon des Champs-Elysées in 1885 and from 1886 until his death he exhibited annually at the Salon des Indépendants.

By 1893 Rousseau retired from the Paris toll service on a small pension and began to paint full-time. The same year the artist met the writer Alfred Jarry, who encouraged him and introduced him into literary circles. In 1899 he wrote a five-act play entitled *La Vengeance d'une Orpheline Russe (A Russian Orphan's Revenge)*. A waltz he composed, "Clémence," was published in 1904. Rousseau became friendly with Robert Delaunay by 1906. 1908 saw the beginning of the musical and family evenings Rousseau held in his studio in the rue Perrel. Late that year Picasso arranged a banquet in honor of Rousseau which Marie Laurencin, Guillaume Apollinaire, Max Jacob and others attended.

By 1909 Rousseau's paintings were acquired by the dealers Ambroise Vollard and Joseph Brummer. His first one-man show was arranged in 1909 by Wilhelm Uhde and took place in a furniture shop in the rue Notre-Dame-des-Champs. Rousseau died on September 2, 1910, in Paris. The same year an exhibition of his work in the collection of Max Weber took place at Alfred Stieglitz' gallery "291" in New York. He was given a retrospective at the Salon des Indépendants in 1911.

2 The Football Players. 1908
(Les Joueurs de football)

60.1583

Oil on canvas, 39½ x 31⅝ in. (100.5 x 80.3 cm.)

Signed and dated l.r.: *Henri Rousseau / 1908*.

PROVENANCE:
Justin K. Thannhauser, Munich, 1912-17
Edwin Suermondt, Burg Drove, Die Eifel, Germany, 1917-23
Mrs. Edwin Suermondt, 1923-26
Galerie Flechtheim, Berlin and Düsseldorf, 1926(?)-28
Paul Rosenberg, Paris and New York, 1928-43
Mrs. Henry D. Sharpe, Providence, Rhode Island, 1943-60, by auction, Sotheby and Co., London, Nov. 23, 1960

The Football Players is the artist's attempt to depict a group of athletes in motion, a rare work among Rousseau's basically static paintings. The tree trunks, symmetrically placed at each side of the composition, mark spatial recession, and the horizontal division of the canvas creates a perspective framework. As Daniel Catton Rich observed, there is something ballet-like in the stylized poses of the football players. The athletes with their striped attire can be perceived as pairs, and the stiffness of their gestures is echoed by the four trees in the background.

Rousseau painted *The Football Players* with surprisingly light, high-keyed color and rendered the foliage with meticulous attention to detail. The artist used to walk from Paris out to the suburban countryside to sketch but finished his work in the studio. In this carefully worked picture, figures and landscape combine to form an otherworldly environment.

EXHIBITIONS:
Paris, Serres du Cours-la-Reine, *Société des Artistes Indépendants: 24ᵐᵉ Exposition*, Mar. 20-May 2, 1908, no. 5261

Berlin, Galerie Flechtheim, *Ausstellung Henri Rousseau*, Mar. 1926, no. 11, repr.

Paris, Galerie Paul Rosenberg, *Exposition Henri Rousseau*, Mar. 3-31, 1937, no. 12

The Art Institute of Chicago, *Henri Rousseau*, Jan. 22-Feb. 23, 1942, traveled to New York, The Museum of Modern Art, Mar. 18-May 3

Venice, XXV Biennale Internazionale d'Arte, *Il Doganiere Rousseau*, June 8-Oct. 15, 1950, no. 15

New York, Wildenstein and Co., Inc., *Henri Rousseau*, Apr. 17-May 25, 1963, no. 49, repr.

Rotterdam, Museum Boymans-van Beuningen, *De Lusthof*

der Naïeven, July 10-Sept. 6, 1964, no. 22, repr., traveled to Paris, Musée National d'Art Moderne, Oct. 14-Dec. 16

New York, The Solomon R. Guggenheim Museum, *Rousseau, Redon, and Fantasy,* May 31-Sept. 8, 1968, color repr.

Amsterdam, Stedelijk Museum, *De grote Naïeven,* Aug. 23-Oct. 20, 1974, no. 11, repr.

New York, The Solomon R. Guggenheim Museum, *Forty Modern Masters: An Anniversary Show,* Dec. 16, 1977-Feb. 5, 1978, no. 118, repr.

REFERENCES:

W. Uhde, *Henri Rousseau,* Paris, 1911, p. 65

D. C. Rich, *Henri Rousseau,* New York, 1946, pp. 51, repr., 52

W. Uhde, *Rousseau,* Bern, 1948, p. 16 and pl. 47

R. Shattuck, *The Banquet Years: Origins of the Avant Garde in France, 1885 to World War I,* rev. ed., New York, 1968, pp. 94-96, 103, 107, 110, 363, no. 45, pl. XIII

Handbook, 1970, pp. 387-389, color repr.

H. Certigny, *La Vérité sur le Douanier Rousseau,* Paris, 1961, p. 315

D. Vallier, *Henri Rousseau,* New York, 1961, p. 111, color repr.

Rudenstine, *Collection Catalogue,* 1976, no. 222, repr.

Edouard Vuillard 1868-1940

Edouard Vuillard was born on November 11, 1868, in Cuiseaux, France. In 1878 his family moved to Paris and Edouard attended the Lycée Condorcet. There he met his future brother-in-law, K.-X. Roussel, as well as Maurice Denis and Lugné-Poe, who was to become a leading theater director. In 1888 he and Roussel attended the Académie Julian, where they joined forces with the artists who would soon call themselves *Nabis*: Paul Sérusier, Paul Ranson, Denis and Bonnard. *"Nabi"* is the Hebrew word for prophet; the *Nabis* used arbitrary color, inspired in large part by Gauguin whom they revered. They sought practical application for their art beyond easel painting to realms such as stage design and architectural decoration. Vuillard began exhibiting with them in 1891 at Le Barc de Boutteville.

In the early years of his career he designed theatrical sets and programs, posters and illustrations. Ambroise Vollard commissioned him to do an album of color lithographs in 1896. The Natanson brothers and Mme Hessel were Vuillard's close friends and important patrons. He accepted commissions to decorate homes and public buildings: the decorations completed in 1913 for the foyer of the newly built Comédie des Champs-Elysées are still in existence. Vuillard exhibited often at the Salon des Indépendants until 1910 and at the Salon d'Automne until 1912. Until the late 1930s his work was rarely shown, except at Bernheim-Jeune, where he exhibited regularly. He executed many paintings of his mother and the interior of the apartment they shared until her death in 1928. The artist continued to live quietly in Paris until the end of his life.

In the late thirties he did decorations for the League of Nations, Geneva, and for the Palais de Chaillot, Paris. In 1938 he was given a major retrospective at the Musée des Arts Décoratifs in Paris. Vuillard died on June 21, 1940, in La Baule.

3 **At the Revue Blanche (Portrait of Félix Fénéon).** 1901
(A La Revue blanche [Portrait de Félix Fénéon])

41.725

Oil on board mounted on gilded board mat with painted cork overlay, 18¼ x 22⅝ in. (46.3 x 57.5 cm.)

Signed l.l.: *à F. Fénéon bien amicale*[ment] *E. Vuillard*; on reverse, possibly by Fénéon: *Edouard Vuillard/1901 /A La revue blanche (Portrait de M. Félix Fénéon).*

PROVENANCE:
from the artist
Félix Fénéon, Paris, 1901-38
Solomon R. Guggenheim, New York, 1938-41
Gift, Solomon R. Guggenheim, 1941

Edouard Vuillard has shown the office in Paris of the periodical, *La Revue blanche,* with Félix Fénéon working at his desk. From 1894 to 1903 Fénéon's name was synonymous with the magazine which contained articles of literary and artistic merit, published books and was closely associated with Vuillard, Bonnard, Toulouse-Lautrec and other artists. Not only Vuillard but also Bonnard and Félix Vallotton portrayed Fénéon at his desk. In the Guggenheim picture Fénéon's tall frame is bent over a stack of papers, and his elegant, dark silhouette stands out against the pale, glowing color of the background. Vuillard has compressed the space of the rooms and presented a detached but evocative portrait of his friend.

In addition to his work at *La Revue blanche,* Félix Fénéon (1861-1944) was an art dealer with the firm of Bernheim-Jeune from 1906 to 1924 and prepared a complete catalogue of Seurat's work.

EXHIBITIONS:
Paris, Bernheim-Jeune, *Portraits d'hommes,* Dec. 16, 1907-Jan. 4, 1908, no. 139
Paris, Galerie les Cadres, *Les Peintres de La Revue blanche,* June 12-30, 1936, no. 50
Paris, Bernheim-Jeune, *Vuillard: oeuvres de 1890 à 1910,* 1938

REFERENCES:
J. Rewald, "Félix Fénéon: II," *Gazette des Beaux-Arts,* vol. XXXIII, Feb. 1948, pp. 116-117, repr.
Rudenstine, *Collection Catalogue,* 1976, no. 250, repr.

Vuillard

4 Place Vintimille. 1908-10

78.2514 T74

Distemper on cardboard mounted on canvas, two panels, 78¾ x 27⅜ in. (200 x 69.5 cm.); 78¾ x 27½ in. (200 x 69.9 cm.)

Not signed or dated.

PROVENANCE:

from the artist
Henry Bernstein, Paris and New York, until 1948
Justin K. Thannhauser, New York, 1948
Gift, Justin K. Thannhauser, 1978

The two panels of *Place Vintimille* were part of a series of eight that Vuillard painted for the playwright Henry Bernstein, who had them installed in his home in Paris. Place Vintimille (now place Adolf Max) was a recurrent subject in Vuillard's work after 1907 when he lived in a fourth floor apartment overlooking the square. Like Bonnard, Vuillard closely observed details of life around him: horse-drawn carriages, dogs, children playing, the chill gray light of Paris and the bare branches of trees.

The origins of the technique employed by Vuillard in *Place Vintimille* can be traced to his early years of painting when he used cardboard and distemper for reasons of economy. He continued to paint with this medium, familiar from set designs, as he favored the absorbency of the support and the resultant matt tonality.

EXHIBITIONS:

Paris, Galerie Charpentier, *Paris,* Dec. 1, 1944-Mar. 1, 1945, nos. 214, 215, repr. (left panel)

New York, The Solomon R. Guggenheim Museum, *The Justin K. Thannhauser Collection,* from Apr. 30, 1965

REFERENCES:

C. Roger-Marx, *Vuillard et son temps,* Paris, 1945, pp. 140, 149, repr. (both panels), 155-157

J. Salomon, *Vuillard, témoignage,* Paris, 1945, p. 57, repr. (right panel)

J. Salomon, *Vuillard admiré,* Paris, 1961, pp. 98, 101, repr. (both panels)

J. Dugdale, "Vuillard the Decorator; The Last Phase: The Third Claude Anet Panel and the Public Commissions," *Apollo,* vol. LXXXVI, Oct. 1967, pp. 272, 274, figs. 5, 6

J. Salomon, *Vuillard,* Paris, 1968, pp. 25, 108, 111, color repr. (both panels), 218

S. Preston, *Vuillard,* New York, 1971, p. 39, fig. 54 (both panels)

J. Russell, *Vuillard,* Greenwich, Conn., 1971, pp. 48, repr. (both panels), 226

H. H. Arnason, *History of Modern Art,* rev. ed., New York, 1977, p. 93 and fig. 153 (both panels)

Barnett, *Thannhauser Catalogue,* 1978, no. 74, color repr. (both panels)

Pierre Bonnard 1867-1947

Pierre Bonnard was born October 3, 1867, at Fontenay-aux-Roses, France. He began law studies in Paris in 1887. That same year Bonnard also attended the Académie Julian and in 1888 entered the Ecole des Beaux-Arts, where he met K.-X. Roussel and Vuillard who became his lifelong friends. Thus Bonnard gave up law to become an artist, and, after brief military service, in 1889 he joined the group of young painters called the *Nabis,* which was organized by Paul Sérusier and included Maurice Denis, Paul Ranson, Roussel, Vuillard and others. The *Nabis,* influenced by Gauguin and Japanese prints, experimented with arbitrary color, expressive line and flat, patterned surfaces.

In 1890 Bonnard shared a studio with Vuillard and Denis, and he began to make color lithographs. The following year he met Toulouse-Lautrec. Also in 1891 he showed for the first time at the Salon des Indépendants and in the *Nabis'* earliest exhibitions at Le Barc de Boutteville. Bonnard exhibited with the *Nabis* until they disbanded in 1900. He worked in a variety of mediums; for example, he frequently made posters and illustrations for *La Revue blanche* and in 1895 he designed a stained-glass window for Louis Comfort Tiffany. His first one-man show, at the Galerie Durand-Ruel in 1896, included paintings, posters and lithographs; in 1897 Ambroise Vollard published the first of many albums of Bonnard's lithographs and illustrated books.

In 1903 Bonnard participated in the first Salon d'Automne and in the Vienna *Secession,* and from 1906 he was represented by Bernheim-Jeune. He traveled abroad extensively and worked at various locations in Normandy, the Seine valley and the south of France (he bought a villa at Le Cannet near Cannes in 1925) as well as in Paris. The Art Institute of Chicago mounted a major Bonnard-Vuillard exhibition in 1933, and The Museum of Modern Art, New York, organized Bonnard retrospectives in 1946 and 1964. Bonnard died at Le Cannet on January 23, 1947.

5 **Dining Room on the Garden.** 1934-35
(Grande salle à manger sur le jardin)

38.432

Oil on canvas, 50 x 53¼ in. (126.8 x 135.3 cm.)

Signed l.l.: *Bonnard.* Not dated.

PROVENANCE:

from the artist
Galerie Bernheim-Jeune, Paris, 1935
Galerie Pierre, Paris, 1937-38

Like his friend Vuillard, Bonnard preferred to paint familiar interior scenes, landscapes and decorative panels. The Guggenheim painting represents the dining room in the villa Bonnard rented only for the summer of 1934 at Bénerville-sur-Mer near Deauville on the Channel coast.

The theme of a still life in front of a window had appeared frequently in the work of Matisse and Picasso. Yet *Dining Room on the Garden* reflects Bonnard's individuality as a painter in the glowing colors with his distinctive value contrasts, in the dominance of the picture plane and in the figure of the artist's wife, Marthe, whose presence is so often felt in his pictures. A very similar painting, *Table before Window* (Collection Edward A. Bragaline, New York), contains a still life, the flattened pattern of a chair in front of the window and Bonnard's wife at the right. In these canvases the windows structure vertically an otherwise indeterminate space. They also provide a visually logical transition between the warm-toned intimacy of the interior and the cool blues outside.

EXHIBITIONS:

Paris, Grand Palais, *Salon d'Automne,* Nov. 1-Dec. 8, 1935, no. 159

Paris, Musée du Petit Palais, *Les Maîtres de l'art indépendant, 1895-1937,* June-Oct. 1937, no. 25

San Francisco Museum of Art, *Art in the Twentieth Century,* June 17-July 10, 1955

London, Tate Gallery, *An exhibition of paintings from The Solomon R. Guggenheim Museum, New York,* Apr. 16-May 26, 1957, no. 2, traveled to The Hague, Gemeentemuseum, June 25-Sept. 1; Helsinki, Ateneumin Taidekokoelmat, Sept. 27-Oct. 20; Rome, Galleria Nazionale d'Arte Moderna, Dec. 5, 1957-Jan. 8, 1958; Cologne, Wallraf-Richartz-Museum, Jan. 26-Mar. 30; Paris, Musée des Arts Décoratifs, Apr. 23-June 1

New York, The Solomon R. Guggenheim Museum, *Inaugural Selection,* Oct. 21, 1959-June 19, 1960

New York, The Museum of Modern Art, *Bonnard and his Environment,* Oct. 7-Nov. 29, 1964, no. 57, repr., traveled to The Art Institute of Chicago, Jan. 8-Feb. 28, 1965; Los Angeles County Museum of Art, Mar. 31-May 30

New York, The Solomon R. Guggenheim Museum, *Gauguin and the Decorative Style,* June 23-Oct. 23, 1966

St. Paul de Vence, France, Fondation Maeght, *Bonnard dans sa lumière,* July 12-Sept. 28, 1975, no. 53, color repr.

New York, The Solomon R. Guggenheim Museum, *Forty Modern Masters: An Anniversary Show,* Dec. 16, 1977-Feb. 5, 1978, no. 7, repr.

REFERENCES:

J. Guenne, "Le Salon d'Automne," *L'Art vivant,* no. 198, Nov. 1935, p. 247, repr.

J. Rewald, *Bonnard,* New York, 1948, p. 116, repr.

A. Terrasse, *Pierre Bonnard,* Paris, 1967, pp. 144-146, color repr.

A. Fermigier, *Pierre Bonnard,* New York, 1969, p. 141, color repr.

Handbook, 1970, pp. 42-43, color repr.

J. and H. Dauberville, *Bonnard: Catalogue raisonné de l'oeuvre peint 1920-1939,* Paris, 1973, vol. III, pp. 409-410, repr., no. 1524

Rudenstine, *Collection Catalogue,* 1976, no. 20, color repr.

H. H. Arnason, *History of Modern Art,* rev. ed., New York, 1977, p. 95 and color pl. 23

Aristide Maillol 1861-1944

Aristide-Jean-Bonaventure Maillol was born on December 9, 1861, in Banyuls-sur-Mer, France. He went to Paris in 1882 to study painting and in 1885 was admitted to the Ecole des Beaux-Arts, where he studied with Jean Léon Gérôme and Alexandre Cabanel. He became dissatisfied with his academic training in 1889, partly due to his discovery of Gauguin's paintings, pottery and wood carving. During the 1890s he concentrated on making tapestries, ceramics and decorative wood carvings, in response to the arts and crafts movement popular in France at the time. In 1896 he showed small carved figures for the first time, at the Salon of the Société Nationale des Beaux-Arts. Maillol became friends with Maurice Denis, Bonnard, Vuillard and the rest of the *Nabis* during the mid-nineties. In 1895 he married Clotilde Narcisse, who became the model for many of his sculptures.

By 1900 deteriorating eyesight forced him to give up tapestry and concentrate on sculpture. Maillol's first one-man exhibition was held at the Galerie Vollard in Paris in 1902. In 1905 his first monumental sculpture, *The Mediterranean,* was shown at the Salon d'Automne, Paris, prompting the German Count Harry Kessler to commission a version in stone. That same year Maillol was commissioned to execute *Action in Chains,* a memorial to Louis-Auguste Blanqui, for the town of Puget-Théniers. In 1907 he completed the relief, *Desire,* and a statue, the *Young Cyclist,* for his patron Kessler. The following year Kessler invited Maillol to Greece and asked him to make woodcut illustrations for Virgil's *Eclogues.*

In 1910 Maillol began a monument to Cézanne that was finally installed in the Tuileries Gardens of Paris in 1929. From 1919 to 1923 he worked on two war memorials for the towns of Céret and Port-Vendres. His first one-man show in the United States took place at the Albright Art Gallery in Buffalo in 1925. In 1930 he received a commission for a war memorial from the town of Banyuls and another for a monument to Debussy in Saint-Germain-en-Laye. Major Maillol retrospectives were held at the Galerie Flechtheim, Berlin, 1928, and the Kunsthalle Basel in 1933. In 1938 he began his last monument commissions, a memorial to aviators entitled *Air,* for the city of Toulouse, and *River,* in memory of Henri Barbusse. Maillol died on September 27, 1944, in Banyuls.

6 **Pomona with Lowered Arms.** Late 1920s
(Pomone aux bras tombants)

58.1513

Bronze, 65¾ in. (167 cm.) high

Signed with monogram: *AM*; inscribed on back of base: *Alexis Rudier Fondeur, Paris.* Not dated.

PROVENANCE:
Estate of the artist
Wildenstein and Co., Inc., New York, 1953-58

Maillol demonstrated a distinct preference for representing the female figure. The composition and pose of *Pomona with Lowered Arms* ultimately derive from Greek art but the voluptuous figure type is that of the women of his native Banyuls. During his lifetime Maillol executed many versions of Pomona. The earliest was a plaster of *Pomona with Raised Arms* which was exhibited at the Salon d'Automne in Paris in 1910; the pose later was used in *The Seasons.* A related draped figure became a World War I memorial at Elne. By the late 1920s Maillol altered the position of the arms in a plaster from which this cast was made.* A marble of Pomona with lowered arms holding apples dates from 1937 (Collection Musée du Petit Palais, Paris).

It was Maillol's practice to return to themes and compositions he had treated earlier. Thus, the sculptures from the 1930s are often new versions of works originally executed during the first decade of the twentieth century.

*conversation with Linda Konheim, Nov. 1978. A photograph of the plaster was taken by Herbert Matter in 1929.

EXHIBITIONS:

Houston, Contemporary Arts Museum, *Monumental Sculpture, the Great-Past and Present,* Oct. 28-Nov. 5, 1957

New York, The Solomon R. Guggenheim Museum, *Inaugural Selection,* Oct. 21, 1959-June 19, 1960

New York, The Solomon R. Guggenheim Museum, *Selected Sculpture and Works on Paper,* July 8-Sept. 14, 1969, p. 136, repr.

New York, The Solomon R. Guggenheim Museum, *Aristide Maillol: 1861-1944,* Dec. 19, 1975-Mar. 21, 1976, no. 105, repr.

REFERENCES:

J. Rewald, *Maillol,* Paris, 1939, pp. 61, repr., 165 (plaster)

J. Charbonneaux, *Maillol,* Paris, 1947, pls. 2, 8 (bronze)

C. Roy, *Maillol vivant,* Geneva, 1947, pl. 52 (bronze)

Handbook, 1959, p. 210, repr.

W. George, *Aristide Maillol,* Greenwich, Conn., 1965, p. 206, repr. (bronze)

Edvard Munch 1863-1944

Edvard Munch was born on December 12, 1863, in Løten, Norway. In 1864 his family moved to Oslo (then Christiania), where both his mother and sister died while he was young. He abandoned engineering studies to dedicate himself to painting in 1880. Munch enrolled in the Royal School of Design in Oslo in 1881 and exhibited for the first time in the autumn salon of Oslo in 1883. During these years he associated with a circle of advanced Norwegian artists and writers. In 1884 he attended an open-air academy in Modum directed by Frits Thaulow.

On a scholarship Thaulow awarded him in 1885, Munch traveled to Paris. The same year he began the themes *The Morning After, Puberty* and *The Sick Child. The Sick Child* created a scandal at Oslo's autumn salon of 1886. In 1889, the year of his first one-man show in Oslo, Munch received the first of three state scholarships and went again to Paris, where he entered Léon Bonnat's art school. As early as 1891 he painted works that would later be included in his *Frieze of Life.* His show at the *Verein Berliner Künstler* in Berlin in 1892 was closed after a week of heated debate. While living in Berlin from 1892 to 1895, Munch produced his first etchings and lithographs and frequented the literary and artistic group which was connected with the periodical *Pan* and included Strindberg and Julius Meier-Graefe. He took part in the Salon des Indépendants in Paris in 1897 and visited Italy two years later. He joined the *Société des Artistes Indépendants* in Paris in 1903 and the *Secession* group in Berlin in 1904.

In 1908 the Nasjonalgalleriet, Oslo, purchased a number of Munch's works. That autumn he suffered a nervous breakdown and entered a clinic in Copenhagen, where he remained for several months. From 1909 to 1914 Munch worked on the *Aula* murals for the Oslo University Assembly Hall; in 1913 his prints were included in the New York Armory Show. Three years later he moved to Ekely at Skøyen, where he spent most of his remaining years. In his work Munch continued such major themes as *The Voice, Kiss, Madonna, Melancholy, The Sick Child* and *Death in the Sickroom.* In 1922 the artist was given a major retrospective at the Kunsthaus Zürich; in 1927 comprehensive exhibitions of his work were held at the Nationalgalerie, Berlin, and the Nasjonalgalleriet, Oslo. Munch died in Skøyen on January 23, 1944; he left all of his work to the city of Oslo.

7 Portrait of Erik Pedersen. 1943

67.1837

Pastel on paper, 9¾ x 17⅞ in. (24.8 x 45.4 cm.)

Signed l.l. of center: *Edv. Munch.* Not dated.

PROVENANCE:
from the artist
Erik Pedersen, Oslo, 1944-57
Estate of Erik Pedersen
Mr. and Mrs. R. Tyler Day, Princeton, New Jersey, mid-1960s-67

Munch sketched the pastel portrait of Erik Pedersen late in 1943 and signed it only nine days before his death in January 1944. At that time Pedersen (1884-1957) was Managing Director of the Freia Chocolade Fabrik in Oslo, where he had been Manager when Munch executed twelve murals for the factory dining room in about 1922.

Munch has minimally indicated the interior setting and has emphasized the head by placing it against the open space of the horizontal format. He captured Pedersen's likeness with a sureness of blue, red, yellow and white lines and a brevity of description. Comparison of the pastel with a photograph of the sitter demonstrates how closely Munch portrayed Pedersen's features. However, he has taken the liberty of making the eyes blue, when they were actually brown.* Pedersen himself recalled that Munch added strong blue shadow to the pastel and commented at the end of the sitting: "Isn't it funny today, I am so weak and feel so bad, I can hardy stand on my feet and then I'm so sensitive that I can make the finest thing." (*Dagbladet,* Nov. 1957)

*conversation with Mrs. R. Tyler Day, Pederson's granddaughter, Jan. 1979. Mrs. Day's mother kindly made a photograph available to the author.

EXHIBITION:
New York, The Solomon R. Guggenheim Museum, *Selected Sculpture and Works on Paper,* July 8-Sept. 14, 1969, p. 68, repr.

REFERENCES:
E. Pedersen, "Det Siste Arbeide," *Kunst og Kultur,* 29 Jg., Hefte 3-4, 1946, pp. 199, repr., 200-204
O. Hølaas, "Munchs siste modell," *Dagbladet* (Oslo), Nov. 29, 1957
Handbook, 1970, pp. 342-343, repr.
T. M. Messer, *Edvard Munch,* New York, 1973, pp. 158-159, color repr.
J. Selz, *E. Munch,* New York, 1974, p. 92, color repr.

II

EARLY DRAWINGS BY MATISSE AND A FAUVE PICTURE
BY BRAQUE. THE CUBIST PAINTINGS OF BRAQUE, PICASSO,
LÉGER, GLEIZES, GRIS AND DUCHAMP. WORKS BY
PICABIA, VILLON, KUPKA AND THE ORPHIC CUBISM OF
DELAUNAY

Henri Matisse 1869-1954

Henri-Emile-Benoît Matisse was born on December 31, 1869, in Le Cateau-Cambrésis, France. He grew up at Bohain-en-Vermandois and studied law in Paris from 1887 to 1889. By 1891 he had abandoned law and started to paint. In Paris Matisse studied art briefly at the Académie Julian and then at the Ecole des Beaux-Arts with Gustave Moreau.

In 1901 Matisse exhibited at the Salon des Indépendants in Paris and met the other future leaders of the Fauve movement, Maurice de Vlaminck and André Derain. His first one-man show took place at the Galerie Vollard in 1904. Both Leo and Gertrude Stein as well as Etta and Claribel Cone began to collect Matisse's work at this time. Like many avant-garde artists in Paris, Matisse was receptive to a broad range of influences; he was one of the first painters to take an interest in primitive art. Matisse abandoned the palette of the Impressionists and established his characteristic style with its flat, brilliant color and fluid line. His subjects were mainly women, interiors and still lifes. In 1913 his work was included in the Armory Show in New York. By 1923 two Russians, Sergei Shchukin and Ivan Morosov, had purchased nearly fifty of his paintings.

From the early twenties until 1939 Matisse divided his time primarily between the south of France and Paris. During this period he worked on painting, sculpture, lithographs and etchings as well as murals for The Barnes Foundation in Pennsylvania, designs for tapestries and for the costumes and sets for Leonide Massine's ballet, *Rouge et Noir (Red and Black)*. While recuperating from two major operations in 1941 and 1942, Matisse concentrated on a technique he had devised earlier, *papiers découpés* (paper cutouts). *Jazz*, written and illustrated by Matisse, was published in 1947. The plates are stencil reproductions of paper cutouts. In 1948 he began the design and decoration of the Chapelle du Rosaire at Vence, which was completed and consecrated in 1951. Matisse continued to make his large paper cutouts, the last of which was a design for the rose window at Union Church of Pocantico Hills, New York. He died in Nice on November 3, 1954.

Matisse

8 Nude. 1898-1901
(Nu)

48.1172 x48

Charcoal on paper, 10⅝ x 8¾ in. (27 x 22.2 cm.)

Signed l.r.: *Henri-Matisse.* Not dated.

PROVENANCE:
Nierendorf Gallery, New York
Estate of Karl Nierendorf, 1948

Both of these drawings belong to the early years of
Matisse's career when he frequented the Académie Carrière, made many drawings from the model and worked
also at sculpture and painting from nature. Like many
drawings of a seated female model, *Nude* is an academic
study in which the solidity of forms is reminiscent of
Cézanne and the play of light is decidedly pictorial.
Male Model represents Bevilaqua, an Italian who posed
hundreds of times while Matisse was working on his
first major bronze, *Le Serf.* The nervous quality of the
line would be accentuated in Matisse's drawings of the
first decade of this century, while he achieves in his later
work great purity of expression in a single line. Although
he is thought of primarily as a colorist, drawing played
a vital role throughout Matisse's oeuvre. Matisse made
studies for paintings and mural decorations as well as
paper cutouts, but drawing remained essentially an end
in itself.

EXHIBITIONS:
Vancouver, B.C., Vancouver Art Gallery, *The Solomon R.
Guggenheim Museum: A Selection from the Museum
Collection,* Nov. 16-Dec. 12, 1954, no. 59, repr.

Philadelphia Museum of Art, *Guggenheim Museum
Exhibition: A Loan Collection of Paintings, Drawings, and
Prints from The Solomon R. Guggenheim Museum, New
York,* Nov. 2, 1961-Jan. 7, 1962, no. 107

REFERENCE:
Handbook, 1959, p. 251, repr.

9 Male Model. ca. 1900
(Homme nu debout)

78.2514 T29

India ink on paper, 12⁵⁄₁₆ x 10⁷⁄₁₆ in. (31.3 x 26.5 cm.)

Signed l.r.: *Henri-Matisse.* Not dated.

PROVENANCE:
Heinz Braune, by 1922-29
Justin K. Thannhauser, Berlin and New York, 1929
Gift, Justin K. Thannhauser, 1978

EXHIBITIONS:
Berlin, Galerien Thannhauser, *Henri Matisse,* Feb.-Mar.
1930
New York, The Solomon R. Guggenheim Museum, *The
Justin K. Thannhauser Collection,* from Apr. 30, 1965

REFERENCES:
R. Schacht, *Henri Matisse,* Dresden, 1922, p. 64, repr.

A. H. Barr, Jr., *Matisse: His Art and His Public,* New York,
1951, pp. 44, repr., 48, 49, 531

H. Geldzahler, "Two Early Matisse Drawings," *Gazette des
Beaux-Arts,* vol. LX, Nov. 1962, pp. 497-502

A. E. Elsen, *The Sculpture of Henri Matisse,* New York,
1972, p. 27, fig. 30

J. Jacobus, *Henri Matisse,* New York, 1972, p. 64, fig. 80

Barnett, *Thannhauser Catalogue,* 1978, no. 29, repr.

Georges Braque 1882-1963

Georges Braque was born in Argenteuil-sur-Seine on May 13, 1882. He grew up in Le Havre and studied evenings at the Ecole des Beaux-Arts there from about 1897 to 1899. He left for Paris to study under a master-decorator to receive his craftsman certificate in 1901. From 1902 to 1904 he painted at the Académie Humbert in Paris where he met Marie Laurencin and Picabia. By 1906 Braque's work was no longer Impressionist but Fauve in style; after spending that summer in Antwerp with Othon Friesz, he showed his Fauve work the following year in the Salon des Indépendants in Paris. His first one-man show was at D.-H. Kahnweiler's gallery in 1908. From 1909 Picasso and Braque worked together in developing Cubism; by 1911 their styles were extremely similar. In 1912 they started to incorporate collage elements into their painting and experiment with the *papier collé* (pasted paper) technique. Their artistic collaboration lasted until 1914. Braque was wounded during World War I; upon his recovery in 1917 he began a close friendship with Gris.

After World War I his work became freer and less schematic. His fame grew in 1922 as a result of a major exhibition at the Salon d'Automne in Paris. In the mid-twenties Braque designed the decor for two Sergei Diaghilev ballets. By the end of the decade he had returned to a more realistic interpretation of nature, although certain aspects of Cubism always remained present in his work. In 1931 Braque made his first engraved plasters and began to portray mythological subjects. His first important retrospective took place in 1933 at the Kunsthalle Basel. He won First Prize at the Carnegie International in Pittsburgh in 1937.

During World War II Braque remained in Paris. His paintings at that time, primarily still lifes and interiors, became more somber. In addition to painting Braque also made lithographs, engravings and sculpture. From the late 1940s Braque treated various recurring themes such as birds, ateliers, landscapes and seascapes. In 1953 he designed stained-glass windows for the church of Varengeville. During the last few years of his life Braque's ill health prevented him from undertaking further large-scale commissions but he continued to paint and make lithographs and jewelry designs. He died in Paris on August 31, 1963.

10 **Landscape near Antwerp.** 1906
(Paysage près d'Anvers)

78.2514 T1

Oil on canvas, 23⅝ x 31⅞ in. (60 x 81 cm.)

Signed l.l.: *G Braque*. Not dated.

PROVENANCE:
Private collection, Paris
Robert Lebel, Paris, ca. 1935-ca. 1951
Justin K. Thannhauser, New York, ca. 1951
Gift, Justin K. Thannhauser, 1978

The Fauve paintings by Matisse and André Derain at the Salon d'Automne in Paris in the autumn of 1905 profoundly impressed Braque. The artist painted his first Fauve works during the summer of 1906, which he spent in Antwerp. The distant harbor on the Scheldt river, complete with masts of ships, is represented in *Landscape near Antwerp*.

Braque employed non-naturalistic color and stylized brushwork in his Fauve paintings: curving contour lines and strokes of contrasting pigment become the visual equivalent for the landscape. In this early Fauve picture the pale violet and green in the sky, the yellow and lavender in the water and the expressive reds, oranges and yellows create a vivid harmony that derives not from the actual landscape but from the imaginative world of the artist. Braque's colors became more extreme and his brushwork more abbreviated in the canvases he painted at L'Estaque in the south of France during the autumn of 1906 and into the winter of 1907. The artist's Fauve manner continued through 1907, but the following year marks the beginning of his Cubist style.

EXHIBITIONS:
Paris, Galerie Pierre, *Georges Braque: Paysages de l'époque fauve (1906)*, Feb. 4-21, 1938

New York, Marie Harriman Gallery, *Les Fauves*, Oct. 20-Nov. 22, 1941, no. 27

New York, Buchholz Gallery, *Early Work by Contemporary Artists*, Nov. 16-Dec. 4, 1943, no. 3

The Toledo Museum of Art, *The Spirit of Modern France: An Essay on Painting in Society 1745-1946*, Nov.-Dec. 1946, no. 67, traveled to The Art Gallery of Toronto, Jan.-Feb. 1947

Venice, XXV Biennale Internazionale d'Arte, *Mostra dei Fauves*, June 8-Oct. 15, 1950, no. 6 bis

New York, Sidney Janis Gallery, *Les Fauves*, Nov. 13-Dec. 23, 1950, no. 2

Pasadena Art Museum, *Georges Braque,* Apr. 20-June 5, 1960, no. 2

New York, The Solomon R. Guggenheim Museum, *The Justin K. Thannhauser Collection,* from Apr. 30, 1965

REFERENCES:

E. C. Oppler, *Fauvism Reexamined,* New York, 1976 (photo reprint of Ph.D. dissertation, Columbia University, 1969), p. 52, fn. 2

H. H. Arnason, *History of Modern Art,* rev. ed., New York, 1977, p. 131 and fig. 210

Barnett, *Thannhauser Catalogue,* 1978, no. 1, color repr.

Braque

11 Violin and Palette. 1909-10
(Violon et palette)

54.1412

Oil on canvas, 36⅛ x 16⅞ in. (91.7 x 42.8 cm.)

Signed on reverse: *Braque*. Not dated.

PROVENANCE:
from the artist
D.-H. Kahnweiler, Paris, 1910
Wilhelm Uhde, Berlin, 1910
Edwin Suermondt, Burg Drove, Die Eifel, Germany,
ca. 1910-23
Mrs. Edwin Suermondt, 1923-ca. 1926
Alex Vömel, Düsseldorf, ca. 1926-53
Fine Arts Associates, New York, 1954

The companion pictures *Violin and Palette* and *Piano and Mandola* (cat. no. 12), painted during the winter of 1909-10, are classic examples of the early phase of Cubism. In both canvases, the objects represented are readily identifiable although their shapes have been fragmented. Braque stated that this fragmentation permitted him "to establish a spatial element as well as a spatial movement." He also remarked that he chose to paint musical instruments not only because he was surrounded by them in his studio but because he was "working towards a tactile space . . . and musical instruments have the advantage of being animated by one's touch." (D. Vallier, "Braque la peinture et nous," *Cahiers d'Art*, XXIXᵉ année, Oct. 1954, p. 16)

Both still lifes exist in rather shallow space, and the forms are rendered with neutral colors, predominantly greens and browns. By limiting the pictorial element through the use of a subdued palette, Braque and Picasso concentrated on a new conception of space, on the disintegration of objects into faceted planes and other essentially formal problems of Analytical Cubism.

EXHIBITIONS:
Cologne, Städtische Ausstellungshalle am Aachenertor, *Internationale Kunstausstellung des Sonderbundes,* May 25-Sept. 30, 1912, no. 231
Moscow, *Bubnovyi valet (Jack of Diamonds),* Mar. 3-Apr. 6, 1913, no. 11
Kunsthalle Basel, *Georges Braque,* Apr. 9-May 14, 1933, no. 22
Kunsthalle Bern, *Georges Braque,* Apr. 25-May 31, 1953, no. 22, traveled to Kunsthaus Zürich, June 7-July 19
Edinburgh, Royal Scottish Academy, *G. Braque,* Aug. 18-Sept. 15, 1956, no. 21, repr., traveled to London, Tate Gallery, Sept. 28-Nov. 11

New York, The Solomon R. Guggenheim Museum, *Inaugural Selection,* Oct. 21, 1959-June 19, 1960
New York, Saidenberg Gallery, *Braque: An American Tribute, Fauvism and Cubism,* Apr. 7-May 2, 1964, no. 14, repr.
Los Angeles County Museum of Art, *The Cubist Epoch,* Dec. 15, 1970-Feb. 21, 1971, no. 19, color pl. 24, traveled to New York, The Metropolitan Museum of Art, Apr. 9-June 8
Paris, Orangerie des Tuileries, *Georges Braque,* Oct. 16, 1973-Jan. 14, 1974, no. 29, repr.
New York, The Solomon R. Guggenheim Museum, *Forty Modern Masters: An Anniversary Show,* Dec. 16, 1977-Feb. 5, 1978, no. 14, repr.

REFERENCES:
D.-H. Kahnweiler, *Der Weg zum Cubismus,* Munich, 1920, p. 24
G. Isarlov, "Georges Braque," *Orbes,* no. 3, spring 1932, no. 70
J. Richardson, *Braque,* Harmondsworth, 1959, pp. 9-10, color pl. 7a
J. Russell, *Georges Braque,* Garden City, 1959, p. 120
J. Leymarie, *Braque,* Lausanne, 1961, p. 48, color repr.
R. Rosenblum, *Cubism and Twentieth-Century Art,* New York, 1961, p. 58
E. Mullins, *The Art of Georges Braque,* New York, 1968, pp. 56-57, repr., 58, 67
Handbook, 1970, pp. 47-48, color repr.
Rudenstine, *Collection Catalogue,* 1976, no. 21, color repr.

12 Piano and Mandola. 1909-10
(Piano et mandore)

54.1411

Oil on canvas, 36⅛ x 16⅞ in. (91.7 x 42.8 cm.)

Signed on reverse: *Braque*. Not dated.

PROVENANCE:
from the artist
D.-H. Kahnweiler, Paris, 1910
Wilhelm Uhde, Berlin, 1910
Edwin Suermondt, Burg Drove, Die Eifel, Germany,
ca. 1910-23
Mrs. Edwin Suermondt, 1923-ca. 1926
Alex Vömel, Düsseldorf, ca. 1926-53
Fine Arts Associates, New York, 1954

EXHIBITIONS:

Cologne, Städtische Ausstellungshalle am Aachenertor, *Internationale Kunstausstellung des Sonderbundes,* May 25-Sept. 30, 1912, no. 232

Moscow, *Bubnovyi valet (Jack of Diamonds),* Mar. 3-Apr. 6, 1913, no. 12

Kunsthalle Basel, *Georges Braque,* Apr. 9-May 14, 1933, no. 21

Kunsthalle Bern, *Georges Braque,* Apr. 25-May 31, 1953, no. 21, traveled to Kunsthaus Zürich, June 7-July 19

Edinburgh, Royal Scottish Academy, *G. Braque,* Aug. 18-Sept. 15, 1956, no. 20, repr., traveled to London, Tate Gallery, Sept. 28-Nov. 11

New York, The Solomon R. Guggenheim Museum, *Inaugural Selection,* Oct. 21, 1959-June 19, 1960

New York, Saidenberg Gallery, *Braque: An American Tribute, Fauvism and Cubism,* Apr. 7-May 2, 1964, no. 15, repr.

Los Angeles County Museum of Art, *The Cubist Epoch,* Dec. 15, 1970-Feb. 21, 1971, no. 18, color pl. 23, traveled to New York, The Metropolitan Museum of Art, Apr. 9-June 8

Paris, Orangerie des Tuileries, *Georges Braque,* Oct. 16, 1973-Jan. 14, 1974, no. 30, repr.

New York, The Solomon R. Guggenheim Museum, *Forty Modern Masters: An Anniversary Show,* Dec. 16, 1977-Feb. 5, 1978, no. 15

REFERENCES:

G. Isarlov, "Georges Braque," *Orbes,* no. 3, spring 1932, no. 76

J. Richardson, *Braque,* Harmondsworth, 1959, pp. 9-10, color pl. 7b

J. Russell, *Georges Braque,* Garden City, 1959, pp. 14, 120

J. Leymarie, *Braque,* Lausanne, 1961, p. 48, color repr.

E. Mullins, *The Art of Georges Braque,* New York, 1968, p. 57, repr.

Handbook, 1970, pp. 48, color repr., 49

Rudenstine, *Collection Catalogue,* 1976, no. 22, color repr.

Pablo Picasso 1881-1973

Pablo Ruiz Picasso was born on October 25, 1881, at Málaga in Andalusia, Spain. The son of an academic painter, José Ruiz Blanco, he began to draw at an early age. In 1895 the family moved to Barcelona, and Picasso studied there at La Lonja, the academy of fine arts. His association with the group at the café Els Quatre Gats in Barcelona from 1898 and his visit to Horta de Ebro of 1898-99 were crucial to his early artistic development. In 1900 Picasso's first exhibition took place in Barcelona, and that autumn he went to Paris for the first of several stays during the early years of the century. Picasso settled in Paris in April 1904 and soon his circle of friends included Max Jacob, Guillaume Apollinaire, Gertrude and Leo Stein as well as two dealers, Ambroise Vollard and Berthe Weill.

His style developed from the Blue Period (1901 to 1904) to the Rose Period (1905) to the pivotal work, *Les Demoiselles d'Avignon* (1907), and the subsequent evolution of Cubism from 1909 into 1911. Picasso's collaboration on ballet and theatrical productions began in 1916. Soon thereafter his work was characterized by neoclassicism and a renewed interest in drawing and figural representation. In the 1920s the artist and his wife Olga (whom he had married in 1918) continued to live in Paris, travel frequently and spend their summers at the beach. From 1925 into the 1930s Picasso was involved to a certain degree with the Surrealists and from the autumn of 1931 he was especially interested in making sculpture. With the large exhibitions at the Galeries Georges Petit in Paris and the Kunsthaus Zürich in 1932 and the publication of the first volume of Zervos' catalogue raisonné the same year, Picasso's fame increased markedly.

By 1936 the Spanish Civil War had a profound effect on Picasso, the expression of which culminated in his painting *Guernica,* 1937. He was also deeply moved by World War II and stayed primarily in Paris during those years. Picasso's association with the Communist party began in 1944. From the late 1940s he lived in the south of France at Vallauris, Cannes and then Vauvenargues. Among the enormous number of Picasso exhibitions that have been held, those at The Museum of Modern Art in New York in 1939 and the Musée des Arts Décoratifs in Paris in 1955 have been most significant. In 1961 the artist married Jacqueline Roque and they moved to Mougins. There Picasso continued his prolific work in painting, drawing, prints, ceramics and sculpture until his death on April 8, 1973.

13 **The End of the Road.** 1898-99
(Au Bout de la route)

78.2514 T33

Oil wash (?) and conté crayon on paper, 18⅜₆ x 12⅛ in.
(47.1 x 30.8 cm.)

Signed l.r.: *P. Ruiz Picasso.* Not dated.

PROVENANCE:
Private collection, Barcelona
Justin K. Thannhauser, New York, by 1957
Gift, Justin K. Thannhauser, 1978

Picasso spent his formative years in Barcelona where
Catalan *modernismo* in general and the artistic activities centered around the cafe El Quatre Gats in particular had a decisive influence. Barcelona's cosmopolitan
cultural environment made accessible the styles of painting and decoration then in fashion: the English Art
Nouveau and Munich's *Jugendstil. The End of the Road*
dates from 1898-99, before the young artist had traveled
outside of Spain. The watercolor shows, from the rear,
a line of poor and crippled people as they proceed down
a road. A row of carriages moves across the landscape
to converge with the procession at the upper right.
There, the winged figure of Death carrying a scythe
waits for them above the walls of a cemetery. Years
later Picasso recalled that "Death waits for all at the
end of the road, even though the rich go there in carriages and the poor on foot." (Richardson, p. 16)

EXHIBITIONS:
New York, The Museum of Modern Art, *Picasso: 75th
Anniversary Exhibition,* May 22-Sept. 8, 1957, p. 14, repr.,
traveled to The Art Institute of Chicago, Oct. 29-Dec. 8

Philadelphia Museum of Art, *Picasso,* Jan. 8-Feb. 23, 1958,
no. 1, repr.

New York, The Museum of Modern Art, *Art Nouveau: Art
and Design at the Turn of the Century,* June 6-Sept. 6, 1960,
no. 222, repr., traveled to Pittsburgh, Museum of Art,
Carnegie Institute, Oct. 13-Dec. 12; Los Angeles County
Museum of Art, Jan. 17-Mar. 5, 1961; The Baltimore
Museum of Art, Apr. 1-May 15

New York, The Solomon R. Guggenheim Museum, *The
Justin K. Thannhauser Collection,* from Apr. 30, 1965

REFERENCES:
H. Seling, ed., *Jugendstil: Der Weg ins 20. Jahrhundert,*
Munich, 1959, pp. 29, 113 and pl. 24

A. Blunt and P. Pool, *Picasso: The Formative Years,* Greenwich, Conn., 1962, p. 30 and pl. 64

J. Richardson, *Pablo Picasso: Watercolours and Gouaches,*
London, 1964, pp. 16-17 and pl. I

P. Daix and G. Boudaille, *Picasso: The Blue and Rose
Periods,* Greenwich, Conn., 1967, no. I.2, pp. 22, 107, repr.

C. Zervos, *Pablo Picasso,* Paris, 1969, vol. 21, no. 79 and
pl. 35

H. H. Arnason, *History of Modern Art,* rev. ed., New York,
1977, p. 125 and fig. 199

P. Daix, *La Vie de peintre de Pablo Picasso,* Paris, 1977,
pp. 29, 33, fn. 6

Barnett, *Thannhauser Catalogue,* 1978, no. 33, color repr.

M. McCully, *Els Quatre Gats: Art in Barcelona around
1900,* exh. cat., Princeton, N.J., 1978, pp. 37-38, repr.

14 Le Moulin de la Galette. Autumn 1900

78.2514 T34

Oil on canvas, 34¾ x 45½ in. (88.2 x 115.5 cm.)

Signed l.r.: *P. R. Picasso.* Not dated.

PROVENANCE:

from the artist
Galerie Berthe Weill, Paris, 1900
Arthur Huc, ca. 1900
Moderne Galerie (Heinrich Thannhauser), Munich, ca. 1909
Paul von Mendelssohn Bartholdy, Berlin, ca. 1910-35
Justin K. Thannhauser, Berlin and New York, ca. 1935
Gift, Justin K. Thannhauser, 1978

Picasso remembered that *Le Moulin de la Galette* was the first canvas he painted after arriving in Paris in October 1900. The World's Fair that year attracted Picasso and several of his Spanish friends to Paris, but they were back in Barcelona for Christmas.

The Moulin de la Galette was a dancing spot at the site of a mill atop Montmartre, not far from where Picasso stayed. Renoir, van Gogh, Toulouse-Lautrec, Théophile-Alexandre Steinlen and Picasso's Spanish friend Ramón Casas had all painted there. Picasso's *Le Moulin de la Galette* is reminiscent not only of Toulouse-Lautrec but also of the latter two artists' work. In this night scene Picasso emphasizes the dancers, who are almost all women, and, through the many black tones and the shrill colors illuminated by electric lights, he creates an unforgettable atmosphere. With *Le Moulin de la Galette* the nineteen-year-old Spaniard captured the excitement of an era.

EXHIBITIONS:

New York, The Museum of Modern Art, *Picasso: Forty Years of His Art,* Nov. 15, 1939-Jan. 7, 1940, no. 5, repr., traveled to The Art Institute of Chicago, Feb 1.-Mar. 3; Boston, Institute of Modern Art, Apr. 27-May 26

New York, M. Knoedler and Co., Inc., *Picasso Before 1907,* Oct. 15-Nov. 8, 1947, no. 3

New York, The Museum of Modern Art, *Picasso: 75th Anniversary Exhibition,* May 22-Sept. 8, 1957, p. 15, repr., traveled to The Art Institute of Chicago, Oct. 29-Dec. 8

Philadelphia Museum of Art, *Picasso,* Jan. 8-Feb. 23, 1958, no. 4, repr.

London, Tate Gallery, *Picasso,* July 6-Sept. 18, 1960, no. 4, pl. Ib

Paris, Grand Palais, *Hommage à Pablo Picasso,* Nov. 1966-Feb. 1967, no. 3, repr.

New York, The Solomon R. Guggenheim Museum, *The Justin K. Thannhauser Collection,* from Apr. 30, 1965

REFERENCES:

C. Zervos, *Pablo Picasso,* Paris and New York, 1932, vol. I, no. 41, pl. 20

B. Weill, *Pan! dans l'Oeil!,* Paris, 1933, p. 67

A. H. Barr, Jr., *Picasso: Fifty Years of His Art,* New York, 1946, pp. 18, repr., 19, 253

A. Cirici Pellicer, *Picasso avant Picasso,* Geneva, 1950, no. 18, repr.

W. Boeck and J. Sabartés, *Picasso,* New York, 1955, p. 117

R. Penrose, *Picasso: His Life and Work,* London, 1958, no. 8, pl. l

H. L. C. Jaffé, *Picasso,* New York, 1964, p. 15

P. Daix and G. Boudaille, *Picasso: The Blue and Rose Periods,* Greenwich, Conn., 1967, no. II. 10, pp. 28, 29, repr., 33, 122

S. Finkelstein, *Der junge Picasso,* Dresden, 1970, pp. 44, 45, 162 and pl. 54

H. H. Arnason, *History of Modern Art,* rev. ed., New York, 1977, p. 125 and fig. 200

P. Daix, *La Vie de peintre de Pablo Picasso,* Paris, 1977, p. 37

Barnett, *Thannhauser Catalogue,* 1978, no. 34, color repr.

Picasso

15 **Woman Ironing.** 1904
(La Repasseuse)

78.2514 T41

Oil on canvas, 45¾ x 28¾ in. (116.2 x 73 cm.)

Signed l.r.: *Picasso.* Not dated.

PROVENANCE:

Ambroise Vollard, Paris
Moderne Galerie (Heinrich Thannhauser), Munich,
ca. 1913
Karl Adler, Berlin and Amsterdam, 1916-late 1930s
Justin K. Thannhauser, late 1930s
Gift, Justin K. Thannhauser, 1978

After several earlier visits, Picasso went back to Paris in
April 1904 and remained there until 1948. He first
stayed in Montmartre at 13, rue Ravignan in the building called the "Bateau-Lavoir," where many artists, including Gris, once lived. The large, haunting picture
from the Thannhauser collection of a woman ironing
dates from this period. Daumier and Degas had treated
the subject before, as had Picasso himself in 1901. The
expressive pose in our painting of the frail woman
pressing down on the iron undoubtedly derives from
Degas' work.

Woman Ironing still retains some of the somber tonality
of Picasso's Blue Period. Both the neutral colors and the
tense, angular figure express poverty, loneliness and suffering. Like Picasso's *Old Guitarist* (Collection The Art
Institute of Chicago), which was painted in Barcelona
in 1903, the woman ironing has one shoulder raised in
a distorted pose, the head lowered and turned to the side
so that it is seen in profile. The model appears in several
of Picasso's canvases of 1904 and has been identified as
Margot, the daughter of Frédé, who owned the café, Le
Lapin Agile, which Picasso and his friends frequented.

EXHIBITIONS:

Munich, Moderne Galerie (Heinrich Thannhauser), *Pablo
Picasso,* Feb. 1913, no. 28

Stuttgart, Kgl. Kunstgebäude, *Grosse Kunstausstellung,*
May-Oct. 1913, no. 420

Berlin, Ausstellungshaus am Kurfürstendamm, *Herbstaus-
stellung,* autumn 1913, no. 171

New York, The Museum of Modern Art, *Picasso: Forty
Years of His Art,* Nov. 15, 1939-Jan. 7, 1940, no. 27, repr.,
traveled to The Art Institute of Chicago, Feb. 1-Mar. 3;
Boston, Institute of Modern Art, Apr. 27-May 26

New York, M. Knoedler and Co., Inc., *Picasso Before 1907,*
Oct. 15-Nov. 8, 1947, no. 18

The Art Gallery of Toronto, *Picasso,* Apr. 1949, no. 2

New York, The Museum of Modern Art, *Picasso: 75th
Anniversary Exhibition,* May 22-Sept. 8, 1957, p. 20, repr.

New York, The Solomon R. Guggenheim Museum, *The
Justin K. Thannhauser Collection,* from Apr. 30, 1965

REFERENCES:

H. Hildebrandt, "Die Frühbilder Picassos," *Kunst und
Künstler,* Jg. II, Apr. 1913, p. 378, repr.

C. Einstein, *Die Kunst des 20. Jahrhunderts,* Berlin, 1926,
vol. I, pl. vii

C. Zervos, *Pablo Picasso,* Paris and New York, 1932, vol. I,
no. 247, pl. lll

A. H. Barr, Jr., *Picasso: Fifty Years of His Art,* New York,
1946, p. 32, repr.

A. Cirici Pellicer, *Picasso avant Picasso,* Geneva, 1950, pp.
179, 183, pl. 180

W. Boeck and J. Sabartés, *Picasso,* New York, 1955, pp.
38-39, 123

R. Penrose, *Picasso: His Life and Work,* London, 1958,
p. 106

H. L. C. Jaffé, *Picasso,* New York, 1964, pp. 19, 70-71,
color repr.

P. Daix and G. Boudaille, *Picasso: The Blue and Rose
Periods,* Greenwich, Conn., 1967, no. XI.6, pp. 56, 64, 65,
240, repr.

E. Steingräber, "La Repasseuse: zur frühesten Version des
Themas von Edgar Degas," *Pantheon,* vol. XXXII, Jan.-
Feb.-Mar. 1974, pp. 52-53, repr.

H. H. Arnason, *History of Modern Art,* rev. ed., New York,
1977, p. 125 and color pl. 41

Barnett, *Thannhauser Catalogue,* 1978, no. 41, color repr.

16 Young Acrobat and Child. March 26, 1905
(Jeune acrobate et enfant)

78.2514 T42

Ink and gouache on gray cardboard, 12⅝₁₆ x 9⅞ in.
(31.3 x 25.1 cm.)

Signed and dated l.r.: *Picasso/Paris 26 Mars 05*; inscribed above signature: *A Mlle/A. Nachmann.*

PROVENANCE:

from the artist
A. Nachmann, Cannes, until 1939
Justin K. Thannhauser, 1939
Gift, Justin K. Thannhauser, 1978

Late in 1904 Picasso again began to paint the harlequins
and saltimbanques that had occupied him in 1901.
Often he chose to portray a family or, as here, children.
This small gouache, executed on gray cardboard, contains various blues and grays as well as the warm brown
and pink hues usually associated with the Rose Period.
In fact, the Rose Period (1905) can be defined not so
much in terms of color as subject matter and mood. At
that time Picasso lived with Fernande Olivier in the
"Bateau-Lavoir," not far from the Cirque Médrano
where he went frequently and made friends with circus people. It was a productive period when Picasso
not only drew and painted in watercolor and gouache
but also experimented with sculpture and printmaking.

EXHIBITION:

New York, The Solomon R. Guggenheim Museum, *The
Justin K. Thannhauser Collection,* from Apr. 30, 1965

REFERENCES:

C. Zervos, "Oeuvres et images inédites de la jeunesse de
Picasso," *Cahiers d'Art,* 25ᵉ année, no. 2, 1950, p. 328, repr.

C. Zervos, *Pablo Picasso,* Paris, 1954, vol. 6, no. 718, pl. 87

P. Daix and G. Boudaille, *Picasso: The Blue and Rose
Periods,* Greenwich, Conn., 1967, no. XII.15, repr.

H. H. Arnason, *History of Modern Art,* rev. ed., New York,
1977, p. 126 and fig. 204

Barnett, *Thannhauser Catalogue,* 1978, no. 42, color repr.

Picasso

17 Carafe, Jug, and Fruit Bowl. Summer 1909
(Carafon, pot et compotier)

37.536

Oil on canvas, 28¼ x 25⅜ in. (71.6 x 64.6 cm.)

Not signed or dated.

PROVENANCE:

from the artist (?)
G. F. Reber, Lausanne, after 1918-35
Zwemmer Gallery, London, 1935-36
Solomon R. Guggenheim, New York, 1936
Gift, Solomon R. Guggenheim, 1937

Carafe, Jug, and Fruit Bowl was painted in Spain during
the summer of 1909. From May to September 1909
Picasso lived in Horta de San Juan (then called Horta
de Ebro), a mountain village in his native Catalonia
where he had spent an earlier crucial period in his development in 1898-99. The Guggenheim painting demonstrates how Picasso had assimilated the influence of
African and Iberian art and the solid monumentality of
Cézanne's work. He endows the still-life objects with a
strong sense of their geometric shapes, their concrete-
ness and individuality. The green fruit in the bowl and
the reddish color of the jug in the background stand out
from the pale grays, tans and whites that dominate the
canvas. The tilting of the table, the narrow space, the
angular planes of the drapery (especially on the table
where faccting is evident) mark a transitional phase
from Picasso's proto-Cubist work to Analytical Cubism.

EXHIBITIONS:

London, Zwemmer Gallery, *Picasso,* May-June 1936, no. 29

Philadelphia Art Alliance, *Solomon R. Guggenheim
Collection of Non-Objective Paintings,* Feb. 8-28, 1937,
no. 190

London, Tate Gallery, *An exhibition of paintings from The
Solomon R. Guggenheim Museum, New York,* Apr. 16-
May 26, 1957, no. 59, traveled to The Hague, Gemeente-
museum, June 25-Sept. 1; Helsinki, Ateneumin Taidekokoel-
mat, Sept. 27-Oct. 20; Rome, Galleria Nazionale d'Arte
Moderna, Dec. 5, 1957-Jan. 8, 1958; Cologne, Wallraf-
Richartz-Museum, Jan. 26-Mar. 30; Paris, Musée des Arts
Décoratifs, Apr. 23-June 1

New York, The Solomon R. Guggenheim Museum,
Inaugural Selection, Oct. 21, 1959-June 19, 1960

The Cleveland Museum of Art, *Paths of Abstract Art,*
Oct. 4-Nov. 13, 1960, no. 18

New York, The Solomon R. Guggenheim Museum,
Cézanne and Structure in Modern Painting, June 5-
Oct. 13, 1963

Houston, The Museum of Fine Arts, *The Heroic Years:
Paris 1908-1914,* Oct. 21-Dec. 8, 1965

New York, The Solomon R. Guggenheim Museum, *Forty
Modern Masters: An Anniversary Show,* Dec. 16, 1977-
Feb. 5, 1978, no. 112

REFERENCES:

C. Zervos, *Pablo Picasso,* Paris, 1942, vol. 2, pt. 1, no. 164
and pl. 81

A. H. Barr, Jr., *Picasso: Fifty Years of His Art,* New York,
1946, p. 283

J. Sabartés, *Picasso: Documents iconographiques,* Geneva,
1954, pl. 187

U. Apollonio, *Fauves et Cubistes,* Bergamo and Paris, 1959,
p. 58, color repr.

Handbook, 1970, pp. 362, repr., 363, 364

Rudenstine, *Collection Catalogue,* 1976, no. 211, repr.

P. Daix and J. Rosselet, *Le Cubisme de Picasso,* Neuchâtel,
1979, no. 298, repr.

18 Accordionist. Summer 1911
(*L'Accordéoniste*)

37.537

Oil on canvas, 51¼ x 35¼ in. (130.2 x 89.5 cm.)

Signed l.l.: *Picasso*; inscribed on reverse: *Picasso/Ceret*. Not dated.

PROVENANCE:
from the artist (?)
Paul Guillaume, Paris, ca. 1920-by 1936
Valentine Gallery, New York, by 1936
Solomon R. Guggenheim, New York, 1936
Gift, Solomon R. Guggenheim, 1937

During the summer of 1911 Picasso and Braque worked closely together at Céret in the French Pyrenees. Picasso's *Accordionist* demonstrates how far he had moved in the direction of abstraction. The traditional relationship between figure and ground has been destroyed and replaced by a unified pictorial configuration. The extreme degree of fragmentation, the flat, shaded planes, non-descriptive regularized brushstrokes, monochromatic color and shallow space are characteristic of Analytical Cubism.

Picasso's *Accordionist* bears strong similarities to Braque's *Man with a Guitar*, summer 1911 (Collection The Museum of Modern Art, New York). As Robert Rosenblum has observed, both paintings have scroll patterns at the lower left, discernible indications of the sitter's fingers and vestiges of facial features. Picasso in particular favored figure painting and often chose to depict people playing musical instruments: for example, the Guggenheim's *Accordionist, "Ma Jolie,"* winter 1911-12 (Collection The Museum of Modern Art, New York), and *The Aficionado*, summer 1912 (Collection Kunstmuseum Basel). In these paintings there is a strong two-dimensional unity of surface, a sense of light emanating from the forms themselves and an articulation of the canvas that is dictated by the inner structure rather than by the arbitrary edges of the support.

EXHIBITIONS:
Philadelphia Art Alliance, *Solomon R. Guggenheim Collection of Non-Objective Paintings*, Feb. 8-28, 1937, no. 187

New York, The Museum of Modern Art, *Picasso: Forty Years of His Art*, Nov. 15, 1939-Jan. 7, 1940, no. 97, repr., traveled to The Art Institute of Chicago, Feb. 1-Mar. 3

The Art Gallery of Toronto, *Picasso*, Apr. 1949, no. 7

Paris, Musée des Arts Décoratifs, *Picasso*, June-Oct. 1955, no. 26, repr.

London, Tate Gallery, *An exhibition of paintings from The Solomon R. Guggenheim Museum, New York*, Apr. 16-May 26, 1957, no. 60, traveled to The Hague, Gemeentemuseum, June 25-Sept. 1; Helsinki, Ateneumin Taidekokoelmat, Sept. 27-Oct. 20; Rome, Galleria Nazionale d'Arte Moderna, Dec. 5, 1957-Jan. 8, 1958; Cologne, Wallraf-Richartz-Museum, Jan. 26-Mar. 30; Paris, Musée des Arts Décoratifs, Apr. 23-June 1

New York, The Solomon R. Guggenheim Museum, *Inaugural Selection*, Oct. 21, 1959-June 19, 1960

New York, Saidenberg Gallery, *Picasso, An American Tribute: Cubism*, Apr. 25-May 12, 1962, no. 5, repr.

New York, The Solomon R. Guggenheim Museum, *Cézanne and Structure in Modern Painting*, June 5-Oct. 13, 1963

New York, The Solomon R. Guggenheim Museum, *Forty Modern Masters: An Anniversary Show*, Dec. 16, 1977-Feb. 5, 1978, no. 113, repr.

REFERENCES:
C. Zervos, *Pablo Picasso*, Paris, 1942, vol. 2, pt. 1, no. 277 and pl. 135

A. H. Barr, Jr., *Picasso: Fifty Years of His Art*, New York, 1946, pp. 74-75, repr.

R. Rosenblum, *Cubism and Twentieth-Century Art*, New York, 1961, pp. 62, 64, pl. 33

Handbook, 1970, pp. 365-367, repr.

Rudenstine, *Collection Catalogue*, 1976, no. 212, color repr.

H. H. Arnason, *History of Modern Art*, rev. ed., New York, 1977, p. 135 and fig. 223

P. Daix and J. Rosselet, *Le Cubisme de Picasso*, Neuchâtel, 1979, no. 424, repr.

Picasso

19 Bottles and Glasses. Winter 1911-12
(Bouteilles et verres)

38.539

Oil on paper mounted on canvas, 25⅜ x 19½ in.
(64.4 x 49.5 cm.)

Signed l.r.: *Picasso.* Not dated.

PROVENANCE:
Gift of the artist
Max Pellequer, Paris, by 1937
Galerie Pierre, Paris, 1937-38
Solomon R. Guggenheim, New York, 1938
Gift, Solomon R. Guggenheim, 1938

Bottles and Glasses, which was executed in the winter
of 1911-12, does not differ significantly in style from the
Accordionist (cat. no. 18) painted earlier the same year.
However, it is more difficult to decipher objects here:
a glass and liqueur bottle at the left and a poster or
sign on the right. Picasso has painted the letters free-
hand instead of stenciling them as he often did from
the winter of 1911-12 on. The intentionally ambiguous
forms are secured with horizontal, vertical and
diagonal restrictions imposed by structural scaffolding.
These shapes exist close to the picture plane within a
sharply contracted space; they are concentrated in the
center of the composition and fade out toward the
edges of the canvas. The emphasis on purely formal
structure is particularly striking in *Bottles and Glasses.*

EXHIBITIONS:
Vancouver, B.C., Vancouver Art Gallery, *The Solomon R.
Guggenheim Museum: A Selection from the Museum Col-
lection,* Nov. 16-Dec. 12, 1954, no. 69, repr.

The Art Gallery of Toronto, *Comparisons,* Jan. 11-Feb. 3,
1957, no. 14c

London, Tate Gallery, *An exhibition of paintings from The
Solomon R. Guggenheim Museum, New York,* Apr. 16-May
26, 1957, no. 62, traveled to The Hague, Gemeentemuseum,
June 25-Sept. 1; Helsinki, Ateneumin Taidekokoelmat, Sept.
27-Oct. 20; Rome, Galleria Nazionale d'Arte Moderna, Dec.
5, 1957-Jan. 8, 1958; Cologne, Wallraf-Richartz-Museum,
Jan. 26-Mar. 30; Paris, Musée des Arts Décoratifs, Apr. 23-
June 1

Dallas Museum of Fine Arts, *The Arts of Man,* Oct. 6-Dec.
31, 1962, not in cat.

Berlin, Neue Nationalgalerie, *Tendenzen der Zwanziger
Jahre,* Aug. 14-Oct. 16, 1977, no. I-20, repr.

REFERENCES:
C. Zervos, *Pablo Picasso,* Paris, 1942, vol. 2, pt. 1, no. 299 and
pl. 145
J. Golding, *Cubism: A History and Analysis, 1907-1914,* rev.
ed., Boston, 1968, p. 113, pl. 13A
Handbook, 1970, pp. 368-369, repr.
Rudenstine, *Collection Catalogue,* 1976, no. 214, repr.
P. Daix and J. Rosselet, *Le Cubisme de Picasso,* Neuchâtel,
1979, no. 446, repr.

20 **Glass and Bottle of Bass.** Early 1914
(Verre et bouteille de Bass)

38.540

Oil, gouache, pencil, sawdust and newspaper on paper mounted on board, 18¾ x 24⅞ in. (47.7 x 62.6 cm.)

Signed l.r.: *Picasso*. Not dated.

PROVENANCE:
Gift of the artist
Max Pellequer, Paris, by 1937
Galerie Pierre, Paris, 1937-38
Solomon R. Guggenheim, New York, 1938
Gift, Solomon R. Guggenheim, 1938

In the summer of 1912 Braque and Picasso made their first *papiers collés* by pasting paper elements onto their compositions. The invention of the collage technique permitted the integration of various extraneous materials—paper, wood, sand, sawdust, newspaper, printed labels—into a work on paper or canvas.

In *Glass and Bottle of Bass,* which dates from early 1914, the glass and bottle are no longer fragmented according to the dictates of their structures but reduced to their simplest two-dimensional silhouettes. The frontal view of the glass is constructed from pieces of white paper (reinforced partly by white paint), while its shape when seen from above is indicated by a circular piece of newspaper. Multiple views of the bottle are suggested by the pencil shading and written word on white paper and by the pencil outline on the sawdust. Another piece of newspaper is pasted below the bottle, and pencil lines connect the various collage elements. The sawdust background provides color and texture in this essentially flat arrangement of objects on the surface.

Around 1913-14 Picasso executed over twenty works showing a bottle of Bass ale.

EXHIBITIONS:
Vancouver, B.C., Vancouver Art Gallery, *The Solomon R. Guggenheim Museum: A Selection from the Museum Collection,* Nov. 16-Dec. 12, 1954

New York, The Solomon R. Guggenheim Museum, *Forty Modern Masters: An Anniversary Show,* Dec. 16, 1977-Feb. 5, 1978, no. 114

REFERENCES:
C. Zervos, *Pablo Picasso,* Paris, 1942, vol. 2, pt. 2, no. 441 and pl. 206
Handbook, 1970, pp. 370, repr., 371

Picasso

21 **Mandolin and Guitar.** 1924
(Mandoline et guitare)

53.1358

Oil with sand on canvas, 55⅜ x 78⅞ in. (140.6 x 200.4 cm.)

Signed and dated l.l.: *Picasso/24.*

PROVENANCE:
from the artist
Paul Rosenberg, Paris, 1924
G. F. Reber, Lausanne, by 1927-53
Jon Nicholas Streep, New York, 1953

During the summers of 1924 and 1925 Picasso painted at least nine large colorful still lifes with an essentially similar motif: an arrangement of objects on a centrally situated table in front of an open window. This theme appeared for the first time in a group of drawings and watercolors Picasso did at Saint-Raphaël in 1919 when he first summered on the Côte d'Azur.

The Guggenheim canvas is structured by means of flat color areas and decorative patterns. Its pictorial organization also depends upon the curved contours of the still-life arrangement and the linear division of the floor and background wall. The bold, bright colors, the lively patterns of the tablecloth and the sky and clouds glimpsed through the window contribute essentially to the picture's vitality.

EXHIBITIONS:
Paris, Galerie Paul Rosenberg, *Exposition d'oeuvres récentes de Picasso,* June-July 1926, no. 29(?)

Paris, Galeries Georges Petit, *Picasso,* June 16-July 30, 1932, no. 156, repr.

Kunsthaus Zürich, *Picasso,* Sept. 11-Oct. 30, 1932, no. 149

Paris, Musée des Arts Décoratifs, *Picasso,* June 3-Oct. 14, 1955, no. 61

London, Tate Gallery, *An exhibition of paintings from The Solomon R. Guggenheim Museum, New York,* Apr. 16-May 26, 1957, no. 64, repr., traveled to The Hague, Gemeente-museum, June 25-Sept. 1; Helsinki, Ateneumin Taidekokoel-mat, Sept. 27-Oct. 20; Rome, Galleria Nazionale d'Arte Moderna, Dec. 5, 1957-Jan. 8, 1958; Cologne, Wallraf-Richartz-Museum, Jan. 26-Mar. 30; Paris, Musée des Arts Décoratifs, Apr. 23-June 1

New York, The Solomon R. Guggenheim Museum, *Inaugural Selection,* Oct. 21, 1959-June 19, 1960

New York, Paul Rosenberg and Co., *Picasso, An American Tribute: The Twenties,* Apr. 25-May 12, 1962, no. 35, repr.

Paris, Grand Palais, *Hommage à Pablo Picasso,* Nov. 18, 1966-Feb. 13, 1967, no. 133, repr.

Amsterdam, Stedelijk Museum, *Picasso,* Mar. 4-Apr. 30, 1967, no. 62, repr.

New York, Marlborough Gallery, *Homage to Picasso,* Oct. 1971, no. 37, color repr.

New York, The Solomon R. Guggenheim Museum, *Forty Modern Masters: An Anniversary Show,* Dec. 16, 1977-Feb. 5, 1978, no. 116

REFERENCES:
Bulletin de l'Effort Moderne, no. 17, July 1925, repr. betw. pp. 8-9

O. Schürer, *Picasso,* Berlin, 1927 [p. 67], repr.

C. Zervos, *Pablo Picasso,* Paris, 1952, vol. 5, no. 220 and pl. 107

R. Penrose, *Picasso: His Life and Work,* London, 1958, pl. XI, no. 4

H. L. C. Jaffé, *Picasso,* New York, 1964, pp. 110-111, color repr.

Handbook, 1970, pp. 374, color repr., 375

Rudenstine, *Collection Catalogue,* 1976, no. 216, color repr.

H. H. Arnason, *History of Modern Art,* rev. ed., New York, 1977, color pl. 142

Picasso

22 Woman with Yellow Hair. December 1931
(Femme aux cheveux jaunes)

78.2514 T59

Oil on canvas, 39⅜ x 31⅞ in. (100 x 81 cm.)

Signed l.l.: *Picasso*; dated on stretcher:
27 Decembre / M.CM.XXXI.

PROVENANCE:

from the artist
Justin K. Thannhauser, Paris and New York, 1937
Gift, Justin K. Thannhauser, 1978

The sleeping woman with yellow hair is Marie-Thérèse
Walter (1909-77). Picasso first met her in 1927 and
portrayed her distinctive profile and sculptural forms
most frequently in the 1930s when she lived with him.
Woman with Yellow Hair portrays Marie-Thérèse's
blonde hair and striking good looks. Picasso has united
forehead and nose in a single curve and has folded the
arms around the sleeping head to form emphatically
sweeping curves and opulent organic shapes. He
associated Marie-Thérèse with the languor, seductive-
ness and inward intensity of sleep and often, in the
paintings of the early 1930s, gave her skin a strong
lavender tonality.

EXHIBITIONS:

New York, The Museum of Modern Art, *Picasso: Forty
Years of His Art*, Nov. 15, 1939 - Jan. 7, 1940, no. 250, trav-
eled to The Art Institute of Chicago, Feb. 1 - Mar. 3; San
Francisco Museum of Art, June 25 - July 22

Buffalo, Albright Art Gallery, *French Paintings of the Twen-
tieth Century, 1900-1939*, Dec. 6 - 31, 1944, no. 50, traveled to
The Cincinnati Art Museum, Jan. 18-Feb. 18, 1945; City
Art Museum of St. Louis, Mar. 8-Apr. 16

The Santa Barbara Museum of Art, *Fiesta Exhibition, 1953:
Picasso, Gris, Miró, Dali*, Aug. 4 - 30, 1953, no. 29

New York, The Solomon R. Guggenheim Museum, *The
Justin K. Thannhauser Collection*, from Apr. 30, 1965

REFERENCES:

J. Cassou, *Picasso*, New York, 1940, p. 137, repr.

C. Zervos, *Pablo Picasso*, Paris, 1955, vol. 7, no. 333 and pl.
138

P. Daix, *La Vie de peintre de Pablo Picasso*, Paris, 1977,
p. 237, fn. 10 and pl. 32

Barnett, *Thannhauser Catalogue*, 1978, no. 59, color repr.

Fernand Léger 1881-1955

Jules Fernand Henri Léger was born February 4, 1881, at Argentan in Normandy. After apprenticing with an architect in Caen from 1897 to 1899, Léger settled in Paris in 1900 and supported himself as an architectural draftsman. He was refused entrance to the Ecole des Beaux-Arts, but nevertheless attended classes there; he also studied at the Académie Julian. Léger's earliest known works, which date from 1905, were primarily influenced by Impressionism. The experience of seeing the Cézanne retrospective at the Salon d'Automne in 1907 and his contact with the early Cubism of Picasso and Braque had an extremely significant impact on the development of his personal style. In 1910 he exhibited with Braque and Picasso at D.-H. Kahnweiler's gallery, where he was given a one-man show in 1912. From 1911 to 1914 Léger's work became increasingly abstract, and he started to limit his color to the primaries and black and white at this time.

Léger served in the military from 1914 to 1917. His "mechanical" period, in which figures and objects are characterized by tubular, machine-like forms, began in 1917. During the early 1920s he collaborated with the writer Blaise Cendrars on films and designed sets and costumes for Rolf de Maré's *Ballet Suédois*; in 1923-24 he made his first film without a plot, *Ballet mécanique*. Léger opened an atelier with Amédée Ozenfant in 1924 and in 1925, at the *Exposition Internationale des Arts Décoratifs,* presented his first murals at Le Corbusier's Pavillon de l'Esprit Nouveau. In 1931 he visited the United States for the first time; in 1935 The Museum of Modern Art, New York, and The Art Institute of Chicago presented exhibitions of his work. Léger lived in the United States from 1940 to 1945 but returned to France after the war. In the decade before his death Léger's wide-ranging projects included book illustrations, monumental figure paintings and murals, stained-glass windows, mosaics, polychrome ceramic sculptures and set and costume designs. In 1955 he won the Grand Prize at the São Paulo Bienal. Léger died August 17, 1955, at his home at Gif-sur-Yvette, France. The Musée National Fernand Léger was founded in 1957 in Biot.

23 **The Smokers.** December 1911-January 1912
(Les Fumeurs)

38.521

Oil on canvas, 51 x 38 in. (121.4 x 96.5 cm.)

Not signed or dated.

PROVENANCE:

from the artist
D.-H. Kahnweiler, Paris, 1912-14, by auction, Hôtel Drouot, Paris, July 4, 1922
Galerie l'Effort Moderne, Paris, 1922
Georges Bernheim, Paris, by 1926-38
Galerie Pierre, Paris, 1938
Solomon R. Guggenheim, New York, 1938
Gift, Solomon R. Guggenheim, 1938

Léger's Cubist works reveal a closer affinity to Delaunay's dynamic Cubism than to the static Cubism of Braque and Picasso. Like many of Robert Delaunay's paintings of Eiffel Towers (for example, cat. nos. 44 and 46), *The Smokers* contains lateral curtains and exhibits multiple points of view from which objects are represented. The volumes of smoke contrast with the flat, angular planes of trees, buildings and faces. Together they function on the picture plane to achieve a decidedly upward movement. Set apart from the dark tonality of urban landscape and foreground figures, the white smoke partakes of an almost sculptural form.

The Smokers is closely related to and slightly earlier in date than *The Wedding,* 1912 (Collection Musée National d'Art Moderne, Paris) and *The Woman in Blue,* late 1912 (Collection Kunstmuseum Basel). Léger's choice of smoke as a subject can be seen within the wider context of an interest on the part of artists at that time in atmospheric phenomena and a wish to give substance to clouds, steam, rain and snow.

EXHIBITIONS:

Paris, Grand Palais, *Société des Artistes Indépendants: Trente ans d'art indépendant 1884-1914,* Feb. 20-Mar. 21, 1926, suppl. no. 2798

Dresden, *Internationale Kunstausstellung,* June-Sept. 1926, no. 114

Kunsthaus Zürich, *Fernand Léger,* Apr. 30-May 25, 1933, no. 55

Paris, Musée du Petit Palais, *Maîtres de l'art indépendant, 1895-1937,* June-Oct. 1937, no. 13

London, Tate Gallery, *An exhibition of paintings from The Solomon R. Guggenheim Museum, New York,* Apr. 16-May 26, 1957, no. 39, traveled to The Hague, Gemeentemuseum, June 25-Sept. 1; Helsinki, Ateneumin Taidekokoelmat, Sept. 27-Oct. 20; Rome, Galleria Nazionale d'Arte Moderna, Dec. 5, 1957-Jan. 8, 1958; Cologne, Wallraf-Richartz-

Museum, Jan. 26-Mar. 30; Paris, Musée des Arts Décoratifs, Apr. 23-June 1

New York, The Solomon R. Guggenheim Museum, *Cézanne and Structure in Modern Painting,* June 6-Oct. 13, 1963

Los Angeles County Museum of Art, *The Cubist Epoch,* Dec. 15, 1970-Feb. 21, 1971, no. 178, color pl. 87, traveled to New York, The Metropolitan Museum of Art, Apr. 9-June 8

Paris, Grand Palais, *Fernand Léger,* Oct. 1971-Jan. 1972, no. 7, repr.

New York, The Solomon R. Guggenheim Museum, *Forty Modern Masters: An Anniversary Show,* Dec. 16, 1977-Feb. 5, 1978, no. 80, repr.

REFERENCES:

G. Apollinaire, *Les Peintres cubistes,* Paris, 1913, p. 65

D. Henry [Kahnweiler], "Fernand Léger," *Jahrbuch der Jungen Kunst,* vol. I, 1920, pp. 301-302, repr.

Bulletin de l'Effort Moderne, no. 9, Nov. 1924, betw. pp. 8-9, repr.

B. Cendrars, "F. Léger," *Cahiers d'Art,* 8e année, no. 3-4, 1933, n.p.

D. Cooper, *Léger et le nouvel espace,* Geneva, Paris and London, 1949, p. 44, repr.

K. Kuh, *Léger,* Urbana, 1953, p. 94, repr.

J. Golding, *Cubism: A History and Analysis, 1907-1914,* Boston, 1968, p. 153, pl. 62

Handbook, 1970, pp. 262, repr., 263, 264

V. Spate, *'Orphism, pure painting, simultaneity': the development of non-figurative painting in Paris, 1908-1914,* Ph.D. dissertation, Bryn Mawr College, 1970, pp. 212-214

C. Green, *Léger and the Avant-Garde,* New Haven and London, 1976, pp. 38-39, 41-45 and pl. 23

Rudenstine, *Collection Catalogue,* 1976, no. 161, color repr.

24 Study for Contrast of Forms. 1913
(Etude pour Contraste de formes)

48.1172 x50

Gouache on paper mounted on board, 19½ x 24 in.
(49.5 x 61 cm.)

Signed and dated l.r.: *F.L. 13.*

PROVENANCE:
Karl Nierendorf, New York, by 1948
Estate of Karl Nierendorf, 1948

From 1913 into 1914 Léger painted many variations
on the theme of *Contrast of Forms* in which the
reduction from visual reality resulted in a seemingly
abstract pictorial vocabulary. The forms may have
originated in landscapes and figure paintings but, in
the development of his individual Cubism, Léger
reordered them in relation to lines, colors and forms.
The essentially monochromatic range in the Guggenheim gouache reinforces Léger's emphasis on geometric
volumes. He contrasts cylindrical shapes and flat
planes, solids and voids. A closely related gouache is
with the Galerie Jan Krugier, Geneva (formerly
Collection Sidney Janis).

EXHIBITIONS:
New York, The Solomon R. Guggenheim Museum, *Selected
Sculpture and Works on Paper,* July 8-Sept. 14, 1969, repr.
New York, The Solomon R. Guggenheim Museum, *Forty
Modern Masters: An Anniversary Show,* Dec. 16, 1977-Feb.
5, 1978, no. 81

REFERENCE:
Handbook, 1970, p. 265, repr.

25 Mural Painting. 1924-25
(Peinture murale)

58.1507

Oil on canvas, 71 x 31⅞ in. (180.2 x 80.2 cm.)

Signed and dated l.r.: *F. LÉGER. 25*; inscribed on reverse: *PEINTURE MURALE / F. LÉGER—24.*

PROVENANCE:
Christian Zervos, Paris, by 1949-58

Léger's desire to use color in a non-restrictive manner as well as his growing interest in abstraction led him to execute several large mural paintings from 1924 to 1926. "In general, pure colors and geometric forms are not compatible with easel painting. Abstraction requires large surfaces, walls. There one can organize an architecture and a rhythm. This is called 'architectonie.' Moreover I would say that easel painting is often limited whereas mural painting is without specific dimensions." (Paris, Musée des Arts Décoratifs, 1956, p. 33)

Here Léger has presented an asymmetrical arrangement of geometric areas of color with strong emphasis on verticals. He has carefully positioned the flat areas of white, gray and black, amplified by reds in the vertical element at the left and balanced by blue at the right. It is not known if the Guggenheim canvas was meant to be seen with another mural painting or if Léger intended it for a specific architectural installation.

EXHIBITIONS:
Paris, Musée National d'Art Moderne, *Fernand Léger, 1905-1949,* Oct. 6-Nov. 13, 1949, no. 45

Kunsthalle Bern, *Fernand Léger,* Apr. 10-May 28, 1952, no. 31

Paris, Musée des Arts Décoratifs, *Fernand Léger, 1881-1955,* June-Oct. 1956, no. 51, repr.

New York, The Solomon R. Guggenheim Museum, *Inaugural Selection,* Oct. 21, 1959-June 19, 1960

New York, The Solomon R. Guggenheim Museum, *Cézanne and Structure in Modern Painting,* June 6-Oct. 13, 1963

REFERENCES:
A. Verdet, *Fernand Léger: le dynamisme pictural,* Geneva, 1955, pl. 22

Handbook, 1970, pp. 266, repr., 267

Rudenstine, *Collection Catalogue,* 1976, no. 166, repr.

26 Woman Holding a Vase. 1927
(Femme tenant un vase)

58.1508

Oil on canvas, 57⅝ x 38⅜ in. (146.3 x 97.5 cm.)

Signed and dated l.r.: *F. LÉGER. 27*; inscribed on reverse: *FEMME TENANT UN VASE / ETAT DÉFINITIF / F LÉGER. 27.*

PROVENANCE:

from the artist (?)
Baron Napoléon Gourgaud, Paris, late 1920s-44
Baroness Gourgaud, Yerre, 1944-57
Sidney Janis Gallery, New York, 1957-58

Woman Holding a Vase is an outstanding example of Léger's attempt to treat human figures with the same plasticity as objects or machines. The arms, the hands, the hair, the breast are all translated into inanimate "values of plastic form." The woman is no longer a figure but an architecture of forms. The interpenetration of woman and vase within an undefined space produces a monumental image.

There are two other extremely similar versions of *Woman Holding a Vase*: one dated 1924 is in the Statens Museum for Kunst, Copenhagen, and another dated 1924-27 is in the Kunstmuseum Basel. Léger indicated that the Guggenheim painting is the final version *(état définitif)*.

EXHIBITIONS:

Kunsthaus Zürich, *Fernand Léger*, Apr. 30-May 25, 1933, no. 116

Paris, Galerie Louis Carré, *La Figure dans l'oeuvre de Fernand Léger,* June 6-July 12, 1952, no. 8

Paris, Musée des Arts Décoratifs, *Fernand Léger, 1881-1955,* June-Oct. 1956, no. 62, repr.

Amsterdam, Stedelijk Museum, *Léger: Wegbereider,* Dec. 11, 1956-Jan. 28, 1957, no. 32

Munich, Haus der Kunst, *Fernand Léger, 1881-1955,* Mar.-May 1957, no. 49, repr.

Kunsthalle Basel, *Fernand Léger,* May 22-June 23, 1957, no. 53, repr.

Kunsthaus Zürich, *Fernand Léger,* July 6-Aug. 17, 1957, no. 68, repr.

New York, The Solomon R. Guggenheim Museum, *Inaugural Selection,* Oct. 21, 1959-June 19, 1960

New York, The Solomon R. Guggenheim Museum, *Cézanne and Structure in Modern Painting,* June 6-Oct. 13, 1963

New York, The Solomon R. Guggenheim Museum, *Forty Modern Masters: An Anniversary Show,* Dec. 16, 1977-Feb. 5, 1978, no. 84

REFERENCES:

B. Dorival, *Les Peintres du XXe siècle,* Paris, 1957, p. 107, color repr.

Handbook, 1970, pp. 268-269, color repr.

Rudenstine, *Collection Catalogue,* 1976, no. 168, color repr.

Léger

27 The Great Parade. 1954
(La Grande parade, état définitif)

62.1619

Oil on canvas, 117¾ x 157½ in. (299 x 400 cm.)

Not signed or dated.

PROVENANCE:
from the artist
Galerie Maeght, Paris, 1955-62

This final version of *The Great Parade,* painted a year before the artist's death, is considered the definitive work of Léger's career. It is the culmination of several themes developed over the preceding fifteen years: *Cyclists, Constructors, Country Outings* and, above all, the *Circus* pictures.

From 1947 Léger made hundreds of preparatory studies for the figures in *The Great Parade* and carefully worked out every detail. Earlier painted versions of the subject are in the collections of the Galerie Louise Leiris in Paris (1952) and the Musée National Fernand Léger in Biot *(The Great Parade Against a Red Background,* 1953). In the Guggenheim's *Great Parade* the acrobats at the upper left can be traced back to a 1940 drawing, and the letter "c" is all that remains from earlier versions in which the word *"cirque"* is spelled out. Léger has imposed free color areas that function independently of the essentially linear figurative composition. He has evolved a synthesis of color, form and rhythm. Not only the immense scale of the final version of *The Great Parade* but the complexity and monumentality of its composition demonstrate Léger's sophistication and command of expression.

EXHIBITIONS:
Paris, Maison de la Pensée Française, *Fernand Léger: Oeuvres récentes 1953-54,* Nov. 1954, no. 47, color repr.

São Paulo, Museu de Arte Moderna, *III Bienal,* summer 1955, no. 28

Paris, Musée des Arts Décoratifs, *Fernand Léger,* June-Oct. 1956, no. 157, repr.

Amsterdam, Stedelijk Museum, *Léger: Wegbereider,* Dec. 11, 1956-Jan. 28, 1957, no. 78

Munich, Haus der Kunst, *Fernand Léger: 1881-1955,* Mar.-May 1957, no. 138

Kunsthalle Basel, *Fernand Léger,* May 22-June 23, 1957, no. 102

Kunsthaus Zürich, *Fernand Léger,* July 6-Aug. 17, 1957, no. 140

New York, The Solomon R. Guggenheim Museum, *Fernand Léger: Five Themes and Variations,* Feb. 28-Apr. 29, 1962, no. 111, color repr.

Paris, Grand Palais, *Fernand Léger,* Oct. 1971-Jan. 1972, no. 240, color pl. xxvii

New York, The Solomon R. Guggenheim Museum, *Forty Modern Masters: An Anniversary Show,* Dec. 16, 1977-Feb. 5, 1978, no. 85

REFERENCES:
D. Vallier, "La Vie fait l'oeuvre de Fernand Léger," *Cahiers d'Art,* 29e année, no. 2, 1954, p. 173

D. Cooper, "La Grande parade de Fernand Léger," *L'Oeil,* no. 1, Jan. 15, 1955, pp. 21-25

A. Verdet, *Fernand Léger: le dynamisme pictural,* Geneva, 1955, pl. 54

A. Liberman, *The Artist in His Studio,* New York, 1960, pp. 50, 52, and pl. 91

P. de Francia, *Léger's "The Great Parade,"* London, 1969, pp. 25-28

Handbook, 1970, pp. 270, repr., 271

Fernand Léger: sa vie, son oeuvre, Milan, 1972, n.p., repr.

H. H. Arnason, *History of Modern Art,* rev. ed., New York, 1977, p. 214, and color pl. 75

Albert Gleizes 1881-1953

Albert Gleizes was born in Paris on December 8, 1881. He worked in his father's fabric design studio after completing secondary school. While serving in the army from 1901 to 1905, Gleizes began to paint seriously. He exhibited for the first time at the Société Nationale des Beaux-Arts, Paris, in 1902, and participated in the Salon d'Automne in 1903 and 1904.

With several friends, including the writer René Arcos, Gleizes founded the Abbaye de Créteil outside Paris in 1906. This utopian community of artists and writers scorned bourgeois society and sought to create a non-allegorical, epic art based on modern themes. The Abbaye closed due to financial difficulties in 1908. In 1909 and 1910 Gleizes met Henri Le Fauconnier, Léger, Robert Delaunay and Jean Metzinger. In 1910 he exhibited at the Salon des Indépendants, Paris, and the *Jack of Diamonds* in Moscow; the following year he wrote the first of many articles. In collaboration with Metzinger, Gleizes wrote *Du Cubisme*, published in 1912. The same year Gleizes helped found the *Section d'Or*.

In 1914 Gleizes again saw military service. His paintings had become abstract by 1915. Travels to New York, Barcelona and Bermuda during the next four years influenced his stylistic evolution. His first one-man show was held at the Galeries Dalmau, Barcelona, in 1916. Beginning in 1918 Gleizes became deeply involved in a search for spiritual values; his religious concerns were reflected in his painting and writing. In 1927 he founded Moly-Sabata, another utopian community of artists and craftsmen, in Sablons. His book, *La Forme et l'histoire*, examines Romanesque, Celtic and Oriental art. In the thirties Gleizes participated in the *Abstraction-Création* group. Later in his career Gleizes executed several large commissions including the murals for the Paris World's Fair of 1937. In 1947 a major Gleizes retrospective took place in Lyon at the Chapelle du Lycée Ampère. From 1949 to 1950 Gleizes worked on illustrations for Pascal's *Pensées*. He executed a fresco, *Eucharist*, for the chapel, Les Fontaines, at Chantilly in 1952. Gleizes died in Avignon on June 23, 1953.

28 **Portrait of an Army Doctor.** 1914-15
(Portrait d'un médecin militaire)

37.473

Oil on canvas, 47¼ x 37⅜ in. (119.8 x 95.1 cm.)

Signed and dated l.r.: *Alb Gleizes / Toul 1914*; inscribed on reverse: *Alb Gleizes / Toul 1914 / exposition de la Triennale* [?] */ 1915.*

PROVENANCE:
from the artist
Galerie René Gimpel, New York, 1937
Gift, Solomon R. Guggenheim, 1937

During Gleizes' year of military service at Toul in France in World War I, he was able to continue painting. The sitter in *Portrait of an Army Doctor* is Dr. Lambert, a surgeon attached to Gleizes' regiment who had taught at the University of Nancy. All but one of the eight surviving studies for the portrait are in the Guggenheim Museum collection.* In the painting Gleizes has carefully arranged the intersecting diagonals and has created circular areas to delineate the figure while focusing on the surgeon's white clothing and his dark hair, eyebrows and mustache. Related in style and conception to the *Portrait of Igor Stravinsky, 1914, Portrait of an Army Doctor* gives a dignified, sober impression of the subject but does not explicitly identify his profession.

* see Rudenstine, pp. 146-147

EXHIBITIONS:
New York, Galerie René Gimpel, *Albert Gleizes,* Dec. 15, 1936-Jan. 15, 1937, no. 8
Philadelphia Art Alliance, *Solomon R. Guggenheim Collection of Non-Objective Paintings,* Feb. 8-28, 1937, no. 166
London, Tate Gallery, *An exhibition of paintings from The Solomon R. Guggenheim Museum, New York,* Apr. 16-May 26, 1957, no. 23, traveled to The Hague, Gemeentemuseum, June 25-Sept. 1; Helsinki, Ateneumin Taidekokoelmat, Sept. 27-Oct. 20; Rome, Galleria Nazionale d'Arte Moderna, Dec. 5, 1957-Jan. 8, 1958; Cologne, Wallraf-Richartz-Museum, Jan. 26-Mar. 30; Paris, Musée des Arts Décoratifs, Apr. 23-June 1
New York, The Solomon R. Guggenheim Museum, *Inaugural Selection,* Oct. 21, 1959-June 19, 1960
New York, The Solomon R. Guggenheim Museum, *Cézanne and Structure in Modern Painting,* June 6-Oct. 13, 1963
New York, The Solomon R. Guggenheim Museum, *Albert Gleizes, 1881-1953: A Retrospective Exhibition,* Sept. 15-Nov. 1, 1964, no. 67, color repr., traveled to Paris, Musée National d'Art Moderne, Dec. 5, 1964-Jan. 31, 1965; Dortmund, Museum am Ostwall, Mar. 13-Apr. 25

New York, The Solomon R. Guggenheim Museum, *Forty Modern Masters: An Anniversary Show*, Dec. 16, 1977-Feb. 5, 1978, no. 46

REFERENCES:
A. Ozenfant and C.-E. Jeanneret, *La Peinture moderne*, Paris, 1924, p. 118, repr.

Handbook, 1970, pp. 136-137, repr.

D. Robbins, *The Formation and Maturity of Albert Gleizes*, Ph.D. dissertation, Institute of Fine Arts, New York University, 1975, pp. 171, 194

Rudenstine, *Collection Catalogue*, 1976, no. 49, color repr.

Gleizes

29 Brooklyn Bridge. 1915

44.942

Oil and gouache on canvas, 40⅛ x 40⅛ in. (102 x 102 cm.)

Signed and dated l.r.: *Brooklyn Bridge / Alb Gleizes 15.*

PROVENANCE:

from the artist
John Quinn, New York, 1916-24
Estate of John Quinn, 1924-27
J. B. Neumann, New York, 1927-44

Gleizes arrived in New York for the first time in the autumn of 1915 and stayed there until late in the spring of 1916. He was fascinated with the New York skyline and the signs and colored lights of Broadway, which were especially exotic since he did not know English. He particularly admired the Brooklyn Bridge and compared its builder to the architect of Notre Dame in Paris. The suspension bridge linking lower Manhattan and Brooklyn was completed in 1883 and inspired numerous other artists—most notably Feininger, Joseph Stella, John Marin and Max Weber—to represent its cables and arches. In our painting Gleizes gives a sense of this remarkable engineering achievement with intersecting diagonals and expresses his own excitement through the boldness and immediacy of his dynamic composition.

In addition to this canvas Gleizes painted two other versions of the Brooklyn Bridge: the final one, produced during a later visit in 1917, is also in the Guggenheim Museum collection.

EXHIBITIONS:

New York, Montross Gallery, *Pictures by Crotti, Duchamp, Gleizes, Metzinger,* Apr. 4-22, 1916, no. 40

New York, The Museum of Modern Art, *Cubism and Abstract Art,* Mar. 2-Apr. 19, 1936, no. 88, repr.

New York, New Art Circle, *Documents of Modern Painting from the Collection of J. B. Neumann,* Sept. 23-Nov. 30, 1940

The Brooklyn Museum, *Brooklyn Bridge: 75th Anniversary Exhibition,* Apr. 29-July 27, 1958

New York, The Solomon R. Guggenheim Museum, *Cézanne and Structure in Modern Painting,* June 6-Oct. 13, 1963

New York, The Solomon R. Guggenheim Museum, *Albert Gleizes, 1881-1953: A Retrospective Exhibition,* Sept. 15-Nov. 1, 1964, no. 84, repr., traveled to Paris, Musée National d'Art Moderne, Dec. 5, 1964-Jan. 31, 1965; Dortmund, Museum am Ostwall, Mar. 13-Apr. 25

New York, The Gallery of Modern Art, *About New York, Night and Day, 1915-1965,* Oct. 19-Nov. 15, 1965

Bordeaux, Musée des Beaux-Arts, *La Peinture française: collections américaines,* May 13-Sept. 15, 1966, no. 96

New York, The Solomon R. Guggenheim Museum, *Forty Modern Masters: An Anniversary Show,* Dec. 16, 1977-Feb. 5, 1978, no. 50, repr.

Washington, D. C., The Hirshhorn Museum and Sculpture Garden, Smithsonian Institution, *"The Noble Buyer:" John Quinn, Patron of the Avant-Garde,* June 15-Sept. 4, 1978, no. 29

REFERENCES:

The Literary Digest, vol. 51, Nov. 27, 1915, p. 1225, repr.

John Quinn, 1870-1925: Collection of Paintings, Watercolors, Drawings and Sculpture, Huntington, N. Y., 1926, p. 10

R. Rosenblum, *Cubism and Twentieth-Century Art,* New York, 1961, fig. 121

Handbook, 1970, pp. 140-141, repr.

Rudenstine, *Collection Catalogue,* 1976, no. 54, repr.

Juan Gris 1887-1927

Juan Gris was born José Victoriano Carmelo Carlos González-Pérez in Madrid on March 23, 1887. He studied mechanical drawing at the Escuela de Artes y Manufacturas in Madrid from 1902 to 1904, during which time he contributed drawings to local periodicals. From 1904 to 1905 he studied painting with the academic artist José Maria Carbonero. In 1906 he moved to Paris, where he lived for most of the remainder of his life. His friends in Paris included Picasso, Braque, Léger and the writers Max Jacob, Guillaume Apollinaire and Maurice Raynal. Although he continued to submit humorous illustrations to journals such as *L'Assiette au Beurre, Le Charivari* and *Le Cri de Paris,* Gris began to paint seriously in 1910. By 1912 he had developed a personal Cubist style.

He exhibited for the first time in 1912: at the Salon des Indépendants in Paris, the Galeries Dalmau in Barcelona, the gallery of Der Sturm in Berlin, the Salon de la Société Normande de Peinture Moderne in Rouen and the Salon de la Section d'Or in Paris. That same year D.-H. Kahnweiler signed Gris to a contract which gave him exclusive rights to the artist's work. Gris became a good friend of Matisse in 1914 and over the next several years formed close relationships with Lipchitz and Jean Metzinger. After Kahnweiler fled Paris at the outbreak of World War I, Gris signed a contract with Léonce Rosenberg in 1916. His first major one-man show was held at Rosenberg's Galerie l'Effort Moderne in Paris in 1919. The following year Kahnweiler returned and once again became Gris' dealer.

In 1922 the painter began commissions for sets and costumes for Sergei Diaghilev. Gris articulated most of his aesthetic theories during 1924 and 1925. He delivered his definitive lecture, "Des Possibilités de la peinture," at the Sorbonne in 1924. Major Gris exhibitions took place at the Galerie Simon in Paris and the Galerie Flechtheim in Berlin in 1923 and at the Galerie Flechtheim in Düsseldorf in 1925. As his health declined, Gris made frequent visits to the south of France. Gris died in Boulogne-sur-Seine on May 11, 1927, at age forty.

30 **Houses in Paris.** 1911
(Maisons à Paris)

48.1172 x 33

Oil on canvas, 20⅝ x 13½ in. (52.4 x 34.2 cm.)

Signed l.l.: *Juan Gris.* Not dated.

PROVENANCE:
from the artist
Marcel Duchamp, Paris
Howard Putzel, San Francisco
Josef von Sternberg, Hollywood
Nierendorf Gallery, New York, by 1948
Estate of Karl Nierendorf, 1948

This urban landscape dates from 1911, when Juan Gris lived in Montmartre in Paris. Soon after his arrival there from Madrid in 1906 he settled at 13, rue Ravignan, in the building called the "Bateau-Lavoir," where his compatriot Picasso also lived. Although Braque and Picasso were his friends, Gris was by no means their follower. His stylistic development evolved toward Cubism in an individual manner and revealed the influence of Cézanne. He painted his first oils in 1911. At that time Gris had his studio on the first floor of the "Bateau-Lavoir," overlooking place Ravignan (now place Emile Goudeau), and *Houses in Paris* may well represent the surrounding area.*

The Guggenheim picture reflects this early moment in Gris' Cubism in the slight flattening of the building, the tilted angle at which architectural elements are presented, in the emphasis on line as an integral part of the design and in the gray tonality which incorporates subtle shades of blue, green and pink. Related works showing buildings in Paris include an oil, *Houses in Paris,* in the Sprengel Collection, Hannover, and a drawing in The Museum of Modern Art, New York, Joan and Lester Avnet Collection.

* first observed by Rudenstine

EXHIBITIONS:
London, Tate Gallery, *An exhibition of paintings from The Solomon R. Guggenheim Museum, New York,* Apr. 16-May 26, 1957, no. 25, traveled to The Hague, Gemeentemuseum, June 25-Sept. 1; Helsinki, Ateneumin Taidekokoelmat, Sept. 27-Oct. 20; Rome, Galleria Nazionale d'Arte Moderna, Dec. 5, 1957-Jan. 8, 1958; Cologne, Wallraf-Richartz-Museum, Jan. 26-Mar. 30; Paris, Musée des Arts Décoratifs, Apr. 23-June 1

New York, The Solomon R. Guggenheim Museum, *Inaugural Selection,* Oct. 21, 1959-June 19, 1960

New York, Leonard Hutton Galleries, *Albert Gleizes and the Section d'Or,* Oct. 28-Nov. 21, 1964, no. 27

Dortmund, Museum am Ostwall, *Juan Gris,* Oct. 23-Dec. 4, 1965, no. 6, repr., traveled to Cologne, Wallraf-Richartz-Museum, Dec. 27, 1965-Feb. 13, 1966

The Baltimore Museum of Art, *From El Greco to Pollock: Early and Late Works by European and American Artists,* Oct. 22-Dec. 8, 1968, no. 107, repr.

New York, The Solomon R. Guggenheim Museum, *Forty Modern Masters: An Anniversary Show,* Dec. 16, 1977-Feb. 5, 1978, no. 51, repr.

REFERENCES:

Handbook, 1970, pp. 144-145, color repr.

Rudenstine, *Collection Catalogue,* 1976, no. 67, repr.

D. Cooper, *Juan Gris,* Paris, 1977, vol. I, pp. 14-15, repr., no. 7

31 Newspaper and Fruit Dish. March 1916
(Journal et compotier)

53.1341

Oil on canvas, 18⅛ x 14⅞ in. (46 x 37.8 cm.)

Signed and dated on reverse: *Juan Gris / 3-16 / I.*

PROVENANCE:

from the artist
Galerie l'Effort Moderne, Paris
Katherine S. Dreier, West Redding, Connecticut, by 1921-52
Gift, Estate of Katherine S. Dreier, 1953

Several still lifes Gris painted in March 1916 contain a newspaper and compotier on a table and a door visible in the background. This group includes another canvas that also belonged to Katherine S. Dreier and is now in the Yale University Art Gallery, New Haven. In *Newspaper and Fruit Dish* not only Gris' use of bright colors but also his technique of dotted brushstrokes in a contrasting color are worthy of special mention. It is well-known that Picasso and Braque had enlivened the surfaces of their work and created decorative effects with patterns of dots around 1914-15. Seurat may have been another source of inspiration: in his letters Gris makes clear his awareness of Seurat's technique, although he does not employ it in relation to color theory as the Neo-Impressionists did. For the most part in our picture Gris applied blue dabs of paint onto yellow areas, some yellow dots over pale pink areas and, at the top, superimposed red dots on yellow, gray and green. The final effect is not scientific but ornamental and colorful.

EXHIBITIONS:

Worcester Art Museum, *Exhibition of Paintings by Members of the Société Anonyme,* Nov. 3-Dec. 5, 1921, no. 20

The Brooklyn Museum, *An International Exhibition of Modern Art,* Nov. 19, 1926-Jan. 1, 1927, no. 206

New York, The Anderson Galleries, *An International Exhibition of Modern Art,* Jan. 25-Feb. 5, 1927, no. 120

New York, Marie Harriman Gallery, *Juan Gris,* opened Feb. 5, 1932, no. 20

New Haven, Yale University Art Gallery, *In Memory of Katherine S. Dreier 1877-1952: Her Own Collection of Modern Art,* Dec. 15, 1952-Feb. 1, 1953, no. 31

London, Tate Gallery, *An exhibition of paintings from The Solomon R. Guggenheim Museum, New York,* Apr. 16-May 26, 1957, no. 26, traveled to The Hague, Gemeentemuseum, June 25-Sept. 1; Helsinki, Ateneumin Taidekokoelmat, Sept. 27-Oct. 20; Rome, Galleria Nazionale d'Arte Moderna, Dec. 5, 1957-Jan. 8, 1958; Cologne, Wallraf-Richartz-Museum, Jan. 26-Mar. 30; Paris, Musée des Arts Décoratifs, Apr. 23-June 1

New York, The Solomon R. Guggenheim Museum, *Neo-Impressionism,* Feb. 9-Apr. 7, 1968, no. 171, repr.

Paris, Orangerie des Tuileries, *Juan Gris,* Mar. 14-July 1, 1974, no. 47

REFERENCES:

U. Apollonio, *Fauves e Cubisti,* Bergamo, 1959, p. 66, color repr.

Handbook, 1970, pp. 146-147, repr.

Rudenstine, *Collection Catalogue,* 1976, no. 68, repr.

D. Cooper, *Juan Gris,* Paris, 1977, vol. I, pp. 246-247, repr., no. 161

Gris

32 Fruit Dish on a Check Tablecloth. November 1917
(Compotier et nappe à carreaux)

38.238

Oil on wood panel, 31¾ x 21¼ in. (80.6 x 53.9 cm.)

Signed and dated l.l.: *Juan Gris / Paris 11-17.*

PROVENANCE:
from the artist
Galerie l'Effort Moderne, Paris
Pierre Faure, Paris
Rose Valland, Paris, by 1938
Solomon R. Guggenheim, New York, 1938
Gift, Solomon R. Guggenheim, 1938

Still lifes figure prominently in Gris' oeuvre. The artist's collage technique is reflected in the placing of compositional elements and in the overlapping planes. In the characteristically colorful *Fruit Dish on a Check Tablecloth,* the white area in the center and adjacent zones of bright green and pale pink are set off against a dark background comprised of various hues. The stylized pink and white checks introduce patterns of rectangles and ovals over the entire canvas. Fragmentation of objects and ornamental patterning create a complexity of design that is visually and intellectually satisfying. Gris' work is based on a schematic organization of color values and a strong sense of logic.

EXHIBITIONS:
New York, The Museum of Modern Art, *Juan Gris,* Apr. 9-June 1, 1958, p. 83, repr.

New York, The Solomon R. Guggenheim Museum, *Inaugural Selection,* Oct. 21, 1959-June 19, 1960

New York, The Solomon R. Guggenheim Museum, *Cézanne and Structure in Modern Painting,* June 6-Oct. 13, 1963

New York, The Solomon R. Guggenheim Museum, *Forty Modern Masters: An Anniversary Show,* Dec. 16, 1977-Feb. 5, 1978, no. 52

REFERENCES:
D.-H. Kahnweiler, *Juan Gris: His Life and Work,* New York, 1947, pl. 42

Handbook, 1970, pp. 149, repr., 150

Rudenstine, *Collection Catalogue,* 1976, no. 70, repr.

D. Cooper, *Juan Gris,* Paris, 1977, vol. I, pp. 348-349, repr., no. 237

Francis Picabia 1879-1953

François Marie Martinez Picabia was born on or about January 22, 1879, in Paris, of a Spanish father and French mother. He was enrolled at the Ecole des Arts Décoratifs in Paris from 1895 to 1897 and later studied with Albert Charles Wallet, Ferdinand Humbert and Fernand Cormon. He began to paint in an Impressionist manner in the winter of 1902-3 and started to exhibit works in this style at the Salon d'Automne and the Salon des Indépendants of 1903. His first one-man show was held at the Galerie Haussmann, Paris, in 1905. From 1908 elements of Fauvism, Neo-Impressionism, Cubism and other forms of abstraction appeared in his painting, and by 1912 he had evolved a personal amalgam of Cubism and Fauvism. Picabia produced his first purely abstract work in 1912.

Picabia became friends with Duchamp and Guillaume Apollinaire and associated with the Puteaux group in 1911-12. He participated in the 1913 Armory Show, visiting New York on this occasion and frequenting avant-garde circles. Alfred Stieglitz gave him a one-man exhibition at his gallery "291" this same year. In 1915, which marked the beginning of Picabia's machinist or mechanomorphic period, he and Duchamp, among others, instigated and participated in Dada manifestations in New York. Picabia lived in Barcelona in 1916-17; in 1917 he published his first volume of poetry and the first issues of *391*, his magazine modeled after Stieglitz's periodical *291*. For the next few years Picabia remained involved with the Dadaists in Zürich and Paris, creating scandals at the Salon d'Automne, but finally denounced Dada in 1921 for no longer being "new." He moved to Tremblay-sur-Mauldre, outside of Paris, the following year and returned to figurative art. In 1924 he attacked Breton and the Surrealists in *391*.

Picabia moved again in 1925, this time to Mougins. During the thirties he became close friends with Gertrude Stein. By the end of World War II Picabia returned to Paris. He resumed painting in an abstract style and writing poetry, and in March 1949 a retrospective of his work was held at the Galerie René Drouin in Paris. Picabia died in Paris on November 30, 1953.

33 Portrait of Mistinguett. ca. 1908-11

66.1801

Oil on canvas, 23⅝ x 19⅜ in. (60 x 49.2 cm.)

Signed and dated l.c.: *Francis Picabia 1907.*

PROVENANCE:
M. Axel, Paris
Pierre Granville, Paris, 1952-66

The Guggenheim's painting almost certainly represents Mistinguett, the famous actress and entertainer whom Picabia knew in the early 1900s. Most likely the artist painted her from memory. Born Jeanne Marie Bourgeois (1875-1956), she appeared in music halls in the 1890s, in comedy roles in 1907 and then at the Moulin Rouge, where she became part proprietor.

Thus, it is probably no coincidence that the *Portrait of Mistinguett* is reminiscent of Toulouse-Lautrec's representations of actresses and dance-hall performers in its emphasis on contour lines, flat areas of unmodeled color and an asymmetrical spatial organization. Picabia painted *Portrait of Mistinguett* at an early point in his career when Fauvism, Japonism and Symbolism exerted a persuasive influence. A certain eclecticism marks Picabia's early work, which evolves from Impressionist landscapes to the boldly contrasting, sensuous colors of the Fauves to Cubism and the theoretical considerations of the abstract art of Orphism and the *Section d'Or.*

EXHIBITIONS:
Paris, Galerie Furstenberg, *Picabia,* June 5-July 5, 1956, not in cat.

New York, The Solomon R. Guggenheim Museum, *Gauguin and the Decorative Style,* June 23-Oct. 23, 1966

New York, The Solomon R. Guggenheim Museum, *Francis Picabia,* Sept. 18-Dec. 6, 1970, no. 9, repr., traveled to Cincinnati Art Museum, Jan. 6-Feb. 7, 1971; Toronto, The Art Gallery of Ontario, Feb. 26-Mar. 28; Detroit Institute of Arts, May 12-June 27

Paris, Grand Palais, *Francis Picabia,* Jan. 23-Mar. 29, 1976, no. 7, repr.

New York, The Solomon R. Guggenheim Museum, *Forty Modern Masters: An Anniversary Show,* Dec. 16, 1977-Feb. 5, 1978, no. 110

REFERENCES:
Handbook, 1970, pp. 358-359, repr.

Rudenstine, *Collection Catalogue,* 1976, no. 209, repr.

W. A. Camfield, *Francis Picabia,* Princeton, N.J., 1979, p. 14 and fig. 29

Picabia

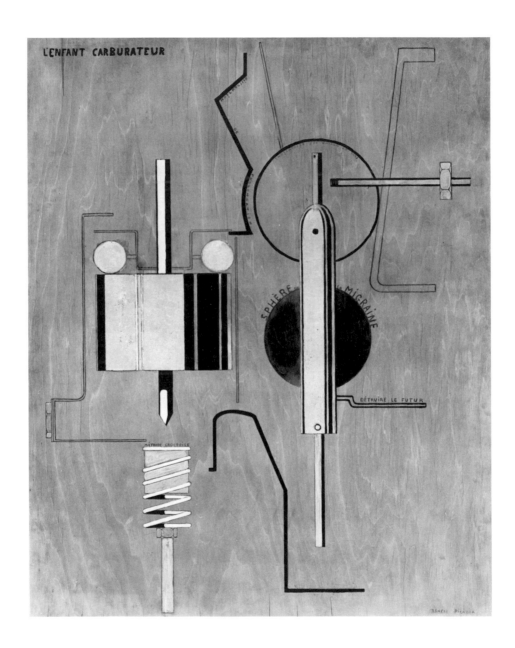

34 The Child Carburetor. 1919
(L'Enfant carburateur)

55.1426

Oil, enamel, metallic paint, gold leaf, pencil and crayon on stained plywood, 49¾ x 39⅞ in. (126.3 x 101.3 cm.)

Signed l.r.: *FRANCIS PICABIA*; inscribed u.l.: *L'ENFANT CARBURATEUR*; elsewhere on surface (left to right and top to bottom): *MÉTHODE CROCO-DILE*; *DISSOLUTION DE PROLONGATION*; *FLUX ET REFLUX DES RÉSOLUTIONS*; *SPHÈRE DE LA MIGRAINE*; *DÉTRUIRE LE FUTUR*; *VALSE EN JAQUETTE*. Not dated.

PROVENANCE:

from the artist
Gabrielle Buffet-Picabia, 1919-40
Peggy Guggenheim, New York, 1940-43
Patricia Matta, New York, 1943-54
Rose Fried Gallery, New York, 1954-55

Picabia's machinist style, which emerged in the summer of 1915 in New York and lasted into 1922, reflects his search for machine equivalents or symbols to comment on man. Picabia's love of cars is well-known as is his adaptation of technical diagrams of machines in his paintings. *Child Carburetor* is based upon the diagram of an actual carburetor, specifically the Racing Claudel.* The carburetor's parts can readily be interpreted in sexual terms. Picabia has altered the actual diagram to suggest two sets of male and female sex organs and to produce a machine that could not work. Not only the forms but also the inscriptions reinforce symbolic meaning and sexual imagery. Nor is the artist's personal life irrelevant, for in the autumn of 1919 both Picabia's wife and his mistress gave birth to his children.

* see Rudenstine

EXHIBITIONS:

Paris, Grand Palais, *Salon d'Automne,* Nov. 1-Dec. 10, 1919, no. 1533

Paris, Galerie de la Cible, *Picabia,* Dec. 10-25, 1920, no. 44

New York, The Museum of Modern Art, *Fantastic Art, Dada and Surrealism,* Dec. 7, 1936-Jan. 17, 1937, no. 462, repr.

New York, Rose Fried Gallery, *Group Exhibition,* Nov. 2-Dec. 1954, no. 11

New York, The Museum of Modern Art, *The Machine as Seen at the End of the Mechanical Age,* Nov. 25, 1968-Feb. 9, 1969, pp. 85, 93, 95, repr.

New York, The Solomon R. Guggenheim Museum, *Francis Picabia,* Sept. 18-Dec. 6, 1970, no. 63, color repr., traveled to Toronto, The Art Gallery of Ontario, Feb. 26-Mar. 28, 1971

Paris, Grand Palais, *Francis Picabia,* Jan. 23-Mar. 29, 1976, no. 80

New York, The Solomon R. Guggenheim Museum, *Forty Modern Masters: An Anniversary Show,* Dec. 16, 1977-Feb. 5, 1978, no. 111, repr.

REFERENCES:

The Little Review, spring 1922, repr. betw. pp. 16 and 17

P. Guggenheim, ed., *Art of this Century,* New York, 1942, p. 60

G. Everling-Picabia, "C'était hier Dada," *Les Oeuvres libres,* Paris, June 1955, p. 129

W. A. Camfield, "The Machine Style of Francis Picabia," *The Art Bulletin,* vol. XLVIII, Sept.-Dec. 1966, p. 320, fig. 32

Handbook, 1970, pp. 360-361, repr.

Rudenstine, *Collection Catalogue,* 1976, no. 210, color repr.

H. H. Arnason, *History of Modern Art,* rev. ed., New York, 1977, p. 350, fig. 544

W. A. Camfield, *Francis Picabia,* Princeton, N. J., 1979, pp. 128-131 and color pl. IX, fig. 169

Marcel Duchamp 1887-1968

Henri-Robert-Marcel Duchamp was born July 28, 1887, near Blainville, France. He joined his artist brothers, Jacques Villon and Raymond Duchamp-Villon, in Paris in 1904 where he studied painting at the Académie Julian until 1905. Duchamp's early works were Post-Impressionist in style, and he exhibited for the first time in 1909 at the Salon des Indépendants and the Salon d'Automne in Paris. His paintings of 1911 were directly related to Cubism but emphasized successive images of a single body in motion. In 1912 he painted the first version of *Nude Descending a Staircase*; this was shown at the Salon de la Section d'Or of that same year and subsequently created great controversy at the Armory Show in New York in 1913. The Futurist show at Galerie Bernheim-Jeune, Paris, in 1912 impressed him profoundly.

Duchamp's radical and iconoclastic ideas predated the founding of the Dada movement in Zürich in 1916. By 1913 he had abandoned traditional painting and drawing for various experimental forms including mechanical drawings, studies and notations that would be incorporated in a major work, the *Large Glass* of 1915-23. In 1914 Duchamp introduced his Readymades—common objects, sometimes altered, presented as works of art—which had a revolutionary impact upon many painters and sculptors. In 1915 Duchamp came to New York where his circle included Katherine Dreier and Man Ray, with whom he founded the Société Anonyme, as well as Louise and Walter Arensberg, Picabia and other avant-garde figures.

After playing chess avidly for nine months in Buenos Aires, Duchamp returned to France in the summer of 1919 and associated with the Dada group in Paris. In New York in 1920 he made his first motor-driven constructions and invented Rrose Sélavy, his feminine alterego. Duchamp moved back to Paris in 1923 and seemed to have abandoned art for chess but in fact continued his artistic experiments. From the mid-1930s he collaborated with the Surrealists and participated in their exhibitions. Duchamp settled permanently in New York in 1942 and became a United States citizen in 1955. During the 1940s he associated and exhibited with the Surrealist emigrés in New York and in 1946 began *Etant donnés*, a major assemblage on which he worked secretly for the next twenty years. Duchamp directly influenced a generation of young Americans. He died in the Paris suburb of Neuilly-sur-Seine on October 2, 1968.

35 Apropos of Little Sister. October 1911
(A propos de jeune soeur)

71.1944

Oil on canvas, 28¾ x 23⅝ in. (73 x 60 cm.)

Signed and dated l.l.: *MARCEL DUCHAMP / Octobre 11*; inscribed on reverse, which shows studies of a nude woman and a girl: *merd*[e].

PROVENANCE:

from the artist
Carroll Galleries, Inc., New York, 1915
John Quinn, New York, 1915-24
Estate of John Quinn, 1924-25
Henri-Pierre Roché and the artist, 1925
Private collection, ca. 1959
Cordier & Ekstrom, New York, 1964
Mary Sisler, New York, 1964-71

The sitter is Magdeleine, the youngest of Marcel Duchamp's brothers and sisters, who was thirteen at the time. She remembers that she was reading while Duchamp painted her.* During the autumn of 1911 Duchamp portrayed his sister in profile in another picture, *Yvonne and Magdeleine Torn in Tatters*, and completed *Sonata* which represents his mother and three sisters. In *Apropos of Little Sister* the delicate, light colors are accentuated by the texture of the canvas itself and the angularity of forms suggests an awareness of Cubism. Painted at his family home in Rouen in October 1911, it follows Duchamp's early work which was influenced by Cézanne, the Fauves and Symbolists but occurs before his interest in successive images of a single body in motion culminated early in 1912 in *Nude Descending a Staircase*.

* correspondence with the author, Feb. 1978

EXHIBITIONS:

New York, Carroll Galleries, Inc., *Third Exhibition of Contemporary French Art*, Mar. 8-Apr. 3, 1915, no. 19

London, New Burlington Galleries, *The International Surrealist Exhibition*, June 11-July 4, 1936, no. 80

Paris, Musée National d'Art Moderne, *Le Cubisme 1907-1914*, Jan. 30-Apr. 9, 1953, no. 63

Paris, Musée Pédagogique, *Pérennité de l'art gaulois*, Feb.-Mar. 1955, no. 464

Paris, Galerie L'Oeil, *Minotaure*, May-June 1962, no. 18

Strasbourg, Château des Rohan, *La Grande aventure de l'art du XXe siècle*, June 8-Sept. 15, 1963, no. 31

New York, Cordier & Ekstrom, *Not Seen and/or Less Seen of/by Marcel Duchamp/ Rrose Sélavy 1904-64: Mary Sisler Collection*, Jan. 14-Feb. 13, 1965, no. 51, color repr.

Philadelphia Museum of Art, *Marcel Duchamp,* Sept. 22-
Nov. 11, 1973, no. 81, repr., traveled to New York, The
Museum of Modern Art, Dec. 3, 1973-Feb. 10, 1974; The
Art Institute of Chicago, Mar. 9-Apr. 21

Paris, Musée National d'Art Moderne, *L'Oeuvre de Marcel
Duchamp,* Jan. 31-May 2, 1977, no. 42, repr.

New York, The Solomon R. Guggenheim Museum, *Forty
Modern Masters: An Anniversary Show,* Dec. 16, 1977-Feb.
5, 1978, no. 29, repr.

REFERENCES:

E. Tériade, "La Peinture surréaliste," *Minotaure,* no. 8, June
15, 1936, p. 4, repr.

R. Lebel, *Marcel Duchamp,* New York, 1959, p. 161, no. 74
and pl. 44

H.-P. Roché, "Adieu, brave petite collection!," *L'Oeil,* no.
51, Mar. 1959, p. 35, repr.

A. Schwarz, *The Complete Works of Marcel Duchamp,*
New York, 1969, pp. 15, 106-107, 427, repr., no. 164

P. Cabanne, *The Brothers Duchamp,* Boston, 1976, p. 47,
color repr.

Raymond Duchamp-Villon 1876-1918

Raymond Duchamp-Villon was born Pierre-Maurice-Raymond Duchamp on November 5, 1876, in Damville, near Rouen. From 1894 to 1898 he studied medicine at the University of Paris. When illness forced him to abandon his studies, he decided to make a career in sculpture, until then an avocation. During the early years of the century he moved to Paris, where he exhibited for the first time at the Salon de la Société Nationale des Beaux-Arts in 1902. His second show was held at the same Salon in 1903, the year he settled in Neuilly-sur-Seine. In 1905 he had his first exhibition at the Salon d'Automne and a show at the Galerie Legrip in Rouen with his brother, the painter Jacques Villon; he moved with Villon to Puteaux two years later.

His participation in the jury of the sculpture section of the Salon d'Automne began in 1907 and was instrumental in promoting the Cubists in the early teens. Around this time he, Villon and their other brother, Marcel Duchamp, attended weekly meetings of the Puteaux group of artists and critics. In 1911 he exhibited at the Galerie de l'Art Contemporain in Paris; the following year his work was included in a show organized by the Duchamp brothers at the Salon de la Section d'Or at the Galerie de la Boétie. Duchamp-Villon's work was exhibited at the Armory Show in New York in 1913 and the Galerie André Groult in Paris, the Galerie S.V.U. Mánes in Prague and the gallery of Der Sturm in Berlin in 1914. During World War I Duchamp-Villon served in the army in a medical capacity, but was able to continue work on his major sculpture *The Horse*. He contracted typhoid fever in late 1916 while stationed at Champagne; the disease ultimately resulted in his death on October 9, 1918, in the military hospital at Cannes.

36 Maggy. 1912
(Tête de Maggy)

57.1464

Bronze, 29⅛ in. (74 cm.) high

Signed and dated on left shoulder: *Duchamp-Villon / 1911*; inscribed on reverse l.l.: *Louis Carré Editeur Paris*; reverse l.r.: *Rudier / Fondeur Paris*.

Third of eight casts made in September 1954 by Rudier Fondeur, Paris, for Louis Carré

PROVENANCE:
Galerie Louis Carré et Cie., Paris, 1954-57

The sitter, Maggy, was the wife of Georges Ribemont-Dessaignes, the Surrealist poet and painter who apparently met the artist in 1909 and was a frequent visitor to Puteaux. Duchamp-Villon has accentuated her prominent features to the point of caricature. The absence of modeling, surface texture, realistic detail and psychological interpretation is immediately apparent. Instead, the emphasis is on essential volumes and their formal relationships. Close in style to the sculptor's head of *Baudelaire* of 1911, *Maggy* displays to an even greater degree the process of reduction and redefinition. The distinctive cylindrical neck, bulging forehead, deep ridges of the eyebrows and cheeks in *Maggy* can be discerned in incipient form in *Baudelaire*. In the distortion of facial features and the Cubist sense of structure, *Maggy* bears a decided resemblance to Matisse's bronzes of *Jeannette*, particularly the third and fourth versions which date from the spring and autumn of 1911.

The plaster head of *Maggy* (Estate of the artist) has been dated 1912 since it was first exhibited in 1914 at the Galerie André Groult in Paris. Other bronze casts of *Maggy* are in The Hirshhorn Museum and Sculpture Garden in Washington, D.C., and the Musée National d'Art Moderne in Paris.

EXHIBITIONS:
New York, The Solomon R. Guggenheim Museum, *Jacques Villon, Raymond Duchamp-Villon, Marcel Duchamp,* Feb. 20-Mar. 10, 1957, repr., traveled to Houston, The Museum of Fine Arts, Mar. 23-Apr. 21

New York, M. Knoedler and Co., Inc., *Raymond Duchamp-Villon 1876-1918,* Oct. 10-Nov. 4, 1967, no. 17, fig. 4

New York, The Solomon R. Guggenheim Museum, *Selected Sculpture and Works on Paper,* July 8-Sept. 14, 1969, p. 116, repr.

New York, The Solomon R. Guggenheim Museum, *Forty Modern Masters: An Anniversary Show,* Dec. 16, 1977-Feb. 8, 1978, no. 31, repr.

REFERENCES:

W. Pach, *Raymond Duchamp-Villon,* Paris, 1924, p. 61, repr. (plaster)

R. Rosenblum, "The Duchamp Family," *Arts,* vol. 31, Apr. 1957, p. 20, repr.

G. H. Hamilton, "Raymond Duchamp-Villon," *L'Oeil,* no. 151-153, Sept. 1967, pp. 51, repr., 52

Handbook, 1970, pp. 106-107, repr.

P. Cabanne, *The Brothers Duchamp,* Boston, 1976, p. 109

H. H. Arnason, *History of Modern Art,* rev. ed., New York, 1977, pp. 125, repr., 195

Jacques Villon 1875-1963

Jacques Villon was born Gaston Duchamp on July 31, 1875, in Damville, Normandy. While still a lycée student in Rouen he began his artistic training under his grandfather, Emile Nicolle, who taught him engraving. In 1894 he began to study law at the University of Paris; that same summer he entered the Ecole des Beaux-Arts in Rouen and shortly thereafter started to send his drawings to local illustrated newspapers. After securing his father's reluctant permission to study art on the condition that he continue his law studies, he returned to Paris where he attended the Atelier Cormon. He adopted the name Jacques Villon in 1895.

For almost ten years he worked largely in graphic media, contributing drawings to Parisian illustrated papers and making color prints and posters. In 1903 he helped organize the drawing section of the first Salon d'Automne. Villon's first gallery exhibition, shared with his brother, sculptor Raymond Duchamp-Villon, took place at Galerie Legrip, Rouen, in 1905. In 1904-5 he studied at the Académie Julian in Paris, painting in a Neo-Impressionist style. He began to spend more time painting around 1906-7 and from 1910 devoted himself primarily to it. In 1906 he settled in Puteaux. There, in 1911, he and Duchamp-Villon started to meet with the Puteaux group, which included their brother Marcel Duchamp, Kupka, Picabia, Gleizes, Robert Delaunay, Léger and others. The same year Villon named and helped found the *Section d'Or*. He exhibited nine paintings at the 1913 New York Armory Show and sold them all.

Villon's first one-man show in America was held at the Société Anonyme, New York, in 1921; by the thirties he was better known in the United States than in Europe. In 1932 he joined the *Abstraction-Création* group and exhibited with them. An important exhibition of Villon's work was held in Paris in 1944 at the Galerie Louis Carré, from that time his exclusive representative. Villon received honors at a number of international exhibitions, including First Prize, Carnegie International, 1950, and Grand Prize for Painting, Venice Biennale, 1956. He designed stained-glass windows for the cathedral at Metz in 1955. Villon died on June 9, 1963, in Puteaux at the age of eighty-seven.

37 **Color Perspective.** 1921
(Perspective colorée)

53.1356

Oil on canvas, 21¼ x 28⅝ in. (54 x 72.7 cm.)

Signed l.r.: *JV*; signed and dated on reverse: *Jacques Villon/21.*

PROVENANCE:
from the artist
Katherine S. Dreier, West Redding, Connecticut, ca. 1922-52
Gift, Estate of Katherine S. Dreier, 1953

Jacques Villon began his career as a printmaker, and line remains a crucial element in his abstractions of about 1919 to 1924. In *Color Perspective* flat, polygonal planes are superimposed on each other and are seen against a flat background. Cognizant of the color theories of M. A. Rosenstiehl and others, Villon explored intricate color relationships, the sensations produced by color disposed on a flat surface and, here, the variations in value and intensity that occur when red is juxtaposed with black and white.

While certain of Villon's paintings from the 1920s appear to be non-objective, a source in nature has been identified for the Jockey series among other works; it is possible, therefore, that other abstractions derive from figuration as well. Villon gave several abstractions the title *Color Perspective*: for example, a painting in The Museum of Modern Art, New York, and two others in the Yale University Art Gallery, New Haven, all dated 1922 and all once in the collection of Katherine S. Dreier.

EXHIBITIONS:
New York, The Museum of Modern Art, *Paintings from New York Private Collections,* July 2-Sept. 22, 1946, p. 5

New Haven, Yale University Art Gallery, *In Memory of Katherine S. Dreier, 1877-1952: Her Own Collection of Modern Art,* Dec. 15, 1952-Feb. 1, 1953, no. 68

New York, The Solomon R. Guggenheim Museum, *Jacques Villon, Raymond Duchamp-Villon, Marcel Duchamp,* Feb. 20-Mar. 10, 1957, repr., traveled to Houston, The Museum of Fine Arts, Mar. 23-Apr. 21

The Cleveland Museum of Art, *Paths of Abstract Art,* Oct. 4-Nov. 13, 1960, no. 34, repr.

Paris, Galerie Charpentier, *Cent tableaux de Jacques Villon,* Apr. 26-June 12, 1961

New York, E. V. Thaw & Co., *Jacques Villon,* Mar. 24-Apr. 18, 1964, no. 4, repr.

REFERENCES:

R. Rosenblum, *Cubism and Twentieth-Century Art,* New York, 1961, p. 156 and fig. 109

Rudenstine, *Collection Catalogue,* 1976, no. 243, repr.

H. H. Arnason, *History of Modern Art,* rev. ed., New York, 1977, p. 217, fig. 370

František Kupka 1871-1957

František Kupka was born September 22, 1871, in Opočno in eastern Bohemia. From 1889 to 1892 he studied at the Prague Academy. At this time he painted historical and patriotic themes. In 1892 Kupka enrolled at the Akademie der bildenden Künste in Vienna where he concentrated on symbolic and allegorical subjects. He exhibited at the Kunstverein, Vienna, in 1894. His involvement with theosophy and Eastern philosophy dates from this period. By spring 1896 Kupka had settled in Paris; there he attended the Académie Julian briefly and then studied with J. P. Laurens at the Ecole des Beaux-Arts.

Kupka worked as an illustrator of books and posters and, during his early years in Paris, became known for satirical drawings for newspapers and magazines. In 1906 he settled in Puteaux, a suburb of Paris, and that same year exhibited for the first time at the Salon d'Automne. Kupka was deeply impressed by the first Futurist Manifesto, published in 1909 in *Le Figaro*. Kupka's work became increasingly abstract around 1910-11, reflecting his theories of motion, color and the relationship between music and painting. In 1911 he participated in meetings of the Puteaux group, which included his neighbors Villon and Duchamp-Villon as well as Duchamp, Gleizes, Jean Metzinger, Picabia, Léger, Guillaume Apollinaire and others. In 1912 he exhibited at the Salon des Indépendants in the Cubist room, although he did not wish to be identified with any movement. Later that same year at the Salon d'Automne his paintings caused critical indignation.

La Création dans les arts plastiques (Creation in the Visual Arts), a book Kupka completed in 1913, was published in Prague in 1923. In 1921 his first one-man show in Paris was held at Galerie Povolozky. In 1931 he was a founding member of *Abstraction-Création* together with van Doesburg, Herbin, Vantongerloo, Hélion, Arp and Gleizes; in 1936 his work was included in the exhibition *Cubism and Abstract Art* at The Museum of Modern Art, New York, and in an important two-man show with Alphonse Mucha at the Jeu de Paume, Paris. A major retrospective of his work took place at the Galerie S.V.U. Mánes in Prague in 1946. The same year Kupka participated in the Salon des Réalités Nouvelles, Paris, where he continued to exhibit regularly until his death. During the early 1950s he gained general recognition and had several one-man shows in New York. Kupka died in Puteaux on June 24, 1957. Important Kupka retrospectives were held at the Musée National d'Art Moderne, Paris, in 1958 and The Solomon R. Guggenheim Museum, New York, in 1975.

38 Planes by Colors, Large Nude. 1909-10
(Plans par couleurs, grand nu)

68.1860

Oil on canvas, 59⅛ x 71⅛ in. (150.1 x 180.8 cm.)

Signed and dated l.r.: *Kupka / 1909*.

PROVENANCE:

from the artist
Mme Eugénie Kupka, Courbevoie, 1957-58
Richard L. Feigen, New York, 1958-61
Mr. and Mrs. Andrew P. Fuller, New York, 1961-68
Gift, Mrs. Andrew P. Fuller, 1968

Over a period of several years, from about 1906 to 1910, Kupka transformed a traditional reclining nude into a formal arrangement of color planes: *Planes by Colors, Large Nude* represents one stage in this metamorphosis. The evolution of this painting can be traced through more than twenty studies.

Although his work reveals a familiarity with Divisionism, Symbolism, Fauvism and Cubism, Kupka was not allied with any artistic movements. In *Planes by Colors, Large Nude* Kupka has eliminated three-dimensional modeling and has constructed the figure with color areas. The pinkish white, green and purple planes differentiate successive positions in depth, although spatial recession is not otherwise indicated. It is a pivotal work, which points in the direction of abstraction and would be followed by other paintings where planes of color are investigated.

EXHIBITIONS:

Paris, Grand Palais, *Salon d'Automne*, Oct. 1-Nov. 8, 1911, no. 811

Paris, Musée des Ecoles Etrangères Contemporains, Jeu de Paume des Tuileries, *F. Kupka-A. Mucha*, June 1936, no. 16, repr.

Prague, Galerie S.V.U. Mánes, *František Kupka*, Nov. 14-Dec. 8, 1946, no. 9

Paris, Grand Palais, *Salon des Indépendants*, Apr. 14-May 9, 1954, no. 1630

São Paulo, Museu de Arte Moderna, *IV Bienal: French Pavilion*, Sept.-Dec. 1957, no. 45

Paris, Musée National d'Art Moderne, *Kupka*, May 27-July 13, 1958, no. 5

New York, The Solomon R. Guggenheim Museum, *František Kupka, 1871-1957: A Retrospective*, Oct. 10-Dec. 7, 1975, no. 42, repr., traveled to Kunsthaus Zürich, Jan. 17-Mar. 14, 1976

New York, The Solomon R. Guggenheim Museum, *Forty Modern Masters: An Anniversary Show*, Dec. 16, 1977-Feb. 5, 1978, no. 74, repr.

REFERENCES:

L. Degand, "Kupka," *Art d'Aujourd'hui,* sér. 3, no. 3-4,
Feb.-Mar. 1952, pp. 55-56, repr.

D. Fédit, *L'Oeuvre de Kupka,* Paris, 1966, p. 48

L. Vachtová, *Frank Kupka: Pioneer of Abstract Art,* New
York, 1968, pp. 73, repr., 103, 299, no. 87

Handbook, 1970, pp. 254-255, color repr.

Rudenstine, *Collection Catalogue,* 1976, no. 158, color repr.

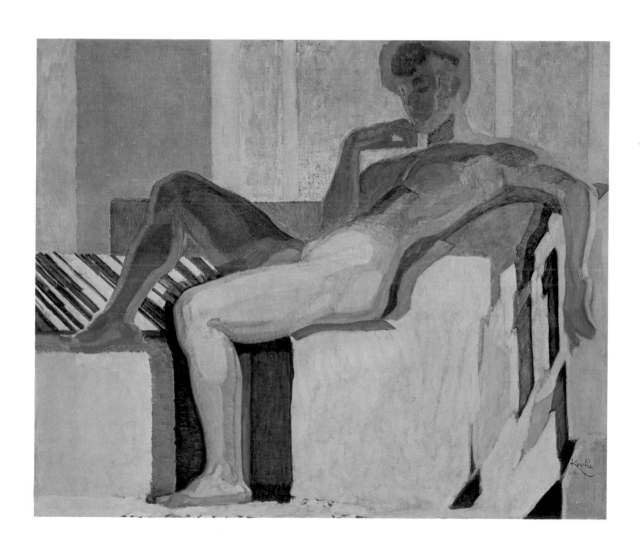

39 The Colored One. ca. 1919-20
(La Colorée)

66.1810

Oil on canvas, 25⅝ x 21¼ in. (65 x 54 cm.)

Signed l.l.: *Kupka.* Not dated.

PROVENANCE:
from the artist
Mme Eugénie Kupka, Courbevoie, 1957-58
Richard L. Feigen, New York, 1958-61
Mr. and Mrs. Andrew P. Fuller, New York, 1961-66
Gift, Mrs. Andrew P. Fuller, 1966

In *The Colored One* Kupka depicts a nude woman lying on her back, her extended legs encircling the golden disc of the sun above. The radiant, translucent color heightens the picture's symbolic aspects while its figurative imagery is rare in Kupka's work after World War I. *The Colored One* reflects Kupka's preoccupation at the time with images of both macrocosmic process and microcosmic germination: for example, *Tale of Pistils and Stamens.**

* see M. Rowell, *Kupka,* exh. cat., New York, 1975, nos. 116-122

EXHIBITIONS:
New York, The Solomon R. Guggenheim Museum, *Gauguin and the Decorative Style,* June 23-Oct. 23, 1966
New York, Spencer A. Samuels and Co., *Frank Kupka,* Mar.-Apr. 1968, no. 40, repr.
New York, The Solomon R. Guggenheim Museum, *František Kupka, 1871-1957: A Retrospective,* Oct. 10-Dec. 7, 1975, no. 116, repr., traveled to Kunsthaus Zürich, Jan. 17-Mar. 14, 1976
New York, The Solomon R. Guggenheim Museum, *Forty Modern Masters: An Anniversary Show,* Dec. 16, 1977-Feb. 5, 1978, no. 78

REFERENCES:
Handbook, 1970, p. 257, repr.
Rudenstine, *Collection Catalogue,* 1976, no. 159, repr.

40 Two Blues II. 1956
(Deux Bleus II)

62.1618

Oil on canvas, 38¼ x 33⅜ in. (97.2 x 84.8 cm.)

Signed and dated l.r.: *Kupka / 1956.*

PROVENANCE:
from the artist
Mme Eugénie Kupka, Courbevoie, 1957-62
Gift, Mme Eugénie Kupka, 1962

In 1955, towards the end of his life, Kupka painted
Two Blues I, 1955 (Collection Musée National d'Art
Moderne, Paris); it was followed the next year by the
Guggenheim's *Two Blues II.* As Kupka's color theories
evolved, he came to associate colors with certain
characteristics. He considered the ideal shape for blue
to be vertical and rectilinear, properties embodied in
the distinctly elongated lozenges of *Two Blues. Two
Blues* continues the theme of earlier works (such as

The Form of Blue, 1929-31) while the simplified,
asymmetrical composition belongs to Kupka's late style.

EXHIBITIONS:
São Paulo, Museu de Arte Moderna, *IV Bienal: French
Pavilion,* Sept.-Dec. 1957, no. 43
New York, The Solomon R. Guggenheim Museum,
František Kupka, 1871-1957: A Retrospective, Oct. 10-Dec.
7, 1975, no. 190, repr., traveled to Kunsthaus Zürich, Jan. 17-
Mar. 14, 1976

REFERENCE:
Handbook, 1970, p. 259, repr.

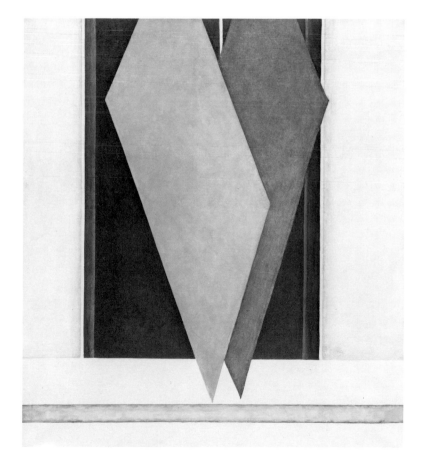

Robert Delaunay 1885-1941

Robert-Victor-Félix Delaunay was born in Paris on April 12, 1885. In 1902, after secondary education, he apprenticed in a studio for theater sets in Belleville. In 1903 he started painting and by 1904 was exhibiting: that year and in 1906 at the Salon d'Automne and from 1904 until World War I at the Salon des Indépendants. Between 1905 and 1907 Delaunay became friendly with Rousseau and Jean Metzinger and studied the color theories of M.-E. Chevreul; he was then painting in a Neo-Impressionist manner. Cézanne's work also influenced Delaunay around this time. From 1907-8 he served in the military in Laon and upon returning to Paris he had contact with the Cubists, who in turn influenced his work. 1909-10 saw the emergence of Delaunay's personal style: he painted his first *Eiffel Tower* in 1909. In 1910 Delaunay married the painter Sonia Terk, who became his collaborator on many projects.

Delaunay's participation in exhibitions in Germany and association with advanced artists working there began in 1911: that year Kandinsky invited him to participate in the first *Blaue Reiter (Blue Rider)* exhibition in Munich. At this time he became friendly with Guillaume Apollinaire, Henri Le Fauconnier and Gleizes. In 1912 Delaunay's first one-man show took place at the Galerie Barbazanges, Paris, and he began his Window pictures. Inspired by the lyricism of color of the Windows, Apollinaire invented the term "Orphism" or "Orphic Cubism" to describe Delaunay's work. In 1913 Delaunay painted his Circular Form or Disc pictures; this year also marks the beginning of his friendship with Blaise Cendrars.

From 1914 to 1920 Delaunay lived in Spain and Portugal and became friends with Sergei Diaghilev, Igor Stravinsky, Diego Rivera and Leonide Massine. He did the decor for the *Ballets Russes* in 1918. By 1920 he had returned to Paris. Here, in 1922, a major exhibition of his work was held at Galerie Paul Guillaume, and he began his second Eiffel Tower series. In 1924 he undertook his Runner paintings and in 1925 executed frescoes for the Palais de l'Ambassade de France at the *Exposition Internationale des Arts Décoratifs* in Paris. In 1937 he completed murals for the Palais des Chemins de Fer and Palais de l'Air at the Paris World's Fair. His last works were decorations for the sculpture hall of the Salon des Tuileries in 1938. In 1939 he helped organize the exhibition *Réalités Nouvelles*. Delaunay died in Montpellier on October 25, 1941.

41 Saint-Séverin No. 3. 1909-10

41.462

Oil on canvas, 45 x 34⅞ in. (114.1 x 88.6 cm.)

Signed l.r.: *r. delaun*[ay]. Not dated.

PROVENANCE:
from the artist
Städtische Kunsthalle Mannheim, 1928-37
Gutekunst und Klipstein, Bern, by 1939
Solomon R. Guggenheim, New York, 1939-41
Gift, Solomon R. Guggenheim, 1941

Robert Delaunay executed seven large oils and numerous drawings of the church of Saint-Séverin in 1909-10: the first instance of a series in his work. The Gothic Church, located in rue des Prêtres Saint-Séverin in Paris, interested the young artist, who painted the canvases in his nearby studio. Like the other versions, *Saint-Séverin No. 3* represents the fifteenth-century ambulatory with its curved vaults, Gothic arches and stained-glass windows. Delaunay chose a view that enabled him to depict tipping arches and bulging columns at the point where the ambulatory curves around the choir and, in addition, permitted him to paint colors modified by the light emanating from the stained-glass windows. The monochromatic color of the Guggenheim's picture appears related to Cézanne's work. In fact, Delaunay spoke of the Saint-Séverin motif as occurring in "a period of transition from Cézanne to Cubism, or rather from Cézanne to the *Windows*." (*Du Cubisme à l'art abstrait,* pp. 86-87)

EXHIBITIONS:
Städtische Kunsthalle Mannheim, *Wege und Richtungen der abstrakten Malerei*, Jan. 30-Mar. 27, 1927, no. 32

New York, The Solomon R. Guggenheim Museum, *Robert Delaunay*, Mar. 22-May 22, 1955, traveled to Boston, Institute of Contemporary Art, June 2-30

Paris, Musée National d'Art Moderne, *Robert Delaunay,* May 25-Sept. 30, 1957, no. 15, traveled to Amsterdam, Stedelijk Museum, Oct. 18-Dec. 1; Eindhoven, Stedelijk van Abbemuseum, Dec. 6, 1957-Jan. 11, 1958; London, Arts Council Gallery, Jan. 25-Feb. 22

New York, The Solomon R. Guggenheim Museum, *Inaugural Selection,* Oct. 21, 1959-June 19, 1960

Kunstverein in Hamburg, *Robert Delaunay,* Jan. 26-Mar. 11, 1962, no. 8, color repr., traveled to Cologne, Wallraf-Richartz-Museum, Mar. 24-May 6; Frankfurter Kunstverein, May 18-June 24

New York, The Solomon R. Guggenheim Museum, *Cézanne and Structure in Modern Painting,* June 6-Oct. 13, 1963

Ottawa, National Gallery of Canada, *Robert and Sonia Delaunay,* Oct. 8-31, 1965, no. 9, repr., traveled to Montreal Museum of Fine Arts, Nov. 10-Dec. 5

New York, The Solomon R. Guggenheim Museum, *Forty Modern Masters: An Anniversary Show,* Dec. 16, 1977-Feb. 5, 1978, no. 22, repr.

REFERENCES:

A. Gleizes, *Kubismus: Bauhausbücher 13,* Munich, 1928, pl. 5

R. Delaunay, *Du Cubisme à l'art abstrait,* ed. P. Francastel, Paris, 1957, pp. 62, 86, 87, 227, 228

G. Habasque, "Catalogue de l'oeuvre de Robert Delaunay," *Du Cubisme à l'art abstrait,* ed. P. Francastel, Paris, 1957, no. 45

G. Vriesen and M. Imdahl, *Robert Delaunay: Light and Color,* New York, 1969, pp. 26, 28, 74, 75 and fig. 10

Handbook, 1970, pp. 86, repr., 87, 88

Rudenstine, *Collection Catalogue,* 1976, no. 32, repr.

H. H. Arnason, *History of Modern Art,* rev. ed., New York, 1977, color pl. 76

M. Hoog, *Robert Delaunay,* New York, 1977, p. 22, color repr.

42 Eiffel Tower with Trees. Summer 1910
(Tour Eiffel aux arbres)

46.1035

Oil on canvas, 49¾ x 36½ in. (126.4 x 92.8 cm.)

Signed and dated l.l.: *r. delaunay 09.*

PROVENANCE:

Sonia Delaunay, Paris, 1946

Delaunay represented the Eiffel Tower at least thirty
times. His earliest version dates from 1909 and was
followed by eight major pictures executed from 1909 to
1911; he returned to the theme once again in the 1920s.
In 1909 the tower was already twenty years old, had
appeared in the paintings of Seurat, Rousseau and
others and was the subject of films. It was, however,
still thought of as a sensational accomplishment of
modern engineering.

For Delaunay the Eiffel Tower was a symbol of
modernism. Not only did it dominate the Paris skyline
but, as Delaunay himself pointed out, the tower was
the tallest structure in the world. Its radio and telegraph
antennas played an important role in communications.

In *Eiffel Tower with Trees* the subdued palette and
fragmentation of forms are reminiscent of Braque and
even Cézanne. The planar handling of clouds and
foliage in this painting will be transformed into the
planar treatment of Paris buildings in the *Eiffel Tower*
of 1911 (see next catalogue entry). Delaunay studied
the tower from many angles and attempted to combine
multiple perspectives in a single composition. Although
it rises upward powerfully, the tower in *Eiffel Tower
with Trees* appears related to its natural surroundings,
whereas the structure in *Eiffel Tower*, because of the
many horizontal and vertical points of view, seems to
be collapsing into itself.

EXHIBITIONS:

New York, The Solomon R. Guggenheim Museum, *Robert
Delaunay,* Mar. 22-May 22, 1955, traveled to Boston, Institute of Contemporary Art, June 2-30

Paris, Musée National d'Art Moderne, *Robert Delaunay,*
May 25-Sept. 30, 1957, no. 17, repr., traveled to Amsterdam,
Stedelijk Museum, Oct. 18-Dec. 1; Eindhoven, Stedelijk van
Abbemuseum, Dec. 6, 1957-Jan. 11, 1958; London, Arts
Council Gallery, Jan. 25-Feb. 22

Kunstverein in Hamburg, *Robert Delaunay,* Jan. 26-Mar. 11,
1962, no. 11, traveled to Cologne, Wallraf-Richartz-Museum,
Mar. 24-May 6; Frankfurter Kunstverein, May 18-June 24

REFERENCES:

F. Gilles de la Tourette, *Robert Delaunay,* Paris, 1950,
pp. 26-28 and pl. 8

"Un texte inédit de Robert Delaunay," *Aujourd'hui,* no. 11,
Jan. 1957, p. 31, repr.

G. Habasque, "Catalogue de l'oeuvre de Robert Delaunay,"
Du Cubisme à l'art abstrait, ed. P. Francastel, Paris, 1957,
no. 70

Handbook, 1959, p. 46, repr.

G. Vriesen and M. Imdahl, *Robert Delaunay: Light and
Color,* New York, 1969, p. 29 and fig. 12

M. Seuphor, *L'Art abstrait,* Paris, 1971, p. 157, repr.

Rudenstine, *Collection Catalogue,* 1976, no. 33, repr.

H. H. Arnason, *History of Modern Art,* rev. ed., New York,
1977, color pl. 77

43 Eiffel Tower. 1911
(Tour Eiffel)

37.463

Oil on canvas, 79½ x 54½ in. (202 x 138.4 cm.)

Signed and dated l.r.: *r delaunay 1910*; inscribed l.l.:
la tour 1910; on reverse: *"la tour 1910" / salle 41
indépendants / 1911 / r. delaunay 19 / Bl. malesherbes.*

PROVENANCE:

from the artist
Solomon R. Guggenheim, New York, 1930
Gift, Solomon R. Guggenheim, 1937

EXHIBITIONS:

Paris, Grand Palais, *Société des Artistes Indépendants,
Trente ans d'art indépendant, 1884-1914,* Feb. 20-Mar. 21,
1926, no. 684

Kunsthaus Zürich, *Abstrakte und Surrealistische Malerei
und Plastik,* Oct. 6-Nov. 3, 1929, no. 21

Charleston, S.C., Carolina Art Association, Gibbes Memorial Art Gallery, *Solomon R. Guggenheim Collection of
Non-Objective Paintings,* Mar. 1-Apr. 12, 1936, no. 112

New York, The Solomon R. Guggenheim Museum, *Robert
Delaunay,* Mar. 22-May 22, 1955, traveled to Boston, Institute of Contemporary Art, June 2-30

Paris, Musée National d'Art Moderne, *Robert Delaunay,*
May 25-Sept. 30, 1957, no. 22, repr., traveled to Amsterdam,
Stedelijk Museum, Oct. 18-Dec. 1; Eindhoven, Stedelijk van
Abbemuseum, Dec. 6, 1957-Jan. 11, 1958; London, Arts
Council Gallery, Jan. 25-Feb. 22

Brussels, Palais des Beaux-Arts, *50 Ans d'art moderne,* Apr.
17-July 21, 1958, no. 69, repr.

New York, The Solomon R. Guggenheim Museum,
Inaugural Selection, Oct. 21, 1959-June 19, 1960

Los Angeles County Museum of Art, *The Cubist Epoch,*
Dec. 15, 1970-Feb. 21, 1971, no. 61, color pl. 79, traveled to
New York, The Metropolitan Museum of Art, Apr. 9-June 8

New York, The Solomon R. Guggenheim Museum, *Forty
Modern Masters: An Anniversary Show,* Dec. 16, 1977-Feb.
5, 1978, no. 23

REFERENCES:

F. Gilles de la Tourette, *Robert Delaunay,* 1950, pl. 9

R. Delaunay, *Du Cubisme à l'art abstrait,* ed. P. Francastel,
Paris, 1957, pp. 79, 227

G. Habasque, "Catalogue de l'oeuvre de Robert Delaunay,"
Du Cubisme à l'art abstrait, ed. P. Francastel, Paris, 1957,
no. 78

J. Golding, *Cubism: A History and Analysis 1907-1914,* rev.
ed., Boston, 1968, pp. 148-149 and pl. 67

M. Martin, *Futurist Art and Theory, 1909-1915,* Oxford,
1968, pp. 106-107 and pl. 74a

U. Laxner, "Robert Delaunay: Tour Eiffel," *Museum Folkwang, Essen, Mitteilungen,* Band 3, 1969, no. 12

Handbook, 1970, pp. 88, 89, repr., 90

Rudenstine, *Collection Catalogue,* 1976, no. 34, color repr.

M. Hoog, *Robert Delaunay,* New York, 1977, p. 12, color
repr.

Delaunay

44 The City. 1911
(La Ville)

38.464

Oil on canvas, 57⅛ x 44½ in. (145 x 111.9 cm.)

Signed and dated l.l.: *la ville 1911 r. delaunay*; inscribed on reverse: *année 1909-10-11-12; Ier exposition / cubiste / Salle 41 aux indépendants / 1911.*

PROVENANCE:
from the artist
Solomon R. Guggenheim, New York, 1938
Gift, Solomon R. Guggenheim, 1938

The composition of *The City* apparently was derived from a photograph Delaunay had which showed the Eiffel Tower from the southwest corner of the top of the Arc de Triomphe. Nevertheless, Delaunay added the lateral curtains he often used. With the exception of the curtain folds framing either side, the painting is situated in slight but undefined depth. The picture demonstrates Delaunay's rapprochement with Cubism—in particular, the close-valued color scheme partakes of Cubist chromatic austerity. However, unlike Braque's and Picasso's Cubism—an essentially graphic form of expression—drawing plays no role in Delaunay's painting; instead light and its effect on color are determining compositional factors. In order to achieve the fragmented modulation of the field, Delaunay used a mosaic-like pointillist technique he had practiced earlier under the influence of the Neo-Impressionists Paul Signac and Henri-Edmond Cross.

EXHIBITIONS:
Paris, Galerie Barbazanges, *Robert Delaunay - Marie Laurencin,* Feb. 28-Mar. 13, 1912, no. 8

Berlin, Der Sturm, *2. Ausstellung,* Apr. 12-May 15, 1912, no. 41

Paris, Les Expositions de "Beaux-Arts," *Les Créateurs du Cubisme,* Mar.-Apr. 1935, no. 27

New York, The Solomon R. Guggenheim Museum, *Robert Delaunay,* Mar. 22-May 22, 1955, traveled to Boston, Institute of Contemporary Art, June 2-30

Paris, Musée National d'Art Moderne, *Robert Delaunay,* May 25-Sept. 30, 1957, no. 26, repr., traveled to Amsterdam, Stedelijk Museum, Oct. 18-Dec. 1; Eindhoven, Stedelijk van Abbemuseum, Dec. 6, 1957-Jan. 11, 1958; London, Arts Council Gallery, Jan. 25-Feb. 22

Kunstverein in Hamburg, *Robert Delaunay,* Jan. 26-Mar. 11, 1962, no. 14, repr., traveled to Cologne, Wallraf-Richartz-Museum, Mar. 24-May 6; Frankfurter Kunstverein, May 18-June 24

Ottawa, National Gallery of Canada, *Robert and Sonia Delaunay,* Oct. 8-31, 1965, no. 14, repr., traveled to Montreal Museum of Fine Arts, Nov. 10-Dec. 5

Los Angeles County Museum of Art, *The Cubist Epoch,* Dec. 15, 1970-Feb. 21, 1971, no. 62, color pl. 83, traveled to New York, The Metropolitan Museum of Art, Apr. 9-June 8

REFERENCES:
R. Delaunay, *Du Cubisme à l'art abstrait,* ed. P. Francastel, Paris, 1957, pp. 73, 79

G. Habasque, "Catalogue de l'oeuvre de Robert Delaunay," *Du Cubisme à l'art abstrait,* ed. P. Francastel, Paris, 1957, no. 87

J. Golding, *Cubism: A History and Analysis 1907-1914,* rev. ed., Boston, 1968, pp. 155-156, pl. 68

Handbook, 1970, pp. 90, repr., 91

Rudenstine, *Collection Catalogue,* 1976, no. 35, color repr.

45 Window on the City No. 3. 1911-12
(La Fenêtre sur la ville no. 3)

47.878

Oil on canvas, 44¾ x 51½ in. (113.5 x 130.7 cm.)

Signed and dated l.r.: *r. delaunay 1910-11*; inscribed on reverse: *r. delaunay / 19 [. . .]-1910-Paris-1911-I [. . .] / fen [. . .] e sur La Ville nº 4.*

PROVENANCE:
Sonia Delaunay, Paris, 1947

Window on the City No. 3 marks a transition from Delaunay's use of light to break up objects in the earlier Eiffel Tower paintings to his concern for pure light as the subject itself in the Window series of 1912. The decorative checkerboard design, previously employed in a more random manner, here becomes an overall grid consistent with the larger patterns of triangles and rectangles.

Delaunay's paintings were enthusiastically received in Germany. *Window on the City No. 3* was included in a Der Sturm gallery exhibition in Berlin early in 1913, and other pictures were shown with works of the *Blaue Reiter (Blue Rider)* group in Munich in December 1911 and subsequently purchased by Jawlensky, Bernhard Koehler and Adolf Erbsloh. Kandinsky corresponded with Delaunay; Klee, Marc and August Macke all visited him in Paris; and Delaunay traveled to Germany at the time of the exhibition at Der Sturm.

EXHIBITIONS:
Berlin, Der Sturm, *12. Ausstellung: R. Delaunay,* Jan. 27-Feb. 20, 1913, no. 15

New York, World's Fair, French Pavilion, *Contemporary French Art,* 1939, no. 42

New York, The Solomon R. Guggenheim Museum, *Robert Delaunay,* Mar. 22-May 22, 1955, traveled to Boston, Institute of Contemporary Art, June 2-30

London, Tate Gallery, *An exhibition of paintings from The Solomon R. Guggenheim Museum, New York,* Apr. 16-May 26, 1957, no. 13, traveled to The Hague, Gemeentemuseum, June 25-Sept. 1; Helsinki, Ateneumin Taidekokoelmat, Sept. 27-Oct. 20; Rome, Galleria Nazionale d'Arte Moderna, Dec. 5, 1957-Jan. 8, 1958; Cologne, Wallraf-Richartz-Museum, Jan. 26-Mar. 30; Paris, Musée des Arts Décoratifs, Apr. 23-June 1

New York, The Solomon R. Guggenheim Museum, *Inaugural Selection,* Oct. 21, 1959-June 19, 1960

The Cleveland Museum of Art, *Paths of Abstract Art,* Oct. 4-Nov. 13, 1960, no. 27, repr.

Bordeaux, Musée des Beaux-Arts, *La Peinture française: collections américaines,* May 13-Sept. 15, 1966, no. 91

New York, The Solomon R. Guggenheim Museum, *Neo-Impressionism,* Feb. 9-Apr. 7, 1968, no. 170, color repr.

Fine Arts Gallery of San Diego, *Color and Form 1909-1914,* Nov. 20, 1971-Jan. 2, 1972, no. 9, color repr., traveled to The Oakland Museum, Jan. 26-Mar. 5; Seattle Art Museum, Mar. 24-May 7

New York, The Solomon R. Guggenheim Museum, *Forty Modern Masters: An Anniversary Show,* Dec. 16, 1977-Feb. 5, 1978, no. 24

REFERENCES:
G. Apollinaire, *Robert Delaunay,* Paris, 1912, no. 15, pl. 5

R. Delaunay, *Du Cubisme à l'art abstrait,* ed. P. Francastel, Paris, 1957, pp. 62, 107, 108, 110

G. Habasque, "Catalogue de l'oeuvre de Robert Delaunay," *Du Cubisme à l'art abstrait,* ed. P. Francastel, Paris, 1957, no. 86

H. B. Chipp, "Orphism and Color Theory," *The Art Bulletin,* vol. XL, Mar. 1958, pp. 59-60 and fig. 2

Handbook, 1959, p. 48, repr.

J. Langner, "Zu den Fenster-Bildern von Robert Delaunay," *Jahrbuch der Hamburger Kunstsammlungen,* Band 7, 1962, pp. 72-73, repr.

W. Haftmann, *Painting in the Twentieth Century,* New York, 1965, pp. 96, 98, color repr.

G. Vriesen and M. Imdahl, *Robert Delaunay: Light and Color,* New York, 1969, pp. 34, 42 and fig. 17

Rudenstine, *Collection Catalogue,* 1976, no. 36, repr.

H. H. Arnason, *History of Modern Art,* rev. ed., New York, 1977, color pl. 78

Delaunay

46 Red Eiffel Tower. 1911-12
(*La Tour rouge*)

46.1036

Oil on canvas, 49¼ x 35⅜ in. (125 x 90.3 cm.)

Signed l.r.: *r. delaun*[ay]. Not dated.

PROVENANCE:
Sonia Delaunay, Paris, 1946

In contrast to the Guggenheim's two earlier representations of the subject, the structure in *Red Eiffel Tower* appears more rigidly upright. This is accentuated by the way Delaunay cuts off the tower at the top and reduces the number of vantage points from which it is seen. The huge structure is emphatically red and thus more colorful than in reality. Delaunay uses the color to differentiate the tower from the surrounding light and to sustain its upward thrust. In the *Red Eiffel Tower* he emphasizes the radiant light streaming down on the tower rather than the iron girders with which it is constructed. To Delaunay the Eiffel Tower was ambitious, monumental and aggressively modern: a symbol of the modern world.

EXHIBITIONS:
Paris, Galerie Barbazanges, *Robert Delaunay - Marie Laurencin,* Feb. 28-Mar. 13, 1912, no. 24

Berlin, Der Sturm, *12. Ausstellung: R. Delaunay,* Jan. 27-Feb. 20, 1913, no. 17

Paris, Musée National d'Art Moderne, *L'Oeuvre du XXe siècle,* May-June 1952, no. 21, traveled to London, Tate Gallery, July 15-Aug. 17

The Arts Club of Chicago, *Robert Delaunay,* Oct. 24-Nov. 21, 1952, no. 11, repr.

New York, The Solomon R. Guggenheim Museum, *Robert Delaunay,* Mar. 22-May 22, 1955, traveled to Boston, Institute of Contemporary Art, June 2-30

London, Tate Gallery, *An exhibition of paintings from The Solomon R. Guggenheim Museum, New York,* Apr. 16-May 26, 1957, no. 16, traveled to The Hague, Gemeentemuseum, June 25-Sept. 1; Helsinki, Ateneumin Taidekokoelmat, Sept. 27-Oct. 20; Rome, Galleria Nazionale d'Arte Moderna, Dec. 5, 1957-Jan. 8, 1958; Cologne, Wallraf-Richartz-Museum, Jan. 26-Mar. 30; Paris, Musée des Arts Décoratifs, Apr. 23-June 1

New York, The Solomon R. Guggenheim Museum, *Inaugural Selection,* Oct. 21, 1959-June 19, 1960

Kunstverein in Hamburg, *Robert Delaunay,* Jan. 26-Mar. 11, 1962, no. 15, color repr., traveled to Cologne, Wallraf-Richartz-Museum, Mar. 24-May 6; Frankfurter Kunstverein, May 18-June 24

The Baltimore Museum of Art, *1914,* Oct. 6-Nov. 15, 1964, no. 40, repr.

New York, The Museum of Modern Art, *The Machine as Seen at the End of the Mechanical Age,* Nov. 25, 1968-Feb. 9, 1969, p. 72, repr., traveled to Houston, University of St. Thomas, Mar. 25-May 18; San Francisco Museum of Art, June 23-Aug. 24

Paris, Orangerie des Tuileries, *Robert Delaunay,* May 25-Aug. 30, 1976, no. 30, color repr., traveled to Staatliche Kunsthalle Baden-Baden, Sept. 25-Nov. 14

REFERENCES:
G. Habasque, "Catalogue de l'oeuvre de Robert Delaunay," *Du Cubisme à l'art abstrait,* ed. P. Francastel, Paris, 1957, no. 89

Handbook, 1959, p. 51, repr.

U. Laxner, "Robert Delaunay: Tour Eiffel," *Museum Folkwang, Essen, Mitteilungen,* Band III, 1969, no. 8

Rudenstine, *Collection Catalogue,* 1976, no. 37, repr.

Delaunay

47 Simultaneous Windows (2nd Motif, 1st Part). 1912
(Les Fenêtres simultanées[2ᵉ motif, 1ʳᵉ partie])

41.464A

Oil on canvas, 21⅝ x 18¼ in. (55.2 x 46.3 cm.)

Signed and dated l.l.: *les fenêtres simultané /
r. delaunay 12*; inscribed on reverse: '*les fenêtres*'
2ᵐ motif 1ʳ partie (1912) r.d. Paris.

PROVENANCE:

from the artist
Hilla Rebay, Greens Farms, Connecticut, by 1936
Solomon R. Guggenheim, New York, 1938
Gift, Solomon R. Guggenheim, 1941

Simultaneous Windows (2nd Motif, 1st Part) is one of
a series of at least seventeen oils Delaunay painted in
1912. By means of overlapping transparent planes of
pure color, he has built up the triangular organization
of *Windows*. Although these planes are set down in an
orderly sequence, their contrasting shades of blue, green
and purple are meant to be perceived simultaneously.

Delaunay was aware of Chevreul's theories involving
complementary colors and simultaneous contrasts in
color harmony. Moreover, simultaneity was a popular
concept around 1912 to 1914, and the term was used
not only by painters but by writers and musicians as
well. Delaunay wrote: "I have dared to create an architecture of color, and have hoped to realize the impulses,
the state of a dynamic poetry while remaining completely within the painterly medium, free from all
literature, from all descriptive anecdote. . . . Color, the
fruit of light, is the foundation of the painter's means of
painting and its language." (G. Vriesen and M. Imdahl,
Robert Delaunay: Light and Color, New York, 1969,
p. 42) Delaunay's *Windows* inspired the poet Guillaume
Apollinaire to write *Les Fenêtres*.

EXHIBITIONS:

Philadelphia, Art Alliance, *Solomon R. Guggenheim Collection of Non-Objective Paintings,* Feb. 8-28, 1937, no. 161

The Arts Club of Chicago, *Robert Delaunay,* Oct. 24-Nov.
21, 1952, no. 12

New York, The Solomon R. Guggenheim Museum, *Robert
Delaunay,* Mar. 22-May 22, 1955, traveled to Boston, Institute of Contemporary Art, June 2-30

London, Tate Gallery, *An exhibition of paintings from The
Solomon R. Guggenheim Museum, New York,* Apr. 16-May
26, 1957, no. 14, traveled to The Hague, Gemeentemuseum,
June 25-Sept. 1; Helsinki, Ateneumin Taidekokoelmat, Sept.
27-Oct. 20; Rome, Galleria Nazionale d'Arte Moderna, Dec.
5, 1957-Jan. 8, 1958; Cologne, Wallraf-Richartz-Museum,
Jan. 26-Mar. 30; Paris, Musée des Arts Décoratifs, Apr. 23-
June 1

New York, The Solomon R. Guggenheim Museum,
Inaugural Selection, Oct. 21, 1959-June 19, 1960

New York, The Solomon R. Guggenheim Museum, *Gauguin
and the Decorative Style,* June 23-Oct. 23, 1966

Buffalo, Albright-Knox Art Gallery, *Color and Field: 1890-
1970,* Sept. 15-Nov. 1, 1970, no. 25, repr., traveled to Dayton Art Institute, Nov. 20, 1970-Jan. 10, 1971; The Cleveland Museum of Art, Feb. 4-Mar. 28

New York, The Solomon R. Guggenheim Museum, *Forty
Modern Masters: An Anniversary Show,* Dec. 16, 1977-
Feb. 5, 1978, no. 25

REFERENCES:

R. Delaunay, *Du Cubisme à l'art abstrait,* ed. P. Francastel,
Paris, 1957, pp. 63, 66-67, 75, 87, 97-98, 108, 170-172, 229-230

G. Habasque, "Catalogue de l'oeuvre de Robert Delaunay,"
Du Cubisme à l'art abstrait, ed. P. Francastel, Paris, 1957,
no. 106

J. Golding, *Cubism: A History and Analysis 1907-1914,* rev.
ed., Boston, 1968, pp. 172-176

Handbook, 1970, pp. 92-93, color repr.

Rudenstine, *Collection Catalogue,* 1976, no. 38, repr.

Delaunay

48 Circular Forms. 1930
(Formes circulaires)

49.1184

Oil on canvas, 50¾ x 76¾ in. (128.9 x 194.9 cm.)

Signed c.l.: *r. delaunay*. Not dated.

PROVENANCE:
Sonia Delaunay, Paris, 1949

Around 1930 Delaunay returned to the abstract circular forms so prevalent in his work of 1913. He first represented the disc in the sky of a 1906 landscape and by 1913 this shape had become the subject of canvases entitled *Sun* and *Moon*.

Circular Forms presents two distinct foci with overlapping circular bands of color, primarily red, blue and yellow. Where the bands intersect, the color changes. The right half of the canvas, showing concentric circles divided into eight segments on which discs are superimposed, is a kaleidoscopic fragmentation of the left half. Delaunay's investigation of schematic concentric circles continued in the 1930s with relief sculpture and paintings of the Rhythm series.

EXHIBITIONS:
The Arts Club of Chicago, *Robert Delaunay,* Oct. 24-Nov. 21, 1954, no. 3

New York, The Solomon R. Guggenheim Museum, *Robert Delaunay,* Mar. 22-May 22, 1955, traveled to Boston, Institute of Contemporary Art, June 2-30

Städtisches Museum Leverkusen, *Robert Delaunay,* June 7-July 15, 1956, no. 37, repr., traveled to Kunstverein Freiburg, July 22 Aug. 19

London, Tate Gallery, *An exhibition of paintings from The Solomon R. Guggenheim Museum, New York,* Apr. 16-May 26, 1957, no. 15, repr., traveled to The Hague, Gemeentemuseum, June 25-Sept. 1; Helsinki, Ateneumin Taidekokoelmat, Sept. 27-Oct. 20; Rome, Galleria Nazionale d'Arte Moderna, Dec. 5, 1957-Jan. 8, 1958; Cologne, Wallraf-Richartz-Museum, Jan. 26-Mar. 30; Paris, Musée des Arts Décoratifs, Apr. 23-June 1

New York, The Solomon R. Guggenheim Museum, *Inaugural Selection,* Oct. 21, 1959-June 19, 1960

New York, The Solomon R. Guggenheim Museum, *Gauguin and the Decorative Style,* June 23-Oct. 23, 1966

REFERENCES:
H. Arp, *Onze peintres,* Zürich, 1949, p. 23, repr.

G. Habasque, "Catalogue de l'oeuvre de Robert Delaunay," *Du Cubisme à l'art abstrait,* ed. P. Francastel, Paris, 1957, no. 270

Handbook, 1970, pp. 94, repr., 95

M. Seuphor, *L'Art abstrait,* Paris, 1971, p. 148, color repr.

Rudenstine, *Collection Catalogue,* 1976, no. 39, repr.

III

Ernst Ludwig Kirchner 1880-1938

Ernst Ludwig Kirchner was born on May 6, 1880, in Aschaffenburg, Germany. After years of travel his family settled in Chemnitz in 1890. From 1901 to 1905 he studied architecture at the Dresden Technische Hochschule and pictorial art in Munich at the Kunsthochschule and an experimental art school established by Wilhelm von Debschitz and Hermann Obrist. While in Munich he produced his first woodcuts; the graphic arts were to become as important to· him as painting. At this time he was drawn to Neo-Impressionism as well as to the old masters.

In 1905 the *Brücke (Bridge)* was founded in Dresden by Kirchner, Fritz Bleyl, Karl Schmidt-Rottluff and Erich Heckel; the group was later joined by Cuno Amiet, Max Pechstein, Nolde and Otto Müller. From 1905 to 1910 Dresden hosted exhibitions of Post-Impressionists, including van Gogh, as well as shows of Munch, Gustav Klimt and the Fauves, which deeply impressed Kirchner. Other important influences were Japanese prints, the Ajanta wall-paintings and African and Oceanic art. Kirchner moved to Berlin with the *Brücke* group in 1911. The following year Marc included works by *Brücke* artists in the second show of the *Blaue Reiter (Blue Rider)* in Munich, thus providing a link between the two groups. In 1913 Kirchner exhibited in the Armory Show in New York, Chicago and Boston, and was given his first one-man shows in Germany, at the Folkwang Museum of Hagen and the Galerie Gurlitt in Berlin. This year also marked the dissolution of the *Brücke.*

During World War I Kirchner was discharged from the army because of a nervous and physical collapse. He was treated at Dr. Kohnstamm's sanatorium in Königstein near Frankfurt, where he completed five wall frescoes in 1916. The artist was severely injured when struck by an automobile in 1917; the next year, during his long period of recuperation, he settled in Frauenkirch near Davos, Switzerland, where he hoped to form a progressive artistic community. Although his plans did not materialize, many young artists, particularly those of the Basel-based *Rot-Blau* group, sought him out during the twenties for guidance. One-man shows of Kirchner's work were held throughout the thirties in Munich, Bern, Hamburg, Basel, Detroit and New York. However, physical deterioration and mental anxiety overtook him again in the middle of the decade. His inclusion in the 1937 Nazi-sponsored show of *Entartete Kunst* (degenerate art) in Munich caused him further distress. Kirchner died by his own hand on June 15, 1938.

49 Woman with Black Hat. 1908
(Dame mit schwarzem Hut)

78.2437

Watercolor on paper, 17¹¹⁄₁₆ x 13⅜ in. (44.9 x 34 cm.)

Not signed or dated. Estate stamp on reverse:
PDre / Ba 4.

PROVENANCE:
Peter Deitsch Gallery, New York, by 1959
Margarete Schultz, Great Neck, New York, 1959-72
Carus Gallery, New York, 1972-74
Phoebe Gibson, California, 1974
Serge Sabarsky Gallery, New York, 1977-78

Kirchner devised linear and planar equivalents for
forms in his rapid sketches from life. In *Woman with
Black Hat* bold black strokes indicate the figure and the
repetition of parallel brushstrokes gives substance to
her arms and torso. Executed primarily in black with
touches of red, the watercolor gives no evidence of the
vivid colorations favored by Kirchner and other artists
of the *Brücke* group. The theme of a woman with large
hat appears in coeval oils Kirchner painted in Dresden
as well as in pictures by van Gogh and Kees van Dongen
exhibited there in 1908 and in Toulouse-Lautrec's
well-known work.

EXHIBITIONS:
Seattle Art Museum, *Ernst Ludwig Kirchner,* Nov. 23, 1968-
Jan. 5, 1969, no. 75, repr., traveled to Pasadena Art Museum,
Jan. 16-Feb. 23; Boston, Museum of Fine Arts, Mar. 20-
Apr. 27
New York, Carus Gallery, *Catalogue Number 5,* Sept. 1972,
no. 42, color repr.

50 **Gerda, Half-Length Portrait.** 1914
(Frauenkopf, Gerda)

78.2421

Oil on canvas, 39 x 29⅝ in. (99.1 x 75.3 cm.)

Signed c.r.: *E. L. Kirchner*; inscribed on reverse: *Frauenkopf / Gerda / 12 / E. L. Kirchner*; Estate stamp: *Be Ba 4.*

PROVENANCE:

Estate of the artist
Curt Valentin Gallery, New York, ca. 1953
Mr. and Mrs. Frederick Zimmerman, New York, ca. 1953-70
La Boetie, Inc., New York, 1970-78
Partial Gift, Mr. and Mrs. Mortimer M. Denker, 1978

Kirchner painted *Gerda, Half-Length Portrait* in Berlin before the outbreak of World War I. Like her younger sister Erna, who was to become the artist's common-law wife, Gerda Schilling was a dancer. In this picture her assertive pose is enhanced by the angular styliza-tions in the background, the hatched patterning of the brushstrokes and the tension between the representation of three-dimensional forms and the two-dimensional picture plane. *Gerda, Half-Length Portrait* shares with Kirchner's Berlin street scenes of 1913-14 not only subject matter but also the intensity and dissonance of color and the use of the background as a dynamic design element.

EXHIBITIONS:

Kunsthalle Bern, *Ernst Ludwig Kirchner*, Mar. 5-Apr. 17, 1933, no. 18

Zürich, Galerie Aktuaryus, *Gedächtnis-Ausstellung Ernst Ludwig Kirchner,* Apr. 30-May 23, 1939, no. 5

Kunstverein in Hamburg, *Ernst Ludwig Kirchner: Werke aus dem Nachlass, zum ersten Male in Deutschland, aus Anlass seines 70. Geburtstages,* Sept. 2-Oct. 8, 1950, no. 11, traveled to Kestner-Gesellschaft Hannover, Oct. 15-Nov. 19; Kunsthalle Bremen, Dec. 3, 1950-Jan. 3, 1951; Wuppertal-Elberfeld, Städtisches Museum, Jan.

Kunsthaus Zürich, *Ernst Ludwig Kirchner 1880-1938,* Mar. 29-May 4, 1952, no. 17

Allentown (Pa.) Art Museum, *The Blue Four and German Expressionism,* Mar. 10-Apr. 21, 1974, no. 54, repr.

New Orleans Museum of Art, *German and Austrian Ex-pressionism,* Nov. 22, 1975-Jan. 18, 1976, no. 29, color repr.

REFERENCES:

W. Grohmann, *Das Werk Ernst Ludwig Kirchners,* Munich, 1926, no. 38, repr.

C. Einstein, *Die Kunst des 20. Jahrhunderts,* 2nd ed., Berlin, 1928, pp. 383, repr., 563

W. Schmalenbach, "Ernst Ludwig Kirchner," *Werk,* 35 Jg., Jan. 1948, p. 20, repr.

D. E. Gordon, *Ernst Ludwig Kirchner,* Cambridge, Mass., 1968, p. 320, no. 375, repr.

Emil Nolde 1867-1956

Emil Nolde was born Emil Hansen on August 7, 1867, in North Schleswig, near Nolde, Germany. He worked as an ornamental carver in furniture factories in Muich, Karlsruhe and Berlin from 1888 to 1890. After a sojourn in Berlin he moved to St. Gallen, Switzerland, in 1891, where he taught ornamental drawing and modeling at the Industrie und Gewerbemuseum. He studied art with Friedrich Fehr in Munich in 1898 and at the Hölzel-Schule in Dachau in 1899, before visiting Paris in the fall of that year to attend the Académie Julian. After stays in Copenhagen, Berlin and Flensburg, Germany, he settled in 1903 on the island of Alsen.

In 1905, after Nolde returned from a trip to Italy, his first one-man show was held at the Galerie Ernst Arnold in Dresden. From 1906 to 1907 he belonged to the Dresden-based *Brücke* group of artists who shared his interest in the graphic arts and his admiration for the work of Munch and van Gogh. Nolde moved to Dresden in 1907 and developed friendships with Kirchner, Max Pechstein and Erich Heckel. That same year the Museum Folkwang in Hagen and the Galerie Commeter in Hamburg presented solo exhibitions of his work. The Berlin *Secession,* which had rejected Nolde's expressionist paintings for several years, expelled him in 1910 after he criticized the association's president. In 1912 he participated in the *Sonderbund* exhibition in Cologne and the second show of the *Blaue Reiter* in Munich. From 1913 to 1914 he traveled across Russia and the Far East to New Guinea. He settled in Berlin in 1915 and spent most winters there until 1940. In 1927 an important traveling retrospective was organized in Dresden, followed the next year by a major one-man show at the Kunsthalle Basel. Nolde's paintings were confiscated by the Nazis in 1937 and he was forbidden to paint, despite his support for the regime. Nolde's first one-man show in the United States was held at Curt Valentin's Buchholz Gallery in New York in 1939. The Kestner-Gesellschaft of Hannover presented a retrospective of his work in 1948. Nolde died on April 13, 1956, in Seebüll, where the Stiftung Seebüll Ada und Emil Nolde was formed shortly thereafter.

51 **Young Horses.** 1916
(Junge Pferde)

79.2551

Oil on canvas, 28½ x 39½ in. (72.4 x 100.3 cm.)

Signed l.r.: *Emil Nolde.* Not dated.

PROVENANCE:

from the artist
National-Galerie, Berlin, 1935-37
Karl Buchholz, Berlin and Bogotá, ca. 1937-39
Francisca Tugendhat de Igler, Caracas, ca. 1939
Doris Igler Boersner, Caracas
Donald Karshan, 1979

In the summer of 1916, during his stay at Utenwarf, Nolde made sketches which he then used for oils he painted on Alsen.* There are five canvases representing pairs of horses that date from 1916. The Guggenheim picture is more abstract than a closely related sketch and another canvas, *Landscape with Young Horses,* both in the Stiftung Seebüll Ada and Emil Nolde.

In our painting two silhouetted shapes of rearing horses stand out against a dark blue-black sky. The green meadow and orange glow at the horizon intensify the dramatic mood. Nolde's landscape resembles the flat, open, rather desolate countryside of his native Schleswig-Holstein. The strong patterns of light and the dark, windswept, overhanging clouds do not merely fill the sky: they impart a mysterious, vital energy and Expressionist force.

* correspondence with Martin Urban, July 1979. See E. Nolde, *Welt und Heimat,* Cologne, 1965, pp. 138-139

EXHIBITIONS:

Vienna, Künstlerhaus, Gesellschaft zur Förderung Moderner Kunst, *Ausstellung Emil Nolde,* Mar. 11-Apr. 8, 1924, no. 6

Dresden, Städtisches Ausstellungsgebäude, *Emil Nolde: Jubiläums-Ausstellung,* Feb. 8-Mar. 24, 1927, no. 111, traveled to Hamburg, Kunstverein, Apr.; Kiel, Schleswig-Holsteinischer Kunstverein, May-June; Essen, Museum Folkwang, July 17-Sept.; Wiesbaden, Nassauischer Kunstverein, Sept.

Frankfurter Kunstverein, *Emil Nolde,* Jan. 1-29, 1928, no. 72

Kunsthalle Basel, *Emil Nolde,* Oct. 11-Nov. 4, 1928, no. 41

Bielefeld, Städtisches Kunsthaus, *Emil Nolde,* Mar.-Apr. 1929

Munich, Haus der deutschen Kunst, *Entartete Kunst,* opened July 19, 1937

Caracas, Fundación Eugenio Mendoza, *Expresionismo en Alemania,* Nov.-Dec. 1959, no. 84, repr.

Brussels, Palais des Beaux-Arts, *Emil Nolde,* May 12-June 18, 1961, no. 28, repr.

Hannover, Kunstverein, *Emil Nolde,* July 16-Sept. 3, 1961, no. 26, repr.

Pforzheim, Kunst und Kunstgewerbeverein, *Emil Nolde, Wilhelm Lehmbruck: Meister der Plastik des 20. Jahrhunderts,* Oct. 20-Nov. 19, 1961, no. 15, repr.

Schleswig, Schleswig-Holsteinisches Landesmuseum, *Die Maler der "Brücke,"* May 6-June 17, 1962, no. 58, traveled to Lübeck, Overbeck-Gesellschaft, June 24-Aug. 12

REFERENCES:

Verzeichnis der Kunstwerke in der neuen Abteilung der National-Galerie im ehemaligen Kronprinzen-Palais, Berlin, 1934, p. 11

P. O. Rave, *Kunstdiktatur im Dritten Reich,* Hamburg, 1949, pp. 81-83

F. Roh, *"Entartete" Kunst: Kunstbarbarei im Dritten Reich,* Hannover, 1962, p. 139

National-Galerie: Gemälde des 20. Jahrhunderts, Berlin, 1976, p. 98

Oskar Kokoschka 1886-1980

Oskar Kokoschka was born on March 1, 1886, in the Austrian town of Pöchlarn. He spent most of his youth in Vienna, where he entered the Kunstgewerbeschule in 1904 or 1905. While still a student he painted fans and postcards for the Wiener Werkstätte, which published his first book of poetry in 1908. That same year Kokoschka was fiercely criticized for the works he exhibited in the Vienna *Kunstschau* and consequently was dismissed from the Kunstgewerbeschule. At this time he attracted the attention of the architect Adolf Loos, who became his most vigorous supporter. In this early period Kokoschka wrote plays that are considered among the first examples of expressionist drama.

His first one-man show was held at Paul Cassirer's gallery in Berlin in 1910, followed later that year by another at the Museum Folkwang in Essen. In 1910 he also began to contribute to Herwarth Walden's periodical *Der Sturm*. Kokoschka concentrated on portraiture, dividing his time between Berlin and Vienna from 1910 to 1914. In 1915, shortly after the outbreak of World War I, he volunteered to serve on the eastern front, where he was seriously wounded. Still recuperating in 1917, he settled in Dresden and in 1919 accepted a professorship at the Akademie there. In 1918 Paul Westheim's comprehensive monograph on the artist was published.

Kokoschka traveled extensively during the 1920s and 1930s in Europe, North Africa and the Middle East. In 1931 he returned to Vienna but, as a result of the Nazis' growing power, he moved to Prague in 1935. He acquired Czechoslovak citizenship two years later. Kokoschka painted a portrait of Czechoslovakia's president Thomas Garrigue Masaryk in 1936, and the two became friends. In 1937 the Nazis condemned his work as "degenerate art" and removed it from public view. The artist fled to England in 1938, the year of his first one-man show in the United States at the Buchholz Gallery in New York. In 1947 he became a British national. Two important traveling shows of Kokoschka's work originated in Boston and Munich in 1948 and 1950 respectively. In 1953 he settled in Villeneuve, near Geneva, and began teaching at the Internationale Sommer Akademie für bildende Kunst, where he initiated his Schule des Sehens. Kokoschka's collected writings were published in 1956, and around this time he became involved in stage design. In 1962 he was honored with a retrospective at the Tate Gallery in London. Kokoschka died February 22, 1980, in Montreux, Switzerland.

52 Knight Errant. 1915
(Der irrende Ritter)

48.1172 x380

Oil on canvas, 35¼ x 70⅛ in. (89.5 x 180.1 cm.)

Signed l.r.: *OK*; on reverse: *OKOXOK*. Not dated.

PROVENANCE:

from the artist
Oskar Reichel, Vienna, by 1916
Otto Kallir, Paris and New York, 1934 - at least 1945
Karl Nierendorf, New York, ca. 1946
Estate of Karl Nierendorf, 1948

The knight in armor appears strangely suspended above the landscape. Kokoschka has confirmed that the knight is a self-portrait and that the canvas was painted before he served in World War I. While the figure of the knight may dominate the picture, its meaning is amplified by the presence of two small figures within the landscape: in the upper center of the composition a bird-man, who also resembles the artist, is perched on a limb which hangs over the ocean; reclining in the landscape at the right is the sphinx-woman who represents Kokoschka's mistress, Alma Mahler. Although Kokoschka had previously depicted bird-man and sphinx-woman close together, they are separated here as if to symbolize the end of the artist's relationship with Alma.* The cloud-filled sky contains the letters "*ES*," which undoubtedly refer to Christ's lament: *Eloi, Eloi, lama sabachthani* ("My God, my God, why hast Thou forsaken me?"). The agitated brushwork and disturbing colors intensify the tumultuous seascape and emphasize the emotional content of Kokoschka's picture.

* see Rudenstine

EXHIBITIONS:
Kunsthaus Zürich, *Oskar Kokoschka*, June 6-July 3, 1927, no. 41
The Arts Club of Chicago, *Kokoschka*, Jan. 3-27, 1941, no. 9
New York, Buchholz Gallery, *Kokoschka*, Oct. 27-Nov. 15, 1941, no. 12
Boston, Institute of Contemporary Art, *Kokoschka*, Oct. 4-Nov. 14, 1948, no. 24, repr.
London, Tate Gallery, *An exhibition of paintings from The Solomon R. Guggenheim Museum, New York,* Apr. 16-May 26, 1957, no. 38, traveled to The Hague, Gemeentemuseum, June 25-Sept. 1; Helsinki, Ateneumin Taidekokoelmat, Sept. 27-Oct. 20; Rome, Galleria Nazionale d'Arte Moderna, Dec. 5, 1957-Jan. 8, 1958; Cologne, Wallraf-Richartz-Museum, Jan. 26-Mar. 30; Paris, Musée des Arts Décoratifs, Apr. 23-June 1
London, Tate Gallery, *Oskar Kokoschka*, Sept. 14-Nov. 11, 1962, no. 46, repr.

Kunstverein in Hamburg, *Oskar Kokoschka,* Dec. 8, 1962-Jan. 27, 1963, no. 24, repr.

Kunsthaus Zürich, *Oskar Kokoschka,* June 1-July 24, 1966, no. 34, repr.

Badischer Kunstverein Karlsruhe, *Oskar Kokoschka: Das Porträt,* Aug. 21-Nov. 20, 1966, no. 27, repr.

New York, The Solomon R. Guggenheim Museum, *Forty Modern Masters: An Anniversary Show,* Dec. 16, 1977-Feb. 5, 1978, no. 73, repr.

REFERENCES:

O. Kokoschka, "Vom Bewusstsein der Gesichte," *Genius: Zeitschrift für Werdende und alte Kunst,* Jg. I, 1919, p. 42, repr.

E. Hoffmann, *Kokoschka: Life and Work,* London, 1947, pp. 123, 153-154, repr. opp. p. 112

P. Selz, *German Expressionist Painting,* Berkeley, 1957, p. 310, pl. 142b

B. Bultmann, *Kokoschka,* London, 1961, p. 32

J. P. Hodin, *Oskar Kokoschka: The Artist and His Time,* Greenwich, Conn., 1966, pp. 7, 58, 134-135, 145-147, 228, repr. opp. p. 53

Handbook, 1970, pp. 250-251, color repr.

"Kokoschka's Early Work, A Conversation between the Artist and Wolfgang Fischer," *Studio International,* vol. 181, Jan. 1971, p. 5

Rudenstine, *Collection Catalogue,* 1976, no. 157, color repr.

Egon Schiele 1890-1918

Egon Schiele was born June 12, 1890, in Tulln, Austria. After attending school in Krems and Klosterneuburg, he enrolled in the Akademie der bildenden Künste in Vienna in 1906. Here he studied painting and drawing but was frustrated by the school's conservatism. In 1907 he met Gustav Klimt who encouraged him and influenced his work. Schiele left the Akademie in 1909 and founded the *Neukunstgruppe* with other dissastisfied students. Upon Klimt's invitation Schiele exhibited at the *Internationale Kunstschau* of 1909 in Vienna, where he encountered the work of van Gogh, Munch, Jan Toroop and others. On the occasion of the first exhibition of the *Neukunstgruppe* in 1909 at the Piska Salon, Vienna, Schiele met the art critic and writer Arthur Roessler who befriended him and wrote admiringly of his work. In 1910 he began a long friendship with the collector Heinrich Benesch. By this time Schiele had developed a personal expressionist portrait and landscape style and was receiving a number of portrait commissions from the Viennese intelligentsia.

Seeking isolation, Schiele left Vienna in 1911 to live in several small villages: he concentrated increasingly on self-portraits and allegories of life, death and sex and produced erotic watercolors. In 1912 he was arrested for "immorality" and "seduction"; during his twenty-four day imprisonment he executed a number of poignant watercolors and drawings. Schiele participated in various group exhibitions, including those of the *Neukunstgruppe* in Prague, 1910, and Budapest, 1912; the *Sonderbund,* Cologne, 1912; and several *Secession* shows in Munich, beginning in 1911. In 1913 the Galerie Hans Goltz, Munich, mounted Schiele's first one-man show. A one-man exhibition of his work took place in Paris in 1914. The following year Schiele married Edith Harms and was drafted into the Austrian Army. He painted prolifically and continued to exhibit during his military service. His one-man show at the Vienna *Secession* of 1918 brought him critical acclaim and financial success. He died several months later in Vienna, at age twenty-eight, on October 31, 1918, a victim of influenza which had claimed his wife three days earlier.

53 Portrait of Johann Harms. 1916
69.1884

Oil with wax on canvas, 54½ x 42½ in. (138.3 x 108 cm.)

Signed and dated l.r.: *EGON/SCHIELE/1916.*

PROVENANCE:

from the artist
Karl Grünwald, Vienna, by 1918-21
Otto Kallir, Vienna and New York, 1921-69
Partial Gift, Dr. and Mrs. Otto Kallir, 1969

Johann Harms (1843-1917) became Schiele's father-in-law in June 1915. Schiele's letters record that in April 1916 he made drawings and worked on the canvas for the seventy-three year-old man's portrait. As is typical of his portraits, there are no props used as clues to the sitter's personality or occupation (master locksmith). While even the chair is sometimes omitted, the one on which Harms sits in this picture was made by Schiele for his studio.

Unlike many Expressionist paintings, the color is somber, almost monochromatic. The color values are used in a hierarchical manner, building up from the dark background to the median gray of the body's bulky diagonal shape and reaching their height in the more vibrant head and hands, always the focal points of Schiele's figure paintings. These small areas succinctly embody his exploration of the sitter's character. In this case the rough, skeletal hands and deeply furrowed brow express a weariness of old age. But the pose of the figure, which seems to be draped over the chair because of the low viewpoint, and the tenderness with which the head rests on the left hand, soften the image and suggest a melancholy peace.

EXHIBITIONS:

Munich, Glaspalast, *Secession,* July-Sept. 1917, no. 2400

Vienna, *XLIX Ausstellung der Vereinigung Bildender Künstler Osterreichs Secession,* Mar. 1918, no. 6

Vienna, Neue Galerie, *Egon Schiele Gemälde und Handzeichnungen,* Nov. 20-Dec. 31, 1923, no. 6

Vienna, Hagenbund, *Gedächtnisausstellung zum 10. Todestag,* Oct.-Nov. 1928, no. 62

Boston, Institute of Contemporary Art, *Egon Schiele,* Oct. 6-Nov. 6, 1960, no. 52, traveled to New York, Galerie St. Etienne, Nov. 15-Dec. 15; Louisville, J. B. Speed Art Museum, Jan. 3-31, 1961; Pittsburgh, Carnegie Institute, Museum of Art, Mar. 1-Apr. 2; The Minneapolis Institute of Arts, Apr. 19-May 21

New York, The Solomon R. Guggenheim Museum, *Gustav Klimt and Egon Schiele,* Feb. 5-Apr. 25, 1965, no. 40, repr.

Munich, Haus der Kunst, *Egon Schiele 1890-1918*, Feb. 22-May 11, 1975, no. 60, repr.

New York, The Solomon R. Guggenheim Museum, *Forty Modern Masters: An Anniversary Show*, Dec. 16, 1977-Feb. 5, 1978, repr.

REFERENCES:

A. Roessler, ed., *Briefe und Prosa von Egon Schiele*, Vienna, 1921, p. 116

O. Nirenstein, *Egon Schiele: Persönlichkeit und Werk*, Vienna, 1930, p. 67, no. 153, pl. 114

O. Kallir, *Egon Schiele: Oeuvre Catalogue of the Paintings*, New York, 1966, no. 213, p. 421

Handbook, 1970, pp. 390-391, repr.

R. Leopold, *Egon Schiele: Paintings, Watercolours, Drawings*, London, 1973, pp. 16, 416, no. 270, pl. 192

A. Comini, *Egon Schiele's Portraits*, Berkeley, Los Angeles, London, 1974, pp. 147-148 and color pl. 142

Rudenstine, *Collection Catalogue*, 1976, no. 223, color repr.

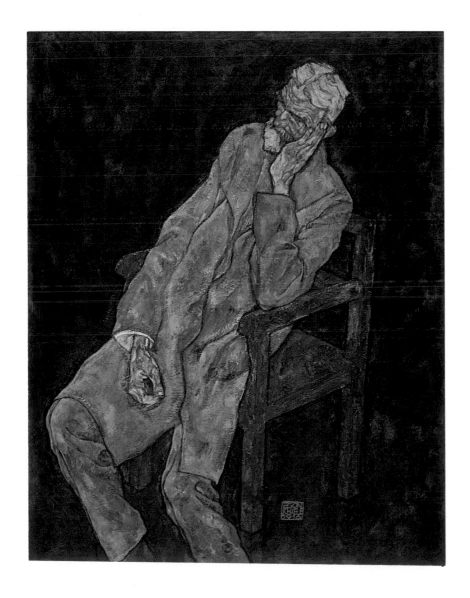

Alexej Jawlensky 1864-1941

Alexej Georgevich Jawlensky was born in or near Torz-hok, Russia, on March 13, 1864, and educated in Moscow. While an army lieutenant, he first studied art at the Academy in St. Petersburg in 1889. In 1896 Jawlensky resigned his military commission to devote himself to painting and moved with Marianne von Werefkin and Helene Nesnakomoff to Munich. From 1896 to 1899 he attended the Ažbe school in Munich, where he first met Kandinsky who had also recently left Russia.

Jawlensky was included in the Munich and Berlin *Secession* exhibitions in 1903. During these years he visited Russia, participating in exhibitions there, and traveled in Europe: in 1905 he met Matisse in Paris and his work was included in the Salon d'Automne. In 1907 he met the *Nabis* Jan Verkade and Paul Sérusier in Munich. Kandinsky and Jawlensky became close friends during the summer of 1908 and the following year the two, together with a number of other artists, founded the *Neue Künstlervereinigung München (NKVM)*. Jawlensky's first one-man exhibition took place in Barmen in 1911. His long friendship with Nolde began in 1912.

The outbreak of World War I forced Jawlensky to flee to Switzerland, where he painted his stylized landscape series, Variations, from 1914 to 1921. In Zürich in 1917 he started his Faces of Saints or Faces of the Saviour series and in Ascona in 1918 he began his constructivist heads. Jawlensky returned to Germany in 1921, settling in Wiesbaden. He married Helene Nesnakomoff, the mother of his twenty year-old son, in 1922. With Klee, Kandinsky and Feininger he was part of the *Blaue Vier (Blue Four)*, founded in 1924. Jawlensky continued to paint constructivist heads during the years in Wiesbaden; from 1934 to 1937 he executed his mystical Meditation series. Crippled by arthritis, Jawlensky was finally forced to cease painting by 1938. He died on March 15, 1941, in Wiesbaden.

54 **Helene with Colored Turban.** 1910
(Helene mit buntem Turban)

65.1773

Oil on board, 37⅛ x 31⅞ in. (94.2 x 81 cm.)

Signed and dated u.l: *A. Jawlensky/1910;* inscribed on reverse, not by the artist: *No. 19 1910/Helene mit/ buntem Turban.*

PROVENANCE:

Estate of the artist, 1941-61
Galerie Wilhelm Grosshennig, Düsseldorf, 1961
Lock Galleries, New York, 1962-65
Leonard Hutton Galleries, New York, 1965

Jawlensky's painting from 1907 to 1910 combined bold Fauvist color and simplified linear structure with an intense personal feeling for the subject. The monumental *Helene with Colored Turban* is a portrait of Helene Nesnakomoff (ca. 1880-1965), who had borne the artist a son in 1902 and whom he was to marry in 1922. This canvas reveals the influence of Matisse's *Red Madras Headdress* (Collection The Barnes Foundation, Merion, Pennsylvania), which is a portrait of Madame Matisse wearing a red turban. Jawlensky has adopted Matisse's brilliant palette and painterly surface treatment but heightens the expressive force of the color and endows the personality of the sitter with an emotional dimension not present in Matisse's work.

On the reverse of this work is *Portrait of a Young Girl,* ca. 1909, an oil sketch of Resi, a neighbor of the artist who often posed for him.

EXHIBITIONS:

Munich, Haus der Kunst, *Der Blaue Reiter*, Sept.-Oct. 1949, no. 36

Düsseldorf, Galerie Wilhelm Grosshennig, *Sonderausstellung Alexej von Jawlensky*, Oct. 3-31, 1961, color repr.

Pasadena Art Museum, *Alexei Jawlensky: A Centennial Exhibition,* Apr. 14-May 19, 1964, no. 18

New York, Leonard Hutton Galleries, *A Centennial Exhibition of Paintings by Alexej Jawlensky, 1864-1941,* Feb. 17-Mar. 1965, no. 14, color repr.

The Baltimore Museum of Art, *A Centennial Exhibition of Paintings by Alexej Jawlensky, 1864-1941: A Selection from Each Year 1901-1917,* Apr. 20-May 23, 1965, no. 10

New York, The Solomon R. Guggenheim Museum, *Gauguin and the Decorative Style,* June 23-Oct. 23, 1966

New York, The Solomon R. Guggenheim Museum, *Forty Modern Masters: An Anniversary Show,* Dec. 16, 1977-Feb. 5, 1978, no. 54, repr.

REFERENCES:

C. Weiler, *Alexej Jawlensky,* Cologne, 1959, pp. 79, color repr., 230, no. 55

Handbook, 1970, pp. 166-167, color repr.

Rudenstine, *Collection Catalogue,* 1976, no. 72, color repr.

H. H. Arnason, *History of Modern Art,* rev. ed., New York, 1977, p. 192 and color pl. 67

Vasily Kandinsky 1866-1944

Vasily Kandinsky was born on December 4, 1866, in Moscow. From 1886 to 1892 he studied law and economics at the University of Moscow, where he lectured after his graduation. In 1896 he declined a teaching position at the University of Dorpat in order to study art in Munich with Anton Ažbe from 1897 to 1899 and at the Akademie with Franz von Stuck in 1900. From 1901 to 1903 Kandinsky taught at the art school of the *Phalanx,* a group he had co-founded in Munich. One of his students was Gabriele Münter, who remained his companion until 1914. In 1902 Kandinsky exhibited for the first time with the Berlin *Secession* and produced his first woodcuts. In 1903-4 he began his travels in Italy, The Netherlands and North Africa and visits to Russia. He showed frequently at the Salon d'Automne in Paris from 1904.

In 1909 Kandinsky was elected president of the newly-founded *Neue Künstlervereinigung München (NKVM)*. Their first show took place at the Moderne Galerie (Thannhauser) in Munich in 1909. In 1911 Kandinsky and Marc withdrew from the *NKVM* and began to make plans for the *Blaue Reiter (Blue Rider) Almanach*. The group's first exhibition was held in December of that year at the Moderne Galerie. He published *Über das Geistige in der Kunst (On the Spiritual in Art)* in 1911. In 1912 the second *Blaue Reiter* show was held at the Galerie Hans Goltz, Munich, and the *Almanach der Blaue Reiter* appeared. Kandinsky's first one-man show was held at the gallery of Der Sturm in Berlin in 1912. In 1913 his works were included in the Armory Show in New York and the *Erster Deutscher Herbstsalon* in Berlin. Except for visits to Scandinavia, Kandinsky lived in Russia from 1914 to 1921, principally in Moscow where he held a position at the People's Commissariat of Education.

Kandinsky began teaching at the Bauhaus in Weimar in 1922. In 1923 he was given his first one-man show in New York by the Société Anonyme, of which he became vice-president. With Klee, Feininger and Jawlensky he was part of the *Blaue Vier (Blue Four)* group, formed in 1924. He moved with the Bauhaus to Dessau in 1925 and became a German citizen in 1928. The Nazi government closed the Bauhaus in 1933 and later that year Kandinsky settled in Neuilly-sur-Seine near Paris; he acquired French citizenship in 1939. Fifty-seven of his works were confiscated by the Nazis in the 1937 purge of *Entartete Kunst* (degenerate art). Kandinsky died on December 13, 1944, in Neuilly.

55 Amsterdam—View from the Window. 1904
(Amsterdam, Blick aus dem Fenster)

Kandinsky Handlist: small oil studies *52, Amsterdam, aus d. Fenster.*

46.1055

Oil on board, 9⅜ x 13 in. (23.9 x 33.1 cm.)

Signed l.r.: *Kandinsky*; inscribed on reverse: *Kandinsky. —Amsterdam Nº 52/1903.*

PROVENANCE:
Hilda Bachrach, Forest Hills, New York, by 1946

During the first years of this century Kandinsky traveled extensively, visiting Holland in May-June 1904. *Amsterdam—View from the Window* records a specific impression: the view from the Americain Hotel on the Leidseplein showing the bridge over the Singel gracht.* Characteristic of his small oil sketches of the period are the high horizon, the vivid yet realistic colors and the rich texture of the paint itself. Kandinsky was already familiar with the work of Monet and the Neo-Impressionists and in his own painting was experimenting with various related techniques.

* see Rudenstine

EXHIBITIONS:
Brussels, Palais des Beaux-Arts, *45 Oeuvres de Kandinsky Provenant du Solomon R. Guggenheim Museum, New York,* May 17-June 30, 1957, repr., traveled to Paris, Musée National d'Art Moderne, Nov. 15, 1957-Jan. 5, 1958; London, Tate Gallery, Jan. 15-Feb. 28; Lyon, Musée des Beaux-Arts, Mar. 8-Apr. 6; Oslo, Kunstnernes Hus, Apr. 18-May 4; Rome, Galleria Nazionale d'Arte Moderna, May 15-June 30

The Art Gallery of Toronto, *Paintings by Kandinsky from the Collection of The Solomon R. Guggenheim Museum,* Apr. 24-May 24, 1959

New York, The Solomon R. Guggenheim Museum, *Vasily Kandinsky, 1866-1944: A Retrospective Exhibition,* Jan. 25-Apr. 7, 1963, no. 3, color repr., traveled to Paris, Musée National d'Art Moderne, Apr. 29-June 24; The Hague, Gemeentemuseum, July 1-Aug. 30; Kunsthalle Basel, Sept. 7-Nov. 7

New York, The Solomon R. Guggenheim Museum, *Kandinsky at the Guggenheim Museum,* May 12-Sept. 5, 1972, color repr., traveled to Los Angeles County Museum of Art, Oct. 3-Nov. 19; Minneapolis, Walker Art Center, May 5-July 15, 1973

Munich, Haus der Kunst, *Wassily Kandinsky 1866-1944,* Nov. 13, 1976-Jan. 30, 1977, no. 8, color repr.

New York, The Solomon R. Guggenheim Museum, *Forty Modern Masters: An Anniversary Show,* Dec. 16, 1977-Feb. 5, 1978, no. 56

REFERENCES:

W. Grohmann, *Wassily Kandinsky: Life and Work,* New York, 1958, p. 342, no. 52, cc 538, repr.

Handbook, 1970, pp. 170-171, repr.

Rudenstine, *Collection Catalogue,* 1976, no. 74, repr.

Kandinsky

56 Blue Mountain. 1908-9
(Der blaue Berg)

Kandinsky Handlist: *1908-1909, 84, Siniaia gora* (in Cyrillic alphabet: Blue Mountain).

41.505

Oil on canvas, 41¾ x 38 in. (106 x 96.6 cm.)

Signed and dated l.r.: *Kandinsky/1908*; signed on stretcher: *Kandinsky*; inscribed, not by the artist: *Nr. 84.*

PROVENANCE:

Herwarth Walden, Berlin, 1914-after 1919
Staatliche Gemäldegalerie, Dresden, 1931-37
Gutekunst und Klipstein, Bern, by 1939
Solomon R. Guggenheim, New York, 1939-41
Gift, Solomon R. Guggenheim, 1941

In 1908 Kandinsky knew the work of Post-Impressionists such as Gauguin and van Gogh as well as that of the *Nabis,* Matisse and other Fauves. His paintings demonstrate an affinity with the *Jugendstil* arts and crafts movement and with religious paintings on glass. *Blue Mountain* dates from 1908-9, a transitional moment in Kandinsky's career. While identifiable forms can still be discerned in this picture, they have lost their impact as representational images and have moved far in the direction of abstraction. The flattened blue, red and yellow forms emphasize the upward thrust of the composition.

The motif of three horsemen and a mountain figures prominently in Kandinsky's oeuvre until 1913. As early as 1902 the image of a single horse and rider appeared in his work.

EXHIBITIONS:

Odessa, *Salon 2: International Exhibition organized by V. A. Izdebsky,* Dec. (?) 1910, no. 200

Berlin, Der Sturm, *Wassily Kandinsky: 1902-1912,* Oct. 2-30, 1912, no. 44

Munich, Moderne Galerie (Heinrich Thannhauser), *Kandinsky,* Jan. 1914

New York, Museum of Non-Objective Painting, *In Memory of Wassily Kandinsky,* Mar. 15-Apr. 29, 1945, no. 1

The Arts Club of Chicago, *Wassily Kandinsky Memorial Exhibition,* Nov. 1945

Lyon, Musée des Beaux-Arts, *45 Oeuvres de Kandinsky Provenant du Solomon R. Guggenheim Museum, New York,* Mar. 8-Apr. 6, 1958, no. 5, traveled to Oslo, Kunstnernes Hus, Apr. 18-May 4; Rome, Galleria Nazionale d'Arte Moderna, May 15-June 30

The Art Gallery of Toronto, *Paintings by Kandinsky from the Collection of The Solomon R. Guggenheim Museum,* Apr. 24-May 24, 1959

New York, The Solomon R. Guggenheim Museum, *Inaugural Selection,* Oct. 21, 1959-June 19, 1960

New York, The Solomon R. Guggenheim Museum, *Vasily Kandinsky, 1866-1944: A Retrospective Exhibition,* Jan. 25-Apr. 7, 1963, no. 9, color repr., traveled to Paris, Musée National d'Art Moderne, Apr. 29-June 24; The Hague, Gemeentemuseum, July 1-Aug. 30; Kunsthalle Basel, Sept. 7-Nov. 7

Montreal, Expo 67, *Man and his World,* Apr. 28-Oct. 27, 1967, no. 92, repr.

New York, The Solomon R. Guggenheim Museum, *Kandinsky at the Guggenheim Museum,* May 12-Sept. 5, 1972, color repr., traveled to Los Angeles County Museum of Art, Oct. 3-Nov. 19; Minneapolis, Walker Art Center, May 5-July 15, 1973

Munich, Haus der Kunst, *Wassily Kandinsky 1866-1944,* Nov. 13, 1976-Jan. 30, 1977, no. 18, repr.

New York, The Solomon R. Guggenheim Museum, *Forty Modern Masters: An Anniversary Show,* Dec. 16, 1977-Feb. 5, 1978, no. 58

REFERENCES:

W. Kandinsky, *Kandinsky 1901-1913,* Berlin, 1913, p. 37, repr.

W. Grohmann, *Kandinsky,* Paris, 1930, p. xxiv

W. Grohmann, *Wassily Kandinsky: Life and Work,* New York, 1958, pp. 263, repr., 331, no. 84

R. C. Washton, *Vasily Kandinsky 1909-1913: Painting and Theory,* Ph.D. dissertation, Yale University, 1968, p. 59, fn. 2

Handbook, 1970, pp. 174-175, color repr.

Rudenstine, *Collection Catalogue,* 1976, no. 79, repr.

H. H. Arnason, *History of Modern Art,* rev. ed., New York, 1977, pp. 180, repr., 189

57 Sketch for "Composition II." 1909-10
(Skizze für Komposition 2)

Kandinsky Handlist: *1909, 89a Eskiz kompozitsii 2* (in Cyrillic alphabet).

45.961

Oil on canvas, 38⅜ x 51⅝ in. (97.5 x 131.2 cm.)

Signed and dated l.r.: *Kandinsky/1910.*

PROVENANCE:

from the artist
Willem Beffie, Amsterdam and Brussels, 1913-at least 1938
Karl Nierendorf, New York, by 1942-45

The Guggenheim painting is the last in a series of numerous studies for *Composition II* (now destroyed). Kandinsky considered the *Compositions* major works which he formulated gradually from preliminary sketches to realize an expression of inner feeling. When he was sick with typhoid fever, Kandinsky visualized a picture which he later strove to reconstruct. The artist felt that *Composition II* came close to capturing that vision.

Although scholars have differed in their interpretations of specific images in the painting, there is general agreement that a catastrophe is depicted on the left and an idyllic scene on the right. Kandinsky himself stated that *Composition II* did not have a theme. He has filled the canvas with a multitude of vibrantly colored, simplified forms and has compressed the imagery to such a degree that it seems to overwhelm its two-dimensional confines.

EXHIBITIONS:

Kunsthalle Bern, *Wassily Kandinsky,* Feb. 21-Mar. 29, 1937, no. 5

London, New Burlington Galleries, *Twentieth Century German Art,* July 1938, no. 76

New York, Nierendorf Gallery, *Kandinsky,* Dec. 1942-Jan. 1943

New York, Museum of Non-Objective Painting, *In Memory of Wassily Kandinsky,* Mar. 15-Apr. 29, 1945, no. 7

The Arts Club of Chicago, *Wassily Kandinsky Memorial Exhibition,* Nov. 1945, no. 3

Brussels, Palais des Beaux-Arts, *45 Oeuvres de Kandinsky Provenant du Solomon R. Guggenheim Museum, New York,* May 17-June 30, 1957, no. 6, traveled to Paris, Musée National d'Art Moderne, Nov. 15, 1957-Jan. 5, 1958; London, Tate Gallery, Jan. 15-Feb. 28

New York, The Solomon R. Guggenheim Museum, *Inaugural Selection,* Oct. 21, 1959-June 19, 1960

New York, The Solomon R. Guggenheim Museum, *Vasily Kandinsky, 1866-1944: A Retrospective Exhibition,* Jan. 25-Apr. 7, 1963, no. 13, color repr., traveled to Paris, Musée National d'Art Moderne, Apr. 29-June 24; The Hague, Gemeentemuseum, July 1-Aug. 30; Kunsthalle Basel, Sept. 7-Nov. 7

University of California at Los Angeles Art Galleries, *Years of Ferment: The Birth of Twentieth Century Art,* Jan. 24-Mar. 7, 1965, no. 89, repr., traveled to San Francisco Museum of Art, Mar. 28-May 16; The Cleveland Museum of Art, July 13-Aug. 22

New York, The Solomon R. Guggenheim Museum, *Kandinsky at the Guggenheim Museum,* May 12-Sept. 5, 1972, color repr.

Munich, Haus der Kunst, *Wassily Kandinsky 1866-1944,* Nov. 13, 1976-Jan. 30, 1977, no. 31, color repr.

New York, The Solomon R. Guggenheim Museum, *Forty Modern Masters: An Anniversary Show,* Dec. 16, 1977-Feb. 5, 1978, no. 60

REFERENCES:

W. Grohmann, *Kandinsky,* Paris, 1930, p. 3, repr.

J. Eichner, *Kandinsky und Gabriele Münter,* Munich, 1957, pp. 111, 113, 114

W. Grohmann, *Wassily Kandinsky: Life and Work,* New York, 1958, pp. 109, color repr., 118, 120-121

Handbook, 1970, pp. 178-179, color repr.

Rudenstine, *Collection Catalogue,* 1976, no. 82, repr.

H. H. Arnason, *History of Modern Art,* rev. ed., New York, 1977, p. 189 and color pl. 59

H. K. Röthel, *Kandinsky,* Paris, 1977, color pl. 9

P. Weiss, "Kandinsky: Symbolist Poetics and Theater in Munich," *Pantheon,* Jg. XXXV, July-Aug.-Sept. 1977, pp. 216-217, repr.

58 Pastorale. February 1911

Kandinsky Handlist: *ii / 1911, 132, Pastoral*
(in Cyrillic alphabet).

45.965

Oil on canvas, 41⅝ x 61⅝ in. (105.8 x 156.7 cm.)

Signed and dated l.r.: *Kandinsky 1911.*

PROVENANCE:

Herwarth Walden, Berlin
Fritz Schön, Berlin and Quebec, before 1930-43
Dominion Gallery, Montreal, 1943
Karl Nierendorf, New York, 1943-45

The three ladies dressed in Biedermeier fashions on the right recall those in such paintings by Kandinsky from 1909 as *Group in Crinolines* (Collection The Solomon R. Guggenheim Museum, New York) and *Group in Crinolines* (Collection State Tretiakov Gallery, Moscow). But in *Pastorale* they are transformed into an attenuated semi-abstraction within an idyllic landscape which includes a horse, a cow, sheep and shepherdess. The implicitly romantic figurative associations merge into a rhythmic whole where forms are modulated by varied shades of white and yellow and accents of red, blue and green. *Pastorale* exemplifies Kandinsky's development from a more decorative style towards abstraction.

EXHIBITIONS:

Berlin, Der Sturm, *Ausstellung von zurückgestellten Bilder des Sonderbundes Köln,* June-July 1912

Berlin, Der Sturm, *Kandinsky,* Sept. 1916, no. 15

New York, Buchholz Gallery, *The Blue Four,* Oct. 31-Nov. 25, 1944, no. 29

New York, Museum of Non-Objective Painting, *In Memory of Wassily Kandinsky,* Mar. 15-Apr. 29, 1945, no. 12

Brussels, Palais des Beaux-Arts, *45 Oeuvres de Kandinsky Provenant du Solomon R. Guggenheim Museum, New York,* May 17-June 30, 1957, repr., traveled to Paris, Musée National d'Art Moderne, Nov. 15, 1957-Jan. 5, 1958; London, Tate Gallery, Jan. 15-Feb. 28; Lyon, Musée des Beaux-Arts, Mar. 8-Apr. 6; Oslo, Kunstnernes Hus, Apr. 18-May 4; Rome, Galleria Nazionale d'Arte Moderna, May 15-June 30

The Art Gallery of Toronto, *Paintings by Kandinsky from the Collection of The Solomon R. Guggenheim Museum,* Apr. 24-May 24, 1959

New York, The Solomon R. Guggenheim Museum, *Inaugural Selection,* Oct. 21, 1959-June 19, 1960

New York, The Solomon R. Guggenheim Museum, *Vasily Kandinsky, 1866-1944: A Retrospective Exhibition,* Jan. 25-Apr. 7, 1963, no. 24, color repr., traveled to Paris, Musée National d'Art Moderne, Apr. 29-June 24; The Hague,

Gemeentemuseum, July 1-Aug. 30; Kunsthalle Basel, Sept. 7-Nov. 7

New York, The Solomon R. Guggenheim Museum, *Kandinsky at the Guggenheim Museum,* May 12-Sept. 5, 1972, color repr., traveled to Los Angeles County Museum of Art, Oct. 3-Nov. 19; Minneapolis, Walker Art Center, May 5-July 15, 1973

Munich, Haus der Kunst, *Wassily Kandinsky 1866-1944,* Nov. 13, 1976-Jan. 30, 1977, no. 36, repr.

New York, The Solomon R. Guggenheim Museum, *Forty-Modern Masters: An Anniversary Show,* Dec. 16, 1977-Feb. 5, 1978, no. 61

REFERENCES:

W. Grohmann, *Kandinsky,* Paris, 1930, pp. xxiv-xxv, 8, repr.

"L'Art non figuratif en Allemagne," *L'Amour de l'Art,* XVᵉ année, Sept. 1934, p. 433

W. Grohmann, *Wassily Kandinsky: Life and Work,* New York, 1958, pp. 112, 114, 127, color repr., 332, no. 132

Handbook, 1970, pp. 180-181, repr.

Rudenstine, *Collection Catalogue,* 1976, no. 86, repr.

P. Weiss, *Kandinsky in Munich: The Formative Jugendstil Years,* Princeton, N. J., 1979, pp. 145-146 and pl. 151

59 Study for "Improvisation 25 (Garden of Love I)." 1912

48.1162

Watercolor on paper, 12⅜ x 18¾ in. (31.3 x 47.6 cm.)

Signed l.r.: *K*. Not dated.

PROVENANCE:
Der Sturm, Berlin
Paul Citroën, Amsterdam, 1917-31
Pierre Alexandre Regnault, Laren, The Netherlands, 1931
J. B. Neumann, New York (?)
Hildegarde Prytek, New York, by 1948

The watercolor represents the theme of the Garden of Love: a curving black line clearly delineates the *hortus conclusus* on the right which encloses two trees and two pairs of lovers. The compositional divisions resemble those in *Improvisation 25* of 1912 (Collection Museum of Smolensk?). According to Kandinsky, *Improvisations* were paintings "produced out of an inner impulse, sudden and unconscious." (Grohmann, p. 103) With blue, green and yellow washes, he has created evocative, elusive, free forms.

EXHIBITIONS:
Brussels, Palais des Beaux-Arts, *45 Oeuvres de Kandinsky Provenant du Solomon R. Guggenheim Museum, New York*, May 17-June 30, 1957, no. 7, repr., traveled to Paris, Musée National d'Art Moderne, Nov. 15, 1957-Jan. 5, 1958; London, Tate Gallery, Jan. 15-Feb. 28; Lyon, Musée des Beaux-Arts, Mar. 8-Apr. 6; Oslo, Kunstnernes Hus, Apr. 18-May 4; Rome, Galleria Nazionale d'Arte Moderna, May 15-June 30

Pasadena Art Museum, *Vasily Kandinsky, 1866-1944: A Retrospective Exhibition* (organized by The Solomon R. Guggenheim Museum, New York), Jan. 15- Feb. 15, 1963, no. 2, traveled to San Francisco Museum of Art, Mar. 1-Apr. 1; Portland (Ore.) Art Museum, Apr. 15-May 15; San Antonio, Marion Koogler McNay Art Institute, June 1-July 1; Colorado Springs Fine Arts Center, July 15-Aug. 25; The Baltimore Museum of Art, Sept. 19-Oct. 20; The Columbus Gallery of Fine Arts, Nov. 5-Dec. 5; St. Louis, Washington University Art Gallery, Dec. 22, 1963-Jan. 6, 1964; Montreal Museum of Fine Arts, Feb. 5-Mar. 5; Worcester Art Museum, Mar. 20-Apr. 20

New York, The Solomon R. Guggenheim Museum, *Kandinsky at the Guggenheim Museum*, May 12-Sept. 5, 1972, color repr., traveled to Los Angeles County Museum of Art, Oct. 3-Nov. 19; Minneapolis, Walker Art Center, May 5-July 15

Munich, Haus der Kunst, *Wassily Kandinsky 1866-1944*, Nov. 13, 1976-Jan. 30, 1977, no. 131, repr.

REFERENCES:
W. Grohmann, *Wassily Kandinsky: Life and Work*, New York, 1958, pp. 75, repr., 118

M. Deutsch, "La Rencontre avec Schoenberg," *XXᵉ siècle*, no. 27, Dec. 1966, p. 29, repr.

Handbook, 1970, pp. 182-183, repr.

H. K. Röthel, *Kandinsky*, Paris, 1977, n.p., repr.

Kandinsky

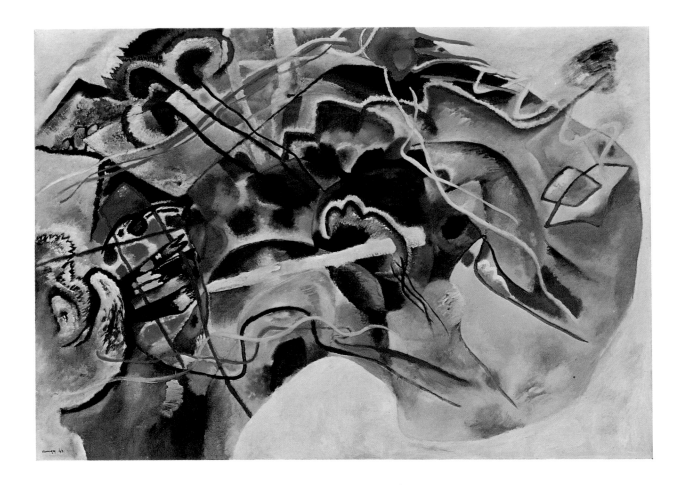

60 Painting with White Border. May 1913
(Bild mit weissem Rand)

Kandinsky Handlist: *v / 1913, 173, Kartina c bel*[oi]
kaimoi (in Cyrillic alphabet: Painting with White
Border).

37.245

Oil on canvas, 55¼ x 78⅞ in. (140.3 x 200.3 cm.)

Signed and dated l.l.: *Kandinsky 1913*; inscribed on
stretcher: *Kandinsky Bild mit weissem Rand (1913) /
N° 173*.

PROVENANCE:
from the artist through Herwarth Walden, Berlin
F. Kluxen, Münster, 1913
Herwarth Walden, Berlin, 1918 or 1919
Solomon R. Guggenheim, New York, 1929-37
Gift, Solomon R. Guggenheim, 1937

In his essay on *Painting with White Border,* Kandinsky
stated that the picture was a translation of impressions
he received on his most recent visit to Moscow. This
Russian subject is directly indicated by the backs of
three horses—a troika—at the upper left. The central
motif is a knight (identified as St. George) on horseback
with a long white lance attacking a serpent or dragon
at the lower left. This image as well as others which
Kandinsky used in paintings of the Last Judgment, Res-
urrection and All Saints' Day appears clearly in the numerous studies for the painting but are sublimated into
abstract forms in this final version.* The white border is
Kandinsky's solution to a compositional problem in
completing the picture.

* see both Rudenstine and Washton

EXHIBITIONS:
Berlin, Der Sturm, *Erster Deutscher Herbstsalon,* Sept.-Nov.
1913, no. 182

Berlin, Der Sturm, *Kandinsky,* Sept. 1916, no. 20

Charleston, S.C., Carolina Art Association, Gibbes Memorial
Art Gallery, *Solomon R. Guggenheim Collection of Non-
Objective Paintings,* Mar. 1-Apr. 12, 1936, no. 67, repr.

New York, Museum of Non-Objective Painting, *In Memory
of Wassily Kandinsky,* Mar. 15-Apr. 29, 1945, no. 24, repr.

London, Tate Gallery, *An exhibition of paintings from The
Solomon R. Guggenheim Museum, New York,* Apr. 16-May
26, 1957, no. 31, traveled to The Hague, Gemeentemuseum,
June 25-Sept. 1; Helsinki, Ateneumin Taidekokoelmat, Sept.
27-Oct. 20; Rome, Galleria Nazionale d'Arte Moderna, Dec.
5, 1957-Jan. 8, 1958; Cologne, Wallraf-Richartz-Museum,
Jan. 26-Mar. 30; Paris, Musée des Arts Décoratifs, Apr. 23-
June 1

New York, The Solomon R. Guggenheim Museum,
Inaugural Selection, Oct. 21, 1959-June 19, 1960

Seattle, World's Fair, *Masterpieces of Modern Art,* Apr. 21-
Sept. 4, 1962, no. 59, repr.

New York, The Solomon R. Guggenheim Museum, *Vasily
Kandinsky, 1866-1944: A Retrospective Exhibition,* Jan. 25-
Apr. 7, 1963, no. 32, repr., traveled to Paris, Musée National
d'Art Moderne, Apr. 29-June 24; The Hague, Gemeentemuseum, July 1-Aug. 30; Kunsthalle Basel, Sept. 7-Nov. 7

New York, The Solomon R. Guggenheim Museum, *Kandinsky at the Guggenheim Museum,* May 12-Sept. 5, 1972,
repr.

Berlin, Nationalgalerie, *Hommage à Schönberg: Der Blaue
Reiter und das Musikalische in der Malerei der Zeit,* Sept.
11-Nov. 4, 1974, no. 17

New York, The Solomon R. Guggenheim Museum, *Forty
Modern Masters: An Anniversary Show,* Dec. 16, 1977-Feb.
5, 1978, no. 63, repr.

REFERENCES:
W. Kandinsky, "Das Bild mit weissem Rand," *Kandinsky
1901-1913,* Berlin, 1913, pp. xxxix-xxxxi, 13, repr.

K. Brisch, *Wassily Kandinsky: Untersuchungen zur Entste-
hung der gegenstandlosen Malerei an seinem Werk von
1900-1921,* Ph.D. dissertation, Rheinische Friedrich-Wilhelm-
Universität, 1955, pp. 228-229, 296, 318

W. Grohmann, *Wassily Kandinsky: Life and Work,* New
York, 1958, pp. 132, 134, 332, no. 173, cc 90, repr.

R. C. Washton, *Vasily Kandinsky 1909-1913, Painting and
Theory,* Ph.D. dissertation, Yale University, 1968, pp.
217-223

P. Overy, *Kandinsky: The Language of The Eye,* New York
and Washington, D.C., 1969, p. 68 and fig. 25

Handbook, 1970, pp. 184, repr., 185

Rudenstine, *Collection Catalogue,* 1976, no. 91, color repr.

H. K. Röthel, *Kandinsky,* Paris, 1977, color pl. 18

P. Weiss, *Kandinsky in Munich: The Formative Jugendstil
Years,* Princeton, N. J., 1979, pp. 131, 147-148 and pl. 138

61 **Black Lines.** December 1913
(Schwarze Linien)

Kandinsky Handlist: *xii / 1913, 189 Chernye shtrikhi* (in Cyrillic alphabet: Black Lines).

37.241

Oil on canvas, 51 x 51¼ in. (129.4 x 131.1 cm.)

Signed and dated l.l.: *Kandinsky 1913*; inscribed on stretcher: *Kandinsky—Schwarze Linien (Dez 1913). (No. 189).*

PROVENANCE:

F. Kluxen, Münster, 1914-18
Herwarth Walden, Berlin, ca. 1918
Georg Muche, Berlin, by 1928
Solomon R. Guggenheim, New York, 1929-37
Gift, Solomon R. Guggenheim, 1937

Black Lines and *Light Picture* in the Guggenheim Museum collection, which were painted in December 1913, are by the artist's own testimony among the earliest examples in his work of "non-objective art."* In *Black Lines* a network of lines articulates the surface, as in two preliminary drawings, and links the red, green, blue, yellow and white spots of color. The black lines themselves consist of oil paint applied in a manner that suggests India ink or prints. Significantly, Kandinsky executed a series of drypoints in 1913-14 which are similar in style to *Black Lines*. The inventiveness of line and the freedom and brilliance of color give the painting its expressive power. The forms seem to float on the surface yet are subtly anchored by the vertical red band at the right.

* see Rudenstine, no. 93

EXHIBITIONS:

Cologne, Kreis für Kunst Köln im Deutschen Theater, *Kandinsky Ausstellung,* Jan. 30-Feb. 15, 1914, no. 3

Berlin, Der Sturm, *Expressionisten, Futuristen, Kubisten,* July 1916, no. 24

Berlin, Nationalgalerie, *Ausstellung Neuerer Deutscher Kunst aus Berliner Privatbesitz,* Apr. 1928, no. 48

Charleston, S.C., Carolina Art Association, Gibbes Memorial Art Gallery, *Solomon R. Guggenheim Collection of Non-Objective Paintings,* Mar. 1-Apr. 12, 1936, no. 69, color repr.

New York, Museum of Non-Objective Painting, *In Memory of Wassily Kandinsky,* Mar. 15-Apr. 29, 1945, no. 27, color repr.

Paris, Musée National d'Art Moderne, *L'Oeuvre du XXᵉ siècle,* May-June 1952, no. 42, repr., traveled to London, Tate Gallery, July 15-Aug. 17

London, Tate Gallery, *An exhibition of paintings from The Solomon R. Guggenheim Museum, New York,* Apr. 16-May 26, 1957, no. 30, repr., traveled to The Hague, Gemeentemuseum, June 25-Sept. 1; Helsinki, Ateneumin Taidekokoelmat, Sept. 27-Oct. 20; Rome, Galleria Nazionale d'Arte Moderna, Dec. 5, 1957-Jan. 8, 1958; Cologne, Wallraf-Richartz-Museum, Jan. 26-Mar. 30; Paris, Musée des Arts Décoratifs, Apr. 23-June 1

New York, The Solomon R. Guggenheim Museum, *Inaugural Selection,* Oct. 21, 1959-June 19, 1960

New York, The Solomon R. Guggenheim Museum, *Vasily Kandinsky, 1866-1944: A Retrospective Exhibition,* Jan. 25-Apr. 7, 1963, no. 35, repr., traveled to Paris, Musée National d'Art Moderne, Apr. 29-June 24; The Hague, Gemeentemuseum, July 1-Aug. 30; Kunsthalle Basel, Sept. 7-Nov. 7

New York, Marlborough-Gerson Gallery, *Artists and Maecenas: A Tribute to Curt Valentin,* Nov. 12-Dec. 27, 1963, not in cat.

New York, The Solomon R. Guggenheim Museum, *Kandinsky at the Guggenheim Museum,* May 12-Sept. 5, 1972, color repr.

Munich, Haus der Kunst, *Wassily Kandinsky 1866-1944,* Nov. 13, 1976-Jan. 30, 1977, no. 46

REFERENCES:

W. Grohmann, *Wassily Kandinsky: Life and Work,* New York, 1958, pp. 138, 141, color repr., 333, no. 189

C. Doelman, *Wassily Kandinsky,* New York, 1964, pp. 36, repr., 75

J. Lassaigne, *Kandinsky,* Geneva, 1964, p. 72, color repr.

K. Kuh, *Break-Up: The Core of Modern Art,* Greenwich, Conn., 1965, pp. 96-97, pl. 66

P. Overy, *Kandinsky: The Language of The Eye,* New York and Washington, D. C., 1969, p. 68 and fig. 24

Handbook, 1970, pp. 190-191, repr.

Rudenstine, *Collection Catalogue,* 1976, no. 94, repr.

Kandinsky

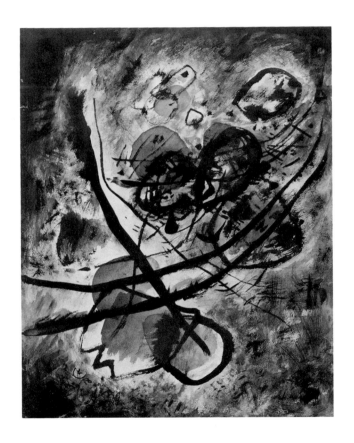

62 Untitled. 1918

49.1236

Watercolor and ink on paper, 11¹⁵⁄₁₆ x 9 in. (28.7 x 22.9 cm.)

Signed and dated l.l.: *K/18.*

PROVENANCE:
Livraria Askanasy Ltda., Rio de Janeiro, 1949

From November 1917 until July 1919 Kandinsky concentrated on drawings, watercolors and paintings on glass. In this small work the intersection of lines and the revolving planet-like orbs form a dense configuration. Although its linear patterning is reminiscent of *Black Lines* (cat. no. 61), the predominantly dark watercolor lacks its spaciousness and vivid coloration.

EXHIBITIONS:
Pasadena Art Museum, *Vasily Kandinsky, 1866-1944: A Retrospective Exhibition* (organized by The Solomon R. Guggenheim Museum, New York), Jan. 15-Feb. 15, 1963, no. 4, traveled to San Francisco Museum of Art, Mar. 1-Apr. 1; Portland (Ore.) Art Museum, Apr. 15-May 15; San Antonio, Marion Koogler McNay Art Institute, June 1-July 1; Colorado Springs Fine Arts Center, July 15-Aug. 25; The Baltimore Museum of Art, Sept. 19-Oct. 20; The Columbus Gallery of Fine Arts, Nov. 5-Dec. 5; St. Louis, Washington University Art Gallery, Dec. 22, 1963 Jan. 6, 1964; Montreal Museum of Fine Arts, Feb. 5-Mar. 5; Worcester Art Museum, Mar. 20-Apr. 20

New York, The Solomon R. Guggenheim Museum, *Kandinsky at the Guggenheim Museum,* May 12-Sept. 5, 1972, repr., traveled to Los Angeles County Museum of Art, Oct. 3-Nov. 19; Minneapolis, Walker Art Center, May 5-July 15, 1973

Munich, Haus der Kunst, *Wassily Kandinsky 1866-1944,* Nov. 13, 1976-Jan. 30, 1977, no. 154, repr.

REFERENCE:
Handbook, 1970, p. 201, repr.

Kandinsky

63 Earth Center. 1921
(Weisses Zentrum)

Kandinsky Handlist: *1921, 236 Belyitsentr* (in Cyrillic alphabet: Earth Center).

71.1936 R98

Signed and dated l.l.: *K 2i*; inscribed on reverse: *K / N°236. / 1921.*

PROVENANCE:

Hans Goltz, Munich, ca. 1925
Maurice J. Speiser, Philadelphia, by 1939
Karl Nierendorf, New York, by 1944
Hilla Rebay, Greens Farms, Connecticut, 1944-67
Estate of Hilla Rebay, 1967-71

The parallel black bands which form a triangle at the lower left establish a movement toward the white center of the picture. There is gravitation toward the center from all directions: the black dagger descending from the upper left aims at a central point which is also the focus of the blue parabola originating at the upper right. The five winged shapes gravitate toward the same destination. It is possible to distinguish overlapping translucent planes of color which define ambiguous spatial relationships.

EXHIBITIONS:

Moscow, *Mir Iskusstva (World of Art),* Oct.-Nov. 1921, no. 44

Munich, Galerie Hans Goltz, *Kandinsky Jubiläums-Ausstellung,* Jan. 1923

New York, The Museum of Modern Art, *Art in Our Time: 10th Anniversary Exhibition,* May-Nov. 1939, no. 180

New York, Nierendorf Gallery, *Gestation-Formation,* Mar. 1944, no. 10

New York, Museum of Non-Objective Painting, *In Memory of Wassily Kandinsky,* Mar. 15-Apr. 29, 1945, no. 43, repr.

The Arts Club of Chicago, *Wassily Kandinsky Memorial Exhibition,* Nov. 1945, no. 34

Paris, Musée National d'Art Moderne, *L'Oeuvre du XXe siècle,* May-June 1952, no. 43, traveled to London, Tate Gallery, July 15-Aug. 17

Bridgeport, Conn., Carlson Gallery, University of Bridgeport, *Homage to Hilla Rebay,* Apr. 8-May 10, 1972, no. 30

New York, The Solomon R. Guggenheim Museum, *Kandinsky at the Guggenheim Museum,* May 12-Sept. 5, 1972

Munich, Haus der Kunst, *Wassily Kandinsky 1866-1944,* Nov. 13, 1976-Jan. 30, 1977, no. 57, repr.

REFERENCES:

W. Grohmann, *Kandinsky,* Paris, 1930, p. 17, repr.

W. Grohmann, *Wassily Kandinsky: Life and Work,* New York, 1958, pp. 168, 334, no. 236, cc 129, repr.

Rudenstine, *Collection Catalogue,* 1976, no. 100, repr.

64 Composition 8. July 1923

Kandinsky Handlist: *vii 1923, 260, Komposition 8.*

37.262

Oil on canvas, 55⅛ x 79⅛ in. (140 x 201 cm.)

Signed and dated l.l.: *K/23*; inscribed on reverse: *K/N° 260/1923.*; on stretcher „*Komposition 8.*"

PROVENANCE:

from the artist
Solomon R. Guggenheim, New York, 1929-37
Gift, Solomon R. Guggenheim, 1937

Kandinsky began to paint the *Compositions* in 1909 and produced the tenth and last one in 1939. In the *Compositions* he sought a significant expression of complex inner feelings. This is articulated in *Composition 8* through the repetition of various geometric elements strewn over the canvas and allowed to interact without a preconceived tectonic unity. Most striking is the large circle in the upper left corner which resonates in the other circular forms and contrasts with the predominating acute angles. Circles first occurred in Kandinsky's work in 1921 and by 1923 assumed a major role in his pictures. He was not so much concerned with circles and triangles as formal elements but as evocations of the spiritual, which he called "the inner."

EXHIBITIONS:

Weimar, *Bauhaus Ausstellung,* Aug.-Sept. 1923

Kunsthalle Mannheim, *Wege und Richtungen der Abstrakten Malerei in Europa,* Jan. 30-May 27, 1927, no. 81

Charleston, S. C., Carolina Art Association, Gibbes Memorial Art Gallery, *Solomon R. Guggenheim Collection of Non-Objective Paintings,* Mar. 1-Apr. 12, 1936, no. 76, repr.

New York, Museum of Non-Objective Painting, *In Memory of Wassily Kandinsky,* Mar. 15-Apr. 29, 1945, no. 57, repr.

Paris, Musée National d'Art Moderne, *L'Oeuvre du XXe siècle,* May-June 1952, no. 44, traveled to London, Tate Gallery, July 15-Aug. 17

New York, The Museum of Modern Art, *German Art of the Twentieth Century,* Oct. 1-Dec. 8, 1957, no. 67, color repr., traveled to City Art Museum of Saint Louis, Jan. 8-Feb. 24, 1958

New York, The Solomon R. Guggenheim Museum, *Vasily Kandinsky, 1866-1944: A Retrospective Exhibition,* Jan. 25-Apr. 7, 1963, no. 53, repr., traveled to Paris, Musée National d'Art Moderne, Apr. 29-June 24; The Hague, Gemeentemuseum, July 1-Aug. 30; Kunsthalle Basel, Sept. 7-Nov. 7

Stuttgart, Würtembergische Kunstverein, *50 Jahre Bauhaus,* May 5-July 28, 1968, no. 111, repr., traveled to London, Royal Academy, Sept. 21-Oct. 27; Amsterdam, Stedelijk Museum, Nov. 30, 1968-Jan. 8, 1969; Paris, Musée National

d'Art Moderne, Apr. 1-June 22; Chicago, Illinois Institute of Technology, Aug. 25-Sept. 26; Toronto, The Art Gallery of Ontario, Dec. 5, 1969-Feb. 8, 1970; Pasadena Art Museum, Mar. 16-May 10; Buenos Aires, Museo Nacional de Bellas Artes, Sept. 1-Oct. 10

New York, The Solomon R. Guggenheim Museum, *Kandinsky at the Guggenheim Museum,* May 12-Sept. 5, 1972, repr.

Munich, Haus der Kunst, *Wassily Kandinsky 1866-1944,* Nov. 13, 1976-Jan. 30, 1977, no. 60, color repr.

New York, The Solomon R. Guggenheim Museum, *Forty Modern Masters: An Anniversary Show,* Dec. 16, 1977-Feb. 5, 1978, no. 64

REFERENCES:

W. Grohmann, *Kandinsky,* Paris, 1930, pp. xxvi, xxviii, 24, repr.

M. Bill, *Wassily Kandinsky,* Paris, 1951, p. 132, repr.

W. Grohmann, *Wassily Kandinsky: Life and Work,* New York, 1958, pp. 119, 188, 189, color repr., 190, 219, 334, no. 260

J. Lassaigne, *Kandinsky,* Geneva, 1964, pp. 97-98

K. Lindsay, "Les Thèmes de l'inconscient," *XXe siècle,* vol. XXVII, Dec. 1966, pp. 46, repr., 48, 49

P. Overy, *Kandinsky: The Language of The Eye,* New York, 1969, pp. 67-68, 83, 107, 108, 121-122 and color pl. 29

Rudenstine, *Collection Catalogue,* 1976, no. 105, repr.

H. K. Röthel, *Kandinsky,* Paris, 1977, color pl. 28

65 **Several Circles.** January-February 1926
(Einige Kreise)

Kandinsky Handlist: *i-ii 1926, 323, Einige Kreise.*

41.283

Oil on canvas, 55¼ x 55⅜ in. (140.3 x 140.7 cm.)

Signed and dated l.l.: *K/26;* inscribed on reverse:
K/N° 323. / 1926 / „Einige Kreise."

PROVENANCE:

from the artist
Staatliche Gemäldegalerie, Dresden, 1926-37
Gutekunst und Klipstein, Bern, by 1939
Solomon R. Guggenheim, New York, 1939-41
Gift, Solomon R. Guggenheim, 1941

From the dark gray, amorphous, nebular environment
emerges a primary form—the large dark blue circle
surrounded by a corona. A black disc is enclosed within
the larger blue one and their circumferences meet at a
tangent. From this matrix many colored circles are
successively generated. They resemble transparent gels.
Those circles that overlap with others change color
where they intersect.

The circle is the most elementary form. Kandinsky
wrote that "the circle is the synthesis of the greatest
oppositions. It combines the concentric and the
excentric in a single form, and in equilibrium."
(Grohmann, 1958, p. 188) For Kandinsky the circle
represents a development in cosmic evolution parallel
to that of spirit taking the form of matter.

EXHIBITIONS:

Dresden, *Internationale Kunstausstellung,* June-Sept. 1926,
no. 519, repr.

New York, Museum of Non-Objective Painting, *In Memory
of Wassily Kandinsky,* Mar. 15-Apr. 29, 1945, no. 97

New York, The Solomon R. Guggenheim Museum, *Vasily
Kandinsky, 1866-1944: A Retrospective Exhibition,* Jan. 25-
Apr. 7, 1963, no. 57, color repr., traveled to Paris, Musée
National d'Art Moderne, Apr. 29-June 24; The Hague,
Gemeentemuseum, July 1-Aug. 30; Kunsthalle Basel, Sept. 7-
Nov. 7

New York, Marlborough-Gerson Gallery, *Artists and
Maecenas: A Tribute to Curt Valentin,* Nov. 12-Dec. 27,
1963, not in cat.

Cambridge, Mass., Busch-Reisinger Museum, Harvard University, *Masters of the Bauhaus,* Nov. 1-Dec. 10, 1966, repr.

New York, The Solomon R. Guggenheim Museum, *Kandinsky at the Guggenheim Museum,* May 12-Sept. 5, 1972,
color repr.

Munich, Haus der Kunst, *Wassily Kandinsky 1866-1944,*
Nov. 13, 1976-Jan. 30, 1977, no. 66

New York, The Solomon R. Guggenheim Museum, *Forty
Modern Masters: An Anniversary Show,* Dec. 16, 1977-Feb.
5, 1978, no. 65

REFERENCES:

Offset, Heft 7, 1926, p. 409, repr.

W. Grohmann, *Kandinsky,* Paris, 1930, pp. xxix, 34, repr.

M. Bill, *Wassily Kandinsky,* Paris, 1951, p. 53, repr.

W. Grohmann, *Wassily Kandinsky: Life and Work,* New
York, 1958, pp. 205, color repr., 206, 335, no. 323

M. Brion, *Kandinsky,* London, 1961, p. 62, repr.

W. Grohmann, "La Grande unité d'une grande oeuvre," *XXᵉ
siècle,* vol. XXVII, Dec. 1966, p. 13, repr. betw. pp. 56-57

Handbook, 1970, pp. 206-207, repr.

Rudenstine, *Collection Catalogue,* 1976, no. 111, color repr.

H. H. Arnason, *History of Modern Art,* rev. ed., New York,
1977, pp. 237, 281 and color pl. 96

H. K. Röthel, *Kandinsky,* Paris, 1977, p. 34, repr.

P. Weiss, *Kandinsky in Munich: The Formative Jugendstil
Years,* Princeton, N. J., 1979, pp. 123, 129 and color pl. VI

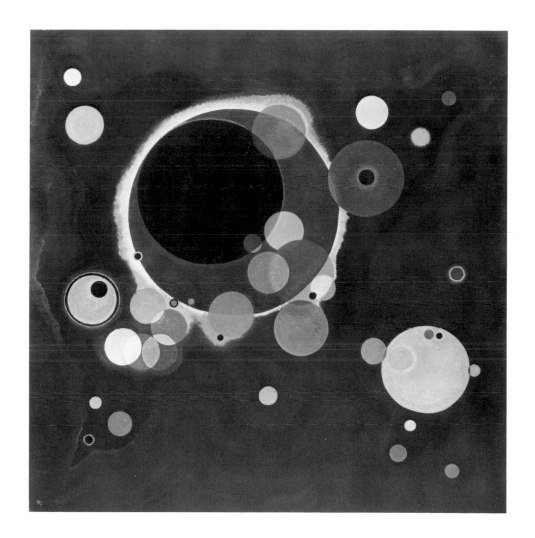

Kandinsky

66 Accompanied Contrast. March 1935
(Contraste accompagné)

Kandinsky Handlist: *iii 1935, 613, Contraste accompagné.*

Oil with sand on canvas, 38¼ x 63⅞ in. (97.1 x 162.1 cm.)

Signed and dated l.l.: *K/35*; inscribed on reverse: *K/N°613 / 1935.*

PROVENANCE:

from the artist
Solomon R. Guggenheim, New York, 1935-37
Gift, Solomon R. Guggenheim, 1937

Far different from Kandinsky's early work, *Accompanied Contrast,* which was done in Paris in 1935, displays cool, delicate color harmonies and a conscious stability of composition. The colored areas containing a mixture of sand and pigment project slightly from the surface and contrast with the smoothly painted background. The raised forms, which are interconnected, function as planes within a self-contained space. The shapes are neither specifically organic nor geometric but partake generally of the abstract style prevalent in Paris in the thirties.

EXHIBITIONS:

Paris, Galerie Cahiers d'Art, *Kandinsky,* June-July 1935

Charleston, S. C., Carolina Art Association, Gibbes Memorial Art Gallery, *Solomon R. Guggenheim Collection of Non-Objective Paintings,* Mar. 1-Apr. 12, 1936, no. 92, repr.

New York, Museum of Non-Objective Painting, *In Memory of Wassily Kandinsky,* Mar. 15-Apr. 29, 1945, no. 210

The Arts Club of Chicago, *Wassily Kandinsky Memorial Exhibition,* Nov. 1945, no. 24

Brussels, Palais des Beaux-Arts, 45 *Oeuvres de Kandinsky Provenant du Solomon R. Guggenheim Museum, New York,* May 17-June 30, 1957, no. 40, repr., traveled to Paris, Musée National d'Art Moderne, Nov. 15, 1957-Jan. 5, 1958; London, Tate Gallery, Jan. 15-Feb. 28

The Art Gallery of Toronto, *Paintings by Kandinsky from the Collection of The Solomon R. Guggenheim Museum,* Apr. 24-May 24, 1959

New York, The Solomon R. Guggenheim Museum, *Inaugural Selection,* Oct. 21, 1959-June 19, 1960

New York, The Solomon R. Guggenheim Museum, *Vasily Kandinsky, 1866-1944: A Retrospective Exhibition,* Jan. 25-Apr. 7, 1963, no. 71, repr., traveled to Paris, Musée National d'Art Moderne, Apr. 29-June 24; The Hague, Gemeentemuseum, July 1-Aug. 30; Kunsthalle Basel, Sept. 7-Nov. 7

New York, The Solomon R. Guggenheim Museum, *Kandinsky at the Guggenheim Museum,* May 12-Sept. 5, 1972, color repr.

REFERENCES:

W. Grohmann, *Wassily Kandinsky: Life and Work,* New York, 1958, p. 340, no. 613, cc 443, repr.

J. Lassaigne, *Kandinsky,* Geneva, 1964, p. 105, color repr.

P. Overy, *Kandinsky: The Language of The Eye,* New York, 1969, p. 175 and color pl. 55

Handbook, 1970, pp. 210-211, repr.

Rudenstine, *Collection Catalogue,* 1976, no. 127, color repr.

67 Dominant Curve. April 1936
(Courbe dominante)

Kandinsky Handlist: *iv 1936, 631, Courbe dominante.*

45.989

Oil on canvas, 50⅞ x 76½ in. (129.4 x 194.2 cm.)

Signed and dated l.l.: *K/36*; inscribed on reverse: *K / N° 63i / 1936 / „Courbe / dominante."*

PROVENANCE:

from the artist
Peggy Guggenheim, London, 1938
Karl Nierendorf, New York, by 1945

Kandinsky regarded *Dominant Curve* as one of his most important works. Forces emanate from the large yellow disc and are governed by the broadly designed curve to the right of center. Block-like steps at the lower right return the compositional flow to this large circle at the upper left. The rectangular tablet with signs in the upper left corner and the three black circles at the upper right firmly anchor the dynamic whole to the picture plane. The palette contains more pastel and high-keyed colors than in Kandinsky's earlier work; many small elements of contrasting hues activate broad expanses of color. Kandinsky's large-scale painting radiates a mystical energy.

EXHIBITIONS:

Paris, Galerie Jeanne Bucher, *Kandinsky,* Dec. 3-19, 1936, no. 7

Kunsthalle Bern, *Kandinsky,* Feb.-Mar. 1937, no. 70

Paris, Jeu de Paume, *Origines et développement de l'art international indépendant,* July 30-Oct. 31, 1937, no. 150

London, Guggenheim Jeune, *Kandinsky,* Mar. 1938, no. 5, repr.

The Arts Club of Chicago, *Wassily Kandinsky Memorial Exhibition,* Nov. 1945, no. 25

Brussels, Palais des Beaux-Arts, *45 Oeuvres de Kandinsky Provenant du Solomon R. Guggenheim Museum, New York,* May 17-June 30, 1957, repr., traveled to Paris, Musée National d'Art Moderne, Nov. 15, 1957-Jan. 5, 1958; London, Tate Gallery, Jan. 15-Feb. 28; Lyon, Musée des Beaux-Arts, Mar. 8-Apr. 6; Oslo, Kunstnernes Hus, Apr. 18-May 4; Rome, Galleria Nazionale d'Arte Moderna, May 15-June 30

The Art Gallery of Toronto, *Paintings by Kandinsky from the Collection of The Solomon R. Guggenheim Museum,* Apr. 24-May 24, 1959

New York, The Solomon R. Guggenheim Museum, *Inaugural Selection,* Oct. 21, 1959-June 19, 1960

New York, The Solomon R. Guggenheim Museum, *Vasily Kandinsky, 1866-1944: A Retrospective Exhibition,* Jan. 25-Apr. 7, 1963, no. 74, repr., traveled to Paris, Musée National d'Art Moderne, Apr. 29-June 24; The Hague, Gemeentemuseum, July 1-Aug. 30; Kunsthalle Basel, Sept. 7-Nov. 7

New York, The Solomon R. Guggenheim Museum, *Kandinsky at the Guggenheim Museum,* May 12-Sept. 5, 1972, color repr.

Munich, Haus der Kunst, *Wassily Kandinsky 1866-1944,* Nov. 13, 1976-Jan. 30, 1977, no. 88

Paris, Musée National d'Art Moderne, Centre National d'Art et de Culture Georges Pompidou, *Paris-New York,* June 1-Sept. 19, 1977, p. 497, repr.

New York, The Solomon R. Guggenheim Museum, *Forty Modern Masters: An Anniversary Show,* Dec. 16, 1977-Feb. 5, 1978, no. 66

REFERENCES:

M. Bill, *Kandinsky,* Paris, 1951, p. 66, repr.

W. Grohmann, *Wassily Kandinsky: Life and Work,* New York, 1958, pp. 228, 231, color repr., 340, no. 631

P. Guggenheim, *Confessions of an Art Addict,* New York, 1960, p. 110

J. Elderfield, "Geometric Abstract Painting and Paris in the Thirties," *Artforum,* vol. VIII, June 1970, pp. 71, repr., 72

Handbook, 1970, pp. 212-213, repr.

Rudenstine, *Collection Catalogue,* 1976, no. 131, repr.

Kandinsky

68 Untitled (No. 673). 1940

48.1172 x89

Watercolor and ink on paper, 18¾ x 12⅛ in. (47.8 x 30.9 cm.)

Signed and dated l.l.: *K/40*; inscribed on reverse by the artist: *N° 673/1940*; and by the artist's widow: *A Hilla de Rebay / En souvenir de Kandinsky / le 1 / VII 48 Paris.*

PROVENANCE:

Karl Nierendorf, by 1948
Estate of Karl Nierendorf, 1948

Kandinsky's late painting is distinguished by a reduction in size, subdued close-ranged hues and an inventive precision in the forms. He has attained a synthesis of the geometric abstraction of his Bauhaus period and the spiritually inspired biomorphic abstraction of his earlier work. In both *No. 673* and *Red Accent* (cat. no. 69), shapes conjure up creatures from animal and vegetable kingdoms. However, the images remain autonomous, a language of private symbols. The compositional elements in *No. 673* are dispersed across the paper and held in precarious balance. In *Red Accent* the canvas is divided vertically into three distinct bands. Left and right are contrasted, forms are repeated and their trajectories cut across the surface. The "red accent," which resembles a painting, is found at the upper left.

EXHIBITIONS:

Bridgeport, Conn., Carlson Gallery, University of Bridgeport, *Homage to Hilla Rebay*, Apr. 8-May 10, 1972, no. 72

New York, The Solomon R. Guggenheim Museum, *Kandinsky at the Guggenheim Museum*, May 12-Sept. 5, 1972, repr., traveled to Los Angeles County Museum of Art, Oct. 3-Nov. 19; Minneapolis, Walker Art Center, May 5-July 15, 1973

Munich, Haus der Kunst, *Wassily Kandinsky 1866-1944*, Nov. 13, 1976-Jan. 30, 1977, no. 194, repr.

69 Red Accent. June 1943
(L'Accent rouge)

Kandinsky Handlist: *vi 1943, 722, L'Accent rouge.*

71.1936 R137

Oil on board mounted on panel,
16½ x 22¾ in. (41.8 x 57.9 cm.)

Signed and dated l.l.: *K/43*; inscribed on reverse,
possibly by the artist: *K/Nº722/1943/58 x 42*; not by
the artist: *Kandinsky / "Composition Marron."*

PROVENANCE:
Hilla Rebay, Greens Farms, Connecticut
Estate of Hilla Rebay, 1967-71

EXHIBITIONS:

Paris, Galerie Raspail [group exhibition], May 1944

Bridgeport, Conn., Carlson Gallery, University of Bridgeport, *Homage to Hilla Rebay,* Apr. 8-May 10, 1972, no. 77

New York, The Solomon R. Guggenheim Museum, *Kandinsky at the Guggenheim Museum,* May 12-Sept. 5, 1972, repr.,
traveled to Los Angeles County Museum of Art, Oct. 3-Nov.
19; Minneapolis, Walker Art Center, May 5-July 15, 1973

Munich, Haus der Kunst, *Wassily Kandinsky 1866-1944,*
Nov. 13, 1976-Jan. 30, 1977, no. 102, repr.

New York , The Solomon R. Guggenheim Museum, *Forty
Modern Masters: An Anniversary Show,* Dec. 16, 1977-Feb.
5, 1978, no. 68

REFERENCES:

W. Grohmann, *Wassily Kandinsky: Life and Work,* New
York, 1958, p. 342, no. 722, cc 521, repr.

Rudenstine, *Collection Catalogue,* 1976, no. 143, repr.

Franz Marc 1880-1916

Franz Marc was born on February 8, 1880, in Munich. The son of a landscape painter, he decided to become an artist after a year of military service interrupted his plans to study philology. From 1900 to 1902 he studied at the Akademie in Munich with Gabriel von Hackl and Wilhelm von Diez. The following year, during a visit to France, he was introduced to Japanese woodcuts and the work of the Impressionists in Paris.

Marc suffered from severe depressions from 1904 to 1907, the year his father died. In 1907 Marc went again to Paris, where he responded enthusiastically to the work of van Gogh, Gauguin, the Cubists and the Expressionists; later he was impressed by the Matisse exhibition in Munich in 1910. During this period he received steady income from the animal anatomy lessons he gave to artists.

In 1910 his first one-man show was held at the Kunsthandlung Brackl in Munich, and Marc met August Macke and the collector Bernhard Koehler. He publicly defended the *Neue Künstlervereinigung München (NKVM),* and was formally welcomed into the group early in 1911, when he met Kandinsky. After internal dissension split the *NKVM,* he and Kandinsky formed the *Blaue Reiter (Blue Rider),* whose first exhibition took place in December 1911 at the Moderne Galerie (Thannhauser) in Munich. Marc invited members of the Berlin *Brücke* group to participate in the second *Blaue Reiter* show two months later at the Galerie Hans Goltz in Munich. The *Almanach der Blaue Reiter* was published with lead articles by Marc in May 1912. When World War I broke out in August 1914, Marc immediately enlisted. He was deeply troubled by Macke's death in action shortly thereafter; during the war he produced his *Sketchbook from the Field.* Marc died at Verdun on March 4, 1916.

70 **White Bull.** 1911
(Stier)

51.1312

Oil on canvas, 39⅜ x 53¼ in. (100 x 135.2 cm.)

Signed and dated on reverse: *Fz. Marc ii / „Stier."*

PROVENANCE:
Bernhard Koehler, Berlin, 1913-27
Bernhard Koehler, Jr., Berlin, 1927-51
Otto Stangl, Munich, 1951

From as early as 1905 Franz Marc represented animals in nature. Not only bulls, cows, horses and pigs but also deer, wolves, foxes and tigers are viewed sympathetically and often with a pantheistic spirit.

White Bull was painted in Sindelsdorf in the Bavarian Alps, probably in July 1911 after Marc's return from England in June, and was definitely completed by August. The large, self-contained form of the bull is seen at rest within a landscape setting. The artist's knowledge of anatomy enabled him to simplify the animal's body into an essential, compact shape. Marc evolved a system of color theories: his intent was to endow colors with both expressive value and symbolic meaning. Thus, as in *Yellow Cow* (cat. no. 71), the image is not naturalistic but spiritual.

EXHIBITIONS:
Munich, Münchner Neue Secession, *Franz Marc Gedächtnisausstellung,* Sept. 14-Oct. 15, 1916, no. 73

Wiesbaden, Nassauischer Kunstverein, Neues Museum, *Franz Marc Gedächtnisausstellung,* Mar.-Apr. 1917, no. 23

Berlin, Nationalgalerie, *Franz Marc,* Mar.-Apr. 1922

Hannover, Kestner-Gesellschaft, *Franz Marc Gedächtnisausstellung,* Mar. 4-Apr. 19, 1936, no. 24

Berlin, Galerie Nierendorf, *Franz Marc,* May 1936, no. 19

Munich, Haus der Kunst, *Der Blaue Reiter,* Sept.-Oct. 1949, no. 230

London, Tate Gallery, *An exhibition of paintings from The Solomon R. Guggenheim Museum, New York,* Apr. 16-May 26, 1957, no. 46, traveled to The Hague, Gemeentemuseum, June 25-Sept. 1; Helsinki, Ateneumin Taidekokoelmat, Sept. 27-Oct. 20; Rome, Galleria Nazionale d'Arte Moderna, Dec. 5, 1957-Jan. 8, 1958; Cologne, Wallraf-Richartz-Museum, Jan. 26-Mar. 30; Paris, Musée des Arts Décoratifs, Apr. 23-June 1

Munich, Städtische Galerie, *Franz Marc,* Aug. 10-Oct. 13, 1963, no. 101, repr.

Kunstverein in Hamburg, *Franz Marc,* Nov. 9, 1963-Jan. 5, 1964, no. 29, repr.

REFERENCES:

W. Kandinsky and F. Marc, eds., *Der Blaue Reiter*, Munich, 1912, opp. p. 91, repr.

C. Einstein, *Die Kunst des 20. Jahrhunderts*, 2nd ed., Berlin, 1928, p. 408, repr.

A. J. Schardt, *Franz Marc*, Berlin, 1936, pp. 87, 89, repr., 163, no. 23, under 1911

August Macke- Franz Marc Briefwechsel, Cologne, 1964, p. 161

K. Lankheit, *Franz Marc: Katalog der Werke*, Cologne, 1970, p. 50, no. 150, repr.

Handbook, 1970, pp. 284-285, color repr.

K. Lankheit, *Franz Marc: Sein Leben und seine Kunst*, Cologne, 1976, p. 77 and color pl. 9

Rudenstine, *Collection Catalogue*, 1976, no. 173, repr.

71 **Yellow Cow.** 1911
(Gelbe Kuh)

49.1210

Oil on canvas, 55⅜ x 74½ in. (140.5 x 189.2 cm.)

Signed on reverse: *Marc*. Not dated.

PROVENANCE:
Herwarth Walden, Berlin, 1915-16
E. Kluxen, Berlin, 1916- ca. 1918
Nell Walden, Berlin and Ascona, Switzerland, ca.
1918-49

Yellow Cow, painted in Sindelsdorf, was shown at the
first *Blaue Reiter* exhibition, which opened in Munich
on December 18, 1911. It is an early example of Marc's
mature style. The sculptured, clearly defined volumes
of the cow show a transitional stage between the artist's
earlier more naturalistic treatment of his subject
matter and the later stylized flattening into planes.
Similarly, the full rounded contours and arabesques
which dominate the composition would soon be
replaced by more concise geometric forms.

The colors have a symbolic value and should be seen
in relation to Marc's theories. In his correspondence
with August Macke in December 1910, Marc specified
that "blue is the *male* principle, severe, bitter, spiritual,
and intellectual. Yellow is the *female* principle, gentle,
cheerful, and sensual. Red is *matter,* brutal and heavy,
the color which must be fought and overcome by the
other two!" (Rudenstine, p. 493) He proceeded to
elaborate on various combinations of colors and their
meanings.

There is an oil sketch for *Yellow Cow* in a private
collection, and an almost identical yellow cow appears
in a painting of 1912, *Cows Red, Green, Yellow,* in the
Städtische Galerie im Lenbachhaus, Munich .

EXHIBITIONS:
Munich, Moderne Galerie (Heinrich Thannhauser), *Der
Blaue Reiter: die erste Ausstellung,* Dec. 18, 1911-Jan. 1,
1912, no. 30, repr.

Berlin, Der Sturm, *43. Ausstellung: Expressionisten, Futuristen, Kubisten,* July 1916, no. 45

Berlin, Der Sturm, *Sammlung Walden,* Oct. 1919, no. 236

Berlin, Galerie Nierendorf, *Franz Marc,* May 1936, no. 8

London, New Burlington Galleries, *Exhibition of Twentieth
Century German Art,* July 1938, no. 164

St. Louis, City Art Museum, *Exhibition of 20th Century
(banned) German Art,* Sept. 1-25, 1939, no. 42, traveled to
Northampton, Smith College Museum of Art, Oct. 1-25;

Kansas City, William Rockhill Nelson Gallery of Art, Nov.
1-25; San Francisco Museum of Art, Feb. 6-26, 1940

Kunstmuseum Bern, *Sammlung Nell Walden aus den Jahren
1919-20,* Oct. 1944-Mar. 1945, no. 344

Munich, Städtische Galerie, *Franz Marc,* Aug. 10-Oct. 13,
1963, no. 100, repr.

Kunstverein in Hamburg, *Franz Marc,* Nov. 9, 1963-Jan. 5,
1964, no. 28, repr.

New York, The Solomon R. Guggenheim Museum, *Forty
Modern Masters: An Anniversary Show,* Dec. 16, 1977-
Feb. 5, 1978, no. 91, repr.

REFERENCES:
T. Däubler, "Franz Marc," *Die Neue Rundschau,* Jg. XXVII,
Apr. 1916, pp. 565-566

H. Walden, ed., *Expressionismus die Kunstwende,* Berlin,
1918, p. 35, repr.

A. J. Schardt, *Franz Marc,* Berlin, 1936, pp. 86, 88, repr., 163,
no. 22, under 1911

N. Walden and L. Schreyer, *Der Sturm: Ein Erinnerungs-
buch an H. Walden und die Künstler aus dem Sturmkreis,*
Baden-Baden, 1954, opp. p. 48, color repr.

P. Selz, *German Expressionist Painting,* Berkeley, 1957, pp.
203, 263 and pl. 81

K. Lankheit, *Franz Marc: Katalog der Werke,* Cologne, 1970,
p. 52, no. 152, repr.

Handbook, 1970, pp. 286-287, repr.

F. S. Levine, *The Apocalyptic Vision: An Analysis of the Art
of Franz Marc,* Ph.D. dissertation, Washington University,
1975, pp. 108-109 and pl. 15

K. Lankheit, *Franz Marc: Sein Leben und seine Kunst,*
Cologne, 1976, pp. 78, 80, 103 and color pl. 10

Rudenstine, *Collection Catalogue,* 1976, no. 174, color repr.

72 The Unfortunate Land of Tyrol. 1913
(Das arme Land Tirol)

46.1040

Oil on canvas, 51⅝ x 78¾ in. (131.1 x 200 cm.)

Inscribed l.l.: *M. / das arme Land Tirol.* Not dated.

PROVENANCE:

from the artist
Willem Beffie, Amsterdam, Brussels and Brooklyn,
before 1916- after 1940
Karl Nierendorf, New York, after 1940-46

Marc made the first sketches for this large painting
during a trip in the Tyrol region in March 1913. *The
Unfortunate Land of Tyrol* was completed by May
22, 1913, when the artist mentioned it in a letter to
his friend August Macke. Marc inscribed the title
on the canvas and combined such images as a graveyard, a house on fire, starved horses, a heraldic eagle
beneath a rainbow and the Austro-Hungarian border
sign to convey a sense of the tension and suffering long
endured by the region. The impact of these ominous
signs is intensified by the jagged black lines and the
discordant colors. Marc's premonitions of World War I
can also be discerned in his painting *Fate of the
Animals* (Collection Kunstmuseum Basel). Themes of
destruction and apocalypse appeared at this time in
the work of other Expressionists such as Kandinsky,
Kokoschka and Beckmann.

Marc painted another canvas entitled *Tyrol* in 1913
but repainted it substantially the following year
(Collection Bayerische Staatsgemäldesammlungen,
Munich).

EXHIBITIONS:

London, New Burlington Galleries, *Exhibition of Twentieth
Century German Art*, July 1938, no. 165

New York, Buchholz Gallery, *Franz Marc*, Nov. 11-Dec. 7,
1940, no. 13

London, Tate Gallery, *An exhibition of paintings from The
Solomon R. Guggenheim Museum, New York*, Apr. 16-May
26, 1957, no. 47, traveled to The Hague, Gemeentemuseum,
June 25-Sept. 1; Helsinki, Ateneumin Taidekokoelmat, Sept.
27-Oct. 20; Rome, Galleria Nazionale d'Arte Moderna, Dec.
5, 1957-Jan. 8, 1958; Cologne, Wallraf-Richartz-Museum,
Jan. 26-Mar. 30; Paris, Musée des Arts Décoratifs, Apr. 23-
June 1

New York, The Solomon R. Guggenheim Museum,
Inaugural Selection, Oct. 21, 1959-June 19, 1960

Munich, Städtische Galerie, *Franz Marc*, Aug. 10-Oct. 13,
1963, no. 159

Kunstverein in Hamburg, *Franz Marc*, Nov. 9, 1963-Jan. 5,
1964, no. 52, repr.

New York, The Solomon R. Guggenheim Museum, *Van
Gogh and Expressionism*, July 1-Sept. 13, 1964

Paris, Musée National d'Art Moderne, Centre National d'Art
et de Culture Georges Pompidou, *Paris-Berlin*, July 12-Nov.
6, 1978, no. 262

REFERENCES:

A. J. Schardt, *Franz Marc*, Berlin, 1936, p. 165, no. 20, 1913

August Macke- Franz Marc Briefwechsel, Cologne, 1964,
p. 163

K. Lankheit, *Franz Marc: Katalog der Werke*, Cologne, 1970,
p. 72, no. 205, repr.

Handbook, 1970, pp. 288-289, repr.

K. Lankheit, *Franz Marc: Sein Leben und seine Kunst*,
Cologne, 1976, pp. 121-122 and color pl. 22

Rudenstine, *Collection Catalogue*, 1976, no. 176, **repr.**

Paul Klee 1879-1940

Paul Klee was born on December 18, 1879, in München-buchsee, Switzerland, into a family of musicians. His childhood love of music was always to remain profoundly important in his life and work. From 1898 to 1901 Klee studied in Munich, first with Heinrich Knirr, then at the Akademie under Franz von Stuck. Upon completing his schooling, he traveled to Italy: this was the first in a series of trips abroad that nourished his visual sensibilities. He settled in Bern in 1902. A series of his satirical etchings was exhibited at the Munich *Secession* in 1906. That same year Klee married and moved to Munich. Here he gained exposure to modern art: he saw the work of Ensor, Cézanne, van Gogh and Matisse. Klee's work was shown at the Kunstmuseum Bern in 1910 and at Heinrich Thann-hauser's Moderne Galerie in Munich in 1911. In 1911 he began to keep a record of his work in his *Oeuvre Catalogue,* with listings from as early as 1884.

Klee met Kandinsky, August Macke, Marc, Jawlensky and other avant-garde figures in 1911; he participated in important shows of advanced art, including the second *Blaue Reiter (Blue Rider)* exhibition, 1912, and the *Erster deutscher Herbstsalon,* 1913. In 1912 he visited Paris for the second time, where he saw the work of Picasso and Braque and met Robert Delaunay, whose essay "On Light" he translated. Klee helped found the *Neue Münchner Secession* in 1914. Color became central to his art only after a revelatory trip to North Africa in 1914.

In 1920 a major Klee retrospective was held at the Galerie Hans Goltz, Munich, his *Schöpferische Konfession (Creative Credo)* was published and he was appointed to the faculty of the Bauhaus. Klee taught at the Bauhaus in Weimar from 1921 to 1926 and in Dessau from 1926 to 1931. During his tenure he was in close contact with other Bauhaus masters such as Kandinsky, Feininger and László Moholy-Nagy. In 1924 the *Blaue Vier (Blue Four),* consisting of Klee, Kandinsky, Feininger and Jawlensky, was founded. Among his notable exhibitions of this period were his first in the United States at the Société Anonyme, New York, 1924; his first major show in Paris the following year at the Galerie Vavin-Raspail; and an exhibition at The Museum of Modern Art, New York, 1930. Klee went to Düsseldorf to teach at the Akademie in 1931, shortly before the Nazis closed the Bauhaus. Forced to leave his position in Düsseldorf by the Nazis in 1933, Klee settled in Bern. Major Klee exhibitions took place in Bern and Basel in 1935 and in Zürich in 1940. Klee died on June 29, 1940, in Muralto-Locarno, Switzerland.

73 Flowerbed. 1913
(Blumenbeet)

Klee Oeuvre Catalogue: *1913, 193, Blumenbeet Öl, auf Pappe A.*

48.1172 x109

Oil on board, 11⅛ x 13¼ in. (28.2 x 33.7 cm.)

Signed and dated u.l.: *Klee / 1913 193.*

PROVENANCE:

from the artist
Hans Goltz, Munich, June-July 1918
Karl Nierendorf, New York, by 1947
Estate of Karl Nierendorf, 1948

Klee's familiarity with Cubist painters, including Robert Delaunay, as well as artists like Matisse is readily apparent in this early canvas. Executed after his stay in Paris in 1912 and before his trip to Tunisia in 1914, *Flowerbed* proceeds from Klee's interest in painting from nature. He has focused on a small segment of landscape where, at the left, parts of flowers emerge. Tightly worked patterns are brought forward to the picture surface and forms are schematized into triangles and wedge shapes. Color is thick and opaque; it ranges in spectrum from pink-rose to dark earth tones.

EXHIBITIONS:

Berlin, Der Sturm, *39. Ausstellung: Albert Block-Paul Klee,* March 1916, no. 55

Munich, *Münchner Neue Secession IV Ausstellung,* 1918, no. 69

New York, The Solomon R. Guggenheim Museum, *Paul Klee, 1879-1940: A Retrospective Exhibition,* Feb. 17-Apr. 30, 1967, no. 14, repr., traveled to Kunsthalle Basel, June 3-Aug. 16

New York, The Solomon R. Guggenheim Museum, *Paul Klee, 1879-1940, in the Collection of The Solomon R. Guggenheim Museum, New York,* June 24-Sept. 5, 1977, no. 9, color repr., traveled to Montreal, Musée d'Art Contemporain, Sept. 18-Oct. 23; Musée de Québec, Nov. 3-Dec. 4; Milwaukee Art Center, Feb. 2-Mar. 18, 1978; University Art Museum, University of California at Berkeley, Apr. 11-June 4; The Cleveland Museum of Art, July 6-Sept. 3; The Baltimore Museum of Art, Sept. 26-Nov. 19; Richmond, Virginia Museum of Fine Arts, Jan. 1-Feb. 18, 1979

REFERENCES:

J. M. Jordan, *Paul Klee and Cubism, 1912-1926,* Ph.D. dissertation, Institute of Fine Arts, New York University, 1974, pp. 265-268, repr.

Rudenstine, *Collection Catalogue,* 1976, no. 146, repr.

74 The Bavarian Don Giovanni. 1919
(Der bayrische Don Giovanni)

Klee Oeuvre Catalogue: *1919, 116 Der bayrische Don Giovanni Aquarell Zeichenpapier (A) verkauft Goltz April 20.*

48.1172 x69

Watercolor on paper, 8⅞ x 8⅜ in. (22.5 x 21.3 cm.)

Signed u.r.: *Klee*; inscribed within picture: *Emma Kathi Mari Cenzl Thères.*

PROVENANCE:
from the artist
Hans Goltz, Munich, 1920
Estate of the artist
Nierendorf Gallery, New York, 1947
Estate of Karl Nierendorf, 1948

Klee's love of music is well-known and is expressed visually throughout his work. Mozart and Bach were his favorite composers and he knew the score of *Don Giovanni.* In the 1920s Klee wanted to design new sets for a production of the opera in Dresden but his project was never undertaken.

Klee painted *The Bavarian Don Giovanni* while he still lived in Munich in Bavaria. The flat, rectilinear organization divides the surface into triangular-shaped colored planes, reminiscent of those in Robert Delaunay's *Windows,* 1912, a painting Klee admired. Yet here the planes can be seen as theatrical curtains which force the viewer to shift from the realm of visual perception to that of the imagination. The ladders link one part of the composition to another and also lead to the names written on the paper. These names, which are characteristically Bavarian, cannot be related to Mozart's *Don Giovanni* but evoke girls one might have once known. Associative and pictorial elements function equally in Klee's work, delighting the eye and amusing the mind.

EXHIBITIONS:
New York, Nierendorf Gallery, *A Comprehensive Exhibition of Works by Paul Klee (from the Estate of the Artist),* Oct. 1947, no. 11
New York, The Solomon R. Guggenheim Museum, *Paul Klee, 1879-1940: A Retrospective Exhibition,* Feb. 17-Apr. 30, 1967, no. 34, repr., traveled to Kunsthalle Basel, June 3-Aug. 16
New York, The Solomon R. Guggenheim Museum, *Paul Klee, 1879-1940, in the Collection of The Solomon R. Guggenheim Museum,* June 24-Sept. 5, 1977, no. 13, color repr., traveled to Montreal, Musée d'Art Contemporain, Sept. 18-Oct. 23; Musée de Québec, Nov. 3-Dec. 4; Milwaukee Art Center, Feb. 2-Mar. 18, 1978; University Art Museum, University of California at Berkeley, Apr. 11-June 4; The Cleveland Museum of Art, July 6-Sept. 3; The Baltimore Museum of Art, Sept. 26-Nov. 19; Richmond, Virginia Museum of Fine Arts, Jan. 1-Feb. 18, 1979

REFERENCES:
W. Grohmann, *Paul Klee,* New York, 1954, p. 389, no. 38, repr.

Handbook, 1970, pp. 220-221, repr.

H. K. Roethel, *Paul Klee in München,* Bern, 1971, no. 125, color repr.

C. Geelhaar, *Paul Klee and the Bauhaus,* Greenwich, Conn., 1973, p. 84

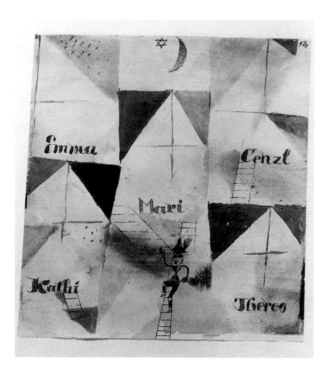

Klee

75 Runner at the Goal. 1921
(Läufer am Ziel)

Klee Oeuvre Catalogue: *1921, 105 Läufer am Ziel Aquarell Deutsches Ingres gelbe.*

48.1172 X55

Watercolor and gouache on yellow Ingres paper mounted on board, 15½ x 12 in. (39.3 x 30.3 cm.)

Signed on support c.r.: *Klee*; inscribed on border of support l.l: *1921 105 Läufer am Zeil*; on mount l.l.: *s.cl.*

PROVENANCE·
Estate of the artist
Nierendorf Gallery, New York, 1947
Estate of Karl Nierendorf, 1948

Wit and imagination animate Klee's simultaneous portrayal of successive movements in *Runner at the Goal.* The exuberance of the winner's pose is punctuated by his upraised arms and red legs. The effect of movement through space is conveyed by the gradation of color from light to dark in the horizontal bands against which the running figure is placed.

Runner at the Goal is based on the same pictorial principles as other works from 1921 such as *Fugue in Red, Crystal Gradation* and *Dream City.* The formal structure of this group of paintings is inspired by the strict pattern of Bach's fugues: the chromatic variations of a single shape resemble the harmonic variations of a single melodic line which are inherent in the fugue.

EXHIBITIONS:
New York, Nierendorf Gallery, *A Comprehensive Exhibition of Works by Paul Klee (from the Estate of the Artist),* Oct. 1947, no. 13

San Francisco Museum of Art, *Art in the 20th Century,* June 17-July 10, 1955

The Arts Club of Chicago, *Wit and Humor,* Feb. 28-Mar. 31, 1962, no. 9, repr.

Pasadena Art Museum, *Paul Klee, 1879-1940: A Retrospective Exhibition* (organized by The Solomon R. Guggenheim Museum, New York), Feb. 21-Apr. 2, 1967, no. 42, repr., traveled to San Francisco Museum of Art, Apr. 13-May 14; The Columbus Gallery of Fine Arts, May 25-June 25; The Cleveland Museum of Art, July 5-Aug. 13; Kansas City, Mo., William Rockhill Nelson Gallery of Art, Sept. 1-30; The Baltimore Museum of Art, Oct. 24-Nov. 19; St. Louis, Washington University Gallery of Art, Dec. 3, 1967-Jan. 5, 1968; Philadelphia Museum of Art, Jan. 15-Feb. 15

New York, The Solomon R. Guggenheim Museum, *Paul Klee, 1879-1940, in the Collection of The Solomon R. Guggenheim Museum,* June 24-Sept. 5, 1977, no. 16, repr., traveled to Montreal, Musée d'Art Contemporain, Sept. 18-Oct. 23; Museé de Québec, Nov. 3-Dec. 4; Milwaukee Art Center, Feb. 2-Mar. 18, 1978; University Art Museum, University of California at Berkeley, Apr. 11-June 4; The Cleveland Museum of Art, July 6-Sept. 3; The Baltimore Museum of Art, Sept. 26-Nov. 19; Richmond, Virginia Museum of Fine Arts, Jan. 1-Feb. 18, 1979

REFERENCE:
Handbook, 1970, p. 223, repr.

76 Night Feast. 1921
(Nächtliches Fest)

Klee Oeuvre Catalogue: *1921, 176 Nächtliches Fest
Öl Papier aufgeklebt auf Carton aufgezogen später auf
Z–Pappe aufgekittet Besitz Frau Bürgi–Bern / 1930.*

73.2054

Oil on paper mounted on board, 19¾ x 23⅝ in. (50
x 60 cm.)

Signed and dated l.l.: *Klee 21*; inscribed on reverse of
mount: *1921 / 176 / "Nächtliches Fest" / Klee
/ Herrn Rolf Bürgi / bei Dr. Schwarz / Junkerngasse
32 / Bern / 21 / 176.*

PROVENANCE:
from the artist
Collection Bürgi, Belp-Bern, 1930-73
Galerie Beyeler, Basel, 1973

Night Feast shows a landscape with church, houses,
trees and mountains, all under skies filled with stars
and astral activity. This is a night of excitement and
intangible mystery. It has been suggested that similar
stars appear on the backdrops of *Weinachtskrippen,*
the models of Nativity scenes seen everywhere in
Germany at Christmastime. Klee's use of a painted
framing device augments the stage-like quality of the
scene. However, it is significant that he has evoked
rather than specified his subject.

Klee employed a dark palette with white highlights
and emphasized the brushwork of the oil paint surface.
Light emanates from the sky and the trees, the
mountains and the pink-red rooftop in the center of
the composition.

Night Feast and *Runner at the Goal* (cat. no. 75), which
were painted in the same year but display strikingly
different pictorial styles, reveal the rich variety of Klee's
art.

EXHIBITIONS:
Berlin, Galerie Flechtheim, *Paul Klee,* Oct. 20-Nov. 15, 1929,
no. 43, repr.
Venice, XVII Biennale Internazionale d'Arte, *German Pa-
vilion,* Apr.-Oct. 30, 1930, no. 50
Kunsthalle Bern, *III. Ausstellung: Paul Klee, Walter Helbig,
M. de Vlaminck, Philipp Bauknecht, Arnold Huggler,* Jan.
18-Feb. 15, 1931, no. 31
Kunsthalle Basel, *Paul Klee,* Oct. 27-Nov. 24, 1935, no. 6
London, The National Gallery, *Paul Klee, 1879-1940,* Dec.
1945, no. 53
Kunstmuseum Basel, *Paul Klee 1879-1940; Ausstellung aus
Schweizer Privatsammlungen zum 10.Todestag, 29 Juni
1950,* June 29-Aug. 15, 1950, no. 7

Berner Kunstmuseum, *Paul Klee,* Aug. 11-Nov. 4, 1956, no.
457
Kunstverein in Hamburg, *Paul Klee,* Dec. 2, 1956-Jan. 27,
1957, no. 116
Lausanne, Palais de Beaulieu, *Chefs d'oeuvres des collections
suisses de Manet à Picasso,* May 1-Oct. 25, 1964, no. 325,
color repr.
New York, The Solomon R. Guggenheim Museum, *Paul
Klee, 1879-1940: A Retrospective Exhibition,* Feb. 17-Apr.
30, 1967, no. 44, color repr., traveled to Kunsthalle Basel,
June 3-Aug. 16
Paris, Musée National d'Art Moderne, *Paul Klee,* Nov. 25,
1969-Feb. 16, 1970, no. 53, repr.
Basel, Galerie Beyeler, *Klee: Kunst ist ein Schöpfungsgleich-
nis,* Sept.-Nov. 1973, no. 18, color repr.
New York, The Solomon R. Guggenheim Museum, *Paul
Klee, 1879-1940, in the Collection of The Solomon R. Gug-
genheim Museum,* June 24-Sept. 5, 1977, no. 18, color repr.,
traveled to Montreal, Musée d'Art Contemporain, Sept. 18-
Oct. 23; Musée de Québec, Nov. 3-Dec. 4; Milwaukee Art
Center, Feb. 2-Mar. 18, 1978; University Art Museum, University of California at Berkeley, Apr. 11-June 4; The Cleveland Museum of Art, July 6-Sept. 3; The Baltimore Museum
of Art, Sept. 26-Nov. 19; Richmond, Virginia Museum of
Fine Arts, Jan. 1-Feb. 18, 1979

REFERENCES:
H. Read, *Klee (1879-1940),* London, 1938, color pl. 8
J. S. Pierce, *Paul Klee and Primitive Art,* New York, 1976
(rev. photo reprint of Ph.D. dissertation, Harvard University,
1961), p. 17

Klee

77 Dance You Monster to My Soft Song! 1922
(Tanze Du Ungeheuer zu meinem sanften Lied!)

Klee Oeuvre Catalogue: *1922, A 54, Tanze Du Ungeheuer zu meinem sanften Lied! Aquarell u. Ölfarbezeichnung. Gaze gipsgrundiert.*

38.508

Watercolor and oil transfer drawing on plaster-grounded gauze mounted on gouache-painted paper, 17⅝ x 12⅞ in. (44.9 x 32.7 cm.)

Inscribed across lower edge of gauze support: *Tanze Du Ungeheuer! Zu meinem sanften Lied;* across lower edge of paper mount: *1922/54 Tanze Du Ungeheüer zu meinem sanften Lied!* Not signed.

PROVENANCE:
St. Annen-Museum, Lübeck, 1927-37
Rudolf Bauer
Solomon R. Guggenheim, New York, 1938
Gift, Solomon R. Guggenheim, 1938

The title, *Dance You Monster to My Soft Song!*, reveals Klee's imagination and the essentially personal, often inexplicable humor of his art. The monster—whose large head, prominent nose, bearded chin and pince-nez bear a certain resemblance to caricatures of Richard Wagner—dominates the composition. His presence hovers over the small figure at a mechanical organ and the inscription which provides the title. Klee has eliminated all conventional spatial and temporal indications and created a world of musical fantasy.

In this work Klee, a technical innovator, employed an oil transfer process on plaster-grounded gauze and then painted the surface with watercolor. The virtually identical drawing which was used in transferring the composition belongs to the Galerie Rosengart, Lucerne.*

* see Rudenstine, p. 400

EXHIBITIONS:
Munich, Galerie Hans Goltz, *Zehn Jahre neue Kunst in München,* Nov.-Dec. 1922, no. 151, repr.
New York, Buchholz Gallery and Willard Gallery, *Paul Klee,* Oct. 9-Nov. 2, 1940, no. 28
New York, The Solomon R. Guggenheim Museum, *Inaugural Selection,* Oct. 21, 1959-June 19, 1960
The Arts Club of Chicago, *Wit and Humor,* Feb. 28-Mar. 31, 1962, no. 11, repr.
New York, The Solomon R. Guggenheim Museum, *Paul Klee, 1879-1940: A Retrospective Exhibition,* Feb. 17-Apr. 30, 1967, no. 51, color repr., traveled to Kunsthalle Basel, June 3-Aug. 16

New York, The Solomon R. Guggenheim Museum, *Paul Klee, 1879-1940, in the Collection of The Solomon R. Guggenheim Museum,* June 24-Sept. 5, 1977, no. 21, color repr.
New York, The Solomon R. Guggenheim Museum, *Forty Modern Masters: An Anniversary Show,* Dec. 16, 1977-Feb. 5, 1978, no. 69

REFERENCES:
C. Giedion-Welcker, *Paul Klee,* New York, 1952, p. 68, pl. 55
W. Grohmann, *Paul Klee Drawings,* New York, 1960, pp. 26-27
M. Huggler, *Paul Klee: Die Malerei als Blick in den Kosmos,* Frauenfeld-Stuttgart, 1969, p. 78, pl. 5
Handbook, 1970, p. 225, repr.
Rudenstine, *Collection Catalogue,* 1976, no. 147, repr.
H. H. Arnason, *History of Modern Art,* rev. ed., New York, 1977, fig. 439

Klee

78 Red Balloon. 1922
(Roter Ballon)

Klee Oeuvre Catalogue: *1922, 179, Roter Ballon Ölbild kleineres Format Nesselstoff auf Pappe geklebt, kreidegrundiert.*

48.1172 x524

Oil (and oil transfer drawing?) on chalk-primed linen gauze mounted on board, 12½ x 12¼ in. (31.7 x 31.1 cm.)

Signed and dated l.l.: *Klee/1922/179*; inscribed on reverse: *1922///179/Roter Ballon/Klee./breiter Rahmen./nicht zu flach/glasen. nicht zu flacher Rahmen/glasen.*

PROVENANCE:
Hermann Lange, Krefeld, by 1931
Karl Nierendorf, New York, by 1947
Estate of Karl Nierendorf, 1948

A red balloon is suspended in space over a cityscape that is simultaneously fantastic and intelligible. The imaginary architectures and illusionary perspectives that were among Klee's major themes are found in this painting of 1922. The same geometric structure and diaphanous color appear in another picture of the same year, *Little Fir-Tree Painting* (Collection Kunstmuseum Basel). Although in earlier works the artist made specific references to houses through details such as windows and slanted roofs, here such images are reduced to a minimum. The resulting schematic rendering anticipates the purely abstract compositions of colored rectangles which Klee began in 1923.

The balloon is a recurrent motif in Klee's work: *The Balloon*, 1926, and *Balloon over Town*, 1928, are other examples of its use. In the Guggenheim picture, Klee took advantage of the weave of the chalk-primed linen gauze and the way this support absorbed the paint to create an enchanting pictorial space.

EXHIBITIONS:
Düsseldorf, Kunstverein für die Rheinlande und Westfalen, *Paul Klee,* June 14-July 6, 1931, no. 17

London, Tate Gallery, *An exhibition of paintings from The Solomon R. Guggenheim Museum, New York,* Apr. 16-May 26, 1957, no. 35, traveled to The Hague, Gemeentemuseum, June 25-Sept. 1; Helsinki, Ateneumin Taidekokoelmat, Sept. 27-Oct. 20; Rome, Galleria Nazionale d'Arte Moderna, Dec. 5, 1957-Jan. 8, 1958; Cologne, Wallraf-Richartz-Museum, Jan. 26-Mar. 30; Paris, Musée des Arts Décoratifs, Apr. 23-June 1

New York, The Solomon R. Guggenheim Museum, *Inaugural Selection,* Oct. 21, 1959-June 19, 1960

New York, The Solomon R. Guggenheim Museum, *Paul Klee, 1879-1940: A Retrospective Exhibition,* Feb. 17-Apr. 30, 1967, no. 58, color repr., traveled to Kunsthalle Basel, June 3-Aug. 16

Des Moines Art Center, *Paul Klee: Paintings and Watercolors from the Bauhaus Years 1921-31,* Sept. 18-Oct. 28, 1973, no. 12, color repr.

New York, The Solomon R. Guggenheim Museum, *Paul Klee, 1879-1940, in the Collection of The Solomon R. Guggenheim Museum,* June 24-Sept. 5, 1977, no. 25, color repr., traveled to Montreal, Musée d'Art Contemporain, Sept. 18-Oct. 23; Musée de Québec, Nov. 3-Dec. 4; Milwaukee Art Center, Feb. 2-Mar. 18, 1978; University Art Museum, University of California at Berkeley, Apr. 11-June 4; The Cleveland Museum of Art, July 6-Sept. 3; The Baltimore Museum of Art, Sept. 26-Nov. 19; Richmond, Virginia Museum of Fine Arts, Jan. 1-Feb. 18, 1979

Kunsthalle Köln, *Paul Klee,* Apr. 11-June 4, 1979, no. 78, color repr.

REFERENCES:
T. M. Messer, *Paul Klee Exhibition at the Guggenheim Museum: A Post-Scriptum,* New York, 1968, pp. 15-16, color repr.

Handbook, 1970, pp. 228-229, color repr.

Rudenstine, *Collection Catalogue,* 1976, no. 149, repr.

H. H. Arnason, *History of Modern Art,* rev. ed., New York, 1977, color pl. 107

79 In the Current Six Thresholds. 1929
(In der Strömung Sechs Schwellen)

Klee Oeuvre Catalogue: *1929, 92 S.2, in der Strömung sechs Schwellen. Tempera = und Ölfarben 43 x 43 Leinw. auf Keil.*

67.1842

Oil and tempera on canvas, 17⅛ x 17⅛ in. (43.5 x 43.5 cm.)

Signed and dated l.r.: *Klee 1929*; inscribed on stretcher: *in der Strömung Sechs Schwellen / Klee / 1929.*

PROVENANCE:

from the artist
D.-H. Kahnweiler, Paris, 1936 or 1937-54
Curt Valentin, New York, 1954
G. David Thompson, Pittsburgh, by 1960
Galerie Beyeler, Basel, 1960-63
Heinz Berggruen, Paris, 1963-67

In the Current Six Thresholds is exceptional in Klee's oeuvre for its austerity and monumentality, its restrained mathematical organization and its dark palette of red and black tonalities. As one of the horizontal band paintings Klee executed after his trip to Egypt in the winter of 1928-29, *In the Current Six Thresholds* bears a distinct relationship to *Monument on the Edge of Fertile Country,* 1929. With reference to the latter Klee wrote: "I am painting a landscape somewhat like the view of the fertile country from the distant mountains of the Valley of the Kings. The polyphonic interplay between earth and atmosphere has been kept as fluid as possible." (W. Grohmann, *Paul Klee,* New York, 1954, p. 273) These paintings are characterized by horizontal bands divided into halves, quarters, eighths and then sixteenths as they proceed from right to left and are crossed by verticals.

EXHIBITIONS:

Düsseldorf, Kunstverein für die Rheinlande und Westfalen, *Paul Klee,* June 14-July 6, 1931, no. 69

Berlin, Galerie Flechtheim, *Paul Klee, neue Bilder und Aquarelle,* Nov. 5-Dec. 10, 1931, no. 2

Paris, Galerie Simon, *Paul Klee,* June 12-25, 1935

Kunsthaus Zürich, *G. David Thompson Collection,* Oct. 15-Nov. 27, 1960, no. 83, traveled to Kunstmuseum Düsseldorf, Dec. 14, 1960-Jan. 29, 1961; The Hague, Gemeentemuseum, Feb. 17-Apr. 9; Turin, Museo Civico, Galleria d'Arte Moderna, Oct.-Nov.

Basel, Galerie Beyeler, *Klee,* Mar.-June 15, 1963, no. 34, repr.

New York, The Solomon R. Guggenheim Museum, *Paul Klee, 1879-1940: A Retrospective Exhibition,* Feb. 17-Apr. 30, 1967, no. 102, color repr., traveled to Kunsthalle Basel, June 3-Aug. 16

Des Moines Art Center, *Paul Klee: Paintings and Watercolors from the Bauhaus Years 1921-1931,* Sept. 18-Oct. 28, 1973, no. 44

New York, The Solomon R. Guggenheim Museum, *Paul Klee, 1879-1940, in the Collection of The Solomon R. Guggenheim Museum,* June 24-Sept. 5, 1977, no. 42, color repr., traveled to Montreal, Musée d'Art Contemporain, Sept. 18-Oct. 23; Musée de Québec, Nov. 3-Dec. 4; Milwaukee Art Center, Feb. 2-Mar. 18, 1978; University Art Museum, University of California at Berkeley, Apr. 11-June 4; The Cleveland Museum of Art, July 6-Sept. 3; The Baltimore Museum of Art, Sept. 26-Nov. 19; Richmond, Virginia Museum of Fine Arts, Jan. 1-Feb. 18, 1979

Kunsthalle Köln, *Paul Klee,* Apr. 7-June 4, 1979, no. 265, repr.

REFERENCES:

J. Spiller, ed., *Paul Klee: The Thinking Eye,* New York, 1964, p. 212

T. M. Messer, *Paul Klee Exhibition at the Guggenheim Museum: A Post-Scriptum,* New York, 1968, p. iv, color repr.

Handbook, 1970, pp. 232-233, repr.

C. Geelhaar, *Paul Klee and the Bauhaus,* Greenwich, Conn., 1973, pp. 122, repr., 126-127

J. Glaesemer, *Paul Klee: Die farbigen Werke in Kunstmuseum Bern,* Bern, 1976, p. 148, fig. d

Rudenstine, *Collection Catalogue,* 1976, no. 151, color repr.

H. H. Arnason, *History of Modern Art,* rev. ed., New York, 1977, color pl. 108

80 **Open Book.** 1930
(*Offenes Buch*)

Klee Oeuvre Catalogue: *1930, 206 E6, Offenes Buch*
Wasserfarben gefirnist Leinwand (Keilrahmen) Weiss-
lack grundiert orig. leisten 0.45 0.42.

48.1172 x526

Gouache over white lacquer on canvas, 18 x 16¾ in.
(45.7 x 42.5 cm.)

Signed l.l.: *Klee*; inscribed on stretcher: *1930. E6*
"Offenes Buch" Klee.

PROVENANCE:
Rolf de Maré, Paris, by 1931
Karl Nierendorf, New York, before 1948
Estate of Karl Nierendorf, 1948

From the complex multiple perspectives, it is possible
to discern the pages of a book being turned or a large
folio volume being opened to an illustration. Although
Klee's title is quite specific, the ambiguity of the image
has led to various interpretations: to Will Grohmann
it suggests an Egyptian tomb rather than a book. The
triangular and drop-shaped signs at the lower left defy
explanation. The book appears yellow with age and
the crosshatching, which first occurs in Klee's painting
of 1923, brings to mind his earlier predilection for
etching. *Open Book* is related to a painting entitled
Open, 1933 (Collection Felix Klee, Bern).

EXHIBITIONS:
London, Tate Gallery, *An exhibition of paintings from The*
Solomon R. Guggenheim Museum, New York, Apr. 16-May
26, 1957, no. 36, repr., traveled to The Hague, Gemeente-
museum, June 25-Sept. 1; Helsinki, Ateneumin Taidekokoel-
mat, Sept. 27-Oct. 20; Rome, Galleria Nazionale d'Arte
Moderna, Dec. 5, 1957-Jan. 8, 1958; Cologne, Wallraf-
Richartz-Museum, Jan. 26-Mar. 30; Paris, Musée des Arts
Décoratifs, Apr. 23-June 1

New York, The Solomon R. Guggenheim Museum,
Inaugural Selection, Oct. 21, 1959-June 19, 1960

Pasadena Art Museum, *Paul Klee, 1879-1940: A Retro-*
spective Exhibition (organized by The Solomon R. Guggenheim Museum, New York), Feb. 21-Apr. 2, 1967, no. 113,
color repr., traveled to San Francisco Museum of Art, Apr.
13-May 14; The Columbus Gallery of Fine Arts, May 25-
June 25; The Cleveland Museum of Art, July 5-Aug. 13;
Kansas City, Mo., William Rockhill Nelson Gallery of Art,
Sept. 1-30; The Baltimore Museum of Art, Oct. 24-Nov. 19;
St. Louis, Washington University Gallery of Art, Dec. 3,
1967-Jan. 5, 1968; Philadelphia Museum of Art, Jan. 15-
Feb. 15

New York, The Solomon R. Guggenheim Museum, *Paul*
Klee, 1879-1940, in the Collection of The Solomon R. Gug-
genheim Museum, June 24-Sept. 5, 1977, no. 43, color repr.

REFERENCES:
C. Einstein, *Die Kunst des 20. Jahrhunderts,* 3rd ed., Berlin,
1931, p. 553, repr.

W. Grohmann, *Paul Klee,* New York, 1967, pp. 118-119,
color repr.

Handbook, 1970, pp. 234-235, repr.

Rudenstine, *Collection Catalogue,* 1976, no. 152, repr.

Klee

81 Hat, Lady and Little Table. 1932
(Hut, Dame und Tischchen)

Klee Oeuvre Catalogue: *1932, 263 (X3) Hut, Dame und Tischchen. Aquarellfarben Sackleinen gipsgrundiert.*

77.2292

Oil and watercolor on gesso-primed burlap mounted on board, 26¼ x 14¼ in. (66.7 x 36.2 cm.)

Signed on support u.l.: *Klee*; inscribed on mount l.l.: *SCl 1932 X3*; c.: *Hut Dame und Tischchen*; u.l.: *für die Monogr. bestimmt Hut Dame und Tischchen.*

PROVENANCE:

from the artist
Private collection, Switzerland, until Bern, Kornfeld und Klipstein, by auction June 19, 1970, no. 676
Edouard Helfer, Bern, 1970-76
Galerie Schindler, Bern, 1977

The artist indicated that he particularly valued *Hat, Lady and Little Table* by inscribing it "*SCl,*" designating it as a painting belonging to a "special class" *(Sonderklasse)* of works which he regarded most highly. Klee, who frequently went back to earlier works and redid them in different sizes or mediums, returned to this composition in 1935 in a painting entitled *Lady Demon* (Klee Stiftung, Kunstmuseum Bern). In the latter the soft color harmonies have been replaced by a darker palette, and the size has been doubled. In both versions the woman has a heart-shaped mouth and her eyes are placed on adjacent but contrasting color areas.

Hat, Lady and Little Table, with its play of a continuous curving line, retains the quality of Klee's drawings. This line forms planes, which have been colored in such a way that they appear suspended on the surface and seem occasionally to overlap each other. Klee has employed gesso-primed burlap to provide surface texture and a delicate color harmony.

EXHIBITIONS:

Kunsthalle Bern, *Paul Klee,* Feb. 23-Mar. 24, 1935, no. 207

New York, The Solomon R. Guggenheim Museum, *Paul Klee, 1879-1940, in the Collection of The Solomon R. Guggenheim Museum,* June 24-Sept. 5, 1977, no. 52, color repr.

New York, The Solomon R. Guggenheim Museum, *Forty Modern Masters: An Anniversary Show,* Dec. 16, 1977-Feb. 5, 1978, no. 71, repr.

REFERENCES:

W. Grohmann, *Paul Klee,* New York, 1954, p. 283

W. Haftmann, *The Mind and Work of Paul Klee,* New York, 1954, p. 166

C. Geelhaar, *Paul Klee: Leben und Werk,* Cologne, 1974, p. 78, color repr.

J. Glaesemer, *Paul Klee: Die farbigen Werke in Kunstmuseum Bern,* Bern, 1976, p. 310, fig. a

Klee

82 New Harmony. 1936
(Neue Harmonie)

Klee Oeuvre Catalogue: *1936, 24 K4 0,93 0,66 Neue Harmonie Ölfarben Leinwand auf Keilrahmen (Tafel).*

71.1960

Oil on canvas, 36⅞ x 26⅛ in. (93.6 x 66.3 cm.)

Signed u.r.: *Klee.* Not dated.

PROVENANCE:

from the artist
D.-H. Kahnweiler, Paris, 1937-39
Nierendorf Gallery, New York, 1939-44
Benjamin Baldwin, New York, by 1949 until New York, Parke-Bernet, by auction Mar. 10, 1971, no. 52
Heinz Berggruen, Paris, 1971
Galerie Beyeler, Basel, 1971

New Harmony is one of only twenty-five works Klee executed in 1936 when he was very ill. One of a series of paintings called "magic squares," it contains the two-dimensional colored rectangles which first appeared in his art in 1923. Essentially it looks back to Klee's color theory of the 1920s and even the title belongs with those works he designated "Architecture, Harmony and Sound." While related to *Ancient Sound,* 1925 (Collection Kunstmuseum Basel), *New Harmony* is based on brighter colors over dark underpainting, which are firmly anchored into a more rigorous grid pattern and now arranged according to the principle of inverted bilateral symmetry. Like so many of his other pictures it reflects the artist's study of musical harmony.

EXHIBITIONS:

Paris, Galerie Simon, *Paul Klee: oeuvres récentes,* Jan. 24-Feb. 5, 1938, no. 1

Amsterdam, Stedelijk Museum, *Tentoonstelling Abstracte Kunst,* Apr. 2-24, 1938, no. 38

London, New Burlington Galleries, *Exhibition of Twentieth Century German Art,* July 1938, no. 92

City Art Museum of Saint Louis, *Exhibition of 20th Century (banned) German Art,* Sept. 1-25, 1939, no. 24, traveled to Northampton, Mass., Smith College Museum of Art, Oct. 1-25; Kansas City, Mo., William Rockhill Nelson Gallery of Art, Nov. 1-25; San Francisco Museum of Art, Feb. 6-26, 1940

New York, Nierendorf Gallery, *Fifth Selection of Works by Paul Klee,* Mar.-June 1942, no. 19

New York, Nierendorf Gallery, *50th Exhibition in New York City: Gestation-Formation,* Mar. 1944, no. 32

New York, The Museum of Modern Art, *Paintings, drawings, and prints by Paul Klee,* Dec. 20, 1949-Feb. 20, 1950, not in cat.

New York, The Solomon R. Guggenheim Museum, *Paul Klee, 1879-1940, in the Collection of The Solomon R. Guggenheim Museum,* June 24-Sept. 5, 1977, no. 56, color repr., traveled to Montreal, Musée d'Art Contemporain, Sept. 18-Oct. 23; Musée de Québec, Nov. 3-Dec. 4; Milwaukee Art Center, Feb. 2-Mar. 18, 1978; University Art Museum, University of California at Berkeley, Apr. 11-June 4; The Cleveland Museum of Art, July 6-Sept. 3; The Baltimore Museum of Art, Sept. 26-Nov. 19; Richmond, Virginia Museum of Fine Arts, Jan. 1-Feb. 18, 1979

REFERENCES:

W. Grohmann, *Paul Klee,* New York, 1954, p. 213

C. Geelhaar, *Paul Klee and the Bauhaus,* Greenwich, Conn., 1973, p. 48

C. Geelhaar, *Paul Klee: Leben und Werk,* Cologne, 1974, p. 82, color repr.

A. Kagan, "Paul Klee's 'Ad Parnassum': The Theory and Practice of Eighteenth-Century Polyphony as Models for Klee's Art," *Arts Magazine,* vol. 52, Sept. 1977, pp. 97, fig. 13, 98-99

Lyonel Feininger 1871-1956

Charles Léonell Feininger was born in New York on July 17, 1871. At age sixteen he traveled to Germany where he studied drawing at the Kunstgewerbeschule in Hamburg. In 1888 he was admitted to the Kunstakademie in Berlin, which he attended intermittently until 1892. As early as 1889 Feininger's drawings were illustrated in Berlin's humorous weeklies, and by the late nineties he had become Germany's leading political cartoonist. In the winter of 1903-4 his drawings were exhibited in the Berlin *Secession*.

In 1906 Feininger moved from Berlin to Paris, where he met Robert Delaunay. The following year he began to paint. In Paris he admired the paintings of van Gogh and Cézanne, and in London in 1908 was deeply impressed by the work of Turner. From 1908 to 1912 the artist resided in Zehlendorf, near Berlin. His paintings were first exhibited at the 1910 Berlin *Secession*. In 1911 Feininger was introduced to Cubism at the Salon des Indépendants in Paris, where six of his own paintings were on view. At Marc's invitation he participated in the 1913 *Erster Deutscher Herbstsalon*, Berlin, with the artists of the *Blaue Reiter (Blue Rider)*. Feininger resettled in Berlin for the war years. His first one-man show was held at the gallery of Der Sturm, Berlin, in 1917. The following year he joined the *Novembergruppe* and met Walter Gropius, with whom he traveled to Weimar in 1919 to serve on the faculty of the newly-founded Bauhaus. In 1921 Feininger, who was always interested in music, composed the first of his thirteen fugues for the organ. In 1924 he joined Klee, Kandinsky and Jawlensky in the *Blaue Vier (Blue Four)* group.

Feininger moved with the Bauhaus to Dessau in 1925 but no longer was obligated to teach. In 1929 his work was included in the first show of The Museum of Modern Art in New York, *Paintings by Nineteen Living Americans*. His sixtieth birthday was observed with a retrospective at the Nationalgalerie of Berlin in 1931. In 1936 he taught a summer course at Mills College in Oakland, California, and in 1937 he fled Germany to settle permanently in New York. The following year he was commissioned to design murals for the New York World's Fair. In 1944 he shared a retrospective with Marsden Hartley at The Museum of Modern Art. He taught at Black Mountain College in Black Mountain, North Carolina, during the summer of 1945, and in 1947 was elected president of the *Federation of American Painters and Sculptors*. Feininger died on January 13, 1956, in New York.

83 Gelmeroda IV. 1915

54.1410

Oil on canvas, 39½ x 31⅜ in. (100 x 79.7 cm.)

Signed and dated l.r.: *Feininger / 15*; inscribed twice on reverse: *Gelmeroda*.

PROVENANCE:

from the artist
Erich Mendelsohn, Berlin and San Francisco, by 1928-53
Mrs. Eric Mendelsohn, San Francisco, 1953-54

The representation of churches, buildings and architectural motifs constitutes a major preoccupation within Feininger's prolific lifelong production. The church at Gelmeroda, a Thuringian village near Weimar, was a recurrent subject from 1906, when Feininger first sketched it, until 1955, when he portrayed it in a lithograph.

Gelmeroda I of 1913 (formerly Pauson Collection, Glasgow) shows the church from the apse side with a large pine tree on the left. *Gelmeroda IV*, which Feininger painted in Berlin, represents the church from the same viewpoint but shifts the two dominant verticals, the steeple and the tree, toward the center of the composition. In this painting the slashing diagonal lines of *Gelmeroda I* have evolved into geometric planes of Cubism, which the artist has employed dynamically to unify the picture surface rather than to pursue a Cubist analysis of space or a Futurist investigation of time. Through the precision of line and the clarity of light, Feininger has created an image of both energy and solidity.

EXHIBITIONS:

Berlin, Der Sturm, 42. *Ausstellung: Lyonel Feininger, Paul Kother, Felix Müller*, June 1916, no. 3

Munich, Galerie Hans Goltz, *Lyonel Feininger*, Oct. 1918, no. 20

New York, The Museum of Modern Art, *Lyonel Feininger, Marsden Hartley*, Oct. 24, 1944-Jan. 14, 1945, pp. 24, repr., 46

London, Tate Gallery, *An exhibition of paintings from The Solomon R. Guggenheim Museum, New York*, Apr. 16-May 26, 1957, no. 19, traveled to The Hague, Gemeentemuseum, June 25-Sept. 1; Helsinki, Ateneumin Taidekokoelmat, Sept. 27-Oct. 20; Rome, Galleria Nazionale d'Arte Moderna, Dec. 5, 1957-Jan. 8, 1958; Cologne, Wallraf-Richartz-Museum, Jan. 26-Mar. 30; Paris, Musée des Arts Décoratifs, Apr. 23-June 1, 1958

New York, The Solomon R. Guggenheim Museum, *Inaugural Selection*, Oct. 21, 1959-June 19, 1960

Pasadena Art Museum, *Lyonel Feininger 1871-1946: A Memorial Exhibition*, Apr. 26-May 29, 1966, no. 13, traveled to Milwaukee Art Center, July 10-Aug. 11; The Baltimore Museum of Art, Sept. 7-Oct. 23

Los Angeles County Museum of Art, *The Cubist Epoch*, Dec. 15, 1970-Feb. 21, 1971, no. 83, color pl. 138, traveled to New York, The Metropolitan Museum of Art, Apr. 9-June 8

Munich, Haus der Kunst, *Lyonel Feininger*, Mar. 24-May 13, 1973, no. 88, repr., traveled to Kunsthaus Zürich, May 25-July 22

New York, The Solomon R. Guggenheim Museum, *Forty Modern Masters: An Anniversary Show*, Dec. 16, 1977-Feb. 1, 1978, no. 35, repr.

REFERENCES:

H. Hess, *Lyonel Feininger*, New York, 1961, pp. 74, 261, no. 146 and pl. 12

P. Krieger, "Lyonel Feiningers Variationen über das Gelmeroda-Motiv," *Zeitschrift des deutschen Vereins für Kunstwissenschaft*, Band XXI, no. 1-2, 1967, pp. 92, 94 and fig. 8

Handbook, 1970, pp. 116-117, repr.

Rudenstine, *Collection Catalogue*, 1976, no. 43, repr.

84 Gelmeroda. August 26, 1927

48.1172 x507

Watercolor and ink on paper, 15½ x 11⅛ in. (39.4 x 28.3 cm.)

Signed l.l.: *Feininger*; inscribed b.c.: *Gelmeroda*; dated l.r.: *26 8 27*.

PROVENANCE:

Karl Nierendorf, New York, by 1948
Estate of Karl Nierendorf, 1948

The watercolor of Gelmeroda was executed more than a decade after Feininger painted the canvas (cat. no. 83). He spent the summer of 1927 at Deep on the Baltic Sea and is not known to have visited Gelmeroda. However, several watercolors of this motif date from that summer and appear to be studies for *Gelmeroda XI* of 1928 (Collection Dr. Laurence Feininger, Trieste).

EXHIBITIONS:

The Art Gallery of Toronto, *A Loan Exhibition from The Solomon R. Guggenheim Museum*, Apr. 2-May 9, 1954, no. 10

Vancouver, B.C., Vancouver Art Gallery, *The Solomon R. Guggenheim Museum: A Selection from the Museum Collection*, Nov. 16-Dec. 12, 1954, no. 6

Munich, Haus der Kunst, *Lyonel Feininger*, Mar. 24-May 13, 1973, no. 212, traveled to Kunsthaus Zürich, May 25-July 22

New York, The Solomon R. Guggenheim Museum, *Forty Modern Masters: An Anniversary Show*, Dec. 16, 1977-Feb. 5, 1978, no. 36

REFERENCE:

Handbook, 1970, p. 118, repr.

IV

Gino Severini 1883-1966

Gino Severini was born April 7, 1883, in Cortona, Italy. He studied at the Scuola Tecnica in Cortona before moving to Rome in 1899. There he attended art classes at the Villa Medici and by 1901 met Umberto Boccioni, who had also recently arrived in Rome and later would be one of the theoreticians of Futurism. Together Severini and Boccioni visited the studio of Giacomo Balla where they were introduced to painting with "divided" rather than mixed color. After settling in Paris in November 1906, Severini studied Impressionist painting and met the Neo-Impressionist Paul Signac.

Severini soon came to know most of the Parisian avant-garde including Modigliani, Gris, Braque and Picasso, Lugné-Poe and his theatrical circle, the poets Max Jacob, Guillaume Apollinaire and Paul Fort and author Jules Romains. After joining the Futurist movement at the invitation of Filippo Tommaso Marinetti and Boccioni, Severini signed the *Technical Manifesto of Futurist Painting* of April 1910 along with Balla, Boccioni, Carlo Carrà and Franco Russolo. However, Severini was less attracted to the subject of the machine than his fellow Futurists and frequently chose the form of the dancer to express Futurist theories of dynamism in art.

Severini helped organize the first Futurist exhibition at Bernheim-Jeune, Paris, in February 1912, and participated in subsequent Futurist shows in Europe and the United States. In 1913 he had one-man exhibitions at the Marlborough Gallery, London, and Der Sturm, Berlin. During the Futurist period Severini acted as an important link between artists in France and Italy. After his last truly Futurist work—a series of paintings on war themes—Severini painted in a Synthetic Cubist mode and by 1920 he was applying theories of Classical balance based on the Golden Section to figurative subjects from the traditional Commedia dell'Arte. He divided his time between Paris and Rome after 1920. He explored fresco and mosaic techniques and executed murals in various mediums in Switzerland, France and Italy during the 1920s. In the 1950s he returned to the subjects of his Futurist years: dancers, light and movement. Throughout his career Severini published important theoretical essays and books on art. Severini died in Paris on February 26, 1966.

85 Red Cross Train Passing a Village. Summer 1915
(Train de la Croix Rouge traversant un village)

44.944

Oil on canvas, 35 x 45¾ in. (88.9 x 116.2 cm.)

Signed l.r.: *G. Severini*; inscribed within picture:
$13 / \dfrac{15}{2317^m} / \dfrac{15}{122^m} /$ *[C]einture AC 247*; on reverse:
*Gino Severini 2 / "Train de la Croix Rouge /
traversant un village„ / 1915.*

PROVENANCE:
from the artist through Alfred Stieglitz, New York
John Quinn, New York, 1917-24
Estate of John Quinn, 1924-27, by auction, American
Art Association, New York, Feb. 9-12, 1927, no. 120
J. B. Neumann, New York, 1927-44

Severini and the other Futurists celebrate the beauty
and dynamism of the machine and modern life in their
paintings. The Futurists believed that their work
should be deeply involved with contemporary life, and
thus sought to express their feelings about World War I
in a series of war paintings or *guerrapittura*. To
express an idea of war in *Red Cross Train Passing a
Village*, Severini selected the train as a symbolic image.
He painted this canvas (as well as another version in
the Stedelijk Museum, Amsterdam) in the summer of
1915 when he lived near a railroad line at Igny and
could watch the trains going to and from the battlefield
with supplies, soldiers and the wounded. Severini's
depiction of road and railway signals and his inscription
of numbers across the landscape add new levels of
meaning to the picture.

Red Cross Train Passing a Village displays the Futurist
concern with movement. The small brushstrokes,
though derived from Neo-Impressionism, seem to have
been applied rapidly and are slanted in varying
directions, thus conveying a vivid sense of motion. The
strong horizontal of the train cuts through the center
of the composition. The feeling of its power and speed
is echoed and heightened by the billowing white smoke
and the shifting, sharp-edged triangular planes that
fragment the landscape.

EXHIBITIONS:
Paris, Galerie Boutet de Monvel, *Iʳᵉ Exposition futuriste
d'art plastique de la guerre et d'autres oeuvres antérieures*,
Jan. 15-Feb. 1916, no. 6
New York, Gallery "291" of the Photo-Secession, *Severini*,
Mar. 6-17, 1917, no. 2

New York, New Art Circle, *Documents of Modern Painting
from the Collection of J. B. Neumann*, Sept. 23-Nov. 30,
1941
London, Tate Gallery, *An exhibition of paintings from The
Solomon R. Guggenheim Museum, New York*, Apr. 16-May
26, 1957, no. 71, traveled to The Hague, Gemeentemuseum,
June 25-Sept. 1; Helsinki, Ateneumin Taidekokoelmat, Sept.
27-Oct. 20; Rome, Galleria Nazionale d'Arte Moderna, Dec.
5, 1957-Jan. 8, 1958; Cologne, Wallraf-Richartz-Museum,
Jan. 26-Mar. 30; Paris, Musée des Arts Décoratifs, Apr. 23-
June 1
Pasadena Art Museum, *The New Renaissance in Italy:
Twentieth Century Italian Art*, Oct. 7-Nov. 16, 1958, no. 95,
repr.
Milan, Palazzo Reale, *Arte italiana del XX secolo da col-
lezioni americane*, Apr. 30-June 26, 1960, no. 175, repr.
Paris, Musée National d'Art Moderne, *Les Sources du XXe
siècle: les arts en Europe de 1884 à 1914*, Nov. 4, 1960-Jan.
23, 1961, no. 668
New York, The Solomon R. Guggenheim Museum, *Forty
Modern Masters: An Anniversary Show*, Dec. 16, 1977-Feb.
5, 1978, no. 124, repr.
Washington, D.C., The Hirshhorn Museum and Sculpture
Garden, Smithsonian Institution, *"The Noble Buyer:" John
Quinn, Patron of the Avant-Garde*, June 15-Sept. 4, 1978, no.
72, repr.

REFERENCES:
*John Quinn, 1870-1925: Collection of Paintings, Water-
colors, Drawings and Sculpture*, Huntington, N.Y., 1926,
p. 15
Handbook, 1970, pp. 412, color repr., 413-414
J. M. Lukach, "Severini's 1917 Exhibition at Stieglitz's
'291,'" *The Burlington Magazine*, vol. CXIII, Apr. 1971,
pp. 199, 203, 205 and fig. 47
J. M. Lukach, "Severini's Writings and Paintings of 1916-
1917 and His Exhibition in New York," *Critica d'Arte*, anno
XX (XXXIX), Nov.-Dec. 1974, pp. 69-70 and fig. 2
Rudenstine, *Collection Catalogue*, 1976, no. 230, color repr.
H. H. Arnason, *History of Modern Art*, rev. ed., New York,
1977, pp. 222, 225 and fig. 379

Marc Chagall b. 1887

Marc Chagall was born on July 7, 1887, in the Russian town of Vitebsk. From 1906 to 1909 he studied in St. Petersburg at the Imperial School for the Protection of the Arts and with Léon Bakst. In 1910 he moved to Paris where he associated with Guillaume Apollinaire and Robert Delaunay and encountered Fauvism and Cubism. He participated in the Salon des Indépendants and the Salon d'Automne in 1912. His first one-man show was held in 1914 at the gallery of Der Sturm in Berlin.

Chagall returned to Russia during the war, settling with his wife Bella (d. 1944) in Vitebsk, where he was appointed Commissar for Art. He founded the Vitebsk Academy and directed it until disagreements with the Suprematists resulted in his resignation in 1920. He moved to Moscow and executed his first stage designs for the State Jewish Kamerny Theater there. After a sojourn in Berlin Chagall returned to Paris in 1923 and met Ambroise Vollard. His first retrospective took place in 1924 at the Galerie Barbazanges-Hodebert, Paris. During the thirties he traveled to Palestine, The Netherlands, Spain, Poland and Italy. In 1933 the Kunsthalle Basel held a major retrospective of his work.

During World War II Chagall fled to the United States; The Museum of Modern Art, New York, gave him a retrospective in 1946. He settled permanently in France in 1948 and exhibited in Paris, Amsterdam and London. During 1951 he visited Israel and executed his first sculptures. The following year the artist traveled in Greece and Italy with his second wife Vava. In 1962 he designed windows for the synagogue of the Hadassah Medical Center near Jerusalem and the cathedral at Metz. He designed a ceiling for the Opéra in Paris in 1964 and murals for the Metropolitan Opera House, New York, in 1965. Chagall now lives and works in St. Paul de Vence, France.

86 The Soldier Drinks. 1911-12
(Le Soldat boit)

49.1211

Oil on canvas, 43 x 37¼ in. (109.1 x 94.5 cm.)

Signed l.r.: *Chagall.* Not dated.

PROVENANCE:
Herwarth Walden, Berlin, 1914-24
Nell Urech-Walden, Ascona, 1924-49

The Soldier Drinks demonstrates a definite Cubist influence in the translation of volumes into planes and the subsequent shallowness of the picture space. Furthermore, the strong horizontals, verticals and diagonals, the importance of a large-scale human figure and the emphasis on rhythmic gestures and details are characteristic of Chagall's work around 1912.

The soldier, who appears in uniform drinking tea, is juxtaposed with a samovar and small figures dancing in the foreground. The picture clearly evokes memories of Russia, although it was painted in Paris where Chagall had been since the late summer of 1910. It was not Chagall's intention to represent the world literally or logically or to portray the reality of everyday life. Rather, his interests lay in the poetic and irrational realm of the imagination.

EXHIBITIONS:
Kunsthalle Basel, *Marc Chagall,* Nov. 4-Dec. 3, 1933, no. 15

Kunstmuseum Bern, *Sammlung Nell Walden aus den Jahren 1912-20,* Oct. 1944-Mar. 1945, no. 278

New York, The Museum of Modern Art, *Marc Chagall,* Apr. 9-June 23, 1946, no. 11, repr., traveled to The Art Institute of Chicago, Nov. 14, 1946-Jan. 12, 1947

Amsterdam, Stedelijk Museum, *Marc Chagall,* Dec. 1947-Jan. 1948, no. 9, traveled to London, Tate Gallery, Feb. 4-29

London, Tate Gallery, *An exhibition of paintings from The Solomon R. Guggenheim Museum, New York,* Apr. 16-May 26, 1957, no. 7, traveled to The Hague, Gemeentemuseum, June 25-Sept. 1; Helsinki, Ateneumin Taidekokoelmat, Sept. 27-Oct. 20; Rome, Galleria Nazionale d'Arte Moderna, Dec. 5, 1957-Jan. 8, 1958; Cologne, Wallraf-Richartz-Museum, Jan. 26-Mar. 30; Paris, Musée des Arts Décoratifs, Apr. 23-June 1

Tokyo, National Museum of Western Art, *Marc Chagall,* Oct. 1-Nov. 10, 1963, no. 18, repr.

Kunsthaus Zürich, *Chagall,* May 6-July 30, 1967, no. 32, repr.

Cologne, Wallraf-Richartz-Museum, *Chagall,* Sept. 2-Oct. 31, 1967, no. 40, repr.

Paris, Grand Palais, *Marc Chagall,* Dec. 13, 1969-Mar. 8, 1970, no. 31, repr.

REFERENCES:

T. Däubler, *Der neue Standpunkt*, Dresden, 1916, pp. 129-131

H. Walden, *Expressionismus, Die Kunstwende*, Berlin, 1918, p. 23, repr.

A. Efross and J. Tugendhold, *Die Kunst Marc Chagalls*, Potsdam, 1921, p. 33, repr.

T. Däubler, *Marc Chagall*, Rome, 1922, pp. 6-7, 9, repr.

H. Walden, *Marc Chagall*, Sturm Bilderbücher No. 1, 2nd ed., Berlin, 1923, p. 9, repr.

L. Venturi, *Chagall*, Geneva, 1956, pp. 37, 40, repr.

F. Meyer, *Marc Chagall*, New York, 1963, pp. 179-180, 184, repr.

J. Cassou, *Chagall*, New York, 1965, p. 102, pl. 71

Handbook, 1970, pp. 66-67, repr.

W. Haftmann, *Chagall*, New York, 1973, pp. 86-87, color repr.

Rudenstine, *Collection Catalogue*, 1976, no. 26, repr.

87 The Flying Carriage. 1913
(La Calèche volante)

49.1212

Oil on canvas, 42 x 47¼ in. (106.7 x 120.1 cm.)

Signed and dated l.r.: *Chagall Paris 13.*

PROVENANCE:
Herwarth Walden, Berlin, 1914-24
Nell Urech-Walden, Ascona, 1924-49

Although this painting has often been called *Burning House,* Chagall himself considers the title *The Flying Carriage* to be correct and has stated that the house is not burning. "There is great ecstasy.... It is calm.* On the left the flying carriage is boldly silhouetted against yellow; on the right the woman in the background has raised her arm in response to the scene. A fiery orange-red sky augments the ecstatic, almost apocalyptic mood. The inscription over the door to the house is *LAV* for *LAVKA* (boutique). The building functions compositionally to stabilize seemingly disparate elements which are unified also by Chagall's intense, vibrant colors.

*conversation with Margit Rowell, Feb. 1974

EXHIBITIONS:
Kunstmuseum Bern, *Sammlung Nell Walden aus den Jahren 1912-20,* Oct. 1944-Mar. 1945, no. 276

New York, The Museum of Modern Art, *Marc Chagall,* Apr. 9-June 23, 1946, no. 17, traveled to The Art Institute of Chicago, Nov. 14, 1946-Jan. 12, 1947

Paris, Musée National d'Art Moderne, *Marc Chagall,* Oct.-Dec. 1947, no. 16, traveled to Amsterdam, Stedelijk Museum, Dec. 1947-Jan. 1948; London, Tate Gallery, Feb. 4-29

London, Tate Gallery, *An exhibition of paintings from The Solomon R. Guggenheim Museum, New York,* Apr. 16-May 26, 1957, no. 8, traveled to The Hague, Gemeentemuseum, June 25-Sept. 1; Helsinki, Ateneumin Taidekokoelmat, Sept. 27-Oct. 20; Rome, Galleria Nazionale d'Arte Moderna, Dec. 5, 1957-Jan. 8, 1958; Cologne, Wallraf-Richartz-Museum, Jan. 26-Mar. 30; Paris, Musée des Arts Décoratifs, Apr. 23-June 1

Tokyo, National Museum of Western Art, *Marc Chagall,* Oct. 1-Nov. 10, 1963, no. 19, repr.

Kunsthaus Zürich, *Chagall,* May 6-July 30, 1967, no. 38

Paris, Grand Palais, *Marc Chagall,* Dec. 13, 1969-Mar. 8, 1970, no. 38, color repr.

REFERENCES:
A. Efross and J. Tugendhold, *Die Kunst Marc Chagalls,* Potsdam, 1921, p. 31, repr.

T. Däubler, *Marc Chagall,* Rome, 1922 [p. 27], repr.

H. Walden, *Marc Chagall,* Sturm Bilderbücher No. 1, 2nd ed., Berlin, 1923, p. 11, repr.

F. Meyer, *Marc Chagall,* New York, 1963, pp. 200, repr., 204

J. Cassou, *Chagall,* New York, 1965, p. 55

Handbook, 1970, pp. 70, repr., 71

W. Haftmann, *Chagall,* New York, 1973, p. 90, color repr.

Rudenstine, *Collection Catalogue,* 1976, no. 27, repr.

Chagall

88 **Paris Through the Window.** 1913
(Paris par la fenêtre)

37.438

Oil on canvas, 53½ x 55¾ in. (135.8 x 141.4 cm.)

Signed and dated l.l.: *Chagall / 1913.*

PROVENANCE:

Herwarth Walden, Berlin, 1914
E. Kluxen, Berlin, 1914
Solomon R. Guggenheim, New York, 1929
Gift, Solomon R. Guggenheim, 1937

While *Paris Through the Window* was painted in Paris, it does not represent what Chagall could see from his studio. Imaginary indoor and outdoor views are inseparably joined on the canvas. The Eiffel Tower, an image also favored by the artist's friends Robert Delaunay and Blaise Cendrars, stands as a metaphor for Paris. The parachutist, the cat with a human head, the double-headed man, the upside-down train, the couple promenading sideways belong to the Paris of Chagall's fantasy. By destroying logical reality Chagall has created a larger psychic reality, for he sought to *"construire psychiquement un tableau"* ("to construct a painting according to psychological considerations").*

* conversation with Margit Rowell, Feb. 1974

EXHIBITIONS:

Charleston, S.C., Carolina Art Association, Gibbes Memorial Art Gallery, *Solomon R. Guggenheim Collection of Non-Objective Paintings,* Mar. 1-Apr. 12, 1936, no. 110

New York, The Museum of Modern Art, *Fantastic Art, Dada, Surrealism,* Dec. 1936-Jan. 1937, repr.

New York, Pierre Matisse Gallery, *Marc Chagall: Paintings and Gouaches 1910-1941,* Nov. 25-Dec. 13, 1941

New York, The Museum of Modern Art, *Marc Chagall,* Apr. 9-June 23, 1946, no. 13, traveled to The Art Institute of Chicago, Nov. 14, 1946-Jan. 12, 1947

Paris, Musée National d'Art Moderne, *Marc Chagall,* Oct.-Dec. 1947, no. 14, traveled to Amsterdam, Stedelijk Museum, Dec. 1947-Jan. 1948; London, Tate Gallery, Feb. 4-29

London, Tate Gallery, *An exhibition of paintings from The Solomon R. Guggenheim Museum, New York,* Apr. 16-May 26, 1957, no. 9, traveled to The Hague, Gemeentemuseum, June 25-Sept. 1; Helsinki, Ateneumin Taidekokoelmat, Sept. 27-Oct. 20; Rome, Galleria Nazionale d'Arte Moderna, Dec. 5, 1957-Jan. 8, 1958; Cologne, Wallraf-Richartz-Museum, Jan. 26-Mar. 30; Paris, Musée des Arts Décoratifs, Apr. 23-June 1

New York, The Solomon R. Guggenheim Museum, *Inaugural Selection,* Oct. 21, 1959-June 19, 1960

New York, Pierre Matisse Gallery, *Marc Chagall: A Celebration,* May 17-June 11, 1977, no. 2, color repr.

New York, The Solomon R. Guggenheim Museum, *Forty Modern Masters: An Anniversary Show,* Dec. 16, 1977-Feb. 5, 1978, no. 17

REFERENCES:

T. Däubler, *Der neue Standpunkt,* Dresden, 1916, pp. 135-136

H. Walden, *Expressionismus, Die Kunstwende,* Berlin, 1918, p. 24, repr.

A. Efross and J. Tugendhold, *Die Kunst Marc Chagalls,* Potsdam, 1921, pp. 43, repr., 52-55

H. Walden, *Marc Chagall,* Sturm Bilderbücher No. 1, 2nd ed., Berlin, 1923, p. 10, repr.

L. Venturi, *Chagall,* Geneva, 1956, pp. 39-42

R. Rosenblum, *Cubism and Twentieth-Century Art,* New York, 1960, p. 242 and fig. 177

F. Meyer, *Marc Chagall,* New York, 1963, pp. 205-206, color repr.

J. Cassou, *Chagall,* New York, 1965, p. 134

Handbook, 1970, pp. 68-69, color repr.

Rudenstine, *Collection Catalogue,* 1976, no. 28, color repr.

H. H. Arnason, *History of Modern Art,* rev. ed., New York, 1977, p. 291 and color pl. 121

89 Birthday. 1923
(Anniversaire)

37.443

Oil on canvas, 31⅞ x 39½ in. (80.8 x 100.3 cm.)

Signed l.r.: *Marc Chagall.* Not dated.

PROVENANCE:
from the artist
Solomon R. Guggenheim, New York, 1936
Gift, Solomon R. Guggenheim, 1937

The Guggenheim's *Birthday* is a version Chagall
executed in Paris in 1923 of a subject he originally
painted in July 1915. The earlier canvas (now Collection The Museum of Modern Art, New York) was in
Chagall's possession in the twenties because its Russian
owner had sent it to Paris for safekeeping. Upon his
return from Russia to Paris in 1923, Chagall re-created
many pictures that had been lost in Germany and France
during the war or had been left behind in the Soviet
Union. *Birthday* was painted from the original, but
others were done from memory, photographs or
sketches.

The circumstances surrounding the painting of
Birthday in July 1915 have been vividly documented
by Chagall's wife Bella *(Lumières allumées,* Paris, 1973,
pp. 258-259). Shortly before their marriage, Bella
arrived at Chagall's room on his birthday carrying a
bunch of flowers. The artist took up a canvas and told
her to stand still as he began to paint. "Suddenly you
lift me off the ground and push with your foot as if
you felt too cramped in the little room. You leap,
stretch out at full length, and fly up to the ceiling. Your
head is turned and you turn mine too. You bend down
behind my ear and whisper something to me. I listen
to the melody of your soft, deep voice. I can even hear
the song in your eyes. And together we rise to the
ceiling of the gaily decked room and fly away...."
(translation from Rudenstine, p. 71)

EXHIBITIONS:
Philadelphia Art Alliance, *Solomon R. Guggenheim Collec-
tion of Non-Objective Paintings,* Feb. 8-28, 1937, no. 146
New York, The Museum of Modern Art, *Marc Chagall,* Apr.
9-June 23, 1946, no. 28, repr., traveled to The Art Institute of
Chicago, Nov. 14, 1946-Jan. 12, 1947
Houston, The Museum of Fine Arts, *Chagall and de Chirico,*
Apr. 3-May 1, 1955, no. 41, repr.
London, Tate Gallery, *An exhibition of paintings from The
Solomon R. Guggenheim Museum, New York,* Apr. 16-May
26, 1957, no. 10, traveled to The Hague, Gemeentemuseum,

June 25-Sept. 1; Helsinki, Ateneumin Taidekokoelmat, Sept.
27-Oct. 20; Rome, Galleria Nazionale d'Arte Moderna, Dec.
5, 1957-Jan. 8, 1958; Cologne, Wallraf-Richartz-Museum,
Jan. 26-Mar. 30; Paris, Musée des Arts Décoratifs, Apr. 23-
June 1
Paris, Musée des Arts Décoratifs, *Marc Chagall,* June 12-
Sept. 30, 1959, no. 92, repr.
Art Center in La Jolla, *Marc Chagall: 75th Anniversary Ex-
hibition,* Oct. 1-Nov. 11, 1962, no. 8, repr.
Tokyo, National Museum of Western Art, *Marc Chagall,*
Oct. 1-Nov. 10, 1963, no. 31, repr.
Montreal, Expo 67, *Man and His World,* Apr. 28-Oct. 27,
1967, no. 74, repr.
Bogotá, Museo de Arte Moderno, *Inaugural Exhibition,* Oct.
29-Dec. 15, 1970

REFERENCES:
W. Erben, *Marc Chagall,* Munich, 1957, p. 60
Handbook, 1959, p. 40, repr.
F. Meyer, *Marc Chagall,* New York, 1963, pp. 237, 324
J. Cassou, *Chagall,* New York, 1965, p. 73, repr.
Rudenstine, *Collection Catalogue,* 1976, no. 30, repr.
H. H. Arnason, *History of Modern Art,* rev. ed., New York,
1977, p. 292 and color pl. 123

90 Green Violinist. 1923-24
(Violoniste)

37.446

Oil on canvas, 78 x 42¾ in. (198 x 108.6 cm.)

Signed l.r.: *Chagall / Marc*; inscribed on trouser cuff in Yiddish: *Oh! Father*. Not dated.

PROVENANCE:

from the artist
Solomon R. Guggenheim, New York, 1936
Gift, Solomon R. Guggenheim, 1937

Chagall has returned often to the theme of the violinist. A similar figure appears in a large canvas from 1912-13 in the Stedelijk Museum, Amsterdam, and in the mural panel *Music,* one of a series Chagall painted in 1919-20 for the State Jewish Kamerny Theater in Moscow and now in the State Tretiakov Gallery there. Executed in Paris in 1923-24, the Guggenheim's *Green Violinist* was done from memory and from sketches Chagall had brought with him from Russia.

The violinist personifies not just music but the arts in general. Years later Chagall remembered he chose the green color of the violinist's face for "psychic and plastic" reasons and said that green is an arbitrary, poetic color.*

* conversation with Margit Rowell, Feb. 1974

EXHIBITIONS:

Kunsthalle Basel, *Marc Chagall,* Nov. 4-Dec. 3, 1933, no. 46

Philadelphia Art Alliance, *Solomon R. Guggenheim Collection of Non-Objective Paintings,* Feb. 8-28, 1937, no. 149

New York, The Museum of Modern Art, *Marc Chagall,* Apr. 9-June 23, 1946, no. 25, repr., traveled to The Art Institute of Chicago, Nov. 14, 1946-Jan. 12, 1947

London, Tate Gallery, *An exhibition of paintings from The Solomon R. Guggenheim Museum, New York,* Apr. 16-May 26, 1957, no. 11, repr., traveled to The Hague, Gemeentemuseum, June 25-Sept. 1; Helsinki, Ateneumin Taidekokoelmat, Sept. 27-Oct. 20; Rome, Galleria Nazionale d'Arte Moderna, Dec. 5, 1957-Jan. 8, 1958; Cologne, Wallraf-Richartz-Museum, Jan. 26-Mar. 30; Paris, Musée des Arts Décoratifs, Apr. 23-June 1

New York, The Solomon R. Guggenheim Museum, *Inaugural Selection,* Oct. 21, 1959-June 19, 1960

New York, The Solomon R. Guggenheim Museum, *Forty Modern Masters: An Anniversary Show,* Dec. 16, 1977-Feb. 5, 1978, no. 19, repr.

REFERENCES:

W. George, *Marc Chagall,* Paris, 1928, pp. 9, 59, repr.

E. Debenedetti, "Saggio di interpretazione del violinista verde di Chagall," *Commentari,* vol. IX, Oct.-Dec. 1958, pp. 298-308 and pl. C

F. Meyer, *Marc Chagall,* New York, 1963, pp. 295, color repr., 333

W. Erben, *Marc Chagall,* rev. ed., New York, 1966, p. 69

Handbook, 1970, pp. 72-73, color repr.

Rudenstine, *Collection Catalogue,* 1976, no. 31, color repr.

H. H. Arnason, *History of Modern Art,* rev. ed., New York, 1977, p. 291 and color pl. 122

Constantin Brancusi 1876-1957

Constantin Brancusi was born on February 19, 1876, in the village of Hobitza, Rumania. He studied art at the Craiova School of Arts and Crafts from 1894 to 1898 and at the Bucharest School of Fine Arts from 1898 to 1901. Eager to continue his education in Paris, Brancusi arrived there in 1904 and enrolled in the Ecole des Beaux-Arts in 1905. The following year his sculpture was shown at the Salon d'Automne, where he met Rodin.

Soon after 1907 his mature period began. The sculptor had settled in Paris but maintained close contact with Rumania throughout this early period, returning frequently and exhibiting in Bucharest almost every year. In Paris his friends included Modigliani, Léger, Matisse, Duchamp and Rousseau. In 1913 five of Brancusi's sculptures were included in the Armory show in New York. Alfred Stieglitz presented the first one-man show of Brancusi's work at his gallery "291" in New York in 1914. By this time a number of Americans, among them Arthur B. Davies, John Quinn, Edward Steichen and the Eugene Meyers, were acquiring his sculpture. Brancusi was never a member of any organized artistic movement, although he associated with Tristan Tzara, Picabia and many other Dadaists in the early 1920s. In 1921 he was honored with a special issue of *The Little Review.* He traveled to the United States twice in 1926 to attend his one-man shows at Wildenstein and at the Brummer Gallery in New York. The following year a major trial was initiated in U. S. Customs Court to determine whether Brancusi's *Bird in Space* was liable for duty as a manufactured object or was a work of art. The court decided in 1928 that the sculpture was a work of art.

Brancusi traveled extensively in the 1930s, visiting India and Egypt as well as European countries. He was commissioned to create a war memorial for a park in Tîrgu Jiu, Rumania, in 1935 and designed a complex which included gates, tables, stools and an *Endless Column.* In 1937 Brancusi discussed a proposed Temple of Meditation in India with the Maharajah of Indore (who had purchased several of his sculptures), but the project was never realized. After 1939 Brancusi worked alone in Paris. His last sculpture, a plaster *Grand Coq,* was completed in 1949. In 1952 Brancusi became a French citizen. He died in Paris on March 16, 1957.

91 **The Sorceress.** 1916-24
(La Sorcière)

56.1448

Wood, 39⅜ in. (100 cm.) high

Signed and dated underneath: *C. Brancusi Paris 1916.*

PROVENANCE:
from the artist, 1956

Although the sculpture bears the date 1916, it appeared unfinished in photographs of Brancusi's studio for several years thereafter. It was the artist's practice to work on a piece for an extended period of time and, as here, to carve directly. The sorceress' face emerges from the grain of the wood, and her pointed headdress and clothing are seen flying behind her. Brancusi may very well have had in mind Rumanian and French folktales about witches.

The Sorceress retains the integrity of the piece of wood he selected and carved to exploit the way the branches grew from the tree trunk. The complex, asymmetrical arrangement of masses stands on a slender leg and maintains perfect equilibrium.

EXHIBITIONS:
London, New Chenil Galleries, *Exhibition of Tri-National Art,* Oct. 1925, no. 2

New York, Wildenstein and Co., Inc., *Exhibition of Sculpture by Brancusi,* Feb. 21-Mar. 3, 1926, no. 4

Moscow, Museum of Modern Western Art, *Contemporary French Art,* May-June 1928, no.5

New York, Brummer Gallery, *Brancusi,* Nov. 17, 1933-Jan. 13, 1934, no. 30

Brussels, Palais des Beaux-Arts, *Exposition Minotaure,* May-June 1934, no. 15, repr.

New York, The Solomon R. Guggenheim Museum, *Constantin Brancusi,* Oct. 26, 1955-Jan. 8, 1956, traveled to Philadelphia Museum of Art, Jan. 27-Feb. 26

New York, The Solomon R. Guggenheim Museum, *Inaugural Selection,* Oct. 21, 1959-June 19, 1960

Philadelphia Museum of Art, *Constantin Brancusi, 1876-1957: A Retrospective Exhibition,* Sept. 25-Nov. 2, 1969, pp. 80-81, color repr., traveled to New York, The Solomon R. Guggenheim Museum (organizer), Nov. 21, 1969-Feb. 15, 1970; The Art Institute of Chicago, Mar. 14-Apr. 26; Bucharest, Muzeul de Arta R. S. R., June 6-Aug. 20

London, Hayward Gallery, *Pioneers of Modern Sculpture,* July 2-Sept. 23, 1973, no. 77

REFERENCES:

This Quarter, vol. I, no. 1, 1925, repr., betw. pp. 246-247

W. Zorach, "The Sculpture of Constantin Brancusi," *The Arts,* vol. IX, Mar. 1926, p. 144, repr.

C. Einstein, *Die Kunst des 20. Jahrhunderts,* 3rd ed., Berlin, 1931, pl. 623

C. Zervos, *Constantin Brancusi,* Paris, 1957, p. 57, repr.

C. Giedion-Welcker, *Constantin Brancusi,* New York, 1959, pp. 32-33 and pls. 78-80

Handbook, 1959, p. 192, repr.

I. Jianou, *Brancusi,* New York, 1963, pp. 100-101 and pl. 65

S. Geist, *Brancusi: A Study of the Sculpture,* New York, 1968, pp. 57, repr., 58, 222, no. 99

A. T. Spear, "Exhibition Review," *Art Quarterly,* vol. XXXIV, summer 1971, p. 239

S. Geist, *Brancusi: The Sculpture and Drawings,* New York, 1975, pp. 26-27, 78, color repr., 181, no. 107

D. Grigorescu, *Brâncusi,* Bucharest, 1977, pp. 64-65, repr.

92 Adam and Eve. 1916-21
(Adam et Eve)

53.1329

Oak and chestnut on limestone base, total 94¼ in.
(239.4 cm.) high; *Eve* (oak), 46¼ in. (118.1 cm.) high;
Adam (chestnut), 34⅞ in. (88.6 cm.) high

Signed on reverse of each section: *C B.* Not dated.

PROVENANCE:

from the artist
John Quinn, New York, 1922-24
Estate of John Quinn, 1924-26
Henri-Pierre Roché, Paris, 1926-53

The wooden sculptures *Adam* and *Eve* were conceived
separately and over a number of years evolved into
their present format. *Eve* was carved as early as 1916
but was reworked in 1920-21. Originally *Adam* was
part of another sculpture that was cut in half and, by
the time it was referred to as "Adambase" and "Adam"
in 1922, it was seen in relation to *Eve*. Although they
were listed and illustrated separately in the Brummer
Gallery's catalogue in 1926, installation shots of the
same exhibition when it appeared in Chicago early in
1927 show *Eve* superimposed on *Adam*. The sculpture's
meaning is determined by the way Brancusi assembled
Adam and Eve.

In *Adam* the angularity and sturdiness of forms convey
a sense of the physical process of hewing the block
and express an essential masculinity. The rounded,
more overtly erotic figure of *Eve* relies without doubt
upon Brancusi's knowledge of African art. Likewise,
the placement of *Eve* on top of *Adam* owes a debt to
primitive art in its vertical articulation.

EXHIBITIONS:

New York, Brummer Gallery, *Brancusi*, Nov. 17-Dec. 15,
1926, nos. 17-18, repr., traveled to The Arts Club of Chicago,
Jan. 4-18, 1927

Paris, Musée National d'Art Moderne, *L'Oeuvre du XXᵉ
siècle*, May-June 1952, no. 117, traveled to London, Tate
Gallery, July 15-Aug. 17

New York, The Solomon R. Guggenheim Museum, *Constantin Brancusi*, Oct. 26, 1955-Jan. 8, 1956, traveled to
Philadelphia Museum of Art, Jan. 27-Feb. 26

New York, The Solomon R. Guggenheim Museum,
Inaugural Selection, Oct. 21, 1959-June 19, 1960

Venice, XXX Biennale Internazionale d'Arte, *Constantin
Brancusi*, June 18-Oct. 16, 1960, no. 8

Philadelphia Museum of Art, *Constantin Brancusi, 1876-
1957: A Retrospective Exhibition*, Sept. 25-Nov. 2, 1969,
pp. 104-105, repr., traveled to New York, The Solomon R.
Guggenheim Museum (organizer), Nov. 21, 1969-Feb. 15,
1970; The Art Institute of Chicago, Mar. 14-Apr. 26; Bucharest, Muzeul de Arta R. S. R., June 6-Aug. 20

The Solmon R. Guggenheim Museum, *Forty Modern Masters: An Anniversary Show*, Dec. 16, 1977-Feb. 5, 1978, no. 9

REFERENCES:

M. M., "Constantin Brancusi: A Summary of Many Conversations," *The Arts*, vol. IV, July 1923, pp. 18, 19, 22, 23, repr.

This Quarter, vol. I, no. 1, 1925, repr. betw. pp. 246-247

*John Quinn 1870-1925: Collection of Paintings, Watercolors,
Drawings and Sculpture*, Huntington, N. Y., 1926, p. 27

J. J. Sweeney, "The Brancusi Touch," *Art News*, vol. 54,
Nov. 1955, pp. 23, 24, repr.

C. Zervos, *Constantin Brancusi*, Paris, 1957, p. 67, repr.

C. Giedion-Welcker, *Constantin Brancusi*, New York, 1959,
p. 33 and pls. 81-84

Handbook, 1959, p. 194, repr.

I. Jianou, *Brancusi*, New York, 1963, p. 105 and pl. 63

S. Geist, *Brancusi: A Study of the Sculpture*, New York,
1968, pp. 61, repr., 78, repr., 79, 80, 222, 225, nos. 105, 134

K. J. Michaelsen, "Brancusi and African Art," *Artforum*,
vol. X, Nov. 1971, p. 76

S. Geist, *Brancusi: The Sculpture and Drawings*, New York,
1975, pp. 97, color repr., 184, 185, no. 138

E. Balas, "The Sculpture of Brancusi in the Light of His
Rumanian Heritage," *Art Journal*, vol. XXXV, winter 1975-
76, pp. 98, 99, repr.

J. Zilczer, *"The Noble Buyer:" John Quinn, Patron of the
Avant-Garde*, exh. cat., Washington, D. C., 1978, p. 151

Brancusi

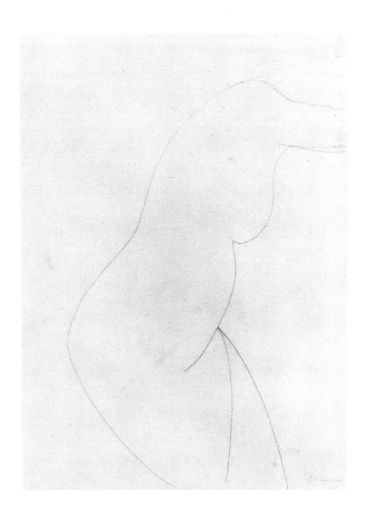

93 Nude. ca. 1920-24
(Nu)

56.1440

Pencil on board, 24¾ x 18 in. (62.9 x 45.7 cm.)

Signed l.r.: *C Brancusi*. Not dated.

PROVENANCE:
from the artist, 1956

It is very difficult to date Brancusi's drawings. Only three examples were dated by the artist and very few can be directly related to his sculptures. In these cases he tended to make drawings after the sculptures rather than preparatory to them.

Angelika Arnoldi* places the Guggenheim *Nude* with a group of pure line drawings of women and considers it slightly earlier than *Female Nude*, 1924 (Collection Muzeul de Arta R.S.R., Bucharest) and *The Dance* (present whereabouts unknown; reproduced in *This Quarter*, no. 1, 1925, no. 85). The pose and the purity of line recall Brancusi's sculptured *Torsos* from at least a decade earlier (1909, 1912 and 1918). The line, which is of extraordinary elegance, achieves a distillation of female form.

* correspondence with the author, Oct. 1978

EXHIBITIONS:
New York, The Solomon R. Guggenheim Museum, *Constantin Brancusi,* Oct. 26, 1955-Jan. 8, 1956, traveled to Philadelphia Museum of Art, Jan. 27-Feb. 26

New York, The Solomon R. Guggenheim Museum, *20th Century Master Drawings,* Nov. 6, 1963-Jan. 5, 1964, no. 14, repr., traveled to Minneapolis, University Gallery, University of Minnesota, Feb. 3-Mar. 15; Cambridge, Mass., The Fogg Art Museum, Harvard University, Apr. 6-May 24

Philadelphia Museum of Art, *Constantin Brancusi, 1876-1957: A Retrospective Exhibition,* Sept. 25-Nov. 2, 1969, pp. 140, repr., 141, traveled to New York, The Solomon R. Guggenheim Museum (organizer), Nov. 21, 1969-Feb. 15, 1970; The Art Institute of Chicago, Mar. 14-Apr. 26; Bucharest, Muzeul de Arta R. S. R., June 6-Aug. 20

Wilhelm-Lehmbruck-Museum der Stadt Duisburg, *Constantin Brancusi: Plastiken-Zeichnungen,* July 11-Sept. 5, 1976, no. 15, repr., traveled to Kunsthalle Mannheim, Sept. 25-Nov. 7

New York, The Solomon R. Guggenheim Museum, *Forty Modern Masters: An Anniversary Show,* Dec. 16, 1977-Feb. 5, 1978, no. 13

REFERENCES:
C. Zervos, *Constantin Brancusi,* Paris, 1957, p. 87, repr.

Handbook, 1959, p. 222, repr.

I. Jianou, *Brancusi,* New York, 1963, p. 114 and pl. 86

S. Geist, *Brancusi: The Sculpture and Drawings,* New York, 1975, p. 36, repr.

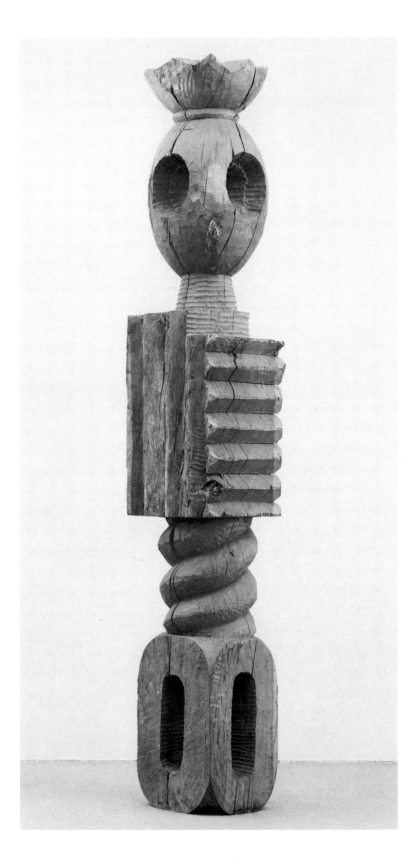

94 King of Kings. Early 1930s
(Le Roi des rois)

56.1449

Oak, 118⅛ in. (300 cm.) high

Not signed or dated.

PROVENANCE:
from the artist, 1956

King of Kings presents problems of dating and difficulties in identifying the forms from which it is composed. According to Carola Giedion-Welcker and Sidney Geist, it was intended for the Temple of Meditation the Maharajah of Indore commissioned in 1933. However, the sculpture was not mentioned in print or photographed until after World War II. As late as 1949 Brancusi had Constantin Antonovici remove some wood from the upper part. Originally called *Spirit of Buddha*, Brancusi referred to it later as *King of Kings*. Thus, not only the sculpture itself but also the title appears to have evolved over a long period of time.

King of Kings has a forbidding, overbearing appearance. The bottom section closely resembles a low table Brancusi had in his studio, while the next segment recalls a wooden screw also in his possession. Its middle zone is not so different from the angular ridges and grooved neck of *Adam*. An oval pierced by large circles surmounted by a crown completes the vertical assemblage. The formal organization of parts is columnar and architectonic and the sculpture rises to a height of almost ten feet.

EXHIBITIONS:
New York, The Solomon R. Guggenheim Museum, *Constantin Brancusi,* Oct. 26, 1955-Jan. 8, 1956, traveled to Philadelphia Museum of Art, Jan. 27-Feb. 26

New York, The Solomon R. Guggenheim Museum, *Inaugural Selection,* Oct. 21, 1959-June 19, 1960

Venice, XXX Biennale Internazionale d'Arte, *Constantin Brancusi,* June 18-Oct. 16, 1960, no. 5, repr.

Philadelphia Museum of Art, *Constantin Brancusi, 1876-1957: A Retrospective Exhibition,* Sept. 25-Nov. 2, 1969, pp. 102-103, repr., traveled to New York, The Solomon R. Guggenheim Museum (organizer), Nov. 1, 1969-Feb. 15, 1970; The Art Institute of Chicago, Mar. 14-Apr. 26; Bucharest, Muzeul de Arta R. S. R., June 6-Aug. 20

New York, The Solomon R. Guggenheim Museum, *Forty Modern Masters: An Anniversary Show,* Dec. 16, 1977-Feb. 5, 1978, no. 10

REFERENCES:
R. V. Gindertael, "Brancusi, l'accessible," *Cimaise,* IIIᵉ sér., no. 3, Jan.-Feb. 1956, p. II, repr.

C. Zervos, *Constantin Brancusi,* Paris, 1957, p. 60, repr.

C. Giedion-Welcker, *Constantin Brancusi,* New York, 1959, pp. 34, 35, 236 and pl. 90

Handbook, 1959, p. 195, repr.

S. Geist, "Brancusi Sanctificatus," *Arts Magazine,* vol. 34, Jan. 1960, p. 28

I. Jianou, *Brancusi,* New York, 1963, p. 111 and pl. 66

S. Geist, *Brancusi: A Study of the Sculpture,* New York, 1968, pp. 73-74, repr., 75, 224, 225, no. 127

S. Geist, *Brancusi: The Sculpture and Drawings,* New York, 1975, pp. 18, 143, color repr., 190, 191, no. 204

E. Balas, "The Sculpture of Brancusi in the Light of His Rumanian Heritage," *Art Journal,* vol. XXXV, winter 1975-76, pp. 95-96, 101, 104

H. H. Arnason, *History of Modern Art,* rev. ed., New York, 1977, p. 146, fig. 258

D. Grigorescu, *Brâncusi,* Bucharest, 1977, pp. 66, 67, repr.

95 **The Seal (Miracle).** 1924-36
(Le Miracle)

56.1450

Marble, 42¾ x 44⅞ x 13 in. (108.6 x 114 x 33 cm.)

Not signed or dated.

PROVENANCE:

from the artist, 1956

Just as *King of Kings* was once known by another title,
the present sculpture was called *Miracle* until the mid-
1950s. Completed by 1936, it was probably begun in
the mid-1920s. Brancusi carved another version of *The
Seal* in blue marble in 1943 (Collection Musée National
d'Art Moderne, Paris). He often represented other animals such as birds, cocks, fish and turtles.

The single, continuous, curved form of the seal is
distinguished by a bent axis. It is meant to be seen on
a broad, round base that can be turned by a motor.
With the assistance of a wedge, the marble sculpture
is balanced on its base so that it stretches forward. The
upward extremity is clearly terminated by a flat plane,
limiting its projection into space.

EXHIBITIONS:

New York, The Museum of Modern Art, *Art in Our Time,*
May 10-Sept. 30, 1939, no. 316, repr.

Philadelphia Museum of Art, *Sculpture International,* May
18-Oct. 1, 1940, no. 47

Philadelphia Museum of Art, *Sculpture of the Twentieth
Century,* Oct. 11-Dec. 7, 1952, no. 17, traveled to The Art
Institute of Chicago, Jan. 22-Mar. 8, 1953; New York, The
Museum of Modern Art, Apr. 29-Sept. 7

New York, The Solomon R. Guggenheim Museum, *Constantin Brancusi,* Oct. 26, 1955-Jan. 8, 1956, traveled to
Philadelphia Museum of Art, Jan. 27-Feb. 26

New York, The Solomon R. Guggenheim Museum,
Inaugural Selection, Oct. 21, 1959-June 19, 1960

New York, The Solomon R. Guggenheim Museum, *Constantin Brancusi, 1876-1957: A Retrospective Exhibition,*
Nov. 21, 1969-Feb. 15, 1970, p. 132, repr.

New York, The Solomon R. Guggenheim Museum, *Forty
Modern Masters: An Anniversary Show,* Dec. 16, 1977-Feb.
5, 1978, no. 11, repr.

REFERENCES:

C. Giedion-Welcker, *Moderne Plastik,* Zürich, 1937, pp. 104-
105, repr.

C. Zervos, *Constantin Brancusi,* Paris, 1957, p. 81, repr.

C. Giedion-Welcker, *Constantin Brancusi,* New York, 1959,
pp. 30, 236 and pls. 54, 56

I. Jianou, *Brancusi,* New York, 1963, p. 111 and pl. 60

S. Geist, *Brancusi: A Study of the Sculpture,* New York,
1968, pp. 115-117, repr., 230, no. 188

S. Geist, *Brancusi: The Sculpture and Drawings,* New York,
1975, p. 149, color repr., 191, no. 212

H. H. Arnason, *History of Modern Art,* rev. ed., New York,
1977, p. 146 and fig. 255

Amedeo Modigliani 1884-1920

Amedeo Modigliani was born July 12, 1884, in Leg-
horn, Italy. The serious illnesses he suffered during his
childhood persisted throughout his life. At age fourteen
he began to study painting. He first experimented with
sculpture during the summer of 1902 and the following
year attended the Istituto di Belle Arti in Venice. Early
in 1906 Modigliani went to Paris where he settled in
Montmartre and attended the Académie Colarossi. His
early work was influenced by Toulouse-Lautrec,
Théophile Alexandre Steinlen, Gauguin and Cézanne.
In the autumn of 1907 he met his first patron, Dr. Paul
Alexandre, who purchased works from him before
World War I. Modigliani exhibited in the Salon
d'Automne in 1907 and 1912 and in the Salon des Indépendants in 1908, 1910 and 1911.

In 1909 Modigliani met Brancusi when both artists
lived in Montparnasse. From 1909 to 1915 the Italian
concentrated on sculpture but he also drew and painted
to a certain extent. However, the majority of his paintings date from 1916 to 1919. Modigliani's circle of
friends first consisted of Max Jacob, Lipchitz and the
Portuguese sculptor Amedeo de Suza Cardoso and later
included Chaim Soutine, Maurice Utrillo, Jules Pascin,
Foujita, Moïse Kisling and the Sitwells. His dealers were
Paul Guillaume (1914 to 1916) and Leopold Zborowski
(by 1917). The only one-man show given the artist during his lifetime took place at the Galerie Berthe Weill
in December 1917.

In March 1917 Modigliani met Jeanne Hébuterne who
became his companion and model. From March or
April 1918 until May 31, 1919, they lived in the south
of France, in both Nice and Cagnes. Modigliani died
in Paris on January 24, 1920.

96 **Head.** 1911-13
(Tête)

55.1421

Limestone, 25 in. (63.5 cm.) high

Not signed or dated.

PROVENANCE:
from the artist
Augustus John, London, 1913-54
Arthur Tooth and Sons, London, 1954
J. J. Klejman Gallery, New York, 1955

Pursuing his wish to be a sculptor, Modigliani carved at least twenty-two heads between 1910 and 1915. In 1911 several heads similar to the Guggenheim example were photographed at Cardoso's studio in Paris in rue du Colonel Combes. A group of seven heads was exhibited as an *"ensemble décoratif"* at the Salon d'Automne the next year. The one in the Guggenheim collection was completed by August 1913 when the English painter Augustus John purchased it from the artist's studio at 216, boulevard Raspail.

Modigliani preferred carving directly into the stone, the technique used by Brancusi, his friend and neighbor in Montparnasse. Influenced by African and archaic sculpture and Brancusi's work, the heads display anonymity, hieratic simplicity and serene passivity. A strong sense of the block of stone is retained in the shape of the head with its stylized hair, elongated nose and cheeks and small mouth.

EXHIBITIONS:
London, Arthur Tooth and Sons, *Recent Acquisitions,* Nov. 15- Dec. 18, 1954, no. 27
Houston, Contemporary Arts Museum, *Totems Not Taboo: An Exhibition of Primitive Art,* Feb. 26-Mar. 29, 1959, repr.
The Cleveland Museum of Art, *Paths of Abstract Art,* Oct. 4-Nov. 13, 1960, no. 36, repr.
Hartford, Wadsworth Atheneum, *Salute to Italy: 100 Years of Italian Art 1861-1961,* Apr. 21-May 28, 1961, repr.
New York, The Solomon R. Guggenheim Museum, *Forty Modern Masters: An Anniversary Show,* Dec. 16, 1977-Feb. 5, 1978, no. 100, repr.

REFERENCES:
A. John, *Chiaroscuro: Fragments of Autobiography,* New York, 1952, p. 131
J. Modigliani, *Modigliani: Man and Myth,* New York, 1958, pp. 55, 59 and pl. 67
A. Werner, *Modigliani the Sculptor,* New York, 1962, pls. 9-11
A. Ceroni, *Amedeo Modigliani: dessins et sculptures,* Milan, 1965, p. 25, no. xxi, pls. 88, 89
A. Werner, *Amedeo Modigliani,* New York, 1966, pl. 25
P. Sichel, *Modigliani,* New York, 1967, pp. 212-213
A. Ceroni, *I dipinti di Modigliani,* Milan, 1970, p. 109, repr., no. xxi
J. Lanthemann, *Modigliani: catalogue raisonné,* Barcelona, 1970, p. 142, no. 625, repr.
Handbook, 1970, pp. 310-311, repr.

97 Beatrice Hastings. 1914-16

41.534

Pencil and conté crayon on paper, 12⅛ x 7¹¹⁄₁₆ in.
(30.8 x 19.5 cm.)

Inscribed l.r.: *BEATRICE*. Not signed or dated.

PROVENANCE:

Félix Fénéon, Paris
Hilla Rebay, New York and Greens Farms, Connecticut,
1930
Solomon R. Guggenheim, New York, 1938
Gift, Solomon R. Guggenheim, 1941

Beatrice Hastings (1879-1943) was originally from Port
Elizabeth, South Africa. After living in London, where
she was a writer and friend of Katherine Mansfield, she
arrived in Paris in the spring of 1914. She was the Paris
correspondent for the English periodical *New Age* and
wrote the column "Impressions de Paris" until August
1916. Beatrice Hastings met Modigliani in July 1914,
and they lived together until 1916. Modigliani drew
and painted her portrait many times during these two
years.

In the Guggenheim drawing the delicacy of her features
is set off by her dark hair and the adjacent background
area. A related drawing inscribed to Beatrice Hastings
and dated "*22 aprile*" is in the collection of James W.
Alsdorf, Winnetka, Illinois. Modigliani often inscribed
paintings as well as drawings with words.

EXHIBITIONS:

Berlin, Galerie Flechtheim, *Seit Cézanne in Paris,* Nov. 23-
Dec. 24, 1929, no. 259

Charleston, S. C., Carolina Art Association, Gibbes Memorial Art Gallery, *Solomon R. Guggenheim Collection of
Non-Objective Paintings,* Mar. 1-Apr. 12, 1936, no. 120

The Baltimore Museum of Art, *Twentieth Century Italian
Art,* Oct. 25-Nov. 27, 1966

New York, The Solomon R. Guggenheim Museum, *Forty
Modern Masters: An Anniversary Show,* Dec. 16, 1977-Feb.
5, 1978, no. 101

REFERENCES:

J. Lipchitz, *Amedeo Modigliani,* New York, 1954, pl. 10

J. Lanthemann, *Modigliani: catalogue raisonné,* Barcelona,
1970, p. 146, no. 715, repr.

Handbook, 1970, pp. 312, repr., 313

98 Nude. 1917
(Nu)

41.535

Oil on canvas, 28¾ x 45⅞ in. (73 x 116.7 cm.)

Signed u.r.: *modigliani*; inscribed on reverse, probably
by the artist: *Modigliani / 3 Joseph Bara / Paris /
1917.*

PROVENANCE:

Leopold Zborowski, Paris
Louis Libaude, Paris
Galerie Bing et Cie, Paris, by 1925
Félix Fénéon, Paris, by 1926
Solomon R. Guggenheim, New York, 1938
Gift, Solomon R. Guggenheim, 1941

Modigliani has shown the reclining female nude asleep:
thus, she does not gaze provocatively at the spectator
as in many of his other paintings of the subject.
Between 1916 and 1919 he painted approximately
twenty-six female nudes. When a group of them
(perhaps including the Guggenheim painting) was
shown at the Galerie Berthe Weill in December 1917,
the police found the paintings to be obscene and closed
the exhibition.

Modigliani's sleeping figure appears self-contained,
sensuous and unaware of the spectator. The warm flesh-
color of her body is set off on one side by the dark
color of the background and on the other by the white
drapery. Her head is described in a rather stylized
manner contrasting with the full, naturalistic modeling
of her torso.

EXHIBITIONS:

Paris, Galerie Bing et Cie, *Modigliani,* Oct. 24-Nov. 15, 1925

Paris, Grand Palais, Société des Artistes Indépendants,
Trente ans d'art indépendant, Feb. 20-Mar. 21, 1926,
no. 3104

New York, The Solomon R. Guggenheim Museum,
Inaugural Selection, Oct. 21, 1959-June 19, 1960

New York, The Solomon R. Guggenheim Museum, *Forty
Modern Masters: An Anniversary Show,* Dec. 16, 1977-Feb.
5, 1978, no. 102

REFERENCES:

W. George, "Modigliani," *L'Amour de l'Art,* VIᵉ année, Oct.
1925, p. 388, repr.

A. Salmon, *Modigliani: sa vie et son oeuvre,* Paris, 1926,
pl. 18

A. Pfannstiel, *Modigliani,* Paris, 1929, pp. 22-23 and foll.
p. 108, repr.

A. Pfannstiel, *Modigliani et son oeuvre,* Paris, 1956, no. 141

J. Modigliani, *Modigliani: Man and Myth,* New York, 1958,
pp. 82-83

A. Ceroni, *Amedeo Modigliani: dessins et sculptures,* Milan,
1965, pp. 18-19, repr.

A. Ceroni, *I dipinti di Modigliani,* Milan, 1970, no. 186, repr.

J. Lanthemann, *Modigliani: catalogue raisonné,* Barcelona,
1970, no. 214 and p. 217, repr.

Handbook, 1970, pp. 314-315, color repr.

Rudenstine, *Collection Catalogue,* 1976, no. 186, repr.

Modigliani

99 Young Girl Seated. 1918-19
(*Jeune fille sur une chaise*)

78.2514 T31

Oil on canvas, 35 ⅞ x 20 ⅞ in. (91.1 x 53 cm.)

Signed u.r.: *modigliani.* Not dated.

PROVENANCE:
Antoine Villard, Paris, until 1928
Bernheim-Jeune, Paris, 1928
Georges Bernheim, Paris, 1928-at least 1934
Renou et Colle, Paris, by 1937
Charles Boyer, Paris, 1937-49
M. Knoedler and Co., Inc., New York, 1949-50
Henry Pearlman, New York, 1950-at least 1954
Justin K. Thannhauser, New York, mid-1950s
Gift, Justin K. Thannhauser, 1978

Young Girl Seated is related to the few landscapes
Modigliani painted in the south of France in 1918-19.
The girl is seen against green grass and a background
wall; her head is tipped to the left, as is the tree trunk. It
was the artist's usual practice to complete each canvas
in a single sitting. His paintings of young people and
children capture their charm and vitality. Modigliani
imbues this picture with the pristine clarity of form
and line characteristic of his portraits.

EXHIBITIONS:
Venice, XVII Biennale Internazionale d'Arte, *Mostra indi-
viduale di Amedeo Modigliani,* 1930, no. 32

Kunsthalle Basel, *Modigliani,* Jan. 7-Feb. 4, 1934, no. 55

Palm Beach, The Society of the Four Arts, *Amedeo Modigliani,* Jan. 8-31, 1954, no. 25, repr., traveled to Miami, The
Lowe Gallery, Feb. 11-28

New York, The Solomon R. Guggenheim Museum, *The
Justin K. Thannhauser Collection,* from Apr. 30, 1965

REFERENCES:
A. Pfannstiel, *Modigliani,* Paris, 1929, p. 35

A. Pfannstiel, *Modigliani et son oeuvre,* Paris, 1956, pp. 123-
124, no. 212

J. Modigliani, *Modigliani: Man and Myth,* New York, 1958,
p. x and pl. 46

A. Ceroni, *Amedeo Modigliani: dessins et sculptures,* Milan,
1965, p. 45 and pl. 194

A. Ceroni, *I dipinti di Modigliani,* Milan, 1970, p. 101,
no. 254

J. Lanthemann, *Modigliani: catalogue raisonné,* Barcelona,
1970, pp. 128, 242, repr., no. 312

Barnett, *Thannhauser Catalogue,* 1978, no. 31, color repr.

Modigliani

100 Jeanne Hébuterne with Yellow Sweater. 1918-19
(Le Sweater jaune)

37.533

Oil on canvas, 39⅜ x 25½ in. (100 x 64.7 cm.)

Signed u.r.: *modigliani*. Not dated.

PROVENANCE:
Leopold Zborowski, Paris(?)
Galerie Bing et Cie, Paris, by 1927
Félix Fénéon, Paris, by 1929
Solomon R. Guggenheim, New York, 1932
Gift, Solomon R. Guggenheim, 1937

Modigliani met Jeanne Hébuterne (1898-1920) in Paris in 1917. As his loyal companion, she was the mother of his only child. As his model, she was the subject of more than twenty portraits between 1917 and 1920. The morning after Modigliani died, Jeanne Hébuterne committed suicide.

Characteristic of the artist's mature style are the long curved neck, the flat, elongated oval face, the empty almond-shaped eyes and the small pursed mouth. Jeanne is seated near the corner of a room; the angle of her head and the curve of her hips and shoulders conform to an S-shaped silhouette, and even the position of her hands reinforces the lively curving shapes. Modigliani has depicted Jeanne's sweater and the background wall in warm light-filled tonalities and with an allover pattern of brushwork in the thinly applied pigment.

EXHIBITIONS:
Kunsthaus Zürich, *Italienische Maler*, Mar. 18-May 1, 1927, no. 109

Charleston, S. C., Carolina Art Association, Gibbes Memorial Art Gallery, *Solomon R. Guggenheim Collection of Non-Objective Paintings*, Mar. 1-Apr. 12, 1936

London, Tate Gallery, *An exhibition of paintings from The Solomon R. Guggenheim Museum, New York*, Apr. 16-May 26, 1957, no. 52, traveled to The Hague, Gemeentemuseum, June 25-Sept. 1; Helsinki, Ateneumin Taidekokoelmat, Sept. 27-Oct. 20; Rome, Galleria Nazionale d'Arte Moderna, Dec. 5, 1957-Jan. 8, 1958; Cologne, Wallraf-Richartz-Museum, Jan. 26-Mar. 30; Paris, Musée des Arts Décoratifs, Apr. 23-June 1

New York, The Solomon R. Guggenheim Museum, *Inaugural Selection*, Oct. 21, 1959-June 19, 1960

Milan, Palazzo Reale, *Arte italiana del XX sècolo da collezioni americane,* Apr. 30-June 26, 1960, no. 147, repr.

Hartford, Wadsworth Atheneum, *Salute to Italy,* Apr. 21-May 28, 1961, p. 32

New York, The Solomon R. Guggenheim Museum, *Forty Modern Masters: An Anniversary Show,* Dec. 16, 1977-Feb. 5, 1978, no. 103

REFERENCES:
A. Pfannstiel, *Modigliani,* Paris, 1929, p. 43, foll. p. 104, color repr.

A. Pfannstiel, *Modigliani et son oeuvre,* Paris, 1956, no. 268

A. Ceroni, *Modigliani,* Milan, 1958, no. 151

F. Russoli, *Modigliani,* London, 1959, pl. 30

F. Russoli, *Modigliani,* Milan, 1963, pls. xiv-xv

A. Ceroni, *I dipinti di Modigliani,* Milan, 1970, no. 220, color pl. lvi

J. Lanthemann, *Modigliani: catalogue raisonné,* Barcelona, 1970, no. 389, repr.

Handbook, 1970, pp. 318-319, repr.

Rudenstine, *Collection Catalogue,* 1976, no. 189, repr.

Alexander Archipenko 1887-1964

Alexander Archipenko was born on May 30, 1887, in Kiev, Ukraine, Russia. He studied painting and sculpture at art school in Kiev, but was expelled in 1905 for criticizing his teachers' academicism. During this time he was impressed by the Byzantine icons, frescoes and mosaics of Kiev. After a sojourn in Moscow Archipenko moved to Paris in 1908. He again rejected academic training and studied independently at the Louvre, where he was drawn to Egyptian, Assyrian, archaic Greek and early Gothic sculpture. In 1910 he began exhibiting at the Salon des Indépendants, Paris, and the following year showed for the first time at the Salon d'Automne.

In 1912 Archipenko was given his first one-man show in Germany at the Folkwang Museum in Hagen. That same year in Paris he opened the first of his many art schools, joined the *Section d'Or* group, which included Picasso, Braque, Léger and Duchamp among others, and produced his first painted reliefs, the *Sculpto-Peintures*. Archipenko made his first prints and exhibited at the Armory Show in New York in 1913. His work was ridiculed by critics at the 1914 Salon des Indépendants and condemned by a Venetian cardinal when exhibited at the Venice Biennale in 1920. During the war years the artist resided in Cimiez, a suburb of Nice. From 1919 to 1921 he traveled to Geneva, Zürich, Paris, London, Brussels, Athens and other European cities to exhibit his work. Archipenko's first one-man show in the United States was held at the Société Anonyme in New York in 1921.

In 1923 he moved from Berlin to the United States where, over the years, he opened art schools in New York City, Woodstock (New York), Los Angeles and Chicago. In 1924 Archipenko invented his first kinetic work, *Archipentura*. For the next thirty years he taught throughout the United States at art schools and universities, including the New Bauhaus School of Industrial Arts in Chicago. He became a United States citizen in 1928. Most of Archipenko's work in German museums was confiscated by the Nazis in their 1937 purge of *Entartete Kunst* (degenerate art). In 1947 he produced the first of his sculptures that are illuminated from within. He accompanied a one-man exhibition throughout Germany in 1955, and at this time began work on the book *Archipenko: Fifty Creative Years 1908-1958*, published in 1960. Archipenko died on February 25, 1964, in New York.

101 Carrousel Pierrot. 1913

57.1483

Painted plaster, 23⅝ in. (60 cm.) high

Signed and dated on base: *Archipenko/ 1913 Paris*; inscribed on right side of sculpture: *venez rire*.

PROVENANCE:

from the artist
Alberto Magnelli, Florence, 1914-57
Mrs. Theo van Doesburg, Meudon, 1957

In *Carrousel Pierrot* the articulation and decoration of smooth plaster surfaces has been achieved through brightly colored, painted patterns. With the introduction of polychromy in his sculpture of the previous year, Archipenko resumed an ancient tradition which had reappeared also in the work of Gauguin and Kirchner and would become influential in the second decade of the twentieth century. However, more immediate sources for Archipenko can be found in contemporary decorative arts both in Russia and France.

The artist recalled that the idea for this sculpture came from a festival when "dozens of carrousels with horses, swings, gondolas and airplanes imitate the rotation of the earth." (Däubler and Goll, p. 13) Indeed, the thrust and counterthrust of the diagonals establish a rotating movement. The inscription *"venez rire"* quite literally invites us to "come laugh."* This introduction of words is apparently related to the Cubist device of adding words and letters to their works. The application of festive colors amplifies the abstract geometry of the figure and accentuates the motion implicit in its pose.

* correspondence with Donald Karshan, Jan. 1979

EXHIBITIONS:

Paris, Société des Artistes Indépendants, Champ de Mars, *Catalogue de la 30ᵐᵉ Exposition*, Mar. 1-Apr. 30, 1914, no. 83

New York, The Solomon R. Guggenheim Museum, *Selected Sculpture and Works on Paper*, July 8-Sept. 14, 1969, p. 90, color repr.

New York, The Solomon R. Guggenheim Museum, *Forty Modern Masters: An Anniversary Show*, Dec. 16, 1977-Feb. 5, 1978, no. 2

REFERENCES:

T. Däubler and I. Goll, *Archipenko-Album*, Potsdam, 1921, p. 13 and pl. 6

Handbook, 1959, pp. 184-185, repr.

A. Archipenko and others, *Archipenko: Fifty Creative Years 1908-1958*, New York, 1960, pls. 3-4

A. E. Elsen, *Origins of Modern Sculpture: Pioneers and Premises,* New York, 1974, pp. 104-105, repr.

D. Karshan, *Archipenko: The Sculpture and Graphic Art,* Tübingen, 1974, pp. 11-12, 15, 18, 24, repr., 34, 36, 39, 40, 156

K. J. Michaelsen, *Archipenko: A Study of the Early Works, 1908-1920,* New York, 1977 (photo reprint of Ph.D. dissertation, Columbia University, 1975), pp. 93-97, 173-174, S46

Archipenko

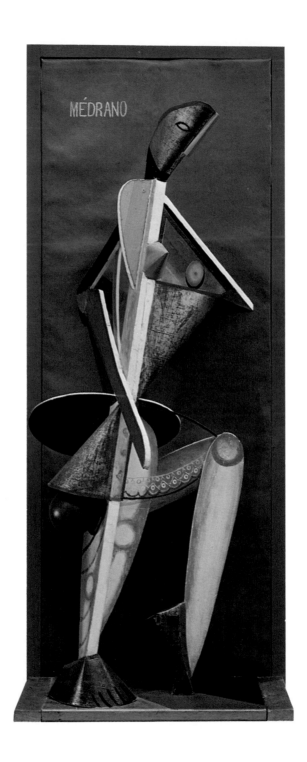

102 Médrano II. 1913

56.1445

Painted tin, wood, glass and painted oilcloth, 49⅞ x 20¼ x 12½ in. (126.6 x 51.5 x 31.7 cm.)

Signed and dated l.r.: *A. Archipenko / 1913 Paris*; inscribed u.l.: *MÉDRANO*.

PROVENANCE:

from the artist
Alberto Magnelli, Florence, 1914-56
Mrs. Theo van Doesburg, Meudon, 1956

The inscription *"MÉDRANO"* refers to the famous circus of that name in boulevard Rochechouart in Paris which many artists frequented. Earlier, in 1912, Archipenko had created *Médrano I* (now destroyed), his first multi-material construction. Made from wood, glass, sheet metal and found objects, it represented a juggler. In *Médrano II* the figure of the dancer is positioned on a base in front of a framed rectangular background that is painted red. Thus, the artist controls the spectator's view of the sculpture. He has assembled carefully selected and precisely crafted materials: reflective metal surfaces in the face and torso, the glass skirt and various pieces of painted wood. He has organized the volumes along a slightly tipped, vertical axis and defined the figure by means of projecting planes. A curved element of wood painted blue determines the angle of the shoulders, a cylindrical tin form and a circle painted on glass indicate her breasts, a projecting wood disc describes the rotation of her hips, and the thrust of her extended leg is parallel to the major vertical axis.

EXHIBITIONS:

Paris, Société des Artistes Indépendants, Champ de Mars, *Catalogue de la 30ᵐᵉ Exposition,* Mar. 1-Apr. 30, 1914, not in cat.

New York, The Solomon R. Guggenheim Museum, *Selected Sculpture and Works on Paper,* July 8-Sept. 14, 1969, pp. 92-93, repr.

London, Hayward Gallery, *Pioneers of Modern Sculpture,* July 20-Sept. 23, 1973, no. 199, color repr.

New York, The Solomon R. Guggenheim Museum, *Forty Modern Masters: An Anniversary Show,* Dec. 16, 1977-Feb. 5, 1978, no. 1, repr.

New York, The Solomon R. Guggenheim Museum, *The Planar Dimension: Europe, 1912-1932,* Mar. 9-May 6, 1979, no. 23, color repr.

REFERENCES:

T. Däubler and I. Goll, *Archipenko-Album,* Potsdam, 1921, pl. 8

C. Einstein, *Die Kunst des 20. Jahrhunderts,* Berlin, 1926, p. 545, repr.

A. Archipenko and others, *Archipenko: Fifty Creative Years 1908-1958,* New York, 1960, pl. 16

R. Rosenblum, *Cubism and Twentieth-Century Art,* New York, 1960, fig. 203

Handbook, 1970, pp. 22, repr., 23

A. E. Elsen, *Origins of Modern Sculpture: Pioneers and Premises,* New York, 1974, p. 145, fig. 161

H. H. Arnason, *History of Modern Art,* rev. ed., New York, 1977, p. 195 and fig. 333

K. J. Michaelsen, *Archipenko: A Study of the Early Works, 1908-1920,* New York, 1977 (photo reprint of Ph.D. dissertation, Columbia University, 1975), pp. 116-122, 179-80, S55

Jacques Lipchitz 1891-1973

Chaim Jacob Lipschitz was born on August 22, 1891, in Druskieniki, Lithuania. At age eighteen he moved to Paris, where he attended the Ecole des Beaux-Arts and the Académie Julian and soon met Picasso, Gris and Braque. In 1912 he began exhibiting at the Salon National des Beaux-Arts and the Salon d'Automne. Lipchitz's first one-man show was held at Léonce Rosenberg's Galerie l'Effort Moderne in Paris in 1920. Two years later he executed five bas-reliefs for The Barnes Foundation in Merion, Pennsylvania. In 1924 the artist became a French citizen and the following year moved to Boulogne-sur-Seine. He received a commission from the Vicomte Charles de Noailles in 1927 for the sculpture *Joy of Life*.

Lipchitz's first important retrospective took place at Jeanne Bucher's Galerie de la Renaissance in Paris in 1930. The Brummer Gallery in New York hosted his first large show in the United States in 1935. In 1941 Lipchitz fled Paris for New York, where he began exhibiting regularly at the Buchholz Gallery (later the Curt Valentin Gallery). He settled in Hastings-on-Hudson, New York, in 1947. In 1954 a Lipchitz retrospective traveled from The Museum of Modern Art in New York to the Walker Art Center in Minneapolis and The Cleveland Museum of Art. In 1958 Lipchitz collaborated with the architect Philip Johnson on the Roofless Church in New Harmony, Indiana. This same year he became a United States citizen. His series of small bronzes, *To the Limit of the Possible,* was shown at Fine Arts Associates in New York in 1959. He visited Israel for the first time in 1963. From 1964 to 1966 Lipchitz showed annually at the Marlborough-Gerson Gallery in New York. Beginning in 1963 he spent several months of each year casting in Pietrasanta, Italy.

From 1970 until 1973 he worked on large-scale commissions for the Municipal Plaza in Philadelphia, Columbia University in New York and the Hadassah Medical Center near Jerusalem. These projects were completed after Lipchitz's death by his wife Yulla. In 1972 the artist's autobiography was published on the occasion of an exhibition of his sculpture at The Metropolitan Museum of Art in New York. Lipchitz died on May 26, 1973, on Capri, and was buried in Jerusalem.

103 **Standing Personage.** 1916
(Personnage debout)

58.1526

Limestone, 42½ in. (108 cm.) high

Signed and dated on front of base: *JL16.*

PROVENANCE:

from the artist through Fine Arts Associates, New York, 1958

More than fifty years after its execution, Lipchitz stated that *Standing Personage* "was completely realized in the round as a three-dimensional object existing in three-dimensional space. Thus, when it is seen in a photograph, it is impossible to understand the work fully. The vertical architectural basis of the structure is apparent.... While this sculpture is in one sense an architectural construction, it is also clearly a figure or figures. The V-shaped curves rising from the sharp vertical in the upper central area reiterate the eyebrows and nose of the slightly earlier head, and the angled elements at the bottom can be either the buttresses supporting a Gothic vault or the legs of a seated figure." (*My Life in Sculpture,* p. 37)

In addition to our version, which was carved from a limestone block, Lipchitz made a plaster of similar dimensions around 1916 (Collection Musée National d'Art Moderne, Paris) that was cast in bronze.

EXHIBITIONS:

Paris, Galerie de la Renaissance, *Cent sculptures par Jacques Lipchitz,* June 13-28, 1930, probably no. 16

New York, The Museum of Modern Art, *The Sculpture of Jacques Lipchitz,* May 18-Aug. 1, 1954, p. 29, repr., traveled to Minneapolis, Walker Art Center, Oct. 1-Dec. 12; The Cleveland Museum of Art, Jan. 25-Mar. 13, 1955

New York, The Solomon R. Guggenheim Museum, *Inaugural Selection,* Oct. 21, 1959-June 19, 1960

New York, The Solomon R. Guggenheim Museum, *Selected Sculpture and Works on Paper,* July 8-Sept. 14, 1969, p. 134, repr.

New York, The Metropolitan Museum of Art, *Jacques Lipchitz: His Life in Sculpture,* June 6-Sept. 12, 1972

New York, The Solomon R. Guggenheim Museum, *Forty Modern Masters: An Anniversary Show,* Dec. 16, 1977-Feb. 5, 1978, no. 86, repr.

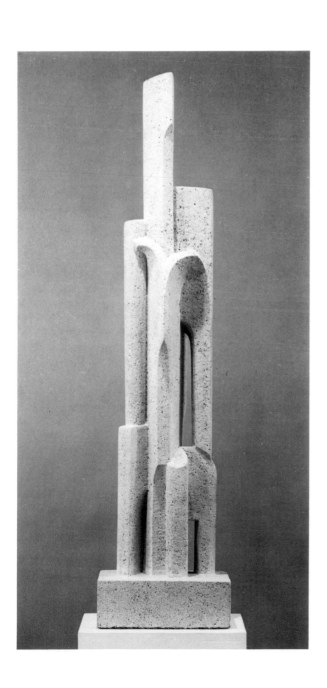

REFERENCES:

J. Baron, "Jacques Lipchitz," *Documents,* 2ᵉ année, no. 1, 1930, p. 19, repr.

M. Raynal, *Jacques Lipchitz,* Paris, 1947, p. 14, repr.

A. M. Hammacher, *Jacques Lipchitz: His Sculpture,* New York, 1960, fig. xxviii

R. Rosenblum, *Cubism and Twentieth-Century Art,* New York, 1960, fig. 210

B. Van Bork, *Jacques Lipchitz: The Artist at Work,* New York, 1966, p. 54, repr.

Handbook, 1970, pp. 274, repr., 275

J. Lipchitz with H. H. Arnason, *My Life in Sculpture,* New York, 1972, pp. 36, repr., 37

A. M. Hammacher, *Jacques Lipchitz,* New York, 1975, pl. 69

H. H. Arnason, *History of Modern Art,* rev. ed., New York, 1977, p. 197, fig. 341

R. E. Krauss, *Passages in Modern Sculpture,* New York, 1977, fig. 45

Mikhail Larionov 1881-1964

Mikhail Larionov was born on May 22, 1881, in Tiraspol, Bessarabia, Russia. From 1898 to 1908 he studied at the Moscow School of Painting, Sculpture and Architecture, where he met Natalia Goncharova; the two lived and worked together until her death in 1962. In 1906 he visited Paris with Sergei Diaghilev, who included his work in the exhibition of Russian artists at the Salon d'Automne of that year. In 1907 Larionov abandoned the Impressionism of his previous work for a neo-primitive style inspired by Russian folk art. With the Burliuk brothers and others he formed the *Blue Rose* group, under whose auspices the review *The Golden Fleece* was published. The first *Golden Fleece* exhibition of 1908 in Moscow introduced many modern French masters to the Russian public. Larionov also organized the avant-garde exhibitions *Link, Jack of Diamonds, Donkey's Tail* and *Target*.

In 1911 Larionov developed a personal abstract style which he defined in his Rayonist Manifesto, published in Moscow in 1913. He participated in the *Erster Deutscher Herbstsalon* at the gallery of Der Sturm in Berlin in 1913, and the following year organized the exhibition *No. 4* in Moscow. In May 1914 Larionov and Goncharova accompanied Diaghilev's *Ballets Russes* to Paris; there Larionov associated with Guillaume Apollinaire. He returned to Russia in July upon the outbreak of World War I and served at the front until his demobilization for health reasons. He then rejoined Diaghilev in Switzerland and devoted himself almost exclusively to designing sets and costumes for the *Ballets Russes*. After Diaghilev died in 1929, Larionov organized a retrospective of maquettes, costumes and decor for his ballets at the Galerie Billiet in Paris in 1930, at which time he published *Les Ballets Russes de Diaghilev* with Goncharova and Pierre Vorms.

In 1938 Larionov became a French citizen. He and Goncharova were given a number of joint exhibitions throughout their careers, among them retrospectives in Paris at the Galerie des Deux-Iles in 1948, the Galerie de l'Institut in 1952 and the Musée National d'Art Moderne in 1963. A one-man exhibition of Larionov's work was held in 1956 at the Galerie de l'Institut. Larionov died on May 10, 1964, at Fontenay-aux-Roses.

104 **Glass.** 1912
(Steklo; Le Verre)

53. 1362

Oil on canvas, 41 x 38¼ in. (104.1 x 97.1 cm.)

Signed l.r.: *M. Larionov*; signed and dated l.l.: *1909. M. L.* (in Cyrillic alphabet); inscribed on reverse: *M. Larionow/ „Le verre" / 1909 / moscou; "Steklo / M. Larionov / Moskva / Palashevshii pr. ugol' Trekhprudnyi per. # 2/7/ (Tverskaia ul.")* (in Cyrillic alphabet); on stretcher: *M. Larionow 43 rue de Seine Paris 6ᵉ.*

PROVENANCE:
from the artist, 1953

Larionov was not only a painter but an organizer of exhibitions and the author of the Rayonist Manifesto. He considered *Glass* to have been his first Rayonist picture. The painting reveals an awareness of Futurism and Cubism: in it Larionov has depicted five tumblers, a goblet and two bottles so that their essential forms are retained and lines represent rays reflected from the objects. As early as 1913 it was observed that Larionov was not painting a still life but "simply 'glass' as a universal condition of glass with all its manifestations and properties—fragility, ease in breaking, sharpness, transparency, brittleness, ability to make sounds, i.e. the sum of all the sensations, obtainable from glass. . . ." (translation from Rudenstine, p. 447)

EXHIBITIONS:
Moscow, *Mir Iskusstva (World of Art)*, Nov. 1912, no. 155b, traveled to St. Petersburg, Jan.-Feb. 1913

Moscow, *Mishen (Target)*, Mar. 24-Apr. 7, 1913, no. 79

Paris, Galerie Paul Guillaume, *Exposition Natalia Gontcharova et Michel Larionov*, June 17-30, 1914, no. 16

Paris, Galerie l'Epoque, *Larionov: peintures et dessins*, Apr. 11-25, 1931, no. 32

Paris, Musée National d'Art Moderne, *L'Oeuvre du XXᵉ siècle*, May-June 1952, no. 53, traveled to London, Tate Gallery, July-Aug.

Los Angeles County Museum of Art, *The Cubist Epoch*, Dec. 15, 1970-Feb. 21, 1971, no. 156, color pl. 160, traveled to New York, The Metropolitan Museum of Art, Apr. 9-June 8

REFERENCES:
E. Eganbyuri, *Natalia Goncharova, Mikhail Larionov*, Moscow, 1913, pp. xxi, 38-39

M. Seuphor, *L'Art abstrait: ses origines, ses premiers maîtres*, Paris, 1950, p. 37

M. Chamot, "The Early Works of Goncharova and Larionov," *The Burlington Magazine,* vol. XCVII, June 1955, p. 173

Handbook, 1959, pp. 100, repr., 101

C. Gray, *The Great Experiment: Russian Art 1863-1922,* New York, 1962, p. 124 and pl. 76

W. George, *Larionov,* Paris, 1966, pp. 116, 123, repr.

T. Loguine, *Gontcharova et Larionov,* Paris, 1971, p. 17, fn. 20

P. Vergo, "A Note on the Chronology of Larionov's Early Work," *The Burlington Magazine,* vol. CXIV, July 1972, p. 479

Rudenstine, *Collection Catalogue,* 1976, no. 160, color repr.

Natalia Goncharova 1881-1962

Natalia Goncharova was born on June 4, 1881, in Nechaevo, Russia. In 1898 she entered the School of Painting, Sculpture and Architecture in Moscow, where she met Mikhail Larionov, who was to become her lifelong companion. Goncharova participated in an exhibition of Russian artists organized by Sergei Diaghilev at the 1906 Salon d'Automne in Paris. Her early work shows the influence of Impressionism, Fauvism and Russian folk sculpture.

From 1907 to 1913 she and Larionov were active in organizing shows in Moscow of new art such as the *Golden Fleece* and *Jack of Diamonds,* which included French as well as Russian artists, and the all-Russian *Link* and *Donkey's Tail* exhibitions. From 1909 to 1911 Goncharova concentrated on religious paintings that reflect her admiration of Russian icons. She rejected French art and adopted Futurist and Rayonist principles around 1911. In 1913, the year Larionov's Rayonist Manifesto was published, Larionov and Goncharova organized the all-Russian exhibition *Target* in Moscow. Goncharova was represented at the second *Blaue Reiter* exhibition in Munich in 1912 and the *Erster Deutscher Herbstsalon* at Der Sturm in Berlin in 1913. Around this time Goncharova and Larionov began their collaboration with Diaghilev and his *Ballets Russes,* which lasted until the impresario's death in 1929. In 1917 they settled permanently in Paris, and the following year their work appeared in the exhibition *L'Art décoratif théâtral moderne* at the Galerie Sauvage, Paris.

Goncharova showed extensively during the twenties and thirties, often with Larionov, in Europe, the United States and Japan. Although she never abandoned painting, much of her creative energy was directed toward stage decoration and book illustration. She designed costumes, settings and drop curtains for international presentations of modern and classical ballets until she was in her seventies. In 1938 Goncharova became a French citizen and in 1955 she married Larionov. The following year she was given a retrospective at the Galerie de l'Institut in Paris. Goncharova died in Paris on October 17, 1962.

105 Cats. 1913
(Koshki; Les Chats)

57. 1484

Oil on canvas, 33¼ x 33 in. (84.4 x 83.8 cm.)

Signed l.r.: *N Gontcharova.*; inscribed on reverse: *N. Gontcharova 43 rue de Seine/ Paris 6ᵉ/ 1910* [1910 written over 1912]. *Rayonisme 1910. „LES CHATS"*; possibly by the artist: *Gontcharav*[a]*/ Katze*[n].

PROVENANCE:

from the artist, 1957

Perhaps to an even greater degree than Larionov's work, Goncharova's painting reveals an understanding of Futurism and Cubism. In *Cats* the forms are represented with faceted planes and the rays by lines of color. The lines of force emanating from objects convey movement and give structure to the composition. A fine example of Goncharova's Rayonist work, *Cats* displays the glowing colors and bold design characteristic of her style. Goncharova was fascinated with Russian folk tales and folk art, and her knowledge of native Russian designs, embroideries and icons is reflected in her painting. In March 1912 Larionov and Goncharova together with Malevich and Vladimir Tatlin organized the *Donkey's Tail* exhibition in Moscow to promote their distinctly Russian school of modernism. Goncharova's peasant pictures exerted a decisive influence on Malevich's development.

EXHIBITIONS:

Moscow, *Mishen (Target),* Mar. 24-Apr. 7, 1913, no. 49

Moscow, *Khudozhestvennyi Salon, Goncharova 1900-1913,* Aug. 1913, no. 645

Berlin, Der Sturm, *Erster Deutscher Herbstsalon,* Sept. 20-Nov. 1, 1913, no. 149

Paris, Galerie Paul Guillaume, *Exposition Natalia Gontcharova et Michel Larionov,* June 17-30, 1914, no. 34

Dresden, *Internationale Kunstausstellung,* June-Sept. 1926, no. 284

Paris, Galerie de l'Institut, *Nathalie Gontcharova: oeuvres anciennes et récentes,* May 4-23, 1956, no. 7, repr.

New York, The Solomon R. Guggenheim Museum, *Inaugural Selection,* Oct. 21, 1959-June 19, 1960

Leeds, City Art Gallery, *Larionov and Goncharova,* Sept. 9-30, 1961, no. 108, repr., traveled to Bristol, City Art Gallery, Oct. 14-Nov. 4; London, Arts Council Gallery, Nov. 16-Dec. 16

Los Angeles County Museum of Art, *The Cubist Epoch,* Dec. 15, 1970-Feb. 21, 1971, no. 105, color pl. 163, traveled to New York, The Metropolitan Museum of Art, Apr. 9-June 8

Berlin, Neue Nationalgalerie, *Tendenzen der Zwanziger Jahre*, Aug. 14-Oct. 16, 1977, no. I/3, repr.

REFERENCES:

E. Eganbyuri, *Natalia Goncharova, Mikhail Larionov*, Moscow, 1913, pp. xii, 11, repr.

M. Seuphor, *L'Art abstrait: ses origines, ses premiers maîtres*, Paris, 1950, p. 154, repr.

Handbook, 1959, p. 67, repr.

C. Gray, *The Great Experiment: Russian Art 1863-1922*, New York, 1962, pl. 80

M. Chamot, *Gontcharova*, Paris, 1972, pp. 54, 57, color repr.

Rudenstine, *Collection Catalogue*, 1976, no. 61, repr.

Kazimir Malevich 1878-1935

Kazimir Severinovich Malevich was born on February 26, 1878, near Kiev, Russia. He studied at the School of Painting, Sculpture and Architecture in Moscow in 1903. During the early years of his career he experimented with various modernist styles and participated in avant-garde exhibitions, among them those of the Artists' Association, Moscow, which included Kandinsky and Larionov, and the 1910 *Jack of Diamonds* show in Moscow. Malevich showed his neo-primitivist paintings of peasants at the exhibition *Donkey's Tail*, 1912. In 1913, with composer M. V. Matyushin and writer Alexej Kruchyonykh, he drafted a manifesto for the First Futurist Congress. That same year Malevich designed the sets and costumes for Matyushin's and Kruchyonykh's opera *Victory over the Sun*. He showed at the Salon des Indépendants, Paris, 1914.

At the *0.10 Last Futurist Exhibition* in Petrograd in 1915 Malevich introduced his non-objective, geometric Suprematist paintings. In 1919 he began to explore the three-dimensional applications of Suprematism in architectural models. Following the Bolshevik Revolution, Malevich and other advanced artists were encouraged by the Soviet government. A state exhibition in Moscow in 1919 focused on Suprematism and other non-objective styles, and later the same year Malevich was given a retrospective in Moscow. In 1919, at the invitation of Chagall, he began teaching at the Vitebsk Academy. Malevich's students at Vitebsk formed the Suprematist group *Unovis*. From 1922 to 1927 he taught at the Institute for Artistic Culture in Petrograd and between 1924 and 1926 he worked primarily on architectural models with his students. He was active also as a theoretician and writer.

In 1927 Malevich traveled with an exhibition of his paintings to Warsaw and also went to Berlin, where his work was shown at the *Grosse Berliner Kunstausstellung*. In Germany he met Arp, Schwitters, Gabo and Le Corbusier and visited the Bauhaus where he met Walter Gropius. Because of his connections with German artists, Malevich was arrested in 1930 and many of his manuscripts were destroyed. In his final period he painted in a representational style. Malevich died in Leningrad on May 15, 1935.

106 **Morning in the Village After Snowstorm.** 1912
(*Utro posle v'yugi v derevne*)

52.1327

Oil on canvas, 31¾ x 31⅞ in. (80.7 x 80.8 cm.)

Signed l.r.: *KM*; inscribed on reverse, not by the artist: "*K. Malevitch/Le matin à la campagne d'après l'orage.*"; inscribed on reverse, possibly by the artist: "*6(—) Peizazh zimoi*" (in Cyrillic alphabet).

PROVENANCE:
the artist until 1927
Rose Fried Gallery, New York, by 1952

Morning in the Village After Snowstorm belongs with Malevich's peasant pictures of 1911-12 which show solid, compact figures tending to daily chores (for example, *In the Fields, The Reaper, Woodcutter* and *Taking in the Rye*). In the Guggenheim painting Malevich has emphasized volume through the shapes of the cylinder, sphere and cone. Even the snowdrifts have been stylized into geometric forms. The colors are predominantly white, red and blue with an almost metallic and decidedly non-naturalistic cast. The geometric and tubular forms suggest those of Léger, whose work Malevich could have known from the *Jack of Diamonds* exhibition in Moscow in February 1912 or through reproductions.

EXHIBITIONS:
Moscow, *Mishen (Target)*, Mar. 24-Apr. 7, 1913, no. 90

St. Petersburg, *Soyuz Molodezhi (Union of Youth)*, Nov. 10, 1913-Jan. 10, 1914, no. 64

Paris, Serres du Cours-la-Reine, *Société des Artistes Indépendants*, Mar. 1-Apr. 30, 1914, no. 2156

Warsaw, Hotel Polonia, *Malevich*, Mar. 8-28, 1927, traveled to Berlin, Lehter Bahnhof, *Grosser Berliner Ausstellung: Sonderausstellung Kasimir Malewitsch*, May 7-Sept. 30

New York, Rose Fried Gallery, *Group Exhibition*, Dec. 15, 1952-Jan. 1953, no. 9

London, Tate Gallery, *An exhibition of paintings from The Solomon R. Guggenheim Museum, New York*, Apr. 16-May 26, 1957, no. 44, traveled to The Hague, Gemeentemuseum, June 25-Sept. 1; Helsinki, Ateneumin Taidekokoelmat, Sept. 27-Oct. 20; Rome, Galleria Nazionale d'Arte Moderna, Dec. 5, 1957-Jan. 8, 1958; Cologne, Wallraf-Richartz-Museum, Jan. 26-Mar. 30; Paris, Musée des Arts Décoratifs, Apr. 23-June 1

New York, The Solomon R. Guggenheim Museum, *Inaugural Selection*, Oct. 21, 1959-June 19, 1960

New York, The Solomon R. Guggenheim Museum, *Kasimir Malevich*, Nov. 16, 1973-Jan. 13, 1974, no. 32, repr., traveled to Pasadena Art Museum, Feb. 4-Mar. 25

New York, The Solomon R. Guggenheim Museum, *Forty Modern Masters: An Anniversary Show,* Dec. 16, 1977-Feb. 5, 1978, no. 88, repr.

Paris, Musée National d'Art Moderne, *Malevitch,* Mar. 14-May 15, 1978, no. 16, color repr.

REFERENCES:

C. Gray, *The Great Experiment: Russian Art 1863-1922,* New York, 1962, pp. 132, 291 and pl. 92

T. Andersen, *Malevich,* Amsterdam, 1970, p. 88, no. 32, repr.

Handbook, 1970, pp. 282-283, color repr.

Rudenstine, *Collection Catalogue,* 1976, no. 170, color repr.

H. H. Arnason, *History of Modern Art,* rev. ed., New York, 1977, p. 227 and color pl. 94

Piet Mondrian 1872-1944

Piet Mondrian was born Pieter Cornelis Mondriaan, Jr. on March 7, 1872, in Amersfoort, The Netherlands. He studied at the Rijksakademie van Beeldende Kunsten, Amsterdam, from 1892 to 1897. Until 1908, when he began to take annual trips to Domburg in Zeeland, Mondrian's work was naturalistic—incorporating successive influences of academic landscape and still-life painting, Dutch Impressionism and Symbolism. In 1909 a major exhibition of his work (with that of C. R. H. Spoor and Jan Sluyters) was held at the Stedelijk Museum, Amsterdam, and that same year he joined the Theosophic Society. In 1909-10 he experimented with Pointillism and by 1911 had begun to work in a Cubist mode. After seeing original Cubist works by Braque and Picasso at the first *Moderne Kunstkring* exhibition in 1911 in Amsterdam, Mondrian decided to move to Paris. In Paris from 1912 to 1914 he began to develop an independent abstract style.

Mondrian was visiting The Netherlands when World War I broke out and prevented his return to Paris. During the war years in Holland he further reduced his colors and geometric shapes and formulated his non-objective Neo-Plastic style. In 1917 Mondrian became one of the founders of *De Stijl*. This group, which included van Doesburg and Vantongerloo, extended its principles of abstraction and simplification beyond painting and sculpture to architecture and graphic and industrial design. Mondrian's essays on abstract art were published in the periodical *De Stijl*. In July 1919 he returned to Paris; there he exhibited with *De Stijl* in 1923 but withdrew from the group after van Doesburg reintroduced diagonal elements into his work around 1925. In 1930 Mondrian showed with *Cercle et Carré (Circle and Square)* and in 1931 joined *Abstraction-Création*.

World War II forced Mondrian to move to London in 1938 and then to settle in New York in October 1940. In New York he joined the *American Abstract Artists* and continued to publish texts on Neo-Plasticism. His late style evolved significantly in response to the city. In 1942 his first one-man show took place at the Valentine Dudensing Gallery, New York. Mondrian died on February 1, 1944, in New York. In 1971 The Solomon R. Guggenheim Museum organized a centennial exhibition of his work.

107 Chrysanthemum. ca. 1908-9

61.1589

Charcoal on paper, 10 x 11¼ in. (25.5 x 28.7 cm.)

Signed l.r.: *PIET MONDRIAAN.* Not dated.

PROVENANCE:
Swetzoff Gallery, Boston, by 1961

Single flower studies such as the Guggenheim's charcoal drawing *Chrysanthemum* and watercolor *Blue Chrysanthemum* (cat. no. 112) were executed by Mondrian as early as 1901 and until the mid-1920s. Among the hundred or so flower pieces Mondrian produced, about half are chrysanthemums. Our drawing probably dates from 1908-9, when the artist produced many notable examples of this subject. Robert Welsh* suggests that the charcoal drawing may be a study for an oil painting (Seuphor, cc 130; Private Collection, Texas, formerly Collection Harry Holtzman).

Although at first glance *Chrysanthemum* seems a descriptive drawing, upon closer examination one becomes aware of a certain amount of stylization. The heavy, angular strokes, the shaded contrasts and the flower's diagonal thrust introduce a kind of expressionist vitality typical of Art Nouveau.

* correspondence with the author, Apr. 1978

EXHIBITIONS:
New York, The Solomon R. Guggenheim Museum, *Selected Sculpture and Works on Paper*, July 8-Sept. 14, 1969, p. 66, repr.

New York, The Solomon R. Guggenheim Museum, *Piet Mondrian, 1872-1944: Centennial Exhibition*, Oct. 8-Dec. 12, 1971, no. 29, repr., traveled to Kunstmuseum Bern, Feb. 9-Apr. 9, 1972

New York, The Solomon R. Guggenheim Museum, *Piet Mondrian at the Guggenheim*, Nov. 19, 1976-Apr. 7, 1977

REFERENCES:
M. Seuphor, *Piet Mondrian: His Life and Work*, New York, 1956, p. 433, no. 642

Handbook, 1970, pp. 324, repr., 325

108 Composition VII. 1913

49.1228

Oil on canvas, $41\frac{1}{8}$ x $44\frac{3}{4}$ in. (104.4 x 113.6 cm.)

Signed l.l.: *MONDRIAN*; on reverse: *Mondrian*; inscribed by the artist, later crossed out by him: *Tableau / N:2*; on stretcher: *Composition. N:VII. Mondrian. Haut.* Not dated.

PROVENANCE:

Rev. Hendricus van Assendelft, Gouda, 1914-28
Mrs. Jacoba van Assendelft-Hoos, Gouda, 1928-47
Jon Nicholas Streep, New York, 1947
Sidney Janis Gallery, New York, 1948-49

Composition VII was painted in Paris in the spring or summer of 1913. Although the ocher-gray colors recall those of Picasso's and Braque's Analytical Cubism of 1911-12, Mondrian's canvas bears no other direct resemblance to the work of the Paris Cubists.

Mondrian's point of departure, unlike that of the Analytical Cubists, was organic structural form, in this instance, trees: two studies of trees in the Gemeentemuseum, The Hague, are related to this canvas. His image is consequently more dynamic—consolidated not only by the contrasts of curves and straight lines but by the swift, uneven, angular and broken strokes—than Braque's and Picasso's basically static compositions.

Mondrian's space is conceived as a close-textured fabric of linear relationships situated on a single plane and organized according to equivalent vertical and horizontal axes. Parisian Cubist space is composed of large, irregular, angled planes which overlap and intersect one another. Furthermore, Mondrian's shading creates zones of contrasting values rather than the spatial ambiguities of the Paris Cubists.

Finally, the progressive fade-out at the borders which occurs in *Composition VII* is certainly influenced by Braque's and Picasso's use of this pictorial device. However, the latter artists employed it to focus attention on a central scaffolded figure or a definitely ovoid composition usually anchored at the bottom edge of the canvas, while Mondrian does not. Consistent with his perfectly balanced and equivalent relationships among all parts, Mondrian has created an evenly ordered, allover pattern recessed equidistantly from all sides.

EXHIBITIONS:

Amsterdam, Stedelijk Museum, *Moderne Kunstkring*, Nov. 7-Dec. 8, 1913, no. 167, repr.

The Hague, Galerie Walrecht, *Mondrian*, ca. June-July 31, 1914

Rotterdam, Rotterdamsche Kunstkring, *Alma, Le Fauconnier, Mondriaan*, Jan. 31-Feb. 28, 1915, no. 58

New York, Sidney Janis Gallery, *Mondrian*, Oct. 10-Nov. 12, 1949, no. 7

New York, The Solomon R. Guggenheim Museum, *Piet Mondrian: the earlier years*, Dec. 11, 1957-Jan. 26, 1958, traveled to San Francisco Museum of Art, Feb. 6-Apr. 14

New York, The Solomon R. Guggenheim Museum, *Inaugural Selection*, Oct. 21, 1959-June 19, 1960

The Santa Barbara Museum of Art, *Piet Mondrian*, Jan. 12-Feb. 21, 1965, no. 42, repr.

Berlin, Nationalgalerie, *Piet Mondrian*, Sept. 15-Nov. 20, 1968, no. 32

Paris, Orangerie des Tuileries, *Mondrian*, Jan. 18-Mar. 31, 1969, no. 42, repr.

New York, The Solomon R. Guggenheim Museum, *Piet Mondrian, 1872-1944: Centennial Exhibition*, Oct. 8-Dec. 12, 1971, no. 56, color repr., traveled to Kunstmuseum Bern, Feb. 9-Apr. 9, 1972

New York, Sidney Janis Gallery, *25th Anniversary Exhibition*, Oct. 2-Nov. 3, 1973, no. 85, repr.

New York, The Solomon R. Guggenheim Museum, *Piet Mondrian at the Guggenheim*, Nov. 19, 1976-Apr. 7, 1977

REFERENCES:

M. Seuphor, *Piet Mondrian: Life and Work*, New York, 1956, pp. 100, 254, repr., no. 374, cc 265

R. P. Welsh, *Piet Mondrian 1872-1944*, exh. cat., Toronto, 1966, pp. 138, 140

Handbook, 1970, pp. 328, repr., 329-330

R. P. Welsh, "The Birth of de Stijl, Part I: Piet Mondrian," *Artforum*, vol. XI, Apr. 1973, p. 50

Rudenstine, *Collection Catalogue*, 1976, no. 202, repr.

Mondrian

109 Composition No. 8. 1914

49.1227

Oil on canvas, 37⅛ x 21⅞ in. (94.4 x 55.6 cm.)

Signed and dated l.l.: *MONDRIAN. 1914*; inscribed on reverse, probably by the artist: *Compositie / 8 / P. Mondriaan.*

PROVENANCE:

Vilmos Huszár, Hierden, The Netherlands, ca. 1918-47
Jon Nicholas Streep, New York, 1947
Sidney Janis Gallery, New York, 1948-49

Composition No. 8 was probably executed in Paris before Mondrian's return to The Netherlands late in the summer of 1914. Like *Composition No. 6* (Collection Gemeentemuseum, The Hague) it derives from studies of building façades in Paris which the artist painted in late 1913 and early 1914. Since these two canvases are further removed from representational subject matter than Mondrian's earlier work, identification of a specific building as their source has not been possible.

Although the space remains unequivocally flat, organized according to a grid of black lines, the grid is larger and more uniform now, the lines are more evenly painted, and there is a noteworthy absence of diagonals. The previous year in *Composition VII* (cat. no. 108) the colors, subdued ochers and grays, appeared in undetermined zones, whereas here the warmer pink tones are more flatly applied and strictly limited to specific grid sections.

EXHIBITIONS:

The Hague, Galerie Walrecht, *Mondrian,* ca. June-July 31, 1914

Rotterdam, Rotterdamsche Kunstkring, *Alma, Le Fauconnier, Mondriaan,* Jan. 31-Feb. 28, 1915, no. 64 ?

Amsterdam, Stedelijk Museum, *Piet Mondrian,* Nov.-Dec. 1946, no. 76, traveled to Kunsthalle Basel, Feb. 6-Mar. 2, 1947

New York, Sidney Janis Gallery, *Mondrian,* Oct. 10-Nov. 12, 1949, no. 11

The Baltimore Museum of Art, *1914: An Exhibition of Paintings, Drawings and Sculpture,* Oct. 6-Nov. 15, 1964, no. 167, repr.

New York, The Solomon R. Guggenheim Museum, *Piet Mondrian, 1872-1944: Centennial Exhibition,* Oct. 8-Dec. 12, 1971, no. 60, repr., traveled to Kunstmuseum Bern, Feb. 9-Apr. 9, 1972

New York, The Solomon R. Guggenheim Museum, *Piet Mondrian at the Guggenheim,* Nov. 19, 1976-Apr. 7, 1977

New York, The Solomon R. Guggenheim Museum, *Forty Modern Masters: An Anniversary Show,* Dec. 16, 1977-Feb. 5, 1978, no. 104

REFERENCES:

M. Seuphor, *Piet Mondrian: Life and Work,* New York, 1956, pp. 259, repr., 404, no. 409, cc 274

L. J. F. Wijsenbeek, *Piet Mondrian,* New York, 1968, pl. 80

Handbook, 1970, pp. 330-331, repr.

Rudenstine, *Collection Catalogue,* 1976, no. 203, repr.

Mondrian

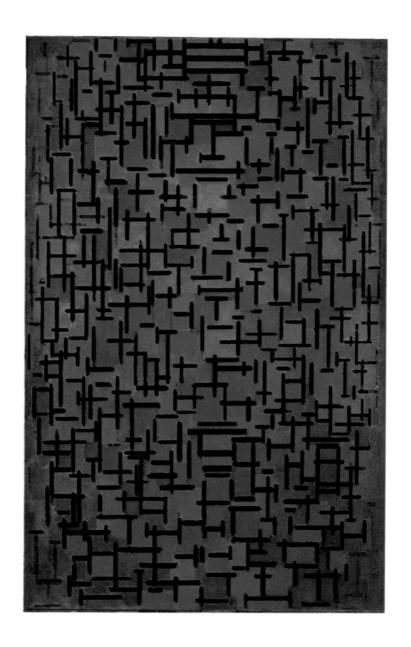

110 Composition 1916. 1916

49.1229

Oil on canvas with wood strip at bottom edge, 46⅞ x
29⅝ in. (119 x 75.1 cm.)

Signed and dated l.l.: *P. MONDRIAAN. '16.*

PROVENANCE:

Rev. Hendricus van Assendelft, Gouda, 1916-28
Mrs. Jacoba van Assendelft-Hoos, Gouda, 1928-47
Jon Nicholas Streep, New York, 1947
Sidney Janis Gallery, New York, 1948-49

During the years 1915 and 1916 Mondrian began to
abandon subjects derived from observable reality such
as trees, dunes, the sea and buildings and concentrated
on purely non-objective compositions. *Composition
1916,* which is his only known work dated 1916,
evolved from a series of charcoal sketches of the church
façade at Domburg on the coast of Dutch Zeeland. The
artist designed a strip frame (now lost) in which the
canvas was meant to be seen. His selection of an ocher,
blue and rose palette with a gray ground appears to
be a movement in the direction of the primary colors:
yellow, blue and red.

Mondrian's work of the war years in Holland is characterized by a breakdown of his familiar grid into an
empirically improvised cross and line pattern, resulting
in a punctuated yet uninterrupted flow of space. Although the black lines are limited to horizontals and
verticals, the areas of color are applied in diagonal ca-
dence. Thus, as was his avowed practice, Mondrian
provoked an opposition or duality of pictorial elements,
to be resolved through a dynamic balance or "plastic
equivalence."

EXHIBITIONS:

Amsterdam, Stedelijk Museum, *Hollandsche Kunstenaars-
kring,* Mar. 11-Apr. 2, 1916

Amsterdam, Stedelijk Museum, *Piet Mondrian,* Nov.-Dec.
1946, no. 78, traveled to Kunsthalle Basel, Feb. 6-Mar. 2,
1947

New York, Sidney Janis Gallery, *Mondrian,* Oct. 10-Nov.
12, 1949, no. 13

New York, The Solomon R. Guggenheim Museum, *Piet
Mondrian: the earlier years,* Dec. 11, 1957-Jan. 26, 1958,
traveled to San Francisco Museum of Art, Feb. 6-Apr. 14

The Santa Barbara Museum of Art, *Piet Mondrian,* Jan. 12-
Feb. 21, 1965, no. 49

The Art Gallery of Toronto, *Piet Mondrian,* Feb. 12-Mar. 20,
1966, no. 80, repr.

New York, The Solomon R. Guggenheim Museum, *Piet
Mondrian, 1872-1944: Centennial Exhibition,* Oct. 8-Dec.
12, 1971, no. 69, color repr., traveled to Kunstmuseum Bern,
Feb. 9-Apr. 9, 1972

New York, The Solomon R. Guggenheim Museum, *Piet
Mondrian at the Guggenheim,* Nov. 19, 1976-Apr. 7, 1977

New York, The Solomon R. Guggenheim Museum, *Forty
Modern Masters: An Anniversary Show,* Dec. 16, 1977-Feb.
5, 1978, no. 105, repr.

REFERENCES:

M. Seuphor, *Piet Mondrian: Life and Work,* New York,
1956, p. 260, repr., no. 424, cc 232

C. Blok, *Mondriaan in de collectie van het Haags Gemeentemuseum,* The Hague, 1964, no. 135

H. L. C. Jaffé, *Piet Mondrian,* New York, 1970, pp. 32, 118,
119, repr.

Handbook, 1970, pp. 332, repr., 333

J. M. Joosten, "Abstraction and Compositional Innovation,"
Artforum, vol. XI, Apr. 1973, pp. 51, color repr., 55

Rudenstine, *Collection Catalogue,* 1976, no. 204, color repr.

Mondrian

111 Composition 2. 1922
(Tableau 2)

51.1309

Oil on canvas, 21⅞ x 21⅛ in. (55.6 x 53.4 cm.)

Signed with monogram and dated l.r.: *PM 22*; inscribed on reverse: *Tableau 2.*

PROVENANCE:

Private collection, Germany
Galerie Springer, Berlin, 1947
Jon Nicholas Streep, New York, 1947-51

By 1921 Mondrian had reduced his palette to the three primary colors, black and gray-white. Organizing his pictures according to a grid of exclusively horizontal and vertical black lines, he structured his compositions around a dominant gray-white square or rectangle framed by black lines and he limited color to smaller marginal zones. 1922 was a year of simplification of both color and line relationships, anticipating the artist's later and generally more austere work.

The format of *Composition 2* is almost square, slightly higher than it is wide. The central area is almost square in opposite proportion, slightly wider than high. The gray background begins to occur frequently around 1921-22 and continues throughout the 1920s when Mondrian lived in Paris. He mixed small amounts of primary color pigment into the non-color zones, thus creating different kinds of chromatic relationships, based not on white but on off-white variants.

A common *De Stijl* device encountered here is the discontinuation of lines before they reach the edge of the canvas. According to the painter Vantongerloo, "the practice originated from a fear that the abstract composition would lose its organic compactness if all lines were carried through to the edge of the composition, bisecting it completely." (R. P. Welsh, *Piet Mondrian 1872-1944,* exh. cat., Toronto, 1966, p. 178) Mondrian was to abandon this pictorial principle by the late 1920s.

EXHIBITIONS:

Boston, Museum of Fine Arts, *European Masters of Our Time,* Oct. 10-Nov. 17, 1957, no. 100, repr.

The Cleveland Museum of Art, *Paths of Abstract Art,* Oct. 4-Nov. 13, 1960, no. 25, repr.

Berlin, Nationalgalerie, *Piet Mondrian,* Sept. 15-Nov. 20, 1968, no. 50, repr.

Paris, Orangerie des Tuileries, *Mondrian,* Jan. 18-Mar. 31, 1969, no. 73, repr.

New York, The Solomon R. Guggenheim Museum, *Piet Mondrian, 1872-1944: Centennial Exhibition,* Oct. 8-Dec. 12, 1971, no. 93, color repr., traveled to Kunstmuseum Bern, Feb. 9-Apr. 9, 1972

New York, The Solomon R. Guggenheim Museum, *Piet Mondrian at the Guggenheim,* Nov. 19, 1970-Apr. 7, 1977

REFERENCES:

Handbook, 1970, pp. 334, 335, color repr.

Rudenstine, *Collection Catalogue,* 1976, no. 205, repr.

K. S. Champa, "Piet Mondrian's 'Painting Number II—Composition with Grey and Black,' " *Arts Magazine,* vol. 52, Jan. 1978, p. 87, repr.

112 Blue Chrysanthemum. ca. early 1920s

frontispiece

61.1588

Watercolor and ink on paper, 10⁹⁄₁₆ x 8¹³⁄₁₆ in. (26.8 x 22.4 cm.)

Signed l.l.: *P. MONDRIAAN.* Not dated.

PROVENANCE:
Swetzoff Gallery, Boston, by 1961

Blue Chrysanthemum probably dates from the early 1920s when Mondrian produced watercolors of single flowers which were favored by Dutch collectors. Its light-blue tonality and overall luminosity indicate a later date than our charcoal drawing of a *Chrysanthemum* (cat. no. 107). Representations of live chrysanthemums such as ours far outnumber dying ones. Around 1908 to 1910 Mondrian also depicted sunflowers, amaryllis and tiger lilies.

Mondrian has isolated a single flower and presented it frontally in a schematic composition so that its parts are distributed along vertical and horizontal axes. According to Robert Welsh,* it was Mondrian's practice in the watercolors and oils to copy (either free-hand or by tracing) a drawing and to add the blue and white colors and ink outlines. With its cool, unified coloration, *Blue Chrysanthemum* is a harmonious synthesis of the form of the flower as a universal species, or, as Mondrian called it, "the universal manifestation of life."

* correspondence with the author, Apr. 1978

EXHIBITIONS:
New York, The Solomon R. Guggenheim Museum, *Selected Sculpture and Works on Paper,* July 8-Sept. 14, 1969, p. 67, color repr.

New York, The Solomon R. Guggenheim Museum, *Piet Mondrian, 1872-1944: Centennial Exhibition,* Oct. 8-Dec. 12, 1971, no. 83, repr., traveled to Kunstmuseum Bern, Feb. 9-Apr. 9, 1972

New York, The Solomon R. Guggenheim Museum, *Piet Mondrian at the Guggenheim,* Nov. 19, 1976-Apr. 7, 1977

New York, The Solomon R. Guggenheim Museum, *Forty Modern Masters: An Anniversary Show,* Dec. 16, 1977-Feb. 5, 1978, no. 106

REFERENCES:
M. Seuphor, *Piet Mondrian: Life and Work,* New York, 1956, p. 433, no. 642

Handbook, 1970, pp. 326-327, color repr.

113 Composition. 1929

53.1347

Oil on canvas, 17¾ x 17⅞ in. (45.1 x 45.3 cm.)

Signed and dated l.r.: *PM 29*; inscribed on stretcher: *Haut / Composition / P. Mondrian.*

PROVENANCE:
Katherine S. Dreier, West Redding, Connecticut
Gift, Estate of Katherine S. Dreier, 1953

The large, enclosed square gray zone was prevalent in Mondrian's paintings from the 1920s and the perfectly square canvas was his favorite format from 1928 to 1932. With the dominant red rectangle in the upper left corner, which echoes the larger gray square, Mondrian resolves the problem of introducing diagonal elements into paintings of purely horizontal and vertical components. While Mondrian still uses marginal rectangles of color, found earlier in *Composition 2* (cat. no. 111), they are beginning to assume a different function. Instead of emphasizing a rectangular grid pattern, they form a diagonal axis, creating an equilibrium of unequal color areas within the canvas.

EXHIBITIONS:
London, Tate Gallery, *An exhibition of paintings from The Solomon R. Guggenheim Museum, New York,* Apr. 16-May 26, 1957, no. 55, traveled to The Hague, Gemeentemuseum, June 25-Sept. 1; Helsinki, Ateneumin Taidekokoelmat, Sept. 27-Oct. 20; Rome, Galleria Nazionale d'Arte Moderna, Dec. 5, 1957-Jan. 8, 1958; Cologne, Wallraf-Richartz-Museum, Jan. 26-Mar. 30; Paris, Musée des Arts Décoratifs, Apr. 23-June 1

Cincinnati, The Taft Museum, *Color: Light to Palette,* Oct. 22-Dec. 6, 1965, no. 55

New York, The Solomon R. Guggenheim Museum, *Piet Mondrian, 1872-1944: Centennial Exhibition,* Oct. 8-Dec. 12, 1971, no. 105, repr., traveled to Kunstmuseum Bern, Feb. 9-Apr. 9, 1972

New York, The Solomon R. Guggenheim Museum, *Piet Mondrian at the Guggenheim,* Nov. 19, 1976-Apr. 7, 1977

REFERENCES:
Handbook, 1970, pp. 336, repr., 337

Rudenstine, *Collection Catalogue,* 1976, no. 206, repr.

K. S. Champa, "Piet Mondrian's 'Painting Number II—Composition with Grey and Black,' " *Arts Magazine,* vol. 52, Jan. 1978, p. 88, repr.

114 Composition I A. 1930

71.1936 R96

Oil on canvas (lozenge), 29⅝ x 29⅝ in. (75.2 x 75.2 cm.)

Signed and dated at center of l.l. edge (on black bar): *PM 30*; inscribed on stretcher: *P. Mondrian accrocher / losangiquement Nº I.*

PROVENANCE:

from the artist
Hilla Rebay, New York and Greens Farms, Connecticut, 1930-67
Estate of Hilla Rebay, 1967-71

Around 1930 to 1933 Mondrian eliminated color in many of his compositions, so that the white plane of the canvas is crossed by a few black lines. These are works of utmost simplicity in which the placement and varying thickness of lines determines the painting's harmony and rhythm.

The lozenge shape of *Composition 1 A* results from rotating a square forty-five degrees. The earliest example of the format dates from 1918, and the majority of these diamond-shaped canvases were painted in 1925-26. The integrity of the rectilinear design survives even when superimposed on and truncated by the contrasting shape of the lozenge. The inherent unity of the square transcends the limits of the canvas and completes itself outside the picture plane. This extension into surrounding space is seen to an even greater degree in *Composition with Yellow Lines,* 1933 (Collection Gemeentemuseum Museum, The Hague), where none of the lines intersect within the canvas.

EXHIBITIONS:

Amsterdam, Stedelijk Museum, *Piet Mondrian,* Nov.-Dec. 1946, no. 107, traveled to Kunsthalle Basel, Feb. 6-Mar. 2, 1947

New York, Sidney Janis Gallery, *Piet Mondrian,* Oct. 10-Nov. 12, 1949, no. 22

New York, The Solomon R. Guggenheim Museum, *Piet Mondrian, 1872-1944: Centennial Exhibition,* Oct. 8-Dec. 12, 1971, no. 111, repr., traveled to Kunstmuseum Bern, Feb. 9-Apr. 9, 1972

New York, The Solomon R. Guggenheim Museum, *Piet Mondrian at the Guggenheim,* Nov. 19, 1976-Apr. 7, 1977

New York, The Solomon R. Guggenheim Museum, *Forty Modern Masters: An Anniversary Show,* Dec. 16, 1977-Feb. 5, 1978, no. 107

REFERENCES:

M. Seuphor, *Piet Mondrian: Life and Work,* New York, 1956, no. 523, cc 408

Rudenstine, *Collection Catalogue,* 1976, no. 207, repr.

Theo van Doesburg 1883-1931

Christian Emil Marie Küpper, who adopted the pseudonym Theo van Doesburg, was born in Utrecht, The Netherlands, on August 30, 1883. His first exhibition of paintings was held in 1908 in The Hague. In the early teens he wrote poetry and established himself as an art critic. From 1914 to 1916 van Doesburg served in the Dutch army, after which time he settled in Leiden and began his collaboration with the architects J.J.P. Oud and Jan Wils. In 1917 they founded the group *De Stijl* and the periodical of the same name; other original members were Mondrian, Vantongerloo, Bart Van der Leck and Vilmos Huszár. Van Doesburg executed decorations for Oud's *De Vonk* project in Noordwijkerhout in 1917.

In 1920 he resumed his writing, using the pen names I. K. Bonset and later Aldo Camini. Van Doesburg visited Berlin and Weimar in 1921 and the following year taught at the Weimar Bauhaus; here he associated with Mies van der Rohe, Le Corbusier, Raoul Hausmann and Hans Richter. He was interested in Dada at this time and worked with Schwitters as well as Arp, Tristan Tzara and others on the review *Mécano* in 1922. Exhibitions of the architectural designs of van Doesburg, Cor van Eesteren and Gerrit Rietveld were held in Paris in 1923 at Léonce Rosenberg's Galerie l'Effort Moderne and in 1924 at the Ecole Spéciale d'Architecture.

The Landesmuseum of Weimar presented a one-man show of van Doesburg's work in 1924. That same year he lectured on modern literature in Prague, Vienna and Hannover, and the Bauhaus published his *Grundbegriffe der neuen gestaltenden Kunst (Principles of Neo-Plastic Art)*. A new phase of *De Stijl* was declared by van Doesburg in his manifesto of Elementarism, published in 1926. During that year he collaborated with Arp and Sophie Taeuber-Arp on the decoration of the restaurant-cabaret L'Aubette in Strasbourg. Van Doesburg returned to Paris in 1929 and began working on a house at Meudon-Val-Fleury with van Eesteren. Also in that year he published the first issue of *Art Concret,* the organ of the Paris-based group of the same name. Van Doesburg was the moving force behind the formation of the group *Abstraction-Création* in Paris. The artist died on March 7, 1931, in Davos, Switzerland.

115 **Composition XI. 1918**

54.1360

Oil on canvas mounted in artist's painted frame, sight, 22⅜ x 39⅞ in. (56.9 x 101.3 cm.)

Signed and dated with monogram l.r.: *1918 VD*; on reverse: *1918 VD*.

PROVENANCE:

Gift of the artist
Evert Rinsema, Drachten, The Netherlands, ca. 1919-47
Jan Meijer, Amsterdam, 1947-53
Mrs. Theo van Doesburg, Meudon, 1953-54

When the painters of the *De Stijl* movement formed a group in the spring of 1917, the similar conclusions each had come to over a period of individual investigation reinforced their unity and, by 1918, they arrived at a reduction of form and color to a pure, elemental level. Van Doesburg's paintings of this time demonstate a synthesis of Mondrian's and Bart Van der Leck's work. As Mondrian had often done, van Doesburg designed a painted frame in which this picture is meant to be seen.

Composition XI is one of van Doesburg's abstract geometric compositions of rectangular color planes floating on the surface of the canvas. Color is limited to subdued red, yellow and blue on an off-white ground: a variation on his more common palette of primaries on white. While a representational origin can be found for most of these abstract works, none has come to light for the Guggenheim picture. In his exploration of the relationship between line, plane and color, van Doesburg has arranged the planes over the background to achieve balance through an intuitive rather than systematic method of placement.

EXHIBITIONS:

Amsterdam, Stedelijk Museum, *De Stijl,* July 6-Sept. 25, 1951
Venice, XXVI Biennale Internazionale d'Arte, *De Stijl,* June 14-Oct. 19, 1952, no. 26
New York, The Museum of Modern Art, *De Stijl: 1917-1928,* Dec. 16, 1952-Feb. 15, 1953
Eindhoven, Stedelijk van Abbemuseum, *Theo van Doesburg,* Dec. 13, 1968-Jan. 26, 1969, no. A17, repr., traveled to The Hague, Gemeentemuseum, Feb. 7-Mar. 24; Kunsthalle Nürnberg, Apr. 16-May 15; Kunsthalle Basel, Aug. 9-Sept. 7
New York, The Solomon R. Guggenheim Museum, *Forty Modern Masters: An Anniversary Show,* Dec. 16, 1977-Feb. 5, 1978, no. 26, repr.

REFERENCES:

H. L. C. Jaffé, *De Stijl, 1917-1931: the Dutch contribution to modern art,* Amsterdam, 1956, p. 48, pl. 13

Handbook, 1970, pp. 98-99, repr.

Rudenstine, *Collection Catalogue,* 1976, no. 41, repr.

Friedrich Vordemberge-Gildewart
1899-1962

Friedrich Vordemberge-Gildewart was born on November 17, 1899, in Osnabrück, Germany. At age twenty he began his studies in architecture and sculpture at the Kunstgewerbeschule and the Technischen Hochschule in Hannover. In 1924 he founded the *K* group with Hans Nitzschke and became a member of *De Stijl* in Leiden and *Der Sturm* in Berlin. That same year Vordemberge-Gildewart met Arp and van Doesburg in Hannover. In 1925 he moved to Paris where he participated in the exhibition *L'Art d'aujourd'hui*. With Schwitters, Nitzschke and Carl Buchheister the artist formed the avant-garde *abstrakten hannover* group in 1927.

Vordemberge-Gildewart's first one-man show was held at the Galerie Povolozky in Paris in 1929. At this time he executed a ceramic project for the refurbished city hospital of Osnabrück. In 1930 he associated with the group *Cercle et Carré (Circle and Square)* which Michel Seuphor organized in Paris. The artist joined the *Abstraction-Création* group in Paris in 1932. In 1937 Vordemberge-Gildewart traveled to Switzerland and in 1938 settled in Amsterdam, eventually becoming a Dutch citizen. His volume of poetry, *millimeter und geraden,* appeared in 1940 and in 1942 he founded Editions Duwaer in Amsterdam, which also published books by Arp and Kandinsky.

In 1949 the first monograph on Vordemberge-Gildewart was published, and he participated in the exhibition *Premiers maîtres de l'art abstrait* at the Galerie Maeght in Paris. He designed window displays for the De Bijenkorf department stores in Amsterdam, The Hague and Rotterdam in 1950. In 1952 Vordemberge-Gildewart taught at the Academie van beeldende Kunsten in Rotterdam. The following year he was awarded Second Prize at the São Paulo Bienal. He became head of the department of Visual Communication at the Hochschule für Gestaltung in Ulm, Germany, in 1954. Vordemberge-Gildewart died on December 19, 1962, in Ulm.

116 **Composition No. 97.** 1935

37.411

Oil on canvas, 31½ x 39⅜ in. (79.9 x 100.1 cm.)

Signed and dated on stretcher: *VORDEMBERGE-GILDEWART / K.N⁰ 97 / 1935.*

PROVENANCE:
from the artist
Rudolf Bauer for The Solomon R. Guggenheim Foundation, 1937
Gift, Solomon R. Guggenheim, 1937

Vordemberge-Gildewart variously combined similar compositional elements in his paintings from 1934 to 1940, where he was investigating the attainment of equilibrium among components of unequal size and pictorial weight. In the Guggenheim painting two isosceles right triangles, one black and one white, occupy the left half of the canvas. The oblique line at the right is parallel to the hypotenuses of the triangles. The thickly painted yellow horizontal bar and the red vertical bar at the lower right serve to define and limit the picture space. Thus, the smaller elements in the composition seem to contain and uplift the heavier ones. Preparatory drawings for the canvas show how the artist experimented with alternative arrangements of the triangles. Three years after completing *Composition 97,* he painted a closely related work, *Composition No. 108* (Collection Israel Museum, Jerusalem).

EXHIBITIONS:
Charleston, S. C., Gibbes Memorial Art Gallery, *Solomon R. Guggenheim Collection of Non-Objective Paintings,* Mar. 12-Apr. 17, 1938, no. 190

New York, Museum of Non-Objective Painting, *European Painters: Otto Nebel, Friedrich Vordemberge-Gildewart, Lotte Konnerth, Hannes Beckmann,* Jan. 18-Feb. 20, 1949, no. 2

London, Tate Gallery, *An exhibition of paintings from The Solomon R. Guggenheim Museum, New York,* Apr. 16-May 26, 1957, no. 75, traveled to The Hague, Gemeentemuseum, June 25-Sept. 1; Helsinki, Ateneumin Taidekokoelmat, Sept. 27-Oct. 20; Rome, Galleria Nazionale d'Arte Moderna, Dec. 5, 1957-Jan. 8, 1958; Cologne, Wallraf-Richartz-Museum, Jan. 26-Mar. 30; Paris, Musée des Arts Décoratifs, Apr. 23-June 1

New York, La Boetie, Inc., *Vordemberge-Gildewart: Paintings, Drawings, Collages,* Sept. 14-Oct. 31, 1971

Dallas Museum of Fine Arts, *Geometric Abstraction: 1926-1942,* Oct. 7-Nov. 19, 1972, no. 57, repr.

REFERENCES:

Circle: International Survey of Constructive Art, J. L. Martin, B. Nicholson, N. Gabo, eds., London, 1937, fig. 13, repr.

M. Bill, "Über Konkrete Kunst," *Das Werk,* Jg. 29, Heft 8, Aug. 1938, p. 250, repr.

Handbook, 1959, p. 176, repr.

H. L. C. Jaffé, *Vordemberge-Gildewart: Mensch und Werk,* Cologne, 1971, Oeuvrekatalog no. 101, repr.

Rudenstine, *Collection Catalogue,* 1976, no. 247, repr.

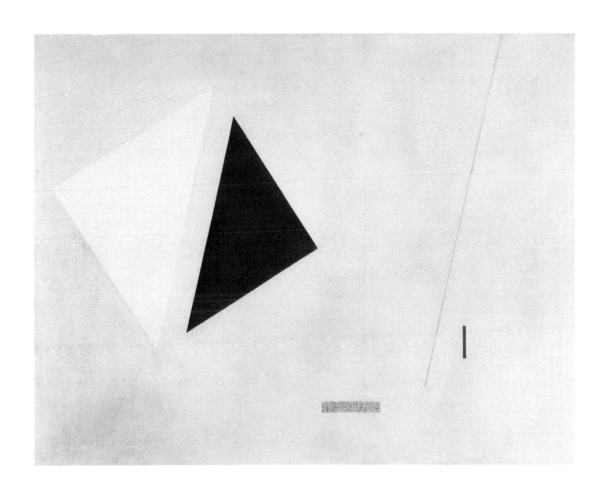

Georges Vantongerloo 1886-1965

Georges Vantongerloo was born on November 24, 1886, in Antwerp. He studied around 1900 at the Académie des Beaux-Arts of Antwerp and of Brussels. He spent the years 1914 to 1918 in The Netherlands, where his work attracted the attention of the Queen. While working on architectural designs there, he met Mondrian, Bart Van der Leck and van Doesburg and collaborated with them on the magazine *De Stijl*, which was founded in 1917. Soon after his return to Brussels in 1918 he moved to Menton, France. In France he developed a close friendship with the artist and architect Max Bill, who was to organize many Vantongerloo exhibitions. In 1924 Vantongerloo published his pamphlet "L'Art et son avenir" in Antwerp.

In 1928 the artist-architect-theorist moved from Menton to Paris; there, in 1931, he became vice-president of the artists' association *Abstraction-Création,* a position he held until 1937. His models of bridges and a proposed airport were exhibited at the Musée des Arts Décoratifs in Paris in 1930. In 1936 he participated in the exhibition *Cubism and Abstract Art* at The Museum of Modern Art in New York. His first one-man show was held at the Galerie de Berri in Paris in 1943. He shared an exhibition with Bill and Pevsner in 1949 at the Kunsthaus Zürich. His seventy-fifth birthday was observed with a solo exhibition at the Galerie Suzanne Bollag in Zürich in 1961. The following year Bill organized a large Vantongerloo retrospective for the Marlborough New London Gallery in London. Shortly after Vantongerloo's death on October 5, 1965, in Paris, the Museo Nacional de Bellas Artes in Buenos Aires held a memorial exhibition of his work.

117 **Composition Green-Blue-Violet-Black.** 1937
(*Composition vert-bleu-violet-noir*)

Vantongerloo Oeuvre Catalogue: *No. 105, Composition vert bleu violet noir. Paris, 1937.*

51.1301

Oil (triplex) on plywood, 25¼ x 39¾ in. (64.2 x 101 cm.)

Signed and dated on reverse: *COMPOSITION / VERT-....-BLEU-VIOLET-....-NOIRE / G. VANTONGERLOO / PARIS 1937 / Nº 105.*

PROVENANCE:

from the artist, 1951

Like other paintings by Vantongerloo, *Composition Green-Blue-Violet-Black* is directly based on the geometric theory of conic sections and the quadratic equations which describe them.* The proportions of the four large white rectangular areas and the central black rectangle are derived from solutions to the quadratic formula $y = -ax^2 + bx + 18$. If the five rectangles were to be arranged, from widest to narrowest, in the shape of a pyramid, a parabolic arc connecting the lower corners of each rectangle would exhibit the equation $y = -x^2 + 7x + 18$ (which results from substituting the constants 1 and 7 for a and b in the formula given above). This equation occurs in Vantongerloo's study for a sculpture.** In the Guggenheim painting the artist has arranged the five rectangles of decreasing width in a counterclockwise spiral beginning at the lower right and ending at the center. This spiral progression is, in turn, a variation of the Golden Section.

 * information supplied by Peter H. Barnett, Jan. 1979

** Rudenstine, p. 665, repr.

EXHIBITIONS:

Kunsthaus Zürich, *Antoine Pevsner, Georges Vantongerloo, Max Bill,* Oct. 15-Nov. 13, 1949, no. 38

Dallas Museum of Fine Arts, *Geometric Abstraction: 1926-1942,* Oct. 7-Nov. 19, 1972, no. 52, repr.

REFERENCES:

Handbook, 1959, p. 171, repr.

Rudenstine, *Collection Catalogue,* 1976, no. 238, repr.

Naum Gabo 1890-1977

Naum Neemia Pevsner was born on August 5, 1890, in Briansk, Russia. From 1910 to 1911 he studied medicine, science and art history at the University in Munich. In 1913 and 1914 he visited Paris, where he saw the work of Gleizes, Jean Metzinger, Léger and Robert Delaunay. During World War I he lived in Oslo with his brother Antoine Pevsner. He executed his first construction in 1915 and signed it "Gabo."

In 1917 Gabo settled in Moscow; there he associated with Vladimir Tatlin, Malevich and Alexander Rodchenko. He and Pevsner published their *Realistic Manifesto* in 1920. In 1922 they participated in the *Erste Russische Kunstausstellung* at the Galerie van Diemen in Berlin. Gabo lived in Berlin for the next decade. The exhibition *Constructivistes russes: Gabo et Pevsner* was held at the Galerie Percier in Paris in 1924. Gabo was given his first one-man show in 1930 at the Kestner-Gesellschaft in Hannover. In 1932 the artist left Germany for Paris, where he became a leading member of the *Abstraction-Création* group. He moved to England in 1936 and the following year collaborated with Nicholson and the architect Leslie Martin on the periodical *Circle: International Survey of Constructivist Art*.

Gabo visited the United States for the first time in 1938, when his sculpture was shown at the Wadsworth Atheneum in Hartford, the Julien Levy Gallery in New York and Vassar College in Poughkeepsie. In 1944 in London he worked with Herbert Read in the Design Research Unit, which promoted cooperation between artists and industry. Gabo moved to the United States in 1946 and two years later shared an exhibition with Pevsner at The Museum of Modern Art in New York. In 1952 he became a United States citizen and from 1953 to 1954 taught at the Harvard University Graduate School of Architecture. During the mid-1950s the artist worked on commissions for the De Bijenkorf building in Rotterdam and for the United States Rubber Company at Rockefeller Center in New York. A retrospective of his work was shown in Amsterdam, Mannheim, Duisburg, Zürich, Stockholm and London in 1965-66, and an important Gabo exhibition toured Europe from 1970 to 1972. In 1973 he received a sculpture commission from the Nationalgalerie of Berlin. The Tate Gallery in London presented a major exhibition of his work in 1976. Gabo died on August 23, 1977, in Middlebury, Connecticut.

118 **Column.** ca. 1923. Reconstructed in 1937

55.1429

Perspex, wood, metal and glass, 41½ x 29 x 29 in. (105.3 x 73.6 x 73.6 cm.)

Not signed or dated.

PROVENANCE:

from the artist, 1949
Addison Gallery of American Art, Phillips Academy, Andover, Massachusetts, 1949-52
Exchanged with the artist
from the artist, 1955

Gabo considered *Column* a work "of great importance not only to my own development, but it can be historically proved that it is a cornerstone in the whole development of contemporary architecture." (letter to Bartlett H. Hayes, Jr., Director, Addison Gallery of American Art, Mar. 13, 1949) He emphasized that the *Column* was the culmination of his "search for an image which would fuse the sculptural element with the architectural element into one unit." (Read and Martin, opp. pl. 26) The vertical elements are rectangular constructions within parabolas which are determined by the dimensions of the bases.

There are several versions of the column: a five inch celluloid model (Collection Tate Gallery, London), three versions approximately eleven inches high (Collections Yale University Art Gallery, New Haven; Sir Leslie Martin and Estate of the artist) and a monumental *Column* over six feet high that was executed in 1975 (Collections Louisiana Museum, Humlebaek, Denmark, and Estate of the artist). It is very difficult to place these sculptures in sequence.

Gabo reconstructed the Guggenheim *Column* in 1937 after it had arrived damaged at The Museum of Modern Art in New York early in 1936.* Since the artist only began to work in perspex in 1936, the perspex parts must date from the time of this reconstruction. He also slightly altered the vertical supports at the rear and the tipped circle at the front of the *Column*: this is evident when photographs published in 1933 and 1936 are compared with reproductions of 1939. Otherwise, the earlier state of the piece appears virtually identical with the Guggenheim's sculpture.

* Museum of Modern Art Photo S-1333 and Registrar's files, loan number 36.53. Confirmed by Miriam Gabo in correspondence with the author, Aug. 1979

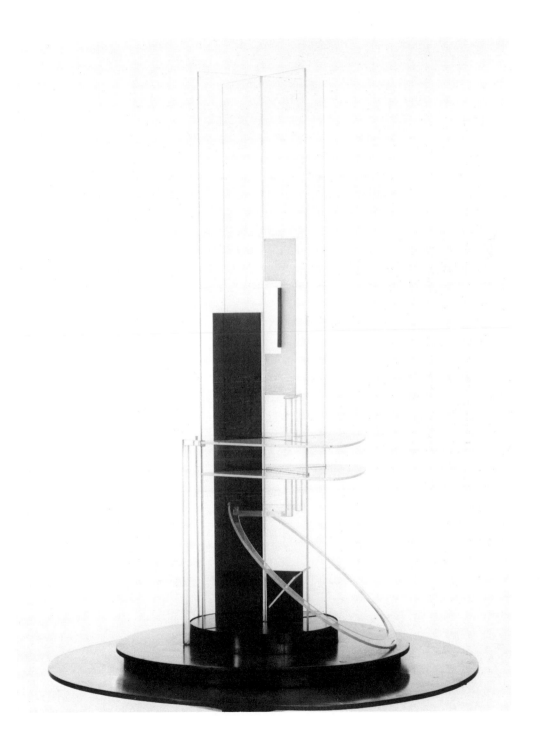

EXHIBITIONS:

Hartford, Wadsworth Atheneum, *Gabo: Constructions in Space,* Mar. 22-30, 1938, no. 1, repr., traveled to New York, Julien Levy Gallery, Apr.; Poughkeepsie, N. Y., Vassar College Art Gallery, May

Extended loan to The Museum of Modern Art, New York, Aug. 23, 1938-May 7, 1948

New York, The Museum of Modern Art, *Art in Our Time,* May 10-Sept. 30, 1939, no. 314, repr.

New York, The Museum of Modern Art, *Art in Progress,* May 24-Oct. 15, 1944, p. 140, repr.

New York, The Museum of Modern Art, *Naum Gabo-Antoine Pevsner,* Feb. 10-Apr. 25, 1948, pp. 26, repr., 47

Andover, Mass., Addison Gallery of American Art, Phillips Academy, *Material and the Immaterial,* winter 1949-50

The Arts Club of Chicago, *Naum Gabo and Josef Albers,* Jan. 29- Feb. 28, 1952

New York, The Museum of Modern Art, *Sculpture of the XX Century,* Apr. 28-Sept. 7, 1953, p. 151, repr.

New York, The Solomon R. Guggenheim Museum, *Selected Sculpture and Works on Paper,* July 8-Sept. 14, 1969, pp. 120-121, color repr.

New York, The Solomon R. Guggenheim Museum, *Forty Modern Masters: An Anniversary Show,* Dec. 16, 1977-Feb. 5, 1978, no. 37, repr.

New York, The Solomon R. Guggenheim Museum, *The Planar Dimension: Europe, 1912-1932,* Mar. 9-May 6, 1979, no. 101, color repr.

REFERENCES:

abstraction-création, no. 2, 1933, p. 16, repr.

N. Gabo, "Constructive Art," *The Listener,* vol. XVI, Nov. 4, 1936, p. 847, repr.

A. H. Barr, Jr., *Cubism and Abstract Art,* exh. cat., New York, 1936, no. 72, repr.

M. Seuphor, *L'Art abstrait: ses origines, ses premiers maîtres,* Paris, 1949, p. 58, repr.

H. Read and L. Martin, *Gabo: Constructions, Sculpture, Paintings, Drawings, Engravings,* Cambridge, Mass., 1957, p. 183 and pl. 26

J. Ernst, "Constructivism and Content," *Studio International,* vol. 171, Apr. 1966, p. 150, repr.

Handbook, 1970, pp. 124-125, color repr.

H. H. Arnason, *History of Modern Art,* rev. ed., New York, 1977, pp. 323-324, fig. 505

R. E. Krauss, *Passages in Modern Sculpture,* New York, 1977, pp. 60-61 and fig. 46

119 Linear Construction No. 1. 1942-43

47.1101

Plexiglass and nylon monofilament, 18 x 18 in.
(45.6 x 45.6 cm.)

Not signed or dated.

PROVENANCE:

from the artist, 1947

Gabo executed many versions of *Linear Construction No. 1* in varying dimensions: examples are in The Hirshhorn Museum and Sculpture Garden, Washington, D.C., and the Estate of the artist. There are also numerous variants characterized by winged or stepped-back sides but otherwise resembling the Guggenheim piece.

Gabo's distinctive use of materials and his preference for plastic and plexiglass are immediately apparent here as in the *Column* (cat. no. 118). The transparency of *Linear Construction No. 1* denies mass and simultaneously defines and makes visible the sculpture's

inner space. The central void both emphasizes the openness of the composition and permits its interaction with surrounding space. George Rickey has observed that Gabo's technique of stretching a series of strings over an open, rigid form created "a *virtual* surface through which the interior space and structure could be clearly seen." ("Naum Gabo 1890-1977," *Artforum*, vol. XVI, Nov. 1977, p. 26)

EXHIBITIONS:

New York, The Solomon R. Guggenheim Museum, *Selected Sculpture and Works on Paper*, July 8-Sept. 14, 1969, p. 122, repr.

New York, The Solomon R. Guggenheim Museum, *Forty Modern Masters: An Anniversary Show*, Dec. 16, 1977-Feb. 5, 1978, no. 39

REFERENCES:

H. Read and L. Martin, *Gabo: Constructions, Sculpture, Paintings, Drawings, Engravings*, Cambridge, Mass., 1957, p. 184, pl. 76

Handbook, 1959, p. 203, repr.

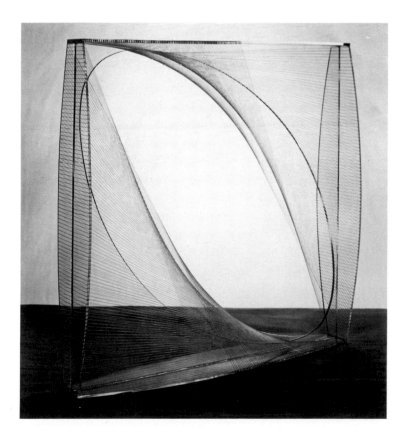

Antoine Pevsner 1884-1962

Antoine Pevsner was born on January 18, 1884, in Orel, Russia. After leaving the Academy of Fine Arts in St. Petersburg in 1911, he traveled to Paris where he saw the work of Robert Delaunay, Gleizes, Jean Metzinger and Léger. On a second visit to Paris in 1913 he met Modigliani and Archipenko who encouraged his interest in Cubism. Pevsner spent the war years 1915 to 1917 in Oslo with his brother Naum Gabo. On his return to Russia in 1917 Pevsner began teaching at the Moscow Academy of Fine Arts with Kandinsky and Malevich.

In 1920 he and Gabo published the *Realistic Manifesto*. Their work was included in the *Erste Russische Kunstausstellung* at the Galerie van Diemen in Berlin in 1922, held under the auspices of the Russian government. The following year Pevsner visited Berlin, where he met Duchamp and Katherine S. Dreier. He then traveled on to Paris; he settled permanently in this city and in 1930 became a French citizen. His work was included in an exhibition at the Little Review Gallery in New York in 1926. He and Gabo designed sets for the ballet *La Chatte,* produced by Sergei Diaghilev in 1927. The two brothers were leaders of the Constructivist members of *Abstraction-Création,* the artists' alliance in Paris whose adherents embraced a variety of abstract styles.

During the 1930s Pevsner's work was shown in Amsterdam, Basel, London, New York and Chicago. In 1946 he, Gleizes, Herbin and others formed the group *Réalités Nouvelles*; their first exhibition was held at the Salon des Réalités Nouvelles in Paris in 1947. That same year Pevsner's first one-man show opened at the Galerie René Drouin in Paris. The Museum of Modern Art in New York presented a *Gabo-Pevsner* exhibition in 1948, and in 1952 Pevsner participated in *Chefs-d'oeuvre du XXᵉ siècle* at the Musée National d'Art Moderne in Paris. The same museum organized a one-man exhibition of his work in 1957. In 1958 he was represented in the French Pavilion at the Venice Biennale. Pevsner died in Paris on April 12, 1962.

120 **Twinned Column.** 1947
(Colonne jumelée)

54.1397

Bronze, 40½ in. (102.9 cm.) high

Signed and dated on front l.l.: *AP47*; inscribed on reverse: *A/P/A.*

PROVENANCE:
from the artist, 1954

Like his brother Gabo, Pevsner experimented with the possibilities of new materials and techniques in his sculpture. In addition to working in plastics, he created many constructions from bronze, brass and tin. Frequently he incorporated more than one substance in a single sculpture to provide color, surface texture and patterning of light and shadow. In *Twinned Column* bronze rods are joined together to form linear configurations reminiscent of the nylon filaments Gabo used. Both *Twinned Column* and *Developable Column of Victory* from the previous year are free-standing sculptures with strong central axes and silhouettes which change when seen from different points of view. The bold symmetry of the compositions and the contrast between solid and void are characteristic of Pevsner's work.

EXHIBITIONS:
Kunsthaus Zürich, *Antoine Pevsner, Georges Vantongerloo, Max Bill,* Oct. 15-Nov. 13, 1949, no. 25

Paris, Musée National d'Art Moderne, *Antoine Pevsner,* Dec. 21, 1956-Mar. 10, 1957, no. 45, repr.

New York, The Solomon R. Guggenheim Museum, *Inaugural Selection,* Oct. 21, 1959-Apr. 4, 1960

The Cleveland Museum of Art, *Paths of Abstract Art,* Oct. 4-Nov. 13, 1960, no. 108, repr.

Tulsa, Okla., Philbrook Art Center, *Twentieth Century Sculpture,* Oct. 1-23, 1962, no. 43

New York, The Solomon R. Guggenheim Museum, *Selected Sculpture and Works on Paper,* July 8-Sept. 14, 1969, p. 149, repr.

New York, The Solomon R. Guggenheim Museum, *Forty Modern Masters: An Anniversary Show,* Dec. 16, 1977-Feb. 5, 1978, no. 109, repr.

REFERENCES:
C. Giedion-Welcker, *Contemporary Sculpture: An Evolution in Volume and Space,* New York, 1955, p. 203, repr.

R. Massat, *Antoine Pevsner et le constructivisme,* Paris, 1956, n.p., repr.

P. Peissi and C. Giedion-Welcker, *Antoine Pevsner,* Neuchâtel, 1961, p. 151, pl. 104

Handbook, 1970, pp. 356-357, repr.

László Moholy-Nagy 1895-1946

László Moholy-Nagy was born on July 20, 1895, in Bacsbarsod, Hungary. In 1913 he began law studies at the University of Budapest but interrupted them the following year to serve in the Austro-Hungarian army. While recovering from a wound in 1917, he founded the artists' group *MA* (today) with Ludwig Kassak and others in Szeged, Hungary, and started a literary magazine called *Jelenkor* (the present). After receiving his law degree, Moholy-Nagy moved to Vienna in 1919, where he collaborated on the *MA* periodical *Horizont*. He traveled to Berlin in 1920 and began making "photograms" and Dada collages.

During the early 1920s Moholy-Nagy contributed to several important art periodicals and co-edited with Kassak *Das Buch neuer Künstler,* a volume of poetry and essays on art. In 1921 he met El Lissitzky in Germany and traveled to Paris for the first time. His first one-man exhibition was organized by Herwarth Walden at Der Sturm in Berlin in 1922. During this period Moholy-Nagy was a seminal figure in the development of Constructivism. While teaching at the Bauhaus in Weimar in 1923, he became involved in stage and book design and with Walter Gropius edited and designed the Bauhausbücher series published by the school. In 1926 he began to experiment with unconventional materials such as aluminum and bakelite. Moholy-Nagy moved with the Bauhaus to Dessau in 1925 and taught there until 1928, when he returned to Berlin to concentrate on stage design and film.

In 1930 he participated in the *Internationale Werkbund Ausstellung* in Paris. The artist moved to Amsterdam in 1934, the year of a major retrospective of his work at the Stedelijk Museum there. In 1935 Moholy-Nagy fled from the growing Nazi threat to London; there he worked as a designer for various companies and on films and associated with Gabo, Barbara Hepworth and Moore. In 1937 he was appointed director of the New Bauhaus in Chicago, which failed after less than a year because of financial problems. Moholy-Nagy established his own School of Design in Chicago in 1938 and in 1940 gave his first summer classes in rural Illinois. He joined the *American Abstract Artists* group in 1941 and in 1944 became a United States citizen. His book *Vision in Motion* was published in 1947, after his death on November 24, 1946, in Chicago.

121 **A II.** 1924

43.900

Oil on canvas, 45⅝ x 53⅝ in. (115.8 x 136.5 cm.)

Signed and dated on reverse: *MOHOLY-NAGY / A*^{II} *(1924) / Moholy = Nagy.*

PROVENANCE:

from the artist, 1943

By 1922 Moholy-Nagy had eliminated all references to representational subject matter. He sought to redefine painting in terms of modern technology. *A II* and *Axl II* (cat. no. 122) are both related to Moholy's coeval experiments in camera-less photography ("photograms"), painting on transparent supports and projection of color transparencies on screens ("painting-with-light"). In *A II* the repetition of the red disc and overlapping parallelograms suggests the light projection of a design on two screens. Likewise, *Axl II* shows two sources of light projected at right angles which form a complex design at the point of intersection. The Constructivist idiom of both pictures reflects Moholy's knowledge of El Lissitzky's and Malevich's work.

EXHIBITIONS:

Dresden, *Internationale Kunstausstellung,* June-Sept. 1926, no. 420

London, London Gallery, *L. Moholy-Nagy,* Dec. 31, 1936-Jan. 27, 1937, no. 19, repr.

New York, The Museum of Modern Art, *Bauhaus 1919-1928,* Dec. 7, 1938-Jan. 30, 1939

New York, Museum of Non-Objective Painting, *In Memoriam Laszlo Moholy-Nagy,* May 15-July 10, 1947, no. 33, repr.

Paris, Palais des Beaux Arts de la Ville de Paris, *Troisième salon internationale des réalités nouvelles,* July 23-Aug. 29, 1948, not in cat.

London, Tate Gallery, *An exhibition of paintings from The Solomon R. Guggenheim Museum, New York,* Apr. 16-May 26, 1957, no. 54, traveled to The Hague, Gemeentemuseum, June 25-Sept. 1; Helsinki, Ateneumin Taidekokoelmat, Sept. 27-Oct. 20; Rome, Galleria Nazionale d'Arte Moderna, Dec. 5, 1957-Jan. 8, 1958; Cologne, Wallraf-Richartz-Museum, Jan. 26- Mar. 30; Paris, Musée des Arts Décoratifs, Apr. 23-June 1

New York, The Solomon R. Guggenheim Museum, *Inaugural Selection,* Oct. 21, 1959-June 19, 1960

The Cleveland Museum of Art, *Paths of Abstract Art,* Oct. 4-Nov. 13, 1960, no. 33, repr.

Chicago, Museum of Contemporary Art, *Laszlo Moholy-Nagy,* May 31-July 12, 1969, not in cat., traveled to Santa Barbara Museum of Art, Aug. 2-Sept. 21; Berkeley, Univer-

sity Art Museum, University of California, Oct. 2-Nov. 2;
Seattle Art Museum, Nov. 20, 1969-Jan. 4, 1970; New York,
The Solomon R. Guggenheim Museum, Feb. 20-Apr. 19

REFERENCES:

S. Giedion, "Notes on the Life and Work of Moholy-Nagy,"
Architects Yearbook, vol. 3, 1949, p. 34, repr.

Handbook, 1970, pp. 320-321, color repr.

Rudenstine, *Collection Catalogue,* 1976, no. 190, repr.

Moholy-Nagy

122 **Axl II.** 1927

64.1754

Oil on canvas, 37 x 29⅛ in. (94.1 x 73.9 cm.)

Signed and dated on reverse: *AXL II / MOHOLY- / NAGY / 1927.*

PROVENANCE:
Sibyl Moholy-Nagy, 1946-60
Galerie Chalette, New York, 1960-61
Mr. and Mrs. Andrew P. Fuller, New York, 1961-64
Gift, Mrs. Andrew P. Fuller, 1964

EXHIBITIONS:

Kunsthaus Zürich, *Abstrakte und Surrealistische Malerei und Plastik,* Oct. 6-Nov. 3, 1929, no. 90

New York, Museum of Non-Objective Painting, *In Memoriam Laszlo Moholy-Nagy,* May 15-July 10, 1947, no. 47

Chicago, Museum of Contemporary Art, *Laszlo Moholy-Nagy,* May 31-July 12, 1969, no. 25, repr., traveled to Santa Barbara Museum of Art, Aug. 2-Sept. 21; Berkeley, University Art Museum, University of California, Oct. 2-Nov. 2; Seattle Art Museum, Nov. 20, 1969-Jan. 4, 1970; New York, The Solomon R. Guggenheim Museum, Feb. 20-Apr. 19

Venice, XXXV Biennale Internazionale d'Arte, *Proposta per una esposizione sperimentale,* June 24-Oct. 25, 1970, no. 26

Dallas, Museum of Fine Arts, *Berlin/Hanover: The 1920s,* Jan. 26-Mar. 13, 1977, no. 31, repr.

REFERENCES:

R. Kostelanetz, *Moholy-Nagy,* New York, 1970, no. 6, repr.

Rudenstine, *Collection Catalogue,* 1976, no. 192, repr.

123 **Dual Form with Chromium Rods.** 1946

48.1149

Plexiglass and chrome-plated steel rods, 36½ x
47⅞ x 22 in. (92.7 x 121.6 x 55.9 cm.)

Not signed or dated.

PROVENANCE:

Estate of the artist, 1948

As early as 1935 Moholy-Nagy created three-
dimensional paintings with transparent plastics. These
"light modulators" evolved into three-dimensional
sculpture about 1941. In *Dual Form with Chromium
Rods*, which dates from the last year of his life, Moholy
has drawn bent chrome rods through the perforations
in a central core of plexiglass. The fish-like shape of
the plexiglass elements occurs frequently in his sculpture of the 1940s. With the free-form lines of chrome
on each side of the plexiglass, the artist achieves an
equilibrium. He has emphasized the light-reflective
properties of materials as well as their capacity to cast
ambiguous patterns of shadow.

This free-standing piece has been exhibited in both
horizontal and vertical positions.

EXHIBITIONS:

New York, Museum of Non-Objective Painting, *In Memoriam Laszlo Moholy-Nagy,* May 15-July 10, 1947, no. 136,
p. 20, repr.

The Art Institute of Chicago, *L. Moholy-Nagy,* Sept. 18-Oct.
26, 1947, no. 19, repr.

Montreal, Expo 67, *International Exhibition of Contemporary Sculpture,* Apr. 28-Oct. 27, 1967, p. 99, repr.

Chicago, Museum of Contemporary Art, *Laszlo Moholy-
Nagy,* May 31-July 12, 1969, no. 123, repr., traveled to Santa
Barbara Museum of Art, Aug. 2-Sept. 21; Berkeley, Univer-
sity Art Museum, University of California, Oct. 2-Nov. 2;
Seattle Art Museum, Nov. 20, 1969-Jan. 4, 1970; New York,
The Solomon R. Guggenheim Museum, Feb. 20-Apr. 19

Venice, XXXV Biennale Internazionale d'Arte, *Proposta
per una esposizione sperimentale,* June 24-Oct. 25, 1970,
no. 34

Washington, D. C., Hirshhorn Museum and Sculpture Garden, Smithsonian Institution, *The Golden Door: Artist-
Immigrants of America, 1876-1976,* May 20-Oct. 20, 1976,
no. 142, repr.

Rochester, Memorial Art Gallery, University of Rochester,
Photographs and Paintings by László Moholy-Nagy, Oct. 21-
Nov. 26, 1978

Buffalo, Albright-Knox Art Gallery, *Modern European
Sculpture 1918-1945: Unknown Beings and Other Realities,*
May 11-June 24, 1979, no. 45, repr., traveled to Minneapolis Institute of Art, July 22-Sept. 2; San Francisco Museum
of Modern Art, Oct. 5-Nov. 18

REFERENCES:

M. Breuning, "Moholy-Nagy Given Memorial Exhibition,"
Art Digest, vol. 21, June 1947, p. 13, repr.

R. Kostelanetz, *Moholy-Nagy,* New York, 1970, p. 55, repr.

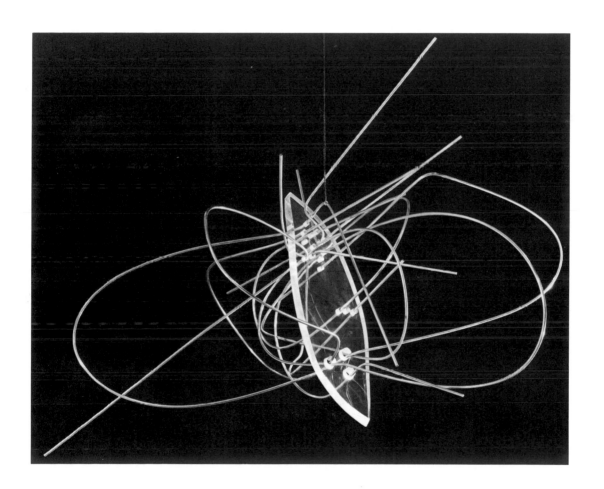

V

Kurt Schwitters 1887-1948

Herman Edward Karl Julius Schwitters was born in Hannover on June 20, 1887. He attended the Kunstgewerbeschule in Hannover from 1908 to 1909 and from 1909 to 1914 studied at the Kunstakademie Dresden. After serving as a draftsman in the military in 1917, Schwitters experimented with Cubist and Expressionist styles. In 1918 he made his first collages and in 1919 invented the term *"Merz,"* which he was to apply to all his creative activities: poetry as well as collage and constructions. This year also marked the beginning of his friendship with Arp and Raoul Hausmann. Schwitters' earliest *Merzbilder* date from 1919, the year of his first exhibition at the gallery of Der Sturm, Berlin, and the first publication of his writings in the periodical *Der Sturm.* Schwitters showed at the Société Anonyme in New York in 1920.

With Arp he attended the *Kongress der Konstructivisten* in Weimar in 1922. There Schwitters met van Doesburg, whose *De Stijl* principles influenced his work. Schwitters' Dada activities included his *Merz-Matineen* and *Merz-Abende* at which he presented his poetry. From 1923 to 1932 he published the magazine *Merz.* Around 1923 the artist started to make his first *Merzbau,* a fantastic structure he built over a number of years; the *Merzbau* grew to occupy much of his Hannover studio. During this period he also worked in typography. Schwitters was included in the *Abstrakte und surrealistische Malerei und Plastik* exhibition at the Kunsthaus Zürich in 1929. The artist contributed to the Parisian review *Cercle et Carré* in 1930; in 1932 he joined the Paris-based *Abstraction-Création* group and wrote for their organ of the same name. He participated in the *Cubism and Abstract Art* and *Fantastic Art, Dada, Surrealism* exhibitions of 1936 at The Museum of Modern Art, New York.

The Nazi regime banned Schwitters' work as *Entartete Kunst* (degenerate art) in 1937. This year the artist fled to Lysaker, Norway, where he constructed a second *Merzbau.* After the German invasion of Norway in 1940, Schwitters escaped to England, where he was interned for over a year. He settled in London following his release, but moved to Little Langdale in the Lake District in 1945. There, helped by a stipend from The Museum of Modern Art, he began work on a third *Merzbau* in 1947. The project was left unfinished when Schwitters died on January 8, 1948, in Kendal, England.

124 Mountain Graveyard. 1919
(Hochgebirgsfriedhof)

62.1617

Oil on board mounted on cork, 36 x 28½ in.
(91.6 x 72.4 cm.)

Signed and dated l.l.: *KS / 19.*

PROVENANCE:

Herwarth Walden, Berlin, by 1921
Frederick M. Stern, Berlin and New York, 1921-62
Gift, Frederick M. Stern, 1962

Mountain Graveyard belongs to the Expressionist
moment in Kurt Schwitters' career which paralleled his
early experiments with abstract collages. Although it
is reminiscent of paintings derived from nature, it anticipates abstractions by such artists as Kandinsky,
Jawlensky and Marc (see cat. no. 72). Schwitters'

images—here mountains, graveyard, church—occurred
also in his poetry. While the picture is not known to
have specific symbolic connotations, it evokes a somber
mood. Schwitters chose to portray the light of sunset
with an intensity of colors and richness of brushwork.

EXHIBITIONS:

Berlin, Der Sturm, *85. Ausstellung: Kurt Schwitters,* 1920,
no. 25

Städtische Kunsthalle Düsseldorf, *Kurt Schwitters,* Jan. 15-
Mar. 3, 1971, no. 8, color repr., traveled to Berlin, Akademie
der Künste, Mar. 12-Apr. 18; Staatsgalerie Stuttgart, May
14-July 18; Kunsthalle Basel, July 31-Sept. 5

REFERENCES:

W. Schmalenbach, *Kurt Schwitters,* Cologne, 1967, pp. 19,
color repr., 80

Rudenstine, *Collection Catalogue,* 1976, no. 224, repr

Schwitters

125 **Merzbild 5 B (Picture-Red-Heart-Church)**
April 26, 1919

(Merzbild 5 B [Bild-Rot-Herz-Kirche])

52.1325

Collage, tempera and crayon on cardboard, 32⅞ x 23¾ in. (83.5 x 60.2 cm.)

Signed and dated l.l.: *KS / 1919*; inscribed on reverse: *(Bild rot Herz-Kirche) / Kt. Schwitters / 26.IV.1919 / Merzbild 5B.*

PROVENANCE:
Hildegarde Prytek, New York, by 1952

In 1919 Schwitters invented the word *"Merz"* to distinguish the collages and assemblages he had been making since the previous year from other types of modern art. He related that he "could not see the reason why old tickets, driftwood, cloak-room tabs, wires and wheel parts, buttons and old rubbish found in the attic and in refuse dumps should not be a material for painting just as good as the colours made in factories. This was, as it were, a social attitude and, artistically speaking, a private hobby, but particularly the last . . . I called my new works that employed any such materials 'MERZ'. This is the second syllable of 'Kommerz.' It arose in the MERZ Picture, a work which showed, underneath abstract shapes, the word MERZ, cut from an advertisement of KOMMERZ-UND PRIVATBANK and pasted on. This word MERZ had itself become part of the picture by adjustment to the other parts, and so it had to be there." (W. Schmalenbach, "Kurt Schwitters," *Art International,* vol. IV, Sept. 1960, p. 58)

In *Merzbild 5B* Schwitters cut several pieces of newspaper and pasted them down, covered them with circular and triangular painted areas, added smaller pieces of paper and a canceled postage stamp and drew three images: a heart, a church and the number 69. The pictorial organization is determined by the arrangement of the printed matter and by the emphatic diagonal and curvilinear elements. Through an additive method of composition involving inventively utilized found objects, Schwitters produced hundreds of works which he called *Merz.*

EXHIBITIONS:
The Art Gallery of Toronto, *A Loan Exhibition from The Solomon R. Guggenheim Museum, New York,* Apr. 2-May 9, 1954, no. 67.

New York, The Solomon R. Guggenheim Museum, *Inaugural Selection,* Oct. 21, 1959-June 19, 1960

New York, Galerie Chalette, *Kurt Schwitters,* Oct. 5-Nov. 30, 1963, no. 10

Städtische Kunsthalle Düsseldorf, *Kurt Schwitters,* Jan. 15-Mar. 3, 1971, no. 23, traveled to Berlin, Akademie der Künste, Mar. 12-Apr. 18; Staatsgalerie Stuttgart, May 14-July 18; Kunsthalle Basel, July 31-Sept. 5

Berlin, Akademie der Künste, *Tendenzen der Zwanziger Jahre,* Aug. 14-Oct. 16, 1977, no. 3-4/3, traveled to Frankfurt, Städelsches Kunstinstitut, Nov. 10, 1977-Jan. 8, 1978

REFERENCES:
W. Schmalenbach, *Kurt Schwitters,* Cologne, 1967, p. 118 and pl. 17

Handbook, 1970, pp. 392-393, repr.

W. S. Lieberman, "Trends of the Twenties," *Art News,* vol. 76, Oct. 1977, p. 41, color repr.

Max Ernst 1891-1976

Max Ernst was born on April 2, 1891, in Brühl, Germany. He enrolled in the University at Bonn in 1909 to study philosophy but soon abandoned this pursuit to concentrate on art. At this time he was interested in psychology and the art of the mentally ill. In 1911 Ernst became friends with August Macke and joined the *Rheinische Expressionisten* group in Bonn. Ernst showed for the first time in 1912 at the Galerie Feldman in Cologne. At the *Sonderbund* exhibition of that year in Cologne he saw the work of van Gogh, Cézanne, Munch and Picasso. In 1913 he met Guillaume Apollinaire and Robert Delaunay and traveled to Paris. Ernst participated that same year in the *Erster Deutscher Herbstsalon*. In 1914 he met Arp, who was to become a lifelong friend.

Despite military service throughout World War I, Ernst was able to continue painting and to exhibit in Berlin at Der Sturm in 1916. He returned to Cologne in 1918. The next year he produced his first collages and founded the short-lived Cologne Dada movement with Johannes Theodor Baargeld; they were joined by Arp and others. In 1921 Ernst exhibited for the first time in Paris, at the Galerie Au Sans Pareil. He was involved in Surrealist activities in the early twenties with Paul Eluard and André Breton. In 1925 Ernst executed his first frottages; a series of frottages was published in his book *Histoire Naturelle* in 1926. He collaborated with Miró on designs for Sergei Diaghilev this same year. The first of his collage-novels, *La Femme 100 têtes,* was published in 1929. The following year the artist collaborated with Dali and Luis Buñuel on the film *L'Age d'or.*

His first American show was held at the Julien Levy Gallery, New York, in 1932. In 1936 Ernst was represented in *Fantastic Art, Dada, Surrealism* at The Museum of Modern Art in New York. In 1939 he was interned in France as an enemy alien. Ernst was able to flee in 1941 to the United States, where he lived until 1953. That year he resettled in France. He received the Grand Prize for Painting at the Venice Biennale in 1954. The artist was honored with numerous major retrospectives in the postwar years, the most recent of which took place at The Solomon R. Guggenheim Museum in 1975. Ernst died on April 1, 1976, in Paris.

126 Landscape. ca. 1914-16 (?)
(Stadt mit Tieren)

48.1172 x280

Oil on burlap, 26¼ x 24½ in. (66.6 x 62.3 cm.)

Signed l.l.: *Max ERNST.* Not dated.

PROVENANCE:
Karl Nierendorf, New York, by 1948
Estate of Karl Nierendorf, 1948

Max Ernst painted this *Landscape* early in his career. It already foreshadows the non-realistic fantasy world of his Surrealist work. At the same time, the verticality of the composition and the manner of representing houses recall Medieval and early Renaissance paintings. The strange, large-eyed animals bring to mind a Nativity scene or suggest the animals depicted by Marc, Chagall and Heinrich Campendonk.

EXHIBITIONS:
New York, The Solomon R. Guggenheim Museum, *Max Ernst: A Retrospective,* Feb. 14-Apr. 20, 1975, no. 17, repr., traveled to Paris, Grand Palais, May 15-Sept. 8

New York, The Solomon R. Guggenheim Museum, *Forty Modern Masters: An Anniversary Show,* Dec. 16, 1977-Feb. 5, 1978, no. 33

Munich, Haus der Kunst, *Max Ernst,* Feb. 17-Apr. 29, 1979, no. 20, repr., traveled to Berlin, Nationalgalerie, May 10-July 15

REFERENCES:
L. R. Lippard, "Dada into Surrealism: Notes of Max Ernst as Proto-Surrealist," *Artforum,* vol. V, Sept. 1966, pp. 13-14, repr.

W. Spies, *Max Ernst-Collagen: Inventar und Widerspruch,* Cologne, 1974, p. 31

W. Spies, *Max Ernst: Werke 1906-1925,* Cologne, 1975, no. 290, repr.

Rudenstine, *Collection Catalogue,* 1976, no. 42, repr.

127 An Anxious Friend. Summer 1944
(Un Ami empressé)

59.1521

Bronze, 26⅜ in. (67 cm.) high

Signed and dated on left side of base: *1944 max ernst.*

Fifth of nine casts made in 1957 from original plaster of 1944 by Modern Art Foundry, Long Island

PROVENANCE:

from the artist
Alexandre Iolas Gallery, New York, 1957
Gift, Dominique and John de Menil, 1959

During the summer of 1944, when he lived in Great River, Long Island, Max Ernst turned his attention to sculpture, a medium in which he had not worked for a decade. He was influenced by the Surrealist sculpture familiar to him in Europe in the 1930s—most notably, the work of his friend Giacometti. Like Giacometti's *Spoon Woman* (cat. no. 135), Ernst's *An Anxious Friend* exhibits the artist's knowledge of primitive art, possesses an emphatic frontality and is amusingly endowed with female attributes. Ernst employed found objects in making the plaster: he decorated the front with drill bits and fashioned the figure's round mouth and eyes from a set of aluminum measuring spoons.*

Although he worked episodically in this medium, Ernst's sculpture is not central to his oeuvre. Consistent with his paintings and drawings, *An Anxious Friend* commands an insistent presence and provokes the imagination.

* correspondence with Julien Levy, Jan. 1979

EXHIBITIONS:

New York, Alexandre Iolas Gallery, *Max Ernst,* Apr.-May 1957
New York, The Solomon R. Guggenheim Museum, *Inaugural Selection,* Oct. 21, 1959-June 19, 1960
Tulsa, Okla., Philbrook Art Center, *Twentieth Century Sculpture,* Oct. 1-23, 1962, no. 21, repr.
New York, The Solomon R. Guggenheim Museum, *Selected Sculpture and Works on Paper,* July 8-Sept. 14, 1969, p. 118, repr.
New York, The Solomon R. Guggenheim Museum, *Forty Modern Masters: An Anniversary Show,* Dec. 16, 1977-Feb. 5, 1978, no. 34, repr.

REFERENCES:

M. Ernst, *Beyond Painting,* New York, 1948, p. 89, repr. (plaster)
J. Russell, *Max Ernst: Life and Work,* New York, 1967, fig. 130
Handbook, 1970, p. 109, repr.
J. Levy, *Memoir of an Art Gallery,* New York, 1976, pp. 271, 273

Jean Arp 1886-1966

Jean (Hans) Arp was born on September 16, 1886, in Strasbourg, Alsace-Lorraine. In 1904, after leaving the Ecole des Arts et Métiers in Strasbourg, he visited Paris and published his poetry for the first time. From 1905 to 1907 Arp studied at the Kunstschule of Weimar and in 1908 went to Paris, where he attended the Académie Julian. In 1909 he moved to Switzerland and, in 1911, was a founder of the *Moderner Bund* group there. The following year he met Robert and Sonia Delaunay in Paris and Kandinsky in Munich. Arp participated in the *Erster Deutscher Herbstsalon* in 1913 at the gallery of Der Sturm in Berlin. After returning to Paris in 1914, he became acquainted with Max Jacob, Picasso and Guillaume Apollinaire. In 1915 he moved to Zürich where he executed collages and tapestries, often in collaboration with his future wife Sophie Taeuber.

In 1916 Hugo Ball opened the Cabaret Voltaire, which was to become the center of Dada activities in Zürich for a group including Arp, Tristan Tzara, Marcel Janco and others. Arp continued his involvement with Dada after moving to Cologne in 1919, contributing to Ernst's periodical *Die Schammade* and creating with him and Johannes Theodor Baargeld their collaborative collages or *Fatagagas*. In 1922 he participated in the *Kongress der Konstructivisten* in Weimar. Soon thereafter he began contributing to magazines such as *Merz, Mécano, De Stijl* and, in 1925, *La Révolution Surréaliste*. Arp's work appeared in the first exhibition of the Surrealist group at the Galerie Pierre in Paris in 1925. With Taeuber and van Doesburg he undertook a commission to decorate the cabaret L'Aubette in Strasbourg in 1926. This same year he settled in Meudon, France.

In 1931 Arp associated with the Paris-based group *Abstraction-Création* and the periodical *Transition*. Throughout the 1930s and until the end of his life he continued to write and publish poetry and essays. In 1942 he fled Meudon for Zürich; he was to make Meudon his primary residence again in 1946. The artist visited New York in 1949 on the occasion of his one-man show at Curt Valentin's Buchholz Gallery. In 1950 he was invited to execute a relief for the Harvard Graduate Center in Cambridge, Massachusetts. In 1954 Arp received the International Prize for Sculpture at the Venice Biennale. He was commissioned to design reliefs for the Ciudad Universitaria in Caracas in 1955. In 1960 he traveled to the Middle East. A large retrospective of his work was held at The Museum of Modern Art in New York in 1958, followed by another at the Musée National d'Art Moderne in Paris in 1962. Arp died on June 7, 1966, in Basel.

128 Constellation with Five White Forms and Two Black, Variation III. 1932
(Constellation aux cinq formes blancs et deux noirs, Variation III)

55.1437

Oil on wood, 23⅝ x 29⅝ in. (60 x 75.3 cm.)

Not signed or dated.

PROVENANCE:

from the artist
Sidney Janis Gallery, New York, by 1955

Arp first made a painted wood relief in 1914; he designed an abstract relief two years later. The wit, vitality and bright contrasting color of his Surrealist work have been replaced here by formal purity, restraint and precision of natural forms. Reduction of color to white and black emphasizes the flat wood shapes superimposed on the wood background.

Arp's three *Constellations*, of which the Guggenheim's is the third variation, contain identical elements in different positions. The two black forms placed at the left here were positioned at the top center in *Variation I* (Collection Munson-Williams-Proctor Institute, Ithaca, New York) and shifted to the right in *Variation II* (Private Collection). Each *Constellation* is a cluster of disparate objects which form a system yet are held apart from one another by the interaction of natural forces.

EXHIBITIONS:

New York, The Solomon R. Guggenheim Museum, *Inaugural Selection*, Oct. 21, 1959-June 19, 1960

The Cleveland Museum of Art, *Paths of Abstract Art*, Oct. 4-Nov. 13, 1960, no. 118, repr.

New York, The Solomon R. Guggenheim Museum, *Jean Arp (1886-1966): A Retrospective Exhibition*, May 16-June 29, 1969

New York, The Solomon R. Guggenheim Museum, *Selected Sculpture and Works on Paper*, July 8-Sept. 14, 1969, p. 94, repr.

New York, The Solomon R. Guggenheim Museum, *Forty Modern Masters: An Anniversary Show*, Dec. 16, 1977-Feb. 5, 1978, no. 3

New York, The Solomon R. Guggenheim Museum, *The Planar Dimension: Europe, 1912-1932*, Mar. 9-May 6, 1979, not in cat.

REFERENCES:

H. Read, *A Concise History of Modern Painting*, New York, 1959, pl. 93

Handbook, 1970, pp. 24-25, repr.

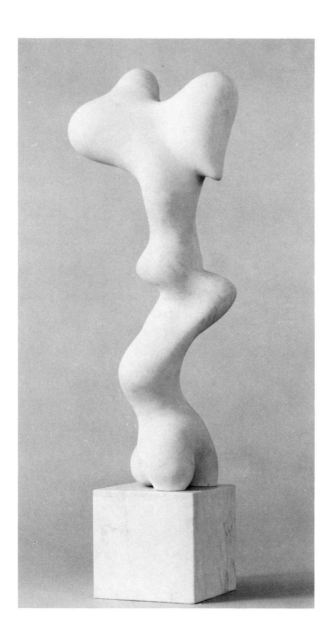

129 Growth. 1938
(Croissance)

53.1359

Marble, 31⅝ in. (80.3 cm.) high

Not signed or dated.

PROVENANCE:
Peter Watson, London, by 1952-53

Perhaps more than any other of the artist's modes of expression, the free forms of Arp's sculpture-in-the-round illustrate one of his basic beliefs: "art is a fruit growing out of man like the fruit out of a plant like the child out of the mother." ("Notes from a Diary," *Transition,* no. 21, Mar. 1932, p. 191) Arp's devotion to abstraction did not derive from formalist ideals; on the contrary, his commitment was to an art which was spontaneous, sensual and irrational, like birth or growth or any other natural process.

His first free-standing sculpture, executed in 1931, was a rhythmically deformed human torso in marble. *Growth* of 1938, with its rhythmic curves, writhing movement and upward thrust, could be considered a later development of the same theme. More exactly, it might be defined as the concrete configuration of an organic entity which is neither vegetal nor animal in origin.

There exist several other versions of *Growth* dated 1938: a slightly larger marble (Collection Sidney Janis, New York) and three bronze casts, one of which is in the Philadelphia Museum of Art.

EXHIBITIONS:
Paris, Musée National d'Art Moderne, *L'Oeuvre du XXᵉ siècle,* May-June 1952, no. 116, traveled to London, Tate Gallery, July 15- Aug. 17

New York, The Solomon R. Guggenheim Museum, *Jean Arp (1886-1966): A Retrospective Exhibition,* May 16-June 29, 1969

New York, The Solomon R. Guggenheim Museum, *Selected Sculpture and Works on Paper,* July 8-Sept. 14, 1969, p. 95, repr.

New York, The Solomon R. Guggenheim Museum, *Forty Modern Masters: An Anniversary Show,* Dec. 16, 1977-Feb. 5, 1978, no. 4, repr.

REFERENCES:
J. Arp, *On My Way: Poetry and Essays, 1912-1947,* New York, 1948, pl. 15b

C. Giedion-Welcker, *Jean Arp,* New York, 1957, p. 109, no. 49

H. Read, *The Art of Jean Arp,* New York, 1968, pp. 94-95, repr.

Handbook, 1970, pp. 26, repr., 27

R. E. Krauss, *Passages in Modern Sculpture,* New York, 1977, p. 141, repr.

Joan Miró 1893-1983

Joan Miró Ferra was born in Barcelona, on April 20, 1893. At the age of fourteen he went to business school in Barcelona and also attended La Lonja, the academy of fine arts in the same city. Upon completing three years of art studies he took a position as a clerk. After suffering a nervous breakdown he abandoned business and resumed his art studies from 1912 to 1915 at Francisc Gali's Escola d'Art in Barcelona. Miró received early encouragement from the dealer José Dalmau, who gave him a small one-man show at his gallery in Barcelona in 1918. In 1917 he met Picabia.

In 1919 Miró made his first trip to Paris, where he met Picasso. From 1920 Miró divided his time between Paris and Montroig. In Paris he associated with the poets Pierre Reverdy, Tristan Tzara and Max Jacob and participated in Dada activities. Dalmau organized Miró's first one-man show in Paris, at the Galerie La Licorne in 1921. His work was included in the Salon d'Automne of 1923. In 1924 Miró joined the Surrealist group. His one-man show at the Galerie Pierre in Paris in 1925 was a major Surrealist event; Miró was included in the first Surrealist exhibition at the Galerie Pierre that same year. He visited The Netherlands in 1928 and began a series of paintings inspired by Dutch Masters. This year he also executed his first *papiers collés* (pasted papers) and collages. In 1929 he started his experiments in lithography, and his first etchings date from 1933. During the early 1930s he made Surrealist sculpture-objects incorporating painted stones and found objects. In 1936 Miró left Spain because of the Civil War; he returned in 1941.

An important Miró retrospective was held at The Museum of Modern Art in New York in 1941. This year Miró began working in ceramics with Lloréns Artigas and started to concentrate on prints: from 1954 to 1958 he worked almost exclusively in these two mediums. In 1959 Miró resumed painting, initiating a series of mural-sized canvases. During the sixties he began to work intensively in sculpture. A major Miró retrospective took place at the Grand Palais in Paris in 1974. Miró died in Palma de Mallorca, Spain, on December 25, 1983.

130 **Prades, the Village.** Summer 1917
(Prades, el poble)

69.1894

Oil on canvas, 25 ⅝ x 28 ⅝ in. (65 x 72.6 cm.)

Signed l.l.: *Miró.* Not dated.

PROVENANCE:

from the artist
Galeries Dalmau, Barcelona, 1918
Pedro Mañach, Barcelona, 1918
Mme Mañach, Barcelona, 1940s-51
Pierre Matisse Gallery, New York, 1951-69
Albert Loeb & Krugier Gallery and
Robert Elkon Gallery, New York, 1969

Miró painted this view of Prades, a village near his family's country home at Montroig in Spain, during the summer of 1917. The restrained yet accurate rendering of the church and adjacent buildings contrasts sharply with the vivid Fauve colors in the foreground. According to the artist* the horizontal bands at the left represent a field plowed and ready for planting, while the wavy lines are string-bean plants climbing up stakes. The stylized patterns and abstract rhythms convey an energy that could not be expressed through naturalistic rendering of forms. It was the earth that captured Miró's imagination in *Prades, the Village*. His attachment to his native Catalan soil will be communicated in many other paintings and elaborated upon in Surrealist works like *The Tilled Field* (cat. no. 131).

* conversation with Margit Rowell, May 1974

EXHIBITIONS:

Barcelona, Galeries Dalmau, *Exposición Joan Miró,* Feb. 16-Mar. 3, 1918, no. 58

New York, Pierre Matisse Gallery, *The Early Paintings of Joan Miró,* Nov. 20-Dec. 15, 1950, no. 6, repr.

New York, The Museum of Modern Art, *Joan Miró,* Mar. 18-May 10, 1959, no. 4, traveled to Los Angeles County Museum of Art, June 10-July 21

Paris, Musée National d'Art Moderne, *Joan Miró,* June 28-Nov. 4, 1962, no. 4

Tokyo, National Museum of Western Art, *Joan Miró,* Aug. 26-Oct. 9, 1966, no. 12, repr., traveled to Kyoto National Museum of Modern Art, Oct. 20-Nov. 30

New York, Robert Elkon Gallery, *New Acquisitions,* Sept. 27-Oct. 29, 1969, no. 16, repr.

New York, Acquavella Galleries, Inc., *Joan Miró,* Oct. 18-Nov. 18, 1972, no. 4, repr.

Berlin, Nationalgalerie, *Tendenzen der Zwanziger Jahre,*
Aug. 14-Oct. 16, 1977, no. 4-120, repr.

New York, The Solomon R. Guggenheim Museum, *Forty
Modern Masters: An Anniversary Show,* Dec. 16, 1977-Feb.
5, 1978, no. 95

REFERENCES:

J. Dupin, *Joan Miró: Life and Work,* New York, 1962, pp.
66, 68, 73, 504, no. 38, repr.

J. Perucho, *Joan Miró and Catalonia,* New York, 1967,
pl. 19

Handbook, 1970, pp. 298-299, repr.

Rudenstine, *Collection Catalogue,* 1976, no. 183, color repr.

131 **The Tilled Field.** 1923-24
(*La Terre labourée*)

72.2020

Oil on canvas, 26 x 36½ in. (66 x 92.7 cm.)

Signed and dated l.l.: *Miró / 1923-24*; inscribed on reverse: *Joan Miró / "La Terre Labourée" / 1923-24.*

PROVENANCE:
from the artist
Jacques Viot, Paris, by 1925
Galerie Pierre, Paris, 1925
André Breton, Paris
René Gaffé, Brussels, by 1928-37
Valerie Cooper, London, by 1938
Pierre Matisse Gallery, New York, 1940-41
Mr. and Mrs. Henry Clifford, Radnor, Pennsylvania, 1941-72
Harold Diamond, New York, 1972

The Tilled Field, which was begun in Spain during the summer of 1923 and completed in Paris the following winter, marks the emergence of Miró's mature style. The new flatness of the spatial implications, the structural division into three horizontal areas and the new richness of imagery demonstrate significant developments in his style since *Prades, the Village* of 1917 (cat. no. 130) or *The Farm* of 1921-22 (Collection Mrs. Ernest Hemingway). While the theme of plowed fields continues in Miró's painting, the subject has become visionary: a vision of a supernatural world, a realm of dream and imagination. The appearance of biomorphism with the isolated eye and ear, the juxtaposition of a folded newspaper and a lizard wearing a conic cap, the stylization of the fig tree at the left and the pine tree at the right where the cone is covered with eyes are examples of Surrealist devices. Miró drew upon Catalan Medieval art as well as contemporary Surrealist works to create his "own unified poetic vision."*

* M. Rowell and R. E. Krauss, *Joan Miró: Magnetic Fields*, exh. cat., New York, 1972-73, no. 1

EXHIBITIONS:
Paris, Galerie Pierre, *Exposition Joan Miró*, June 12-27, 1925, no. 9
London, New Burlington Galleries, *The International Surrealist Exhibition*, June 11-July 4, 1936, no. 215
New York, Pierre Matisse Gallery, *Joan Miró*, Mar. 12-31, 1940, no. 12, repr.
New York, The Museum of Modern Art, *Joan Miró*, Nov. 18, 1941-Jan. 11, 1942, pp. 22, 26, 27, repr.
New York, The Museum of Modern Art, *Joan Miró*, Mar. 18-May 10, 1959, no. 21, traveled to Los Angeles County Museum of Art, June 10-July 21
Paris, Musée National d'Art Moderne, *Joan Miró*, June 28-Nov. 4, 1962, no. 23
London, Tate Gallery, *Joan Miró*, Aug. 27-Oct. 11, 1964, no. 31, repr., traveled to Kunsthaus Zürich, Oct. 31-Dec. 6
New York, The Museum of Modern Art, *Dada, Surrealism and their Heritage*, Mar. 27-June 9, 1968, no. 223, repr.
New York, The Solomon R. Guggenheim Museum, *Joan Miró: Magnetic Fields*, Oct. 26, 1972-Jan. 21, 1973, no. 1, repr.
Paris, Grand Palais, *Joan Miró*, May 17-Oct. 13, 1974, no. 17
New York, The Solomon R. Guggenheim Museum, *Forty Modern Masters: An Anniversary Show*, Dec. 16, 1977-Feb. 5, 1978, no. 96
Madrid, Museo Español de Arte Contemporaneo, *Joan Miró: Pintura*, May 4-July 23, 1978, no. 14, color repr.

REFERENCES:
M. Leiris and M. Morise, "Rêves," *La Révolution Surréaliste*, no. 5, Oct. 15, 1925, p. 10, repr.
A. Breton, *Le Surréalisme et la peinture*, Paris, 1928, pl. 58
R. Gaffé, "Réflexions d'un collectionneur," *Cahiers de Belgique*, 2e année, Feb. 1929, p. 55, repr.
J. Dupin, *Joan Miró: Life and Work*, New York, 1962, pp. 134, 135, repr., 136-142
W. S. Rubin, *Dada and Surrealist Art*, New York, 1968, pp. 152, 153, repr., 154-155
R. Penrose, *Miró*, New York, 1969, pp. 34, 35, color repr.
M. Rowell, *Miró*, New York, 1970, pp. 11-12
M. Rowell, "Miró, Apollinaire and 'L'Enchanteur pourrissant,'" *Art News*, vol. 71, Oct. 1972, pp. 64, repr., 65-67

132 Landscape (The Hare). Autumn 1927
(*Paysage [Le Lièvre]*)

57.1459

Oil on canvas, 51 x 76⅝ in. (129.6 x 194.6 cm.)

Signed and dated l.r.: *Miró / 1927*; inscribed on reverse: *Joan Miró. / "Paysage" / 1927.*

PROVENANCE:
from the artist
Galerie Pierre, Paris, 1927-at least 1933
Max Pellequer, Paris, after 1933-ca. 1950
Galerie Maeght, Paris, ca. 1950-57

Miró's *Landscape* shows a hare, a dotted spiral, purple-red earth and orange sky. The artist recalled* that the motif was suggested when, on a summer evening in Montroig, he saw a hare streak across an unplanted field as the sun was setting. The Guggenheim picture strongly resembles another 1927 *Landscape* (Collection Mr. and Mrs. Gordon Bunshaft, New York) in composition and in the presence of a strange animal preoccupied with a transcendent object. Thus, the meaning of the spiral form transcends that of merely a sun to suggest a comet or an apparition of female sexuality.**

 * conversation with Margit Rowell, May 1974
** M. Rowell and R. E. Krauss, *Joan Miró: Magnetic Fields,* exh. cat., New York, 1972-73, no. 27

EXHIBITIONS:
Paris, Galerie Georges Bernheim, *Miró,* May 1-15, 1928
Krefeld, Kaiser Wilhelm Museum, *Joan Miró,* Jan. 10-Feb. 14, 1954, no. 3, traveled to Stuttgart, Würtembergische Staatsgalerie, Feb. 21-Mar. 28; Berlin, Haus am Waldsee, Apr. 18-May 2
Brussels, Palais des Beaux-Arts, *Joan Miró,* Jan. 6-Feb. 7, 1956, no. 32, repr.
Rome, Galleria Nazionale d'Arte Moderna, *An exhibition of paintings from The Solomon R. Guggenheim Museum, New York,* Dec. 26, 1957-Jan. 8, 1958, traveled to Cologne, Wallraf-Richartz-Museum, Jan. 26-Mar. 30; Paris, Musée des Arts Décoratifs, Apr. 23-June 1
New York, The Solomon R. Guggenheim Museum, *Inaugural Selection,* Oct. 21, 1959-June 19, 1960
Paris, Musée National d'Art Moderne, *Joan Miró,* June 28-Nov. 4, 1962, no. 43
London, Tate Gallery, *Joan Miró,* Aug. 27-Oct. 11, 1964, no. 70, traveled to Kunsthaus Zürich, Oct. 31-Dec. 6, 1964
Tokyo, National Museum of Western Art, *Joan Miró,* Aug. 26-Oct. 9, 1966, no. 32, repr., traveled to Kyoto National Museum of Modern Art, Oct. 20-Nov. 30

New York, The Solomon R. Guggenheim Museum, *Joan Miró: Magnetic Fields,* Oct. 26, 1972-Jan. 21, 1973, no. 27, repr.
Paris, Grand Palais, *Joan Miró,* May 17-Oct. 13, 1974, no. 32, color repr.
London, Hayward Gallery, *Dada and Surrealism Reviewed* (organized by Arts Council of Great Britain), Jan. 11-Mar. 27, 1978, no. 9-59

REFERENCES:
S. Dali, "Joan Miró," *Cahiers de Belgique,* 2ᵉ année, June 1929, p. 207, repr.
J. Prévert and G. Ribemont-Dessaignes, *Joan Miró,* Paris, 1956, p. 116, color repr.
J. Dupin, *Joan Miró: Life and Work,* New York, 1962, pp. 178-179, 225, repr., 515, no. 184, repr.
Handbook, 1970, pp. 302-303, repr.
Rudenstine, *Collection Catalogue,* 1976, no. 185, repr.

Miró

133 Painting. 1953
(Peinture)

55.1420

Oil on canvas, 76¾ x 148¾ in. (195 x 378 cm.)

Signed l.r.: *Miró*; signed and dated on reverse:
Miró / 1953 / peinture.

PROVENANCE:

from the artist through Pierre Matisse Gallery,
New York, 1955

Painting of 1953 is a pivotal work in Miró's career. It
is situated between his relatively reflective and reserved
art of the 1940s and the freer, more spontaneous
expressiveness of the late fifties and sixties. Constant
to Miró's total oeuvre are the bold imaginative figures
and the emphatic cohesive grounds. Specific to this
particular period of 1953-54 are the energetic gestural
treatment, the intentional clumsiness of the images and
the predominance of bright, raw hues. The artist has
used disconnected dotted lines to underscore or inflect
certain parts of the composition within the overall
rhythmic pattern.

EXHIBITIONS:

Paris, Galerie Maeght, *Miró,* June-Aug. 1953, no. 15

New York, Pierre Matisse Gallery, *Miró: Recent Paintings,*
Nov. 17-Dec. 19, 1953, no. 15

London, Tate Gallery, *An exhibition of paintings from The
Solomon R. Guggenheim Museum, New York,* Apr. 16-May
26, 1957, no. 51, repr., traveled to The Hague, Gemeente-
museum, June 25-Sept. 1; Helsinki, Ateneumin Taidekokoel-
mat, Sept. 27-Oct. 20; Rome, Galleria Nazionale d'Arte
Moderna, Dec. 5, 1957-Jan. 8, 1958; Cologne, Wallraf-
Richartz-Museum, Jan. 26-Mar. 30; Paris, Musée des Arts
Décoratifs, Apr. 23-June 1

New York, The Museum of Modern Art, *Joan Miró,* Mar.
18-May 10, 1959, no. 101a

Paris, Grand Palais, *Joan Miró,* May 17-Oct. 13, 1974, no. 70

New York, The Solomon R. Guggenheim Museum, *Forty
Modern Masters: An Anniversary Show,* Dec. 16, 1977-Feb.
5, 1978, no. 98

REFERENCES:

R. Motherwell, "The Significance of Miró," *Art News,* vol.
58, May 1959, p. 33, repr.

J. Dupin, *Joan Miró: Life and Work,* New York, 1962, pp.
389, color repr., 434, 435, 561, no. 805

J. Lassaigne, *Miró,* Geneva, 1963, p. 100

R. Penrose, *Miró,* New York, 1969, pp. 120, 122-123, color
repr.

Handbook, 1970, pp. 304-305, color repr.

H. H. Arnason, *History of Modern Art,* rev. ed., New York,
1977, p. 361 and color pl. 156

Miró and Artigas

Executed with Joseph Lloréns Artigas

134 Alicia. 1965-67

67.1844

Ceramic tile, 97 x 228½ in. (246.4 x 580.5 cm.)

Signed l.r.: *Miró Artigas.* Not dated.

PROVENANCE:

commissioned from the artist, 1965
Gift, Harry F. Guggenheim in memory of his wife
Alicia Patterson Guggenheim, 1967

In 1965 Miró began work on a ceramic mural commissioned by Harry F. Guggenheim, President of The Solomon R. Guggenheim Foundation, in memory of his wife Alicia Patterson Guggenheim, who had died in 1963. Almost two hundred ceramic plaques were executed in Spain by Miró in collaboration with his old friend Lloréns Artigas, the Spanish ceramicist. The mural was designed to occupy the first wall encountered as one ascends the Guggenheim's spiral ramp, and it is partially visible as one enters the Museum's rotunda.

Miró and Artigas integrated the motif with the medium. The distinctive and spontaneous use of black lines recalls Miró's *Painting* (cat. no. 133). The artist has interwoven letters of Mrs. Guggenheim's first name into the bold calligraphy and brightly colored design of the mural.

EXHIBITIONS:

Installed at The Solomon R. Guggenheim Museum, May 18, 1967, and often on view

New York, The Solomon R. Guggenheim Museum, *Selected Sculpture and Works on Paper,* July 8-Sept. 14, 1969, p. 139, repr.

New York, The Solomon R. Guggenheim Museum, *Forty Modern Masters: An Anniversary Show,* Dec. 16, 1977-Feb. 5, 1978, no. 99, repr.

REFERENCES:

J. Perucho, *Joan Miró and Catalonia,* New York, 1967, pls. III-119

Handbook, 1970, pp. 308, repr., 309

J. Pierre and J. Corredor-Matheos, *Céramiques de Miró et Artigas,* Paris, 1974, pp. 174, repr., 184 and pl. 342

Alberto Giacometti 1901-1966

Alberto Giacometti was born on October 10, 1901, in Borgonovo, Switzerland, and grew up in the nearby town of Stampa. His father Giovanni was a Post-Impressionist painter. From 1919 to 1920 he studied painting at the Ecole des Beaux-Arts and sculpture and drawing at the Ecole des Arts et Métiers in Geneva. In 1920 he traveled to Italy, where he was impressed by the Cézannes and Archipenkos at the Venice Biennale. He was also deeply affected by primitive and Egyptian art and by the masterpieces of Giotto and Tintoretto. In 1922 Giacometti settled in Paris, making frequent visits to Stampa. From time to time over the next several years he attended Bourdelle's sculpture classes at the Académie de la Grande Chaumière.

In 1927 the artist moved into a studio with his brother Diego, his lifelong companion and assistant, and exhibited his sculpture for the first time at the Salon des Tuileries, Paris. His first show in Switzerland, shared with his father, was held at the Galerie Aktuaryus in Zürich in 1927. The following year Giacometti met Masson and by 1930 he was a participant in the Surrealist circle. His first one-man show took place in 1932 at the Galerie Pierre Colle in Paris. In 1934 his first American solo exhibition opened at the Julien Levy Gallery in New York. During the early 1940s he became friends with Picasso, Jean-Paul Sartre and Simone de Beauvoir. From 1942 Giacometti lived in Geneva, where he associated with the publisher Albert Skira.

He returned to Paris in 1946. In 1948 he was given a one-man show at the Pierre Matisse Gallery in New York. The artist's friendship with Samuel Beckett began around 1951. In 1955 he was honored with major retrospectives at the Arts Council Gallery in London and The Solomon R. Guggenheim Museum in New York. He received the Sculpture Prize at the Carnegie International in Pittsburgh in 1961 and the First Prize for Sculpture at the Venice Biennale of 1962, where he was given his own exhibition area. In 1965 Giacometti exhibitions were organized by the Tate Gallery in London, The Museum of Modern Art in New York, the Louisiana Museum in Humlebaek, Denmark, and the Stedelijk Museum in Amsterdam. That same year he was awarded the Grand National Prize for Art by the French government. Giacometti died on January 11, 1966, in Chur, Switzerland.

135 **Spoon Woman.** 1926
(Femme-cuiller)

55.1414

Bronze, 57 in. (144.7 cm.) high

Signed on reverse: *A. Giacometti*; on reverse of base: *Alberto Giacometti 3/6*. Not dated.

Third of six casts made in 1954 from original plaster of 1926 by Susse Fondeur, Paris

PROVENANCE:
from the artist through Pierre Matisse Gallery, New York, 1955

For a short time in the mid-1920s Giacometti experimented with Cubism; he soon developed his personal Cubist sculptural style. In *Spoon Woman* he assimilates the Cubist innovations of Lipchitz and Henri Laurens. Yet the work also reveals the influence of primitive art and Surrealism. There are clear similarities to Cycladic sculpture and to certain formal characteristics of African sculpture—such as the equivalence of convexity and concavity and arbitrary figure proportions—which had already been absorbed into Cubist sculpture itself. However, the enlargement of the female torso into an oversized, spoon-like hollow, with its inverted reference to pregnancy, foreshadows Giacometti's brilliant explorations during the later 1920s and 1930s of a Surrealist world arising from subconscious dreams and emotions.

EXHIBITIONS:
New York, The Solomon R. Guggenheim Museum, *Alberto Giacometti*, June 7-July 17, 1955

Vienna, Museum des 20. Jahrhunderts, *Kunst von 1900 bis heute*, Sept. 21-Nov. 4, 1962, no. 137, repr.

Washington, D. C., The Phillips Collection, *Alberto Giacometti*, Feb. 2-Mar. 4, 1963, no. 2

New York, The Solomon R. Guggenheim Museum, *Selected Sculpture and Works on Paper*, July 8-Sept. 14, 1969, p. 124, repr.

New York, The Solomon R. Guggenheim Museum, *Forty Modern Masters: An Anniversary Show*, Dec. 16, 1977-Feb. 5, 1978, no. 40, repr.

Buffalo, Albright-Knox Art Gallery, *Modern European Sculpture 1918-1945: Unknown Beings and Other Realities*, May 11-June 24, 1979, no. 21, repr., traveled to Minneapolis Institute of Art, July 22-Sept. 2; San Francisco Museum of Modern Art, Oct. 5-Nov. 18

REFERENCES:

J. Dupin, *Alberto Giacometti,* Paris, 1962, pp. 39, 193, repr. (plaster)

Handbook, 1970, pp. 126-127, repr.

R. Hohl, *Alberto Giacometti,* New York, 1971, pp. 39, repr. (plaster), 78-79

H. H. Arnason, *History of Modern Art,* rev. ed., New York, 1977, fig. 635

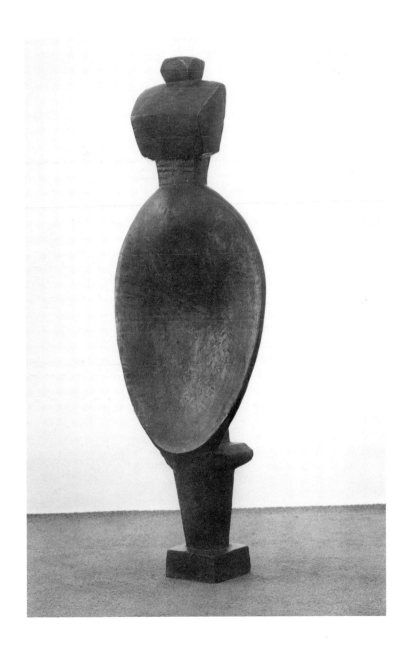

136 Nose. 1947
(Le Nez)

66.1807

Bronze, wire, rope and steel, 15 x 3 x 26 in.
(38 x 7.5 x 66 cm.)

Signed on bottom: *Alberto Giacometti / 5/6 / Susse Fondeur/Paris.* Not dated.

Fifth of six casts made in 1965 from plaster by Susse Fondeur, Paris

PROVENANCE:
from the artist through Pierre Matisse Gallery, New York, 1966

About 1947 Giacometti ceased making minute sculptures, and his tall, thin skeletal figures began to appear. In *Nose* and *Hand*, both done in 1947, the artist enlarged a detail to such a degree that it would be impossible for him to realize the whole figure. As in *Hand* and *Man Pointing* of the same year, he has elongated forms for expressive effect and in accordance with his perception of the subject. Through the introduction of a steel cage in our sculpture, Giacometti has located the head within spatial confines, although the nose protrudes beyond them. The investigation of space preoccupies the artist here as it had in the early 1940s, when he made extremely small figures on large bases, and as it would during the next years in group compositions like *City Square* and *The Cage.*

EXHIBITIONS:
New York, The Solomon R. Guggenheim Museum, *Selected Sculpture and Works on Paper,* July 8-Sept. 14, 1969, p. 126, repr.

Bogotá, Museo de Arte Moderno, *Quatro Maestros Contemporaneos: Giacometti, Dubuffet, de Kooning, Bacon* (organized by The Museum of Modern Art, New York), May 30-June 28, 1973

New York, The Solomon R. Guggenheim Museum, *Alberto Giacometti: A Retrospective Exhibition,* Apr. 5-June 23, 1974, no. 51, repr., traveled to Minneapolis, Walker Art Center, July 13-Sept. 1; The Cleveland Museum of Art, Sept. 24-Oct. 28; Ottawa, National Gallery of Canada, Nov. 15, 1974-Jan. 5, 1975; Des Moines Art Center, Jan. 27-Mar. 2; Montreal, Musée d'Art Contemporain, Mar. 27-May 4

Duisberg, Wilhelm-Lehmbruck-Museum, *Alberto Giacometti: Plastiken, Gemälde, Zeichnungen,* Sept. 17-Nov. 27, 1977, no. 19, repr.

New York, The Solomon R. Guggenheim Museum, *Forty Modern Masters: An Anniversary Show,* Dec. 16, 1977-Feb. 5, 1978, no. 41

REFERENCE:
Handbook, 1970, p. 129, repr.

Giacometti

137 Diego. 1953

55.1431

Oil on canvas, 39½ x 31¾ in. (100.5 x 80.5 cm.)

Not signed or dated.

PROVENANCE:
from the artist through Galerie Maeght, Paris, 1955

The sitter is the artist's brother Diego (born 1902). From 1927 Diego lived in Alberto's studio at 46, rue Hippolyte-Maindron in Paris and assisted him with sculpture. He set up armatures, patinated the bronzes and made plaster casts in addition to designing and building modern furniture. Between 1935 and 1940 Diego posed every morning for Alberto, who was working from the model during that period. The artist later observed that, when he worked from memory, his heads ultimately became essentially Diego's head, because he had done it most often.

From time to time Giacometti abandoned painting for certain intervals: for example, no canvases exist from the late thirties to mid-forties, while many paintings date from the fifties until the mid-sixties. The frontal pose of the seated figure in an interior setting and the neutral palette of grays, tans and browns are characteristic of Giacometti's paintings. Likewise, the inner frame painted on the canvas, employed earlier by Ferdinand Hodler, appears in most of the paintings of the 1950s. This device enables the artist to locate the figure in the space within the picture plane and to keep the figure separate from the distance between viewer and picture. During the many sittings for a portrait, Giacometti paints over the figure and re-creates it again and again. Thus, a painting evolves through many states, fluctuating in degrees of precision and vagueness, until he ceases to rework it.

EXHIBITIONS:
New York, The Solomon R. Guggenheim Museum, *Alberto Giacometti,* June 7-July 17, 1955

London, Tate Gallery, *An exhibition of paintings from The Solomon R. Guggenheim Museum, New York,* Apr. 16-May 26, 1957, no. 21, repr., traveled to The Hague, Gemeentemuseum, June 25-Sept. 1; Helsinki, Ateneumin Taidekokoelmat, Sept. 27-Oct. 20; Rome, Galleria Nazionale d'Arte Moderna, Dec. 5, 1957-Jan. 8, 1958; Cologne, Wallraf-Richartz-Museum, Jan. 26-Mar. 30; Paris, Musée des Arts Décoratifs, Apr. 23-June 1

San Francisco, California Palace of the Legion of Honor, *Man: glory, jest and riddle, a survey of human form through the ages,* Nov. 10, 1964-Jan. 3, 1965, no. 251

New York, The Solomon R. Guggenheim Museum, *Alberto Giacometti: A Retrospective Exhibition,* Apr. 5-June 23, 1974, no. 129, repr., traveled to Minneapolis, Walker Art Center, July 13-Sept. 1; The Cleveland Museum of Art, Sept. 24-Oct. 28; Ottawa, National Gallery of Canada, Nov. 15, 1974-Jan. 5, 1975; Des Moines Art Center, Jan. 27-Mar. 2; Montreal, Musée d'Art Contemporain, Mar. 27-May 4

New York, The Solomon R. Guggenheim Museum, *Forty Modern Masters: An Anniversary Show,* Dec. 16, 1977-Feb. 5, 1978, no. 42

REFERENCES:
Handbook, 1959, p. 61, repr.

J. Dupin, *Alberto Giacometti,* Paris, 1962, p. 134, repr.

Giacometti

138 Portrait of Douglas Cooper. Late April-May 1956

57.1478

Pencil on paper, 25¾ x 19¾ in. (65.4 x 50.2 cm.)

Signed and dated l.r.: *Alberto Giacometti / 1957.*

PROVENANCE:

from the artist through Pierre Matisse Gallery,
New York, 1957

Although the drawing is dated 1957, Douglas Cooper distinctly remembers* sitting for Giacometti approximately six times within a ten day period in Paris at about the same time that Helene and G. David Thompson were married. There are two very similar drawings of Douglas Cooper, one of which belonged to Mrs. Thompson and is inscribed by the artist and dated *"Paris le 8 mai 1956."*** Apparently it was never Giacometti's intention to paint the portrait in oil.

The artist has aligned the composition along strong vertical and horizontal axes so as to focus upon the art historian's face. While the interior space is only alluded to minimally, the freely moving line firmly defines the figure.

  * correspondence with the author, Feb. 1978
 ** correspondence with Helene Thompson, Apr. 1978

EXHIBITIONS:

Kunsthalle Bern, *Alberto Giacometti,* June 16-July 22, 1956, no. 85

Houston, Contemporary Arts Museum, *Personal Contacts: A Decade of Contemporary Drawings,* Nov. 20, 1958-Jan. 4, 1959

New York, The American Federation of Arts, *Images of Praise,* Dec. 12, 1963-Jan. 2, 1964

St. Louis, Gallery of Art, Washington University, *Nineteenth and Twentieth Century Artists as Draughtsmen,* Mar. 13-Apr. 8, 1966

New York, The Solomon R. Guggenheim Museum, *Selected Sculpture and Works on Paper,* July 8-Sept. 14, 1969, p. 23, repr.

Bogotá, Museo de Arte Moderno, *Quatro Maestros Contemporaneos: Giacometti, Dubuffet, de Kooning, Bacon* (organized by The Museum of Modern Art, New York), May 30-June 28, 1973

New York, The Solomon R. Guggenheim Museum, *Alberto Giacometti: A Retrospective Exhibition,* Apr. 5-June 23, 1974, no. 180, repr., traveled to Minneapolis, Walker Art Center, July 13-Sept. 1; The Cleveland Museum of Art, Sept. 24-Oct. 28; Ottawa, National Gallery of Canada, Nov. 15, 1974-Jan. 5, 1975; Des Moines Art Center, Jan. 27-Mar. 2; Montreal, Musée d'Art Contemporain, Mar. 27-May 4

New York, The Solomon R. Guggenheim Museum, *Forty Modern Masters: An Anniversary Show,* Dec. 16, 1977-Feb. 5, 1978, no. 43

REFERENCE:

Handbook, 1970, p. 132, repr.

Giacometti

139 Mountain. ca. 1956-57
(La Montagne)

57.1481

Pencil on paper, 19¾ x 25¾ in. (50.2 x 65.4 cm.)

Signed and dated l.r.: *Alberto Giacometti / 1957.*

PROVENANCE:

from the artist through Pierre Matisse Gallery,
New York, 1957

The mountain is Piz Margna as Giacometti saw it from
his summer retreat at Maloja near Stampa in Switzerland.* The nervous energy of the individual pencil
marks expresses the upward thrust of the mountain
peak. The viewpoint from which the summit is shown
is reminiscent of Cézanne's drawings of Mont Sainte-
Victoire as seen from Les Lauves near Aix-en-Provence.

In sketches like *Mountain* one can speak neither of
perspective nor flatness, as the image tends to dissolve
the picture plane. Nonetheless, a distance which defies
measurement, as well as an inevitable presence of
objects or figures remain; it is the same distance which
separates us from Giacometti's sculptures and the same
presence with which these sculptures are endowed.

* conversation with Herbert Matter, Apr. 1978

EXHIBITIONS:

New York, The Museum of Modern Art, *Alberto Giacometti,* June 9-Oct. 10, 1965, no. 131, repr., traveled to The
Art Institute of Chicago, Nov. 5-Dec. 12; Los Angeles County
Museum of Art, Jan. 11-Feb. 20, 1966; San Francisco Museum
of Art, Mar. 10-Apr. 24

New York, The Solomon R. Guggenheim Museum, *Selected
Sculpture and Works on Paper,* July 8-Sept. 14, 1969, p. 25,
repr.

Paris, Orangerie des Tuileries, *Alberto Giacometti,* Oct. 24,
1969-Jan. 12, 1970, no. 267, repr.

New York, The Solomon R. Guggenheim Museum, *Alberto
Giacometti: A Retrospective Exhibition,* Apr. 5-June 23,
1974, no. 181, repr., traveled to Minneapolis, Walker Art
Center, July 13-Sept. 1; The Cleveland Museum of Art, Sept.
24-Oct. 28; Ottawa, National Gallery of Canada, Nov. 15,
1974-Jan. 5, 1975; Des Moines Art Center, Jan. 27-Mar. 2;
Montreal, Musée d'Art Contemporain, Mar. 27-May 4

New York, The Solomon R. Guggenheim Museum, *Forty
Modern Masters: An Anniversary Show,* Dec. 16, 1977-Feb.
5, 1978, no. 45

REFERENCES:

A. du Bouchet, *Alberto Giacometti: dessins 1914-1965,* Paris,
1969, p. 71, repr.

Handbook, 1970, p. 133, repr.

J. Lord, *Alberto Giacometti Drawings,* Greenwich, Conn.,
1971, no. 94

Max Beckmann 1884-1950

Max Beckmann was born in Leipzig on February 12, 1884. He began to study art with Carl Frithjof Smith at the Grossherzogliche Kunstschule in Weimar in 1900 and made his first visit to Paris in 1903-4. During this period Beckmann began his lifelong practice of keeping a diary or *Tagebuch*. In the autumn of 1904 he settled in Berlin.

In 1913 the artist's first one-man show took place at the Galerie Paul Cassirer in Berlin. He was discharged for reasons of health from the medical corps of the German army in 1915 and settled in Frankfurt. In 1925 Beckmann's work was included in the exhibition of *Die Neue Sachlichkeit* (New Objectivity) in Mannheim, and he was appointed professor at the Städelsches Kunstinstitut in Frankfurt. His first show in the United States took place at J. B. Neumann's New Art Circle in New York in 1926. A large retrospective of his work was held at the Kunsthalle Mannheim in 1928. From 1929 to 1932 he continued to teach in Frankfurt but spent time in Paris in the winters. It was during these years that Beckmann began to use the triptych format. When the Nazis came to power in 1933, Beckmann lost his teaching position and moved to Berlin. In 1937 his work was included in the Nazis' exhibition of *Entartete Kunst* (degenerate art). The day after the show opened in Munich in July 1937, the artist and his wife left Germany for Amsterdam, where they remained until 1947. In 1938 he was given the first of numerous exhibitions at Curt Valentin's Buchholz Gallery in New York.

Beckmann traveled to Paris and the south of France in 1947 and later that year went to the United States to teach at the School of Fine Arts at Washington University in St. Louis. The first Beckmann retrospective in the United States took place in 1948 at the City Art Museum of St. Louis. The artist taught at the University of Colorado in Boulder during the summer of 1949 and that autumn at the Brooklyn Museum School. Thus, in 1949, the Beckmanns moved to New York and the artist was awarded First Prize in the exhibition *Painting in the United States, 1949,* at the Carnegie Institute in Pittsburgh. He died on December 27, 1950, in New York.

140 Paris Society. 1931
(Gesellschaft Paris)

70.1927

Oil on canvas, 43 x 69⅛ in. (109.3 x 175.6 cm.)

Signed and dated u.l.: *Gesellschaft / Paris 31 / Beckmann.*

PROVENANCE:
Estate of Max Beckmann
Catherine Viviano Gallery, New York, 1955-63
Stanley J. Seeger, Jr., Frenchtown, New Jersey, 1963-70

Paris Society dates primarily from 1931 when Beckmann was in Frankfurt and Paris during the winter. However, its conception originated as early as 1925, and the artist reworked the canvas in Amsterdam in 1947. Fifteen people are presented in a room with mirrors on the rear wall; two small background figures and the large chandelier are actually reflections of activity taking place in front of the picture plane. Not only the compressed space but also the bold, black outlines create tensions within the picture.

Although the figures are not portraits, certain individuals can be identified. In the center is Beckmann's friend Prince Rohan; a drawing for this figure dated October 30, 1931, is in the collection of Catherine Viviano, New York. The German ambassador in Paris, Leopold von Hoesch, is depicted with his hands covering his face at the right. The character as well as the title of the picture assumed its present form in 1931.*

* Information supplied by Mathilde Q. Beckmann in correspondence with the author, May 1979

EXHIBITIONS:
Berlin, Galerie Flechtheim, *Max Beckmann,* Mar. 5-24, 1932, no. 2

Paris, Galerie Bing, *Max Beckmann,* 1932, no. 6

Kunsthalle Bern, *Max Beckmann, Marguerite Frey-Surbek, Martin Christ, Fernand Riard,* Feb. 19-Mar. 20, 1938, no. 2

City Art Museum of Saint Louis, *Max Beckmann,* May-June 1948, no. 20

New York, Catherine Viviano Gallery, *Max Beckmann,* Jan. 9-27, 1962, no. 3, repr.

Boston, Museum of Fine Arts, *Max Beckmann,* Oct. 1-Nov. 15, 1964, no. 34, traveled to New York, The Museum of Modern Art, Dec. 14, 1964-Jan. 31, 1965; The Art Institute of Chicago, Mar. 12-Apr. 11; Hamburg, Kunstverein, May 15-July 11; Frankfurter Kunstverein, July 15-Sept. 9; London, Tate Gallery, Oct. 1-Nov. 7

New York, The Solomon R. Guggenheim Museum, *Forty Modern Masters: An Anniversary Show,* Dec. 16, 1977-Feb. 5, 1978, no. 5

REFERENCES:
B. Reifenberg and W. Hausenstein, *Max Beckmann,* Munich, 1949, p. 73, no. 302

F. W. Fischer, *Max Beckmann: Symbol und Weltbild,* Munich, 1972, pp. 90, 169

E. Göpel and B. Göpel, *Max Beckmann: Katalog der Gemälde,* Bern, 1976, vol. I, pp. 243-244, no. 346 and vol. II, pl. 119

S. Lackner, *Beckmann,* New York, 1977, pp. 110, 111, repr.

141 **Alfi with Mask.** 1934
(Alfi mit Maske)

76.2202

Oil on canvas, 30⅞ x 29¾ in. (78.4 x 75.5 cm.)
Signed and dated u.l.: *Beckmann/ 34.*

PROVENANCE:

Galerie Nierendorf, Berlin, by 1936
Ludwig Mies van der Rohe, Berlin and Chicago,
1936-69
Estate of Mies van der Rohe, 1969-73
Georgia van der Rohe, New York, 1973-75
Partial Gift, Georgia van der Rohe, 1975

Alfi with Mask represents a sensuous reclining female
model. The mask conceals the woman's identity and
gives her an air of mystery. Apparently Beckmann
painted no other picture of Alfi, whose identity remains
unknown. The name itself is puzzling since it is not
used for women in German, but is a variation on the
man's name Alf.

In the 1920s the artist had included masked people and
even a masked self-portrait in his paintings. Such
enigmatic figures appear also in his work of the 1940s.
Beckmann was fascinated with the borderline between
reality and unreality and loved Mardi Gras balls,
masquerade parties and cabarets.

The Guggenheim picture was painted in 1934 in Berlin
where Beckmann led a secluded life. It was presented
to the architect Mies van der Rohe on the occasion of
his fiftieth birthday on March 27, 1936.

EXHIBITION:

New York, The Solomon R. Guggenheim Museum, *Forty
Modern Masters: An Anniversary Show,* Dec. 16, 1977-Feb.
5, 1978, no. 6, repr.

REFERENCES:

B. Reifenberg and W. Hausenstein, *Max Beckmann,* Munich,
1949, p. 74, no. 337
E. Göpel and B. Göpel, *Max Beckmann: Katalog der
Gemälde,* Bern, 1976, vol. I, pp. 269-270, no. 402 and vol.
II, pl. 134

Henry Moore b. 1898

Henry Spencer Moore was born July 30, 1898, in Castleford, Yorkshire, the son of a miner. Despite an early desire to become a sculptor, Moore began his career as a teacher in Castleford. After military service in World War I he attended Leeds School of Art on an ex-serviceman's grant. In 1921 he won a Royal Exhibition Scholarship to study sculpture at the Royal Academy of Art in London. Moore became interested in the Mexican, Egyptian and African sculpture he saw at the British Museum. He was appointed Instructor of Sculpture at the Royal Academy in 1924, a post he held for the next seven years. A Royal Academy traveling scholarship allowed Moore to visit Italy in 1925; there he saw the frescoes of Giotto and Masaccio and the late sculpture of Michelangelo. Moore's first one-man show of sculpture was held at the Warren Gallery, London, in 1928.

In the 1930s Moore was a member of *Unit One*, a group of advanced artists organized by Paul Nash, and was close friends with Nicholson, Barbara Hepworth and the critic Herbert Read. From 1932 to 1939 he taught at the Chelsea School of Art. He was an important force in the English Surrealist movement, although he was not entirely committed to its doctrines; Moore participated in the *International Surrealist Exhibition* at the New Burlington Galleries, London, in 1936. In 1940 Moore was appointed an official war artist and was commissioned by the War Artists Advisory Committee to execute drawings of life in underground bomb shelters. From 1940 to 1943 the artist concentrated almost entirely on drawing. His first retrospective took place at Temple Newsam, Leeds, in 1941. In 1943 he received a commission from the Church of St. Matthew, Northampton, to carve a *Madonna and Child*; this sculpture was the first in an important series of family group sculptures. Moore was given his first major retrospective abroad by The Museum of Modern Art, New York, in 1946. He won the International Prize for Sculpture at the Venice Biennale of 1948.

Moore executed several important public commissions in the 1950s, among them *Reclining Figure*, 1956-58, for the UNESCO Building in Paris. In 1963 the artist was awarded the British Order of Merit. A major retrospective of his sculpture was held at the Forte di Belvedere, Florence, in 1972. Moore now lives and works at Perry Green, Much Hadham, Hertfordshire.

142 Upright Figure. 1956-60

60.1582

Elm wood, 111 in. (282 cm.) high

Not signed or dated.

PROVENANCE:
commissioned from the artist, 1956

When he was commissioned by The Solomon R. Guggenheim Foundation in 1956, Henry Moore commenced to carve a horizontal reclining figure which was related to his bronze *Reclining Figure* of 1956. As he worked, the artist transformed the Guggenheim sculpture into a vertical composition. He has stated that "although, of course, I changed it considerably, it shows the great importance of gravity in sculpture. Lying down, the figure looked static, whilst upright it takes on movement, and because it is working against gravity it looks almost as though it is climbing." (Hedgecoe and Moore, p. 280)

The towering female figure is attached to the elm block and can, therefore, be defined as a high relief. The sculpture's rough surface bears visible evidence of how Moore carved directly into the wood, a technique not often encountered in his mature work.

EXHIBITIONS:
New York, The Solomon R. Guggenheim Museum, *Guggenheim International Award, 1960*, Nov. 1, 1960-Jan. 29, 1961, not in cat.

New York, The Solomon R. Guggenheim Museum, *Selected Sculpture and Works on Paper*, July 8-Sept. 14, 1969, p. 142, repr.

New York, The Solomon R. Guggenheim Museum, *Forty Modern Masters: An Anniversary Show*, Dec. 16, 1977-Feb. 5, 1978, no. 108, repr.

REFERENCES:
W. Grohmann, *Henry Moore*, Berlin, 1960, pl. 62

J. Russell, *Henry Moore: Stone and Wood Carvings*, London, 1961, pls. 56, 56A

A. Bowness, ed., *Henry Moore: Sculpture and Drawings*, New York, 1965, vol. 3, p. 23, no. 403, pls. 33-36

H. Read, *Henry Moore: A Study of His Life and Work*, New York, 1966, pp. 208- 209, pls. 193, 194

J. Hedgecoe and H. Moore, *Henry Moore*, New York, 1968, pp. 280-285, repr.

J. Russell, *Henry Moore*, New York, 1968, p. 178, pls. 181, 182

R. Melville, *Henry Moore: Sculpture and Drawings 1921-1969*, New York, 1970, p. 362, pls. 597-599

Handbook, 1970, pp. 338-339, repr.

H. Seldis, *Henry Moore in America*, New York, 1973, p. 145

303

Ben Nicholson 1894-1982

Ben Nicholson was born on April 10, 1894, in Denham, Buckinghamshire, England. Both his parents were painters. Nicholson attended the Slade School of Fine Art in London in 1910-11; between 1911 and 1914 he traveled in France, Italy and Spain. He lived briefly in Pasadena in 1917-18. His first one-man show was held at the Adelphi Gallery in London in 1922. Shortly thereafter he began abstract paintings influenced by Synthetic Cubism. By 1927 he had initiated a primitive style inspired by Rousseau and early English folk art.

From 1931 Nicholson lived in London; his association with Moore and Barbara Hepworth dates from this period. In 1932 he and Hepworth visited Brancusi, Arp, Braque and Picasso in France. Herbin and Hélion encouraged them to join *Abstraction-Création* in 1933. Nicholson made his first wood relief in 1933; the following year, after meeting Mondrian, he geometricized his forms and restricted his palette to white. Hepworth and Nicholson married in 1934. In 1937 Nicholson edited *Circle: International Survey of Constructivist Art,* which he had conceived in 1935.

After moving to Cornwall in 1939, Nicholson resumed painting landscapes and added color to his abstract reliefs. In 1945-46 he turned from reliefs to linear, abstract paintings. Nicholson was commissioned to paint a mural for the Time-Life Building in London in 1952. He was honored with retrospectives at the Venice Biennale in 1954, and at the Tate Gallery, London, and the Stedelijk Museum, Amsterdam, in 1955. Nicholson moved to Ticino, Switzerland, in 1958 and began to concentrate once more on painted reliefs. In 1964 he made a concrete wall relief for the *Documenta III* exhibition in Kassel, Germany, and in 1968 was awarded the Order of Merit by Queen Elizabeth. The Albright-Knox Art Gallery, Buffalo, organized a retrospective of his work in 1978. Ben Nicholson returned to England in 1972, settling first in Cambridge and later in Hampstead. He died on February 6, 1982.

143 December 1955 (night façade). 1955

57.1461

Oil on board, 42½ x 45¾ in. (108 x 116.2 cm.)

Signed and dated on reverse: *Dec 55 / Ben Nicholson / (night façade).*

PROVENANCE:

from the artist through Galerie de France, Paris, 1957

Ben Nicholson's still lifes from the 1950s retain a residual Cubism in the disposition of forms and elaborate the artist's synthesis of abstraction and still life. While the Guggenheim picture originated with a simple arrangement of objects on a table, it exhibits decidedly architectural elements which are alluded to in the title. The smoothly painted, dark background area contrasts with the colorful, textured surface of the vestigial table top. The spare, linear outlines of forms and the differentiated planes of color create a complex and spatially ambiguous composition.

In assigning titles to his work, the artist prefers to state the date first in the manner designated here.

EXHIBITIONS:

Paris, Galerie de France, *Ben Nicholson,* Apr. 1956

Paris, Musée des Beaux-Arts de la Ville de Paris, *11ème Salon des Réalités Nouvelles-Nouvelles Réalités,* June 29-Aug. 5, 1956, not in cat.

New York, The Solomon R. Guggenheim Museum, *Inaugural Selection,* Oct. 21, 1959-June 19, 1960

Dallas Museum of Fine Arts, *Ben Nicholson,* Apr. 15-May 17, 1964, no. 43

The Arts Club of Chicago, *Ben Nicholson,* Sept. 20-Oct. 29, 1976, no. 8, repr.

Buffalo, Albright-Knox Art Gallery, *Ben Nicholson: Fifty Years of His Art,* Oct. 21-Nov. 26, 1978, no. 61, color repr., traveled to Washington, D.C., Hirshhorn Museum and Sculpture Garden, Smithsonian Institution, Dec. 21, 1978-Feb. 18, 1979; The Brooklyn Museum, Mar. 17-May 13

REFERENCES:

H. Read, *Ben Nicholson: Work Since 1947,* London, 1956, vol. II, pl. 129

J. Russell, *Ben Nicholson: Drawings, Paintings and Reliefs 1911-1968,* New York, 1969, color pl. 64

Handbook, 1970, pp. 346-347, repr.

H. H. Arnason, *History of Modern Art,* rev. ed., New York, 1977, p. 541, fig. 932

Jean Hélion b. 1904

Jean Hélion was born on April 21, 1904, in Couterne, France. He entered the Institut Industriel du Nord in Lille to study chemistry in 1920 but left the following year to become an architectural apprentice in Paris. He painted while working as an architectural draftsman in the early 1920s. Hélion attracted the attention of the collector Georges Bine in 1925 and was soon able to devote himself entirely to painting. In 1927 he met Torres-García, who collaborated on *L'Acte,* a short-lived magazine founded by Hélion and others.

Hélion first exhibited at the Salon des Indépendants in 1928. Shortly thereafter he became acquainted with Arp, Pevsner and Mondrian. By 1929 his work was non-figurative. With van Doesburg and others in 1930 he formed the artists' association and periodical *Art Concret,* which was succeeded by the *Abstraction-Création* group the next year. In 1931, after traveling through Europe and the Soviet Union, Hélion returned to Paris, where he met Ernst, Tristan Tzara and Duchamp. His first one-man show was held at the Galerie Pierre in Paris in 1932. That same year Hélion made his first visit to New York, where he was given a one-man exhibition at the John Becker Gallery at the end of 1933. After returning to Europe from a second trip to the United States in 1934, he met Miró, Lipchitz and Nicholson. In 1936 he settled in the United States, dividing his time between Virginia and New York. That year one-man shows of his work took place at the Galerie Cahiers d'Art in Paris and the Valentine Gallery in New York. The artist traveled to Paris in 1938 on the occasion of his solo exhibition at the Galerie Pierre, and he became friends with Tanguy, Paul Eluard and Matta.

He joined the French army in 1940 and was taken prisoner a short time later. Hélion escaped internment camp in 1942 and that same year made his way to Virginia. In 1943 he began to paint in a figurative style again. His book *They Shall Not Have Me* was published in 1943, a year in which he was given one-man shows in Chicago and New York. Hélion returned to Paris in 1946. Throughout the 1950s and 1960s his work was shown in Europe and New York. During the 1970s he exhibited almost exclusively in France. Hélion now lives in Paris and in Châteauneuf en Thymerais, France.

144 Composition. April-May 1934

61.1586

Oil on canvas, 56¾ x 78¾ in. (144.3 x 199.8 cm.)

Signed and dated on reverse: *TOP HAUT / Hélion / Paris 34.*

PROVENANCE:

from the artist
Paul Nelson, Paris, 1935-61
Joseph Cantor, Carmel, Indiana, 1961

During the brief period of 1932 to 1935 Hélion executed a series of abstract canvases similar to *Composition* and referred to as the Equilibrium group. The earlier paintings were composed of squares, rectangles and lines organized in a continuous chain on a white ground. Gradually the shapes and their spatial articulation became more fluid and complex. These canvases were characterized by an allover design of interlocking forms and a closer integration of figures and field. As in other Equilibrium paintings, the subtle modulation of color creates curved forms. Shapes are rhythmically disposed in a sequence of irregular horizontal alignments on a gray ground.

EXHIBITIONS:

Paris, Galerie Cahiers d'Art, *Hans Arp-Ghika, Jean Hélion, S. H. Taueber-Arp,* July 3-Aug. 2, 1934

Kunstmuseum Luzern, *Thèse, Antithèse, Synthèse,* Feb. 24-Mar. 31, 1935, no. 50

New York, The Solomon R. Guggenheim Museum, *Cézanne and Structure in Modern Painting,* June 6-Oct. 13, 1963

New York, Gallery of Modern Art, *Paintings by Jean Hélion, 1928-1964,* Nov. 3-Dec. 2, 1964, no. 6, repr.

Paris, Grand Palais, *Hélion: cent tableaux 1928-1970,* Dec. 11, 1970-Feb. 1, 1971, p. 25, repr.

REFERENCES:

G. Grigson, "Painting and Sculpture," *The Arts Today,* 1935, opp. p. 92, repr.

T. M. Messer, *Elements of Modern Painting,* New York, 1961, color repr.

Handbook, 1970, pp. 158-159, color repr.

"Letters from 31 Artists to the Albright-Knox Art Gallery," E. Moore, ed., *Albright-Knox Gallery Notes,* vol. XXXII, spring 1970, p. 15

M. S. Schipper, *Jean Hélion: The Abstract Years, 1929-1939,* Ph.D. dissertation, University of California at Los Angeles, 1974, pp. 115-117

Rudenstine, *Collection Catalogue,* 1976, no. 71, repr.

H. H. Arnason, *History of Modern Art,* rev. ed., New York, 1977, p. 412 and color pl. 180

Auguste Herbin 1882-1960

Auguste Herbin was born in Quiévy, France, on April 29, 1882. After studying at the Ecole des Beaux-Arts in Lille, Herbin moved to Paris in 1901. There he painted in Impressionist and Fauve styles and became close friends with the art dealer Wilhelm Uhde. In 1909 Herbin took a studio in the "Bateau Lavoir" in Montmartre, where his neighbors included Picasso, Braque and Gris. Under their influence Herbin experimented briefly with Analytical Cubism. Later he rejected this style in favor of the Synthetic Cubism of the *Section d'Or* group with which he exhibited in Paris in 1912. The same year he showed at the Galerie Der Sturm in Berlin and in 1913 he participated in the Armory Show in New York. His one-man show at the Galerie Moderne in Paris in 1914 established Herbin's reputation, and the following year he signed a contract with Léonce Rosenberg. Thereafter, Herbin was given frequent one-man exhibitions at Rosenberg's Galerie l'Effort Moderne in Paris.

Herbin continued to work within the Cubist style and by 1917 had begun a series of stereometric abstractions based on the Orphic Cubism of Robert Delaunay. He also made colored geometric reliefs of concrete, wood, and cement. In the early 1920s Herbin painted for a brief period in a figurative manner. Herbin returned to pure abstraction in 1926, and the next year was given an important exhibition at the Galerie Mak in Amsterdam. In 1931 Herbin, with van Doesburg and others, founded the *Abstraction-Création* group in Paris. Herbin also served as editor of the group's magazine of the same name.

In the 1940s Herbin began to formulate a personal theory of abstract art based on the unification of vivid color, geometric form and ideological content. He developed his "plastic alphabet" in 1943. Herbin elucidated his theories in his book *L'Art non-figuratif, non-objectif*, published in 1949. In 1952 he designed twelve tapestries which were exhibited at the Galerie Denise René in Paris. Herbin showed often in international art exhibitions in the 1950s, and in 1956 the Palais des Beaux-Arts in Brussels organized a major retrospective of his paintings. Herbin died in Paris on January 31, 1960.

145 Composition on the Name "Rose." 1947
(Composition sur le nom "Rose")

49.1183

Oil on canvas, 32 x 25¾ in. (81.3 x 65.4 cm.)

Signed and dated l.r.: *herbin 1947*; inscribed b.c.: *"rose."*

PROVENANCE:
from the artist, 1949

From the early 1940s until his death in 1960, Herbin created many paintings inspired by words: for example, *Amour* (love), *Blé* (wheat), *Mer* (sea), *Minuit* (midnight), *Nöel* (Christmas), *Oiseau* (bird) and *Vin* (wine). Following his renunciation of the object and his espousal of colorful geometric patterns, Herbin formulated his theory of a "plastic alphabet." Every letter of the alphabet was associated with specific colors, shapes and sounds. The artist studied forms and color relationships and imaginatively endowed words and letters with a visual reality and levels of spiritual meaning.

Here, the canvas is divided into four sections, each painted a different color. Various shades of blue predominate and are contrasted with reds and greens and accented by three pink circles. Herbin's flat, brightly colored work would have an impact on Op and Hard-Edge painters as well as color theorists.

EXHIBITION:
New York, The Solomon R. Guggenheim Museum, *Inaugural Selection*, Oct. 21, 1959-June 19, 1960

REFERENCE:
Handbook, 1970, pp. 160-161, repr.

Joaquín Torres-García 1874-1949

Joaquín Torres-García was born on July 28, 1874, in Montevideo, Uruguay. The father was Catalan and moved his family to Mataró, near Barcelona, in 1891. Torres-García attended the Academia de Bellas Artes in Barcelona in 1894. His first one-man show, consisting of drawings and posters, was held at the Salón La Vanguardia there in 1897. The following year he met Julio González and Picasso among other artists and frequented the café Els Quatre Gats. Beginning in 1904 Torres-García assisted Antonio Gaudí on the Sagrada Familia and in designing stained-glass windows. He was commissioned to paint several murals in and near Barcelona in 1908 and for the Uruguayan Pavilion at the *Exposition Universelle de Bruxelles* in 1910. On his way back to Spain, Torres-García visited Paris; he traveled to Italy in 1912, soon after the Catalan National Movement commissioned him to execute a major mural series for the Salón de San Jorge in Barcelona. His first book, *Notes sobre art,* was published in 1913 and he wrote consistently from that time. He worked on the San Jorge murals until 1917. In 1918 the Galeries Dalmau in Barcelona exhibited paintings in his new style as well as toys made by the artist. His long friendship with Miró began at about that time.

From 1920 to 1922 Torres-García lived in New York, where his work was shown at the Whitney Studio Club. He settled in Paris in 1926 and met Mondrian in 1929. Around this time he developed his style of Universal Constructivism. In 1930 he founded the group *Cercle et Carré (Circle and Square)* with Michel Seuphor and wrote his essay "Vouloir construire" ("The Will to Construct"). Torres-García returned to Montevideo in 1934 to communicate his theories of art. The following year he founded the *Asociación de Arte Constructivo (Association of Constructivist Art),* which encouraged modern art in South America through its school and lectures. Torres-García completed his stone *Monumento Cósmico* in Rodó Park, Montevideo, in 1938. In 1944 he opened the Taller Torres-García (workshop), published *Universalismo Constructivo* and was awarded the Grand National Prize for Painting by the Uruguayan government. He died on August 8, 1949, in Montevideo.

146 **Composition.** 1938
(*Composición*)

77.2395

Gouache on cardboard, 32 x 39⅞ in. (81.3 x 101.3 cm.)

Signed and dated l.l.: *J. TG 38*; inscribed l.l.: ∧∧G [*Asociación de Arte Constructivo*].

PROVENANCE:
Estate of the artist, 1949-60
Rose Fried Gallery, New York, 1960-64
Mr. and Mrs. Walter Nelson Pharr, New York, 1964-77
Gift, Mr. and Mrs. Walter Nelson Pharr, 1977

Following his contact with van Doesburg, Mondrian, Hélion, Vantongerloo and Michel Seuphor, Torres-García formulated his concept of Universal Constructivism. He organized symbols and abstract notations along vertical and horizontal axes and frequently divided his canvas into an irregular grid structure. Although grid lines are absent from this *Composition,* it displays an essentially architectonic enregistration. Most striking is the restriction of the palette to a monochromatic range of various warm and cool shades of gray. Here, as in other paintings from the time, volumetric forms emerge as if in relief from the background. The fish, bottle and zigzag recur in other works. Torres-García's pictorial vocabulary drew upon pre-Columbian and various primitive as well as natural sources. In accordance with the tenets of Universal Constructivism, the placement of signs within a pictorial construction conveys a metaphysical sense of the universe.

EXHIBITIONS:
New York, Rose Fried Gallery, *J. Torres-García: Paintings from 1930-1949,* Mar. 1-26, 1960, no. 12
Amsterdam, Stedelijk Museum, *Joaquín Torres-García,* Dec. 1961-Jan. 1962, no. 18, traveled to Staatliche Kunsthalle Baden-Baden, Mar. 2-Apr. 1
New York, Parke-Bernet, *Review of the Season 1962-63,* June 18-July 26, 1963
Ottawa, National Gallery of Canada, *Joaquín Torres-García: 1879-1949,* Oct. 2-Nov. 1, 1970, no. 39, repr., traveled to New York, The Solomon R. Guggenheim Museum, Dec. 12, 1970-Jan. 31, 1971; Providence, Museum of Art, Rhode Island School of Design, Feb. 16-Mar. 31

REFERENCE:
R. Raoul, "New York Letter, Art Dealers on Parade: The Show at Parke Bernet," *Apollo,* vol. 78, July 1963, p. 63, repr.

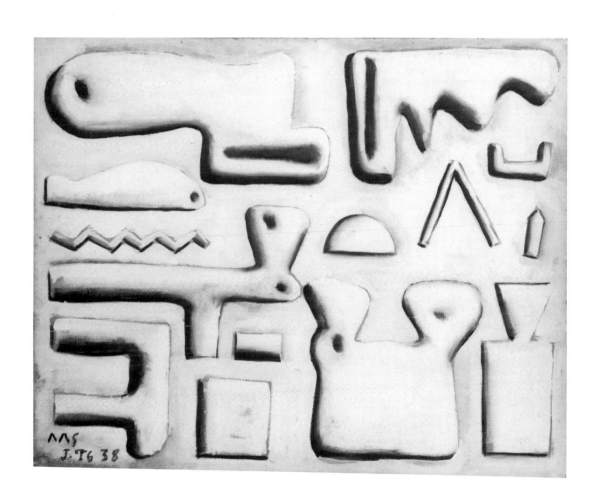

Salvador Dali b. 1904

Dali was born Salvador Felipe Jacinto Dali y Domenech in the Catalonian town of Figueras, Spain, on May 11, 1904. In 1921 he enrolled in the Real Academia de Bellas Artes de San Fernando in Madrid, where he became friends with Federico García Lorca and Luis Buñuel. His first one-man show was held in 1925 at the Galeries Dalmau in Barcelona. In 1926 Dali was expelled from the Academia and the following year he visited Paris and met Picasso. He collaborated with Buñuel on the film *Un Chien Andalou* in 1928. At the end of the year he returned to Paris and met Tristan Tzara and Paul Eluard. About this time Dali produced his first Surrealist paintings, and met André Breton and Louis Aragon. He worked with Buñuel and Ernst on the film *L'Age d'or* in 1930. During the 1930s the artist contributed to various Surrealist publications and illustrated the works of Surrealist writers and poets. His first one-man show in the United States took place at the Julien Levy Gallery in New York in 1933.

Dali was censured by the Surrealists in 1934. Toward the end of the decade he made several trips to Italy to study the art of the sixteenth and seventeenth centuries. In 1940 Dali fled to the United States, where he worked on theatrical productions, wrote, illustrated books and painted. A major retrospective of his work opened in 1941 at The Museum of Modern Art in New York and traveled through the United States. In 1942 Dali published his autobiography and began exhibiting at Knoedler in New York. He returned to Europe in 1948, settling in Port Lligat, Spain. His first paintings with religious subjects date from 1948-49. In 1954 a Dali retrospective was held at the Palazzo Pallavicini in Rome and in 1964 an important retrospective of his work was shown in Tokyo, Nagoya and Kyoto. He continued painting, writing and illustrating during the late 1960s. The Salvador Dali Museum in Cleveland was inaugurated in 1971, and the Dalinian Holographic Room opened at M. Knoedler and Co., New York, in 1973. The artist now lives in Port Lligat.

147 Paranoiac-critical Study of Vermeer's "Lacemaker."
1955
(Etude paranoïaque critique de la "Dentellière" de Vermeer)

76.2206

Oil on canvas, 10¾ x 8¾ in. (27.1 x 22.1 cm.)

Not signed or dated.

PROVENANCE:
Anonymous Gift, 1976

By 1954 Dali's fascination with Vermeer's painting of *The Lacemaker* merged with his interest in the logarithmic spiral as exemplified by the rhinoceros horn. That year Dali and Robert Descharnes collaborated on a film, *The Prodigious Story of the Lacemaker and the Rhinoceros,* and the following December the artist gave a lecture at the Sorbonne in Paris on "Phenomenological Aspects of the Paranoiac-Critical Method." Dali painted the Guggenheim's picture only after studying Vermeer's original in the Louvre, observing a rhinoceros at the zoo and painting a more representational copy of *The Lacemaker* (The Robert Lehman Collection, The Metropolitan Museum of Art, New York). He remembers that he did our *Paranoiac-critical Study* in two days in Spain.*

Little remains of the prototype in the Guggenheim painting: there is only the lacemaker's face surrounded by exploding forms which resemble rhinoceros horns. As early as 1934 Dali painted canvases with "paranoiac images" and defined the "paranoiac-critical" method "as a great art of playing upon all one's own inner contradictions with lucidity by causing others to experience the anxieties and ecstasies of one's life in such a way that it becomes gradually as essential to them as their own." *(The Unspeakable Confessions of Salvador Dali,* p. 17)

* conversation with the author, Apr. 1978

EXHIBITIONS:
New York, Carstairs Gallery, *Salvador Dali,* Dec. 4, 1956-Jan. 5, 1957, no. 6
Tokyo, Prince Hotel Gallery, *Salvador Dali,* Sept. 8-Oct. 18, 1964, no. 52, color repr., traveled to Nagoya, Prefectural Museum of Art, Oct. 23-30; Kyoto, Municipal Art Gallery, Nov. 3-29
New York, Gallery of Modern Art, *Salvador Dali 1910-1965,* Dec. 18, 1965-Feb. 28, 1966, no. 142, repr.
New York, The Solomon R. Guggenheim Museum, *Special Installation: Salvador Dali,* May 25-July 11, 1976
New York, The Solomon R. Guggenheim Museum, *Forty Modern Masters: An Anniversary Show,* Dec. 16, 1977-Feb. 5, 1978, no. 21, repr.

REFERENCES:
A. R. Morse, *Dali: a study of his life and work,* Greenwich, Conn., 1958, p. 81 and fig. 75
R. Descharnes, *The World of Salvador Dali,* New York, 1962, pp. 52-55, color repr.
S. Dali and A. Parinaud, *The Unspeakable Confessions of Salvador Dali,* New York, 1976, pp. 232-233, 297
R. Descharnes, *Salvador Dali,* New York, 1976, pp. 45, 152 and fig. 141
U. Kultermann, "Vermeer, versions modernes," *Connaissance des Arts,* no. 302, Apr. 1977, p. 96, color repr.

Yves Tanguy 1900-1955

Raymond Georges Yves Tanguy was born on January 5, 1900, in Paris. While attending lycée during the teens, he met Pierre Matisse, his future dealer and lifelong friend. In 1918 he joined the Merchant Marine and traveled to Africa, South America and England. During military service at Lunéville in 1920, Tanguy became friends with the poet Jacques Prévert. He returned to Paris in 1922 after volunteer service in Tunis and began sketching café scenes that were praised by Maurice de Vlaminck. After Tanguy saw Giorgio de Chirico's work in 1923, he decided to become a painter. In 1924 he, Prévert and Marcel Duhamel moved into a house that was to become a gathering place for the Surrealists. Tanguy became interested in Surrealism in 1924 when he saw the periodical *La Révolution Surréaliste*. André Breton welcomed him into the Surrealist group the following year.

Despite his lack of formal training, Tanguy's art developed quickly and his mature style emerged by 1927. His first one-man show was held in 1927 at the Galerie Surréaliste in Paris. In 1928 he participated with Arp, Ernst, André Masson, Miró, Picasso and others in the Surrealist exhibition at the Galerie Au Sacre du Printemps, Paris. Tanguy incorporated into his work the images of geological formations he had observed during a trip to Africa in 1930. He exhibited extensively during the 1930s in one-man and Surrealist group shows in New York, Brussels, Paris and London.

In 1939 Tanguy met the painter Kay Sage in Paris and later that year traveled with her to the American Southwest. They married in 1940 and settled in Woodbury, Connecticut. In 1942 Tanguy participated in the *Artists in Exile* show at the Pierre Matisse Gallery in New York, where he exhibited frequently until 1950. In 1947 his work was included in the exhibition *Le Surréalisme en 1947*, organized by Breton and Duchamp at the Galerie Maeght in Paris. He became a United States citizen in 1948. In 1953 he visited Rome, Milan and Paris on the occasion of his one-man shows in those cities. The following year he shared an exhibition with Kay Sage at the Wadsworth Atheneum in Hartford and appeared in Hans Richter's film *8 x 8*. A retrospective of Tanguy's work was held at The Museum of Modern Art in New York eight months after his death on January 15, 1955, in Woodbury.

148 Untitled. 1949

63.1663

Ink and paper collage on paper, 19⅞ x 14⅝ in. (50.5 x 37.4 cm.)

Signed and dated l.r.: *YVES TANGUY 49.*

PROVENANCE:
from the artist
Kay Sage Tanguy, Woodbury, Connecticut
Gift, Estate of Kay Sage Tanguy, 1963

Multiplicity of detail and precision of line characterize this drawing and others of a group Tanguy executed in 1949. Line cannot be separated from form in these works. The very shapes and the manner in which they are linked together occur also in coeval oil paintings: *Fear* (Collection Whitney Museum of American Art, New York) and *Flashing Fire* (Estate of Kay Sage Tanguy). Although the complex structure gives the initial impression of stability, it is in a precarious state, tenuously balanced on spindly points. Possessing aspects of a fantastic machine engaged in an undecipherable activity, it fills the page vertically and moves back into depth. This drawing can be related to Tanguy's Surrealist landscapes with lateral architectural aggregations of the late 1940s and early 1950s.

EXHIBITIONS:
Milan, Galleria del Naviglio, *Yves Tanguy,* Mar. 28-Apr. 1953
New York, Pierre Matisse Gallery, *Exhibition of Gouaches and Drawings by Yves Tanguy,* Mar. 26-Apr. 13, 1963, no. 64, repr.
New York, The Solomon R. Guggenheim Museum, *Selected Sculpture and Works on Paper,* July 8-Sept. 14, 1969, p. 86, repr.

REFERENCE:
Handbook, 1970, pp. 426-427, repr.

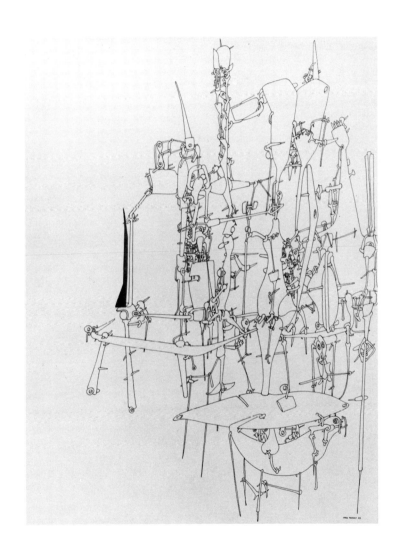

Matta b. 1911

Roberto Sebastian Antonio Matta Echaurren was born on November 11, 1911, in Santiago, Chile. After studying architecture at the Universidad Católica in Santiago, Matta went to Paris in 1934 to work as an apprentice to the architect Le Corbusier. By the mid-thirties he knew the poet Federico García Lorca, Dali and André Breton; in 1937 he left Le Corbusier's atelier and joined the Surrealist movement. This same year Matta's drawings were included in the Surrealist exhibition at Galerie Wildenstein in Paris. In 1938 he began painting with oils, executing a series of fantastic landscapes which he called "inscapes" or "psychological morphologies."

Matta fled Europe for New York in 1939, where he associated with other Surrealist emigrés including Ernst, Tanguy, André Masson and Breton. The Julien Levy Gallery in New York presented a one-man show of his paintings in 1940, and he was included in the *Artists in Exile* exhibition at the Pierre Matisse Gallery in New York in 1942. During the forties Matta's painting anticipated many innovations of the Abstract Expressionists and significantly influenced a number of New York School artists, in particular his friends Gorky and Motherwell. Towards the end of the war he evolved increasingly monstrous imagery; the appearance of mechanical forms and cinematic effects in Matta's work reflects the influence of Duchamp, whom he met in 1944. He broke with the Surrealists in 1948 and returned to Europe, settling in Rome in 1953. A mural for the UNESCO Building in Paris was executed by the artist in 1956. In 1957 he was honored with a major retrospective at The Museum of Modern Art in New York. His work was exhibited in Berlin in 1970 and Hannover in 1974. The artist now lives in Tarquinia, Italy, and Paris.

149 **Years of Fear.** 1941

72.1991

Oil on canvas, 44 x 56 in. (111.8 x 142.2 cm.)

Not signed or dated.

PROVENANCE:
from the artist
Pierre Matisse Gallery, New York, 1942-late 1950s
Private collection, New York, late 1950s-1968
Harold Diamond, New York, 1968-72

Like other canvases Matta painted early in the 1940s, *Years of Fear* contains changing, amorphic shapes within a landscape space which lacks either precise topography or a horizon line. He has thinly applied pigment in swirling patterns, focusing on colorful, sometimes jewel-like nuggets and structuring the canvas with web-like lines. The linear patterns establish spatial recession, link various parts of the composition and contribute a strong stabilizing element. The artist recalls that he painted *Years of Fear* in New York at the beginning of 1941, before going to Mexico in May.* After his Mexican sojourn, the yellow and gray tonalities of this picture would be replaced by more intense and brilliant colors. Although his pictorial vocabulary has evolved over the decades, Matta's plastic imagination remains consistent and his meaning continues to elude specific interpretation.

* correspondence with the author, Apr. 1979

EXHIBITIONS:
New York, Pierre Matisse Gallery, *Matta,* Mar. 31-Apr. 21, 1942, no. 9
The Arts Club of Chicago, *Matta,* Jan. 4-29, 1944, no. 16
New York, Andrew Crispo Gallery, *Matta: A Totemic World,* Jan. 11-Feb. 15, 1975, no. 5, repr.
London, Hayward Gallery, *Dada and Surrealism Reviewed,* Jan. 11-Mar. 27, 1978, no. 15.31, color repr.

REFERENCE:
A. Smith, "New York Letter," *Art International,* vol. 16, Oct. 1972, p. 52, repr.

150 Nature is Hostile. ca. 1951

74.2096

Pencil, charcoal and wax crayon on paper, 14 1/16 x 19 5/8 in. (35.7 x 49.8 cm.)

Inscribed l.r.: *There is a contradiction between fantasy and reality—Nature is hostile—a life has to HOLD to keep a form. Nov. 11.* Not signed or dated.

PROVENANCE:

Daniel Catton Rich, Worcester, Massachusetts, and New York, by 1970
Gift, Daniel Catton Rich, 1974

Matta dates this drawing 1951 and relates it to his large canvas, *The Spherical Roof around Our Tribe* of 1952 (Collection The Museum of Modern Art, New York), which has similar compositional elements, as well as to certain of his other paintings of the time.* The landscape associations of his earlier work have now been replaced by suggestions of human figures: for example, the raised arms at top center and upper right in the drawing resemble those in the painting *Les Evanisseur qui nui eve* (Collection Laureati, Rome). Matta articulates forms and defines movement in space with deftly placed pencil lines, smudged and erased in some places and broken into rows of dots in others. There are accents in red and yellow crayon only at the lower left and center of the page, where shapes collide with almost explosive force.

* correspondence with the author, Apr. 1979

Victor Brauner 1903-1966

Victor Brauner was born on June 15, 1903, in Piatra-Neamt, Rumania. His father was involved in spiritualism and sent Brauner to evangelical school in Braïla from 1916 to 1918. In 1921 he briefly attended the School of Fine Arts in Bucharest, where he painted Cézannesque landscapes. He exhibited paintings in his subsequent expressionist style at his first one-man show at the Galerie Mozart in Bucharest in 1925. Brauner helped found the Dadaist review 75 HP in Bucharest. He went to Paris in 1925 but returned to Bucharest approximately a year later. In Bucharest in 1929 Brauner was associated with the Dadaist and Surrealist review UNU.

Brauner settled in Paris in 1930 and became friends with his compatriot Brancusi. Then he met Tanguy who introduced him to the Surrealists by 1933. André Breton wrote an enthusiastic introduction to the catalogue for Brauner's first Parisian one-man show at the Galerie Pierre in 1934. The exhibition was not well-received, and in 1935 Brauner returned to Bucharest where he remained until 1938. That year he moved to Paris, lived briefly with Tanguy and painted a number of works featuring distorted human figures with mutilated eyes. Some of these paintings, dated as early as 1931, proved gruesomely prophetic when he lost his own eye in a scuffle in 1938. At the outset of World War II Brauner fled to the south of France, where he maintained contact with other Surrealists in Marseille. Later he sought refuge in Switzerland; unable to obtain suitable materials there, he improvised an encaustic from candle wax and developed a graffito technique.

Brauner returned to Paris in 1945. He was included in the *Exposition Internationale du Surréalisme* at the Galerie Maeght in Paris in 1947. His postwar painting incorporated forms and symbols based on Tarot cards, Egyptian hieroglyphics and antique Mexican codices. In the fifties Brauner traveled to Normandy and Italy, and his work was shown at the Venice Biennale in 1954 and 1966. He died in Paris on March 12, 1966.

151 **Spread of Thought.** July 1956
(*L'Etendue de la pensée*)

59.1517

Oil on canvas, 28¾ x 23½ in. (73.1 x 59.7 cm.)

Signed and dated l.r.: *V.B. VII. 1956.*

PROVENANCE:

from the artist
Alexandre Iolas Gallery, New York, by 1958
Gift, Dominique and John de Menil, 1959

Brauner often selected titles which referred to abstract concepts, inner states or mental faculties. Not interested in representing objects per se, he concentrated on psychological states, usually endowing them with a totemic or iconic morphology.

Spread of Thought is rather unusual among Brauner's mature works, where simplified compositions on a flat, single-toned ground are far more common. The angular stylization of the figure as well as the repetitive hatched motifs of the background are distinctly reminiscent of primitive art. The figure's static and hieratic frontality and the decorative hatching recur from time to time in other paintings and drawings from 1956 to 1960.

EXHIBITIONS:

New York, The Solomon R. Guggenheim Museum, *Inaugural Selection,* Oct. 21, 1959-June 19, 1960
New York, The Solomon R. Guggenheim Museum, *Elements of Modern Art,* Oct. 3-Nov. 12, 1961 and Jan. 9-25, 1962

REFERENCES:

L. Hoctin, "A propos de Victor Brauner," *Cahiers d'Art,* 31-32ᵉ années, 1956-57, p. 387, repr.
Handbook, 1970, pp. 50, repr., 51

Wifredo Lam 1902-1982

Wifredo Oscar de la Concepción Lam y Castilla was born in Sagua la Grande, Cuba, on December 8, 1902. His family moved in 1916 to Havana, where he attended the Escuela de Bellas Artes. During the early 1920s he exhibited at the Salón de la Asociación de Pintores y Escultores in Havana. In 1923 Lam traveled to Madrid; there he studied with Fernández Alvarez de Sotomayor and at the Academia Libre in the Pasaje de la Alhambra. He was impressed with the prehistoric art in the Museo Arqueológico and with the works of Bruegel, Bosch and El Greco in the Museo del Prado.

In 1938 the artist moved to Paris. He met Picasso, who introduced him to Chagall, Miró, Léger, Matisse, Tristan Tzara, Paul Eluard and others. Lam shared an exhibition with Picasso at the Perls Galleries in New York in 1939. That same year Lam's first one-man show in Paris was held at the Galerie Pierre Loeb, and he joined the Surrealist group. In 1941 he boarded a ship with hundreds of intellectuals fleeing Europe from Marseille. After a period of detention near Martinique, Lam eventually made his way to Havana in 1942. From 1942 to 1950 he was given one-man exhibitions regularly at the Pierre Matisse Gallery in New York.

After a stay of several months in Haiti, in 1946 Lam returned to France via New York, where he met James Johnson Sweeney, Gorky, Duchamp, Nicolas Calas and Calder. He traveled extensively until 1952, when he settled in Paris. In 1953 a one-man show of his work was held at Galerie Maeght in Paris. In 1955 he resumed his travels, visiting Sweden, South America, Cuba, the United States, France and Mexico. From 1960 Lam maintained a studio in Albisola, Italy. The artist went to Cuba in 1963 on the invitation of the revolutionary government. In 1964 and 1965 he visited Italy and France. During the second half of the decade he was given numerous retrospectives in Europe. Several one-man shows of Lam's work were held in 1970, primarily in Italy. His ceramics were exhibited for the first time in 1975. Lam died in Paris on September 11, 1982.

152 **Rumblings of the Earth.** 1950
(Rumor de la tierra)

59.1525

Oil on canvas, 59¾ x 112 in. (151.7 x 284.5 cm.)

Not signed or dated.

PROVENANCE:
from the artist
Gift, Mr. and Mrs. Joseph Cantor, Indianapolis, 1959

Both *Rumblings of the Earth* and another canvas Lam painted in 1950, *Zambezia-Zambezia* in the Guggenheim Museum collection, were inspired by Surrealist images and primitive art. The artist stated in May 1969 that "this picture took form in 1950, without any definite or 'literary' idea behind it, by emerging, as it were, from the day-to-day strivings of a painter who, faced with a canvas, constructs an organic composition out of the simple elements and complex forms of his language. It was only afterwards that these forms became strictly poetical symbols, such as carnal love, materialized as flames in the right-hand side of the picture. I call this work *Rumblings of the Earth* by which I mean the earth and its imperatives, the substances of which it is composed and the forms they assume: unending transmutations, fertilizations, births and deaths." (New York, Center for Inter-American Relations, 1969, p. 18)

EXHIBITIONS:
Havana, Parque Central, *Lam: Obras Recientes 1950,* Oct. 2-15, 1950, no. 9

London, ICA Gallery, *Wifredo Lam,* 1952, no. 8

Paris, Galerie Maeght, *Wifredo Lam,* Feb. 1953, no. 2

New York, The Solomon R. Guggenheim Museum, *Inaugural Selection,* Oct. 21, 1959-June 19, 1960

Notre Dame, Ind., University of Notre Dame Art Gallery, *Wifredo Lam,* Jan. 8-29, 1961, repr.

New York, Art Gallery, Center for Inter-American Relations, *Latin American Paintings From the Collection of The Solomon R. Guggenheim Museum,* July 2-Sept. 14, 1969, pp. 18-19, repr.

REFERENCES:
W. Lam, "Oeuvres récentes de Wifredo Lam," *Cahiers d'Art,* 26e année, 1951, p. 181, repr.

Medium, no. 4, Jan. 1955, opp. p. 17, repr.

M. Leiris, *Wifredo Lam,* Milan, 1970, no. 108, color repr.

Handbook, 1970, pp. 260-261, repr.

M.-P. Fouchet, *Wifredo Lam,* Barcelona, 1976, pp. 92-93, pl. 98

Rufino Tamayo b. 1899

Rufino Tamayo was born August 26, 1899, in Oaxaca, Mexico. Orphaned by 1911, he moved to Mexico City to live with an aunt who sent him to commercial school. Tamayo began taking drawing lessons in 1915 and by 1917 had left commercial school to devote himself entirely to the study of art. In 1921 he was appointed Head of the Department of Ethnographic Drawing at the Museo Nacional de Arqueología, Mexico City, where his duties included drawing pre-Columbian objects in the museum's collection. Tamayo integrated the forms and slatey tones of pre-Columbian ceramics into his early still lifes and portraits of the men and women of Mexico.

The first exhibition of Tamayo's work in the United States was held at the Weyhe Gallery, New York, in 1926. He received the first of many mural commissions from the Escuela Nacional de Música in Mexico City in 1932. In 1936 the artist moved to New York, and throughout the late thirties and early forties the Valentine Gallery, New York, gave him shows. He taught for nine years, beginning in 1938, at the Dalton School in New York. In 1948 Tamayo's first retrospective took place at the Instituto de Bellas Artes, Mexico City. Tamayo was influenced by European modernism during his stay in New York and later when he traveled in Europe and settled in Paris in 1957. He executed a mural for the UNESCO Building in Paris in 1958. Tamayo returned to Mexico City in 1964, making it his permanent home. The French government named him Chevalier and Officier de la Légion d'Honneur in 1956 and 1969 respectively, and he has been the recipient of numerous other honors and awards. His work has been exhibited internationally in group and one-man shows, one of the most important of which was a retrospective at the 1977 São Paulo Bienal. In 1979 Tamayo was honored with a retrospective at The Solomon R. Guggenheim Museum. The artist lives and works in Mexico City.

153 **Woman in Grey.** 1959
(Mujer en gris)

59.1563

Oil on canvas, 76¾ x 51 in. (195 x 129.5 cm.)

Signed and dated l.l.: *Tamayo / o-59.*

PROVENANCE:
from the artist through M. Knoedler and Co., Inc., New York, 1959

Tamayo's orientation toward School of Paris artists does not obscure the inspiration of his Mexican heritage. *Woman in Grey* combines austerity and warm earthiness of palette with a female figure reminiscent of Picasso's work of the late 1920s and early 1930s. The stylized contour of the woman's body is repeated in the decorative background pattern, and a consistently painted surface unifies the canvas. Tamayo's commitment to figure painting is demonstrated in a related contemporary painting, *Woman in White* of 1959 (Collection Milwaukee Art Center), and in later canvases such as *Dancer* of 1977 (Collection The Solomon R. Guggenheim Museum).

EXHIBITIONS:
New York, M. Knoedler and Co., Inc., *Tamayo,* Nov. 17-Dec. 12, 1959, no. 13

Ann Arbor, Museum of Art, University of Michigan, *Images at Mid-Century,* Apr. 13-June 12, 1960

New York, The Solomon R. Guggenheim Museum, *Guggenheim International Award, 1960,* Nov. 1, 1960-Jan. 29, 1961

Mexico City, Museo de Arte Moderno, *Rufino Tamayo,* Sept. 1964, no. 25

Ithaca, N. Y., Andrew Dickson White Museum of Art, Cornell University, *The Emergent Decade: Latin American Painters and Painting in the 1960s,* Oct. 8-Nov. 8, 1965, traveled to Dallas Museum of Fine Arts, Dec. 18, 1965-Jan. 18, 1966; Ottawa, National Gallery of Canada, Apr. 1-May 1; New York, The Solomon R. Guggenheim Museum (organizer), May 20-June 19; Champaign-Urbana, Krannert Art Museum, University of Illinois, Sept. 16-Oct. 9; Lincoln, Mass., De Cordova Museum, Nov. 6-Dec. 4; Sarasota, John and Mable Ringling Museum of Art, Apr. 9-May 7, 1967

Phoenix Art Museum, *Tamayo,* Mar. 1968, no. 69, color repr.

New York, Art Gallery, Center for Inter-American Relations, *Latin American Paintings From the Collection of The Solomon R. Guggenheim Museum,* July 2- Sept. 14, 1969, pp. 34-35, repr.

Paris, Musée d'Art Moderne de la Ville de Paris, *Tamayo: Peintures, 1960-1974,* Nov. 27, 1974-Feb. 2, 1975, no. 3

São Paulo, XIV Bienal, *Rufino Tamayo,* Oct. 1-Dec. 18, 1977

Washington, D.C., The Phillips Collection, *Rufino Tamayo: Fifty Years of His Painting,* Oct. 6- Nov. 18, 1978, no. 23, color repr., traveled to San Antonio, Marion Koogler McNay Art Institute, Jan. 6-Feb. 17, 1979

New York, The Solomon R. Guggenheim Museum, *Rufino Tamayo: Myth and Magic,* May 18-Aug. 12, 1979, no. 62, color repr.

REFERENCES:

E. Genauer, *Rufino Tamayo,* New York, 1974, color pl. 51

H. H. Arnason, *History of Modern Art,* rev. ed., New York, 1977, p. 577, fig. 1009

Julius Bissier 1893-1965

Julius Heinrich Bissier was born on December 3, 1893, in Freiburg-im-Breisgau, Germany. He first studied art history at the University in his native city in 1913 but decided to become an artist and enrolled in the Kunstakademie Karlsruhe the following year. His artistic training was cut short after a few months by World War I; after serving throughout the conflict, Bissier began to paint independently. Bissier's first one-man show was held at the Kunstverein, Freiburg-im-Breisgau, in 1920. He was awarded the Prize for Painting at the Deutsche Künstlerbund exhibition in Hannover in 1928. He taught at the University of Freiburg-im-Breisgau from 1929 to 1933. The Orientalist Ernst Grosse introduced Bissier to Far Eastern art, and Willi Baumeister stimulated his interest in modern abstract painting. He visited Paris and met Brancusi in 1933. In the early 1930s Bissier made his first abstract brush paintings, a form of expression to which he devoted himself almost exclusively from 1932 to 1947.

The artist's long friendship with Oskar Schlemmer began in 1933. Bissier did not exhibit between 1933 and 1945 because of the political situation. In 1934 nearly all of his work was destroyed in a fire at the University of Freiburg-im-Breisgau. In 1939, after several trips to Italy, Bissier moved to Hagnau, Germany, on the shores of Lake Constance; there he started to make designs for tapestries and fabrics. He executed his first color monotypes in 1947 and in the early fifties began to experiment with egg-tempera, which he used in his "miniatures" of 1955-56. His friendship with Arp dated from 1957. In 1958 the first major Bissier retrospective was held at the Kestner-Gesellschaft Hannover and traveled to other German cities. The artist executed a mural for the University in Freiburg-im-Breisgau in 1959-60. He was honored with one-man exhibitions at the Venice Biennale in 1960 and the São Paulo Bienal the following year. He became friends with Nicholson and Mark Tobey in this period. In 1961 Bissier moved to Ascona, Switzerland, where he died on June 18, 1965.

154 **Cista (Archaic Symbol).** 1937
(Cista [archaisches Symbol])

76.2239

India ink on paper, 9¾ x 7¼ in. (24.7 x 18.2 cm.)

Signed and dated l.c.: *37 / Julius Bissier*; inscribed l.l.: *Cista (archaisches Symbol) 1937 / wertvolles Blatt*; l.r.: *unten.*

PROVENANCE:

Estate of the artist, 1965-76
Gift, Mrs. Lisbeth Bissier, Ascona, 1976

In the early 1930s Bissier began to make drawings with India ink and a brush on Japanese papers, a category of work he designated *"kleine Tuschen."* Cognizant of the art and thought of China and Japan, Bissier manifests an original calligraphy in his work. He deftly places the black symbol on the white page and appends his emblematic signature, the imprint of an inked cork. During the 1930s Bissier executed several brush drawings entitled *Cista* which are inspired by Johann Jakob Bachofen's analysis of symbolism in antiquity.* He probably added the title and date to the Guggenheim drawing after World War II.

* W. Schmalenbach, *Julius Bissier,* Cologne, 1974, p. 79

EXHIBITION:

Kestner-Gesellschaft Hannover, *Julius Bissier,* Oct. 24-Nov. 30, 1958, no. 6

Bissier

155 Dark Whitsunday. May 21, 1961
(Dunkler Pfingsttag)

76.2258

Egg-oil tempera on batiste, 17⅜ x 19 in. (44.2 x 48.2 cm.)

Signed and dated c.l.: *dunkler Pfingsttag 61 Julius Bissier.*

PROVENANCE:

from the artist
Lefebre Gallery, New York, 1961
Mr. and Mrs. L. F. Gittler, New York, 1961-70
Lefebre Gallery, New York, 1970
Mrs. Andrew P. Fuller, New York, 1970-76
Gift, Mrs. Andrew P. Fuller, 1976

The bold asceticism of Bissier's brush drawings stands in contrast to the colorfulness of his late work. The subtle harmony of delicate shades arises in part from his practice of mixing dry pigment and egg-oil emulsion and then applying it to a ground of powdered chalk and poppy-seed oil treated with synthetic varnish. He obtains an irregular network of wrinkles by soaking and later wringing out the cloth support.

Like many of the "miniatures" Bissier painted between 1956 and 1965, *Dark Whitsunday* represents an aggregation of containers: pitcher, vase, bottles and glass. Not only the letters (YRN) but also the inscription (title, date and signature) become integral parts of the composition. As indicated by the title, Bissier executed the work on Whitsunday, which fell on May 21 in 1961.

EXHIBITIONS:

New York, Lefebre Gallery, *Julius Bissier,* Nov. 7-Dec. 2, 1961

San Francisco Museum of Art, *Julius Bissier, 1893-1965: A Retrospective Exhibition,* Sept. 18-Oct. 27, 1968, no. 135, color repr., traveled to Washington, D.C., The Phillips Collection, Nov. 18-Dec. 22; Pittsburgh, Museum of Art, Carnegie Institute, Jan. 20-Feb. 23, 1969; Dallas Museum of Fine Arts, Mar. 19-Apr. 20; New York, The Solomon R. Guggenheim Museum, May 16-June 29

Wols 1913-1951

Wols was born Alfred Otto Wolfgang Schulze on May 27, 1913, in Berlin. In 1919 the family moved to Dresden, where he developed his considerable talent in music. During a visit to Berlin in 1932 Wols met Moholy-Nagy, on whose advice he settled in Paris. There he supported himself as a photographer and became acquainted with Léger, Arp, Giacometti and Amédée Ozenfant. After moving to Spain in 1933, he was ordered back to Germany for labor service; his refusal to return resulted in lifelong expatriation. Wols was imprisoned in Barcelona in 1935 for his controversial political attitudes. Upon his release several months later he was sent back to France.

In 1937 Wols was an official photographer at the *Exposition internationale* in Paris. The same year he exhibited his photographs at a small Parisian gallery. This success was immediately followed by the outbreak of war and his internment in several French camps. When Wols was freed in 1940, he settled in the coastal town of Cassis. As the fighting drew nearer in 1942, he fled inland to Dieulefit where he befriended the poet Henri-Pierre Roché. In 1945 Roché brought Wols' work to the attention of René Drouin, who gave him a one-man show later that year. Wols visited Paris for the exhibition and remained there, becoming friends with the painters Camille Bryen and Georges Mathieu. In 1947 he exhibited his first large paintings in a second one-man show at the Galerie René Drouin and received praise from Jean-Paul Sartre. That same year he participated in the Salon des Réalités Nouvelles and illustrated books by Sartre, Antonin Artaud and Kafka. The artist's dependency on alcohol, which apparently developed in the internment camps, became so severe that he underwent treatment in 1951. On recovering, Wols moved to Champigny, in the country near Paris. He was given a solo exhibition in 1951 at the Galerie Nina Dausset in Paris. Wols died on September 1, 1951, at age thirty-eight, in Champigny.

156 **Houses.** 1942
(Maisons)

48.1172 x423

Watercolor and ink on paper, 6¼ x 4¼ in.
(15.9 x 10.9 cm.)

Signed l.r.: *WOLS*; inscribed on reverse, not by the artist: *Wols / "Houses."* Not dated.

PROVENANCE:

from the artist (?)
Karl Nierendorf, New York, by 1948
Estate of Karl Nierendorf, 1948

Wols has filled the small dimensions of this watercolor with a fantastic landscape of houses and rocky cliffs. Houses and cities recur in his oeuvre and often, as here, they are seen as if from a ship. Werner Haftmann thinks* that our watercolor was executed in 1942, during the last year of Wols' stay at Cassis, a coastal town with quarries and cliffs near Marseille on the Mediterranean.

Wols is essentially a graphic artist. With great delicacy and precision his line records and communicates. His images originate from his inner resources: he explores and evokes a strange dream-like world of the subconscious.

* correspondence with the author, Feb. 1979

EXHIBITIONS:

New York, The Solomon R. Guggenheim Museum, *European Drawings,* Feb. 24-Apr. 17, 1966, no. 141, repr., traveled to Minneapolis, University Gallery, University of Minnesota, May 10-31; Lincoln, Mass., De Cordova Museum, June 26-Sept. 4; Providence, Museum of Art, Rhode Island School of Design, Sept. 14-Oct. 8; Ottawa, National Gallery of Canada, Nov. 28-Dec. 25; Milwaukee Art Center, Jan. 5-Feb. 5, 1967; Atlanta, The High Museum of Art, Mar. 1-31; Dallas Museum of Fine Arts, Apr. 15-May 15, Champaign-Urbana, Krannert Art Museum, University of Illinois, May 28-June 25; Raleigh, North Carolina Museum of Art, July 15-Aug. 20
New York, The Solomon R. Guggenheim Museum, *Selected Sculpture and Works on Paper,* July 8-Sept. 14, 1969, p. 87, repr.

REFERENCE:
Handbook, 1970, p. 435, repr.

Henri Michaux b. 1899

Henri Michaux was born on May 24, 1899, in Namur, Belgium. His early childhood was spent in Brussels and his adolescence in a country boarding school where he majored in Flemish studies. In 1914 Michaux returned to German-occupied Brussels, and during this period he began to write. His writings were first published in 1922, and Michaux had already gained recognition as an author when he moved to Paris in 1924. In Paris Michaux saw the work of Ernst, Giorgio de Chirico and Klee. Between 1925 and 1927 he began to draw and paint in his spare time, although he had no formal artistic training. In 1927 Michaux traveled to Ecuador with his poet friend Alfredo Gangoténa, and this same year his first important book, *Qui je fus,* was published in Paris.

For the next ten years Michaux traveled extensively, visiting Turkey, South America, India and China, and wrote numerous books about his journeys. In 1937 he began to paint on a regular basis and was given his first exhibition at the Galerie Pierre, Paris. The artist for the most part uses India ink but has also worked in other media such as oil and pastel. His series include the Alphabets, 1924 to 1934, Black Backgrounds, 1937-38, Frottages, 1944 to 1947, and Movements, 1950-51. In 1954 Michaux began to experiment with hallucinogens and from this time until 1962 he attempted to depict his drug-induced visions. Michaux has also given written accounts of these experiences in books such as *Misérable Miracle* of 1957. In 1964 a major Michaux retrospective was held at the Musée National d'Art Moderne, Paris, and his work was the subject of the film *H.M. ou l'Espace du Dedans.* In 1966 the Galerie Le Point Cardinal, Paris, began to represent Michaux and showed his work regularly throughout the next decade. In 1978 the Musée National d'Art Moderne, Paris, held an important Michaux retrospective which traveled in part to The Solomon R. Guggenheim Museum and the Musée d'Art Contemporain, Montreal. Michaux lives in Paris.

157 Untitled. 1948

65.1772

Pencil and watercolor on paper, 15⅜ x 11½ in. (39.1 x 29.2 cm.)

Signed l.r.: *HM.* Not dated.

PROVENANCE:

from the artist
Le Point Cardinal, Paris, 1965

Soon after his wife's death in a tragic accident, within two months time Michaux executed hundreds of pen and ink and wash drawings similar to this example. The artist's sense of despair is expressed visually through the monstrous organic shape which resembles a head, the jarring introduction of red, lavender and turquoise tints and the fuzzy line which erodes form. A head-like image which disappears only to reemerge is a recurrent theme although it is most prevalent in Michaux's early work. Likewise, he consistently favors gouache and watercolor as mediums because of the freedom and fluidity they permit.

EXHIBITIONS:

New York, The Solomon R. Guggenheim Museum, *Selected Sculpture and Works on Paper,* July 8-Sept. 14, 1969, p. 61, repr.

New York, The Solomon R. Guggenheim Museum, *Henri Michaux,* Sept. 8-Oct. 15, 1978, no. 163

REFERENCE:
Handbook, 1970, p. 294, repr.

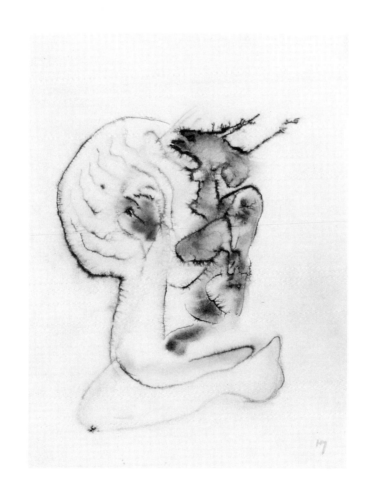

158 Untitled. June 1960

74.2082

India ink on paper, 29⅛ x 43¼ in. (74 x 109.9 cm.)

Signed l.r.: *HM*; dated on reverse: *Juin 1960*.

PROVENANCE:
from the artist
Daniel Cordier, Paris
Anonymous Gift, 1974

Michaux has demonstrated a predilection for India ink since its appearance in his work of the mid-1950s. A prolific quantity of drawings similar to this example is concentrated around 1960. In these, the artist first dropped or flung ink blots onto the paper and then shaped and elaborated upon them with lines. Randomly scattered over the page, the ink blots form a quite dense, allover pattern. Within the horizontal, block-like format they establish an intense, agitated rhythm. Michaux's work is characterized by an abstract calligraphy reminiscent of the Surrealist technique of automatic writing.

EXHIBITION:
New York, The Solomon R. Guggenheim Museum, *Henri Michaux*, Sept. 8-Oct. 15, 1978, no. 164

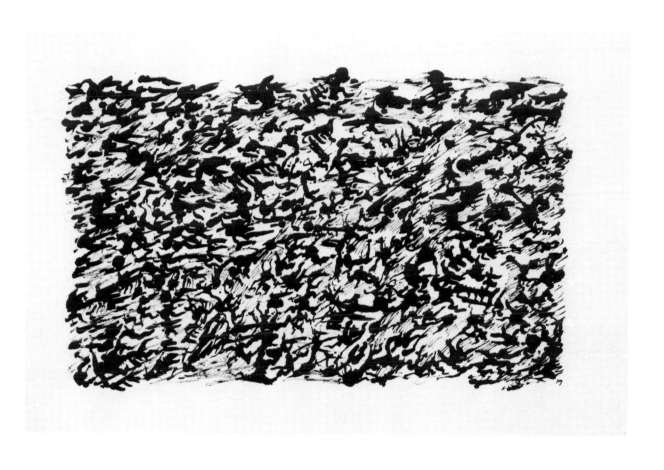

Jiří Kolář b. 1914

Jiří Kolář was born on September 24, 1914, in Protivín in southern Bohemia. As a young man he learned carpentry and worked at a variety of odd jobs. He was interested in literature and decided to become a poet after reading Marinetti's *Les mots en liberté futuristes* in Czech translation in 1930. In 1934 Kolář began to experiment with collage; some of these early works were exhibited in 1937 at the Mozarteum in Prague.

It was as a poet that Kolář initially distinguished himself. His first volume of poetry, *Křestný list (Birth Certificate)*, was published in 1942. The following year he was a founding member of *Group 42*, comprised of Czech artists, photographers and art historians interested in the role of modern urban society in their work. After the war years Kolář moved to Prague, became an editor of the weekly *Lidová kultůra (Popular Culture)* and continued to write poetry. His poems were published in several books including *Dny v roce (Days in a Year)* of 1948. His first trip outside Czechoslovakia took him to England and Scotland. In the early 1950s Kolář experimented with various collage techniques. In 1953 he was imprisoned for several months because his poetry was regarded as anti-Stalinist; he was forbidden to publish until 1964. He worked primarily on concrete poems and collages where unrelated texts and images are juxtaposed. An important one-man show was held in 1962 at the Galerie S.V.U. Mánes in Prague; he has subsequently exhibited frequently in Europe. The forms of his art multiplied with crazygrammes, rollages, chiasmages, crumplages, banners and veiled intercollages. In 1967 Kolář began making daily collages, an outgrowth of the daily journal he had kept since 1946. He received First Prize at the São Paulo Bienal in 1969 and the following year traveled to the United States, Canada and Japan. Major exhibitions of his work were organized by The Solomon R. Guggenheim Museum in 1975 and the Albright-Knox Art Gallery in Buffalo in 1978. The artist lives in Paris.

159 **Mirror from the book "Bilderspiegel."** 1966

77.2375

Scratched mirror and paper collage, 3⅜ x 3⅜ in. (8.6 x 8.6 cm.)

Signed and dated on mount l.r.: *Jiří Kolář 66.*

PROVENANCE:

from the artist
Galerie Wendtorf-Swetec, Düsseldorf, 1973
Hubertus Schoeller, Düsseldorf, 1973-76
Mr. and Mrs. William C. Edwards, Jr., Dallas, 1976-77
Gift, Mr. and Mrs. William C. Edwards, Jr., 1977

Kolář transformed this little mirror with an image for a book he designed. Entitled *Bilderspiegel (Picture mirror)*, this book of poems by Konrad Balder Schäuffelen was published by Wolfgang Hake in Cologne in 1966. Our mirror is number twenty-five in an edition of one hundred. Kolář has scratched the reverse of the mirror so that a glimpse of the reproduction he has glued to the back appears on the reflective surface. Each page of the small volume has a square opening; thus, the mirror inside the back cover is always visible.*

The artist's collaboration on this publication grew out of his love of books and his vocation as a poet. The mirror becomes a form of collage, since the tiny face of the man pictured becomes part of our own reflection. Likewise, the trompe l'oeil effect Kolář achieves with rollage, one of many variations of collage he has developed, is related to the distorted appearances produced by trick mirrors. His work is characterized by the inventiveness and diversity of his elaborations upon collage techniques and the resulting spatial and metaphysical ambiguities.

* confirmed by Kolář in correspondence with Thomas M. Messer, Apr. 1979

EXHIBITIONS:

New York, The Solomon R. Guggenheim Museum, *Jiří Kolář,* Sept. 12-Nov. 9, 1975, no. 109

Buffalo, Albright-Knox Art Gallery, *Jiří Kolář: Transformations,* Apr. 28-May 29, 1978, no. 28, repr., traveled to Toronto, Art Gallery of Ontario, June 9-July 9; Athens, Georgia Museum of Art, The University of Georgia, Oct. 29-Dec. 3

160 Reverence to Columbus. 1968-69

72.1992

Paper collage on plaster and board (chiasmage), three objects, total 35½ x 81½ x 48¼ in. (90.2 x 207 x 122.5 cm.)

Signed and dated on reverse: *JIŘI KOLAŘ—POCTA KOLUMBOVI 1968-69.*

PROVENANCE:
from the artist
Art Centrum, Prague, 1969
Willard Gallery, New York, 1969-72

Reverence to Columbus consists of three objects: a large egg, a small head and a flat base where a collage of cartographic fragments creates a fantastic map. Each part is completely covered with small pieces of torn, printed paper reassembled to form patterns. Since the mid-1960s Kolář's application of this technique, which he calls "chiasmage," to free-standing objects negates their three-dimensionality and often alters their meanings. Apples and pears as well as eggs are his favorite subjects for chiasmaged objects. *Reverence to Columbus* refers to an apocryphal story in which Christopher Columbus smashed an egg down on its large end to make it stand up straight (as it does here).

EXHIBITIONS:
New York, Willard Gallery, *Chiasmagen, Collages, Objects, Muchlages, Photo Screen, Rollages, 1966-69,* Dec. 2, 1969-Jan. 3, 1970
Dublin, Royal Dublin Society, *ROSC '71,* Oct. 24-Dec. 29, 1971, no. 70, repr.
New York, The Solomon R. Guggenheim Museum, *Jiři Kolář,* Sept. 12-Nov. 9, 1975, no. 191, repr.

Francis Bacon b. 1909

Francis Bacon was born in Dublin on October 28, 1909. At the age of sixteen he moved to London and subsequently lived for about two years in Berlin and Paris. Bacon never attended art school but began to draw and work in watercolor about 1926-27. A Picasso exhibition he saw at Paul Rosenberg's gallery in Paris in 1926 and Picasso's work in general had a decisive influence on his painting until the mid-1940s. Upon his return to London in 1929 he established himself as a furniture designer and interior designer. He began to use oils in the autumn of that year and exhibited furniture and rugs as well as a few paintings in his studio. His work was included in group exhibitions in London at the Mayor Gallery in 1933 and Thos. Agnew and Sons in 1937.

Bacon's mature style emerged around 1944, and his first one-man show took place at the Hanover Gallery in London in 1949. From the mid-1940s into the 1950s Bacon's work reflects the influence of Surrealism and reveals the artist's predilection for figures in interior spaces. He avoids the static image of traditional figure painting and attempts to show his subjects in motion, frequently using blurring to suggest mobility. He has dwelt upon images of a screaming person and an open mouth. In the 1950s Bacon drew on such sources as Velázquez's *Portrait of Pope Innocent X,* van Gogh's *The Painter on the Road to Tarascon* and Muybridge's photographs. Receptive to photographic images in the conception of his paintings, Bacon clips illustrations from newspapers and magazines. Friends such as Lucien Freud and George Dyer have posed for him. Since the mid-1960s his canvases reveal a greater sense of depth, brighter and more varied colors and the use of foreshortened and twisting forms to create a nightmare vision. Major retrospectives of Bacon's work opened at The Solomon R. Guggenheim Museum in 1963 and at the Grand Palais in Paris in 1971; paintings from 1968 to 1974 were exhibited at The Metropolitan Museum of Art, New York, in 1975. The artist lives in London.

161 Three Studies for a Crucifixion. March 1962

64.1700

Oil with sand on canvas, three panels, each 78 x 57 in. (198.2 x 144.8 cm.)

Not signed or dated.

PROVENANCE:

from the artist through Marlborough Fine Art Ltd., London, 1964

Bacon first grouped three panels together in 1944 in the major work *Three Studies for Figures at the Base of a Crucifixion* (Collection Tate Gallery, London). Eighteen years later he returned to the triptych format with the Guggenheim's *Three Studies for a Crucifixion*. While the artist was undoubtedly aware of representations of the Crucifixion by Grünewald, Picasso and by his friend Roy de Maistre, he does not believe in its Christian meaning. For Bacon it is not a religious subject but the ultimate example of man's inhuman behavior to man.

Bacon worked on the three panels separately during a two week period in March 1962 when he was drinking heavily. As he completed them, they evolved into a triptych and were finished together; parts of the left panel were reworked later the same month. Bacon finds that many images come to him at once, and that the triptych format allows for such groupings without implying any narrative sequence. As the artist has explained, the undulating figure in the right panel was inspired by Christ in Cimabue's Crucifixion, which always reminded him of a worm crawling down the cross. The significance of the two figures in the left panel remains mysterious, while the foreground images of meat and the slaughterhouse are associated with the physical aspects of the Crucifixion. The violence in the center panel has decidedly modern connotations made explicit by the victim's smashed head, the bullet holes and bloodstained bed and intensified by the expressive reds, oranges and blacks of the three panels.

EXHIBITIONS:

London, Tate Gallery, *Francis Bacon,* May 24-July 1, 1962, no. 90, color repr., traveled to Kunsthalle Mannheim, July 18-Aug. 26; Turin, Galleria Civica d'Arte Moderna, Sept. 11-Oct. 14; Kunsthaus Zürich, Oct. 27-Nov. 25; Amsterdam, Stedelijk Museum, Jan. 11-Feb. 18, 1963

London, Tate Gallery, *British Painting in the Sixties,* June 1-30, 1963, no. 4

New York, The Solomon R. Guggenheim Museum, *Francis Bacon,* Oct. 18, 1963-Jan. 12, 1964, no. 57, repr., traveled to The Art Institute of Chicago, Jan. 24-Feb. 23

Paris, Grand Palais, *Francis Bacon,* Oct. 26, 1971-Jan. 10, 1972, no. 41, traveled to Städtische Kunsthalle Düsseldorf, Mar. 7-May 7

REFERENCES:

R. Alley, "Francis Bacon," *Cimaise,* 10e année, Jan.-Feb. 1963, pp. 22-23, repr.

J. Rothenstein and R. Alley, *Francis Bacon,* London, 1964, pp. 144-145, repr., 146, 274, no. 201

Handbook, 1970, pp. 29-31, repr.

J. Russell, *Francis Bacon,* Greenwich, Conn., 1971, pp. 89, 173-174, 207-208 and color pl. 18

H. Geldzahler, "Introduction," *Francis Bacon: Recent Paintings 1968-1974,* exh. cat., New York, 1975, p. 12

L. Trucchi, *Francis Bacon,* Milan, 1975, pl. 77

D. Sylvester, *Francis Bacon: Interviewed by David Sylvester,* New York, 1975, pp. 13, repr., 14, 22, 23, 44, 46, 54, 84, 86

H. H. Arnason, *History of Modern Art,* rev. ed., New York, 1977, p. 560, figs. 981-983

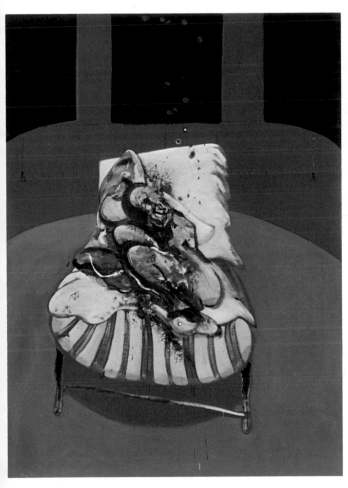 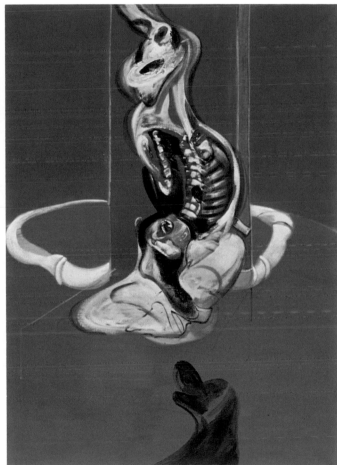

Jean Dubuffet b. 1901

Jean Dubuffet was born in Le Havre on July 31, 1901. He attended art classes in his youth and in 1918 moved to Paris to study at the Académie Julian, which he left after six dissatisfying months. During this time Dubuffet met Suzanne Valadon, Raoul Dufy, Léger and Max Jacob and became fascinated with Hans Prinzhorn's book on psychopathic art; he was also interested in literature, music, philosophy and linguistics. In 1923 and 1924 he traveled to Italy and South America respectively. Then Dubuffet gave up painting for about ten years, supporting himself first as an industrial draftsman and thereafter entering the family wine business. After much vacillation between careers in art and business, he committed himself entirely to becoming an artist in 1942.

Dubuffet's first one-man exhibition was held at the Galerie René Drouin in Paris in 1944. During the forties the artist associated with Charles Ratton, Jean Paulhan, Georges Limbour and André Breton. His style and subject matter in this period owed a debt to Klee and Alfred Jarry. From 1945 he collected *Art Brut,* spontaneous, direct works by individuals (often mental patients) not influenced by professional artists. The Pierre Matisse Gallery gave him his first one-man show in New York in 1947.

From 1951 to 1952 Dubuffet lived in New York; he then returned to Paris, where a retrospective of his work took place at the Cercle Volney in 1954. His first museum retrospective occurred in 1957 at the Schloss Morsbroich, Leverkusen, Germany. Major Dubuffet exhibitions have since been held at the Musée des Arts Décoratifs, Paris, The Museum of Modern Art, New York, The Art Institute of Chicago, the Stedelijk Museum, Amsterdam, the Tate Gallery, London, and The Solomon R. Guggenheim Museum in New York. His paintings of *L'Hourloupe,* a series begun in 1962, were exhibited at the Palazzo Grassi in Venice in 1964. A collection of Dubuffet's writings, *Prospectus et tous écrits suivants,* was published in 1967, the same year he started his architectural structures. Soon thereafter he began numerous commissions for monumental outdoor sculptures, some of which were shown at The Art Institute of Chicago in 1969. In 1971 he produced his first theater props, the *"practicables."* The following year his *Group of Four Trees* was erected at Chase Manhattan Plaza, New York, and he gave his collection of *Art Brut* to the city of Lausanne. Dubuffet lives and works in Paris and Périgny.

162 **Will to Power.** January 1946
(Volonté de puissance)

74.2076

Oil, pebbles, sand and glass on canvas, 45¾ x 35 in. (116.2 x 88.9 cm.)

Signed and dated u.l.: *J. Dubuffet / 1946.*

PROVENANCE:

from the artist
Henri-Pierre Roché, Paris, 1946-59
Mme Roché, Paris, 1959-67
Galerie Paul Facchetti, Paris, 1967-68
Morris Pinto, Paris, 1968
Baron Elie de Rothschild, Paris, 1968-74

In *Will to Power* the frontal male nude fills the canvas from top edge to bottom, overwhelming the pictorial space. This *"personnage incivil,"* as Dubuffet called the figure, is seen against "a sky of trivial and violent blue." (Paris, Galerie René Drouin, 1946, p. 56) The stocky, muscular man with his arms behind his back presents an image of masculine brutality. Dubuffet used a variety of materials to create the coarse, gritty, heavily impastoed surface and employed stones for the man's teeth and shiny inlaid glass fragments for his eyes.

Dubuffet's title, *Will to Power,* refers to a central concept in the philosophy of Friedrich Nietzsche. The concept was popularized after Nietzsche's death and in this attenuated form was incorporated into the ideology of Nazism. Thus, Dubuffet's image appears to be a caricature of the "will to power" interpreted as romanticized masculine aggression.

EXHIBITIONS:

Paris, Galerie René Drouin, *Mirobolus, Macadam & Cie: Hautes Pâtes de J. Dubuffet,* May 3-June 1, 1946, pp. 55, repr., 56

New York, The Museum of Modern Art, *The Work of Jean Dubuffet,* Feb. 19-Apr. 8, 1962, no. 27, traveled to The Art Institute of Chicago, May 11-June 17; Los Angeles County Museum of Art, July 10-Aug. 12

New York, The Solomon R. Guggenheim Museum, *Jean Dubuffet: A Retrospective,* Apr. 26-July 29, 1973, no. 20, repr., traveled to Paris, Grand Palais, Sept. 27-Dec. 20

New York, The Solomon R. Guggenheim Museum, *Forty Modern Masters: An Anniversary Show,* Dec. 16, 1977- Feb. 5, 1978, no. 27, repr.

REFERENCES:

J. Fitzsimmons, "Jean Dubuffet: A Short Introduction to His Work," *Quadrum,* no. 4, 1957, p. 31, repr.

L. Trucchi, *L'Occhio di Dubuffet,* Rome, 1965, fig. 63

M. Loreau, *Catalogue des travaux de Jean Dubuffet. Fascicule II: Mirobolus, Macadam et Cie,* Paris, 1966, fig. 100

M. Loreau, *Jean Dubuffet: Délits, déportements, lieux de haut jeu,* Paris, 1971, p. 40, repr.

H. H. Arnason, *History of Modern Art,* rev. ed., New York, 1977, fig. 952

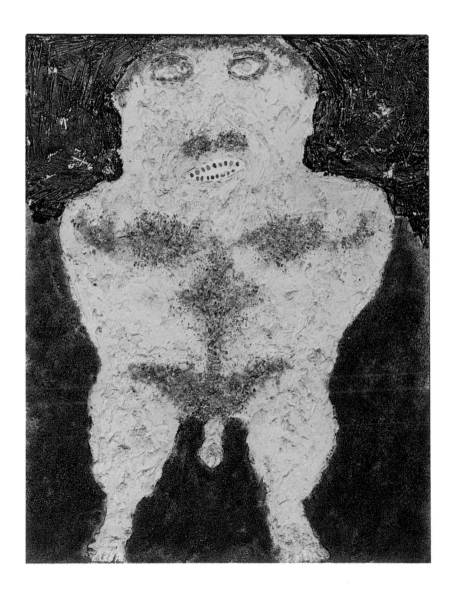

Dubuffet

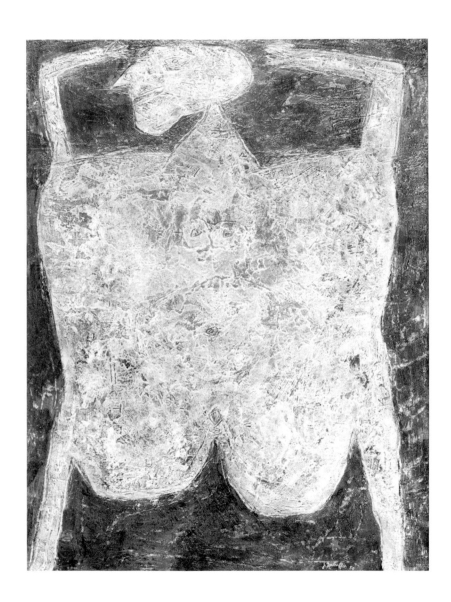

163 Triumph and Glory. December 1950
(Triomphe et gloire)

71.1973

Oil on canvas, 51 x 38 in. (129.5 x 96.5 cm.)

Signed and dated l.r.: *J. Dubuffet* 50; inscribed on reverse: *Triomphe et Gloire / Corps de Dame / J. Dubuffet / Décember 50.*

PROVENANCE:

from the artist
Alfonso S. Ossorio, East Hampton, New York, 1951-71

The *Corps de dames* series comprises thirty-six oil paintings plus gouaches and drawings of female bodies executed between April 1950 and February 1951. Even more than Picasso's female nudes of the 1930s and 1940s, Dubuffet's figures violate the traditional artistic image of female beauty. One cannot help but react to the ugliness, the primitive imagery and the crude, graffiti-like drawing of this series. Dubuffet has explained: "I intended the line not to give the figure a definite shape, but just the reverse—it ought to prevent the figure taking on any particular shape, so that it remains in the state of a general concept and something immaterial. I was interested (and I think this is true of all my pictures) in the brutal juxtaposition, in these female bodies, of the generalized and the particular, the subjective and the objective, the metaphysical and the trivial-grotesque. The one is strengthened by the presence of the other, I feel." (London, Tate Gallery, *Jean Dubuffet: Paintings,* exh. cat., 1966, p. 29)

EXHIBITION:
New York, The Solomon R. Guggenheim Museum, *Jean Dubuffet: A Retrospective,* Apr. 26-July 29, 1973, no. 46, color repr.

REFERENCE:
M. Loreau, *Catalogue des travaux de Jean Dubuffet. Fascicule VI: Corps de dames,* Paris, 1965, fig. 115

164 Door with Couch Grass. October 31, 1957
(Porte au chiendent)

59.1549

Oil on canvas with assemblage, 74½ x 57½ in.
(189.2 x 146 cm.)

Signed and dated u.l.: *J. Dubuffet 57*; l.c.: *J. Dubuffet 57*.

PROVENANCE:

from the artist through Pierre Matisse Gallery, New York, 1959

After moving to Vence in the south of France in 1955, Dubuffet became interested in doors and even bought a large dilapidated one from a peasant so he could study it at home. Dubuffet took one of the canvases he was using at this time for studies of earth stratification and geographical topography, cut it down and transformed it into a door. To this he added parts of other paintings so as to "represent a wall, a doorstep, and the ground. Certain of these elements, intended for my assemblages, were the result of a special technique. It consisted in shaking a brush over the painting spread out on the floor, covering it with a spray of tiny droplets. This is the technique, known as 'Tyrolean,' that masons use in plastering walls to obtain certain mellowing effects. . . . I combined this technique with others —successive layers, application of sheets of paper, scattering sand over the painting, scratching it with the tines of a fork. In this way I produced finely worked sheets that gave the impression of teeming matter, alive and sparkling, which I could use to represent a piece of ground. . . ." (J. Dubuffet, "Memoir on the Development of My Work from 1952," *The Work of Jean Dubuffet*, exh. cat., New York, 1962, pp. 132, 137)

EXHIBITIONS:

New York, Pierre Matisse Gallery, *Jean Dubuffet,* Feb. 4-22, 1958, no. 19, repr.

The Cleveland Museum of Art, *Some Contemporary Works of Art,* Nov. 11-Dec. 31, 1958, no. 9, repr.

New York, The Solomon R. Guggenheim Museum, *Inaugural Selection,* Oct. 21, 1959-June 19, 1960

New York, The Museum of Modern Art, *The Work of Jean Dubuffet,* Feb. 19-Apr. 18, 1962, no. 141, repr., traveled to The Art Institute of Chicago, May 11-June 17; Los Angeles County Museum of Art, July 10-Aug. 12

Venice, XXXII Biennale Internazionale d'Arte, *Today's Art in Museums: The Solomon R. Guggenheim Museum,* June 20-Oct. 18, 1964, no. 5

New York, Cordier & Ekstrom, *Doors,* Mar. 19-Apr. 20, 1968

New York, The Solomon R. Guggenheim Museum, *Jean Dubuffet: A Retrospective,* Apr. 26-July 29, 1973, no. 90, repr., traveled to Paris, Grand Palais, Sept. 27-Dec. 20

REFERENCES:

Art International, vol. II, no. 1, 1958, p. 52, repr.

"Quelques introductions au Cosmorama de Jean Dubuffet," *Cahiers du Collège de Pataphysique,* nos. 10-11, 1960, p. 35, repr.

L. Trucchi, *L'Occhio di Dubuffet,* Rome, 1965, fig. 201

M. Loreau, *Catalogue des travaux de Jean Dubuffet. Fascicule XIII: Célébration du sol I, lieux cursifs, texturologies, topographies,* Paris, 1969, fig. 102

Handbook, 1970, pp. 100-101, repr.

M. Loreau, *Jean Dubuffet: Délits, déportements, lieux de haut jeu,* Paris, 1971, p. 248, repr.

H. H. Arnason, *History of Modern Art,* rev. ed., New York, 1977, fig. 954

165 Nunc Stans. May 16-June 5, 1965

66.1818

Vinyl on canvas, three panels, each 63¾ x 107⅞ in.
(161.9 x 274 cm.)

Signed and dated on third panel l.l.: *J. Dubuffet 65.*

PROVENANCE:

from the artist
Galerie Beyeler, Basel, and Galerie Jeanne Bucher,
Paris, 1966

Dubuffet created *Nunc Stans* in May-June 1965, for a
commission for wall decorations in the entrance hall
of the new Faculté des Lettres at Nanterre, France. Although the project was later abandoned, many studies
exist for *Nunc Stans* and *Epokhê*. Dubuffet used primary colors plus black and white vinyl paint in the
large-scale Guggenheim panels. The smooth surface,
the bold, decorative quality and the pattern of interlocking pictographs are typical of the *Hourloupe* cycle.
Dubuffet invented the name *"L'Hourloupe"* to refer to
the series he began in July 1962. In this cycle traditional
figure-ground relationship is destroyed; instead, there
is a play of image against image.

EXHIBITIONS:

Paris, Galerie Jeanne Bucher, *Nunc Stans, Epokhê, cycle de
l'Hourloupe,* Apr.-May 1966, color repr.

Amsterdam, Stedelijk Museum, *Jean Dubuffet,* June 10-
Aug. 28, 1966, no. 121, repr.

New York, The Solomon R. Guggenheim Museum, *Jean
Dubuffet 1962-66,* Oct. 27, 1966-Feb. 5, 1967, no. 70, repr.

New York, The Solomon R. Guggenheim Museum, *Jean
Dubuffet: A Retrospective,* Apr. 26-July 29, 1973, no. 132,
repr., traveled to Paris, Grand Palais, Sept. 27-Dec. 20

REFERENCES:

D. Rodgers, "Recent Museum Acquisitions," *The Burlington Magazine,* vol. CIX, Sept. 1967, p. 534 and fig. 51

M. Loreau, *Catalogue des travaux de Jean Dubuffet. Fascicule XXI: L'Hourloupe II,* Paris, 1968, p. 57 and fig. 143

Handbook, 1970, pp. 102, repr., 103

M. Loreau, *Jean Dubuffet: Délits, déportements, lieux de
haut jeu,* Paris, 1971, pp. 456, 457, repr.

H. H. Arnason, *History of Modern Art,* rev. ed., New York,
1977, fig. 956

166 Bidon l'Esbroufe. December 11, 1967

70.1920

Acrylic on fiberglas-reinforced polyester resin, 65¾ in. (167 cm.) high

Signed and dated on left side of left foot: *J.D. 67.*

PROVENANCE:
Gift of the artist in honor of Mr. and Mrs. Thomas M. Messer, 1970

In November and December of 1967 Dubuffet executed a series of six three-dimensional standing personages, of which *Bidon l'Esbroufe* is the final one. With his usual sense of fantasy and invention, Dubuffet has endowed each sculpture with a name which defies not only translation but any attempt to paraphrase it: *Béniquet Trompette, Canotin Mâche-oeil, Papa Loustic, Brûle Savate,* and *Fiston la Filoche.* These titles are humorous, poetic and onomatopoeic. They are comparable to children's freely concocted nicknames in their irrational combinations of words and images and their rhythmic resonance.

Characteristic of Dubuffet's *Hourloupe* sculpture is a particular kind of three-dimensionality, which can be generally described as resulting from the juxtaposition of flat cutouts with colored designs at oblique angles. The red, white and blue-black colors accentuate this effect by flattening the forms rather than modeling them.

EXHIBITIONS:
Kunsthalle Basel, *Jean Dubuffet: L'Hourloupe,* June 6-Aug. 10, 1970, not in cat.

New York, The Solomon R. Guggenheim Museum, *Jean Dubuffet: A Retrospective,* Apr. 26-July 29, 1973, no. 270, repr., traveled to Paris, Grand Palais, Sept. 27-Dec. 20

REFERENCES:
G. Bonnefoi, "Sculptures, murs et demeures pour un nouveau Minotaure," *XXe siècle,* XXXIe année, no. 32, June 1969, p. 29, repr.

Handbook, 1970, pp. 104-105, repr.

M. Loreau, *Catalogue des travaux de Jean Dubuffet. Fascicule XXIV: Tour aux figures, amoncellements, cabinet logologique,* Paris, 1973, fig. 32

Asger Jorn 1914-1973

Asger Jorn was born Asger Oluf Jørgensen in Vejrum, Jutland, Denmark, on March 3, 1914. He visited Paris in the autumn of 1936, where he studied at Léger's Académie Contemporaine. During the war Jorn remained in Denmark, painting canvases that reflect the influence of Ensor, Kandinsky, Klee and Miró and contributing to the magazine *Helhesten*.

Jorn traveled to Swedish Lapland in the summer of 1946, met Constant in Paris that autumn and spent six months in Djerba, Tunisia, in 1947-48. His first one-man exhibition in Paris took place in 1948 at the Galerie Breteau. At about the same time the COBRA (an acronym for Copenhagen, Brussels, Amsterdam) movement was founded by Appel, Constant, Corneille, Christian Dotremont, Jorn and Joseph Noiret. The group's unifying doctrine was complete freedom of expression with emphasis on color and brushwork. Jorn edited monographs of the Bibliothèque Cobra before disassociating himself from the movement.

In 1951 Jorn returned, poor and ill, to Silkeborg, his hometown in Denmark. He began his intensive work in ceramics in 1953. The following year he settled in Albisola, Italy, and participated in a continuation of COBRA called *Mouvement International pour un Bauhaus Imaginiste*. Jorn's activities included painting, collage, book illustration, prints, drawings, ceramics, tapestries, commissions for murals and, in his last years, sculpture. He participated in the *Situationist International* movement from 1957 to 1961 and worked on a study of early Scandinavian art between 1961 and 1965. After the mid-1950s Jorn divided his time between Paris and Albisola. His first one-man show in New York took place in 1962 at the Lefebre Gallery. From 1966 Jorn concentrated on oil painting and traveled frequently, visiting Cuba, England and Scotland, the United States and the Orient. Jorn died on May 1, 1973, in Aarhus, Denmark.

167 Green Ballet. 1960
(Il balletto verde)

62.1608

Oil on canvas, 57⅛ x 78⅞ in. (145 x 200 cm.)

Signed l.r.: *Jorn*; inscribed on reverse: *il balletto verde / Jorn / 60 / the green ballet*

PROVENANCE:
from the artist
Jon Nicholas Streep, New York, 1960-62

Jorn's painting is generally less figurative in inspiration than that of his COBRA colleagues. In this canvas, where bright colors are applied in a seeming frenzy, control is established by the large sweeping movements and asymmetrically balanced color shapes. The artist's title suggests the floating, turning shapes and the figures splayed out across the canvas. The palette of predominant greens with red, yellow and blue is frequently encountered in Jorn's work, as is the expressive function of the heavily applied pigment. A sense of genesis, produced by the balance between creative and destructive forces, emerges as the artist's primary concern.

EXHIBITIONS:
New York, The Solomon R. Guggenheim Museum, *Van Gogh and Expressionism,* July 1-Sept. 13, 1964
San Francisco Museum of Art, *Colorists 1950-1965,* Oct. 15-Nov. 21, 1965
New York, Gruenebaum Gallery, *Asger Jorn: The Crucial Years 1954-1964,* Nov. 1-Dec. 3, 1977, no. 12

REFERENCES:
Handbook, 1970, pp. 168-169, repr.
H. H. Arnason, *History of Modern Art,* rev. ed., New York, 1977, fig. 992
G. Atkins, *Asger Jorn: The crucial years 1954-1964,* London, 1977, no. 1308, fig. 221

Karel Appel b. 1921

Karel Appel was born on April 25, 1921, in Amsterdam. From 1940 to 1943 he studied at the Rijksakademie van Beeldende Kunsten in Amsterdam. In 1946 his first one-man show was held at Het Beerenhuis in Groningen, The Netherlands, and he participated in the *Jonge Schilders* exhibition at the Stedelijk Museum of Amsterdam. Around this time Appel was influenced first by Picasso and Matisse, then by Dubuffet. He was a member of the *Nederlandse Experimentele Groep* and established the COBRA movement in 1948 with Constant, Corneille and others. In 1949 Appel completed a fresco for the cafeteria of the city hall in Amsterdam, which created such controversy that it was covered for ten years.

In 1950 the artist moved to Paris; there the writer Hugo Claus introduced him to Michel Tapié, who organized various exhibitions of his work. Appel was given a one-man show at the Palais des Beaux-Arts in Brussels in 1953. He received the UNESCO Prize at the Venice Biennale of 1954, and was commissioned to execute a mural for the restaurant of the Stedelijk Museum in 1956. The following year Appel traveled to Mexico and the United States and won a graphics prize at the Ljubljana Biennial in Yugoslavia. He was awarded an International Prize for Painting at the São Paulo Bienal in 1959. The first major monograph on Appel, written by Claus, was published in 1962. In the late 1960s the artist moved to the Château de Molesmes, near Auxerre, southeast of Paris. Solo exhibitions of his work were held at the Centre National d'Art Contemporain in Paris and the Stedelijk Museum in Amsterdam in 1968 and at the Kunsthalle Basel and the Palais des Beaux-Arts in Brussels in 1969. During the 1950s and 1960s he executed numerous murals for public buildings. A major Appel show opened at the Centraal Museum in Utrecht in 1970, and a retrospective of his work toured Canada and the United States in 1972. Appel lives in Paris and New York.

168 **Two Heads.** 1953
(*Deux têtes*)

54.1363

Oil on canvas, 78¾ x 29½ in. (200 x 75 cm.)

Signed and dated l.r.: *K. Appel '53.*

PROVENANCE:
from the artist, 1954

The motif of two heads occurs frequently in Appel's paintings of the 1950s. In this canvas he crowds two heads into a vertical format. Thickly and vigorously applied, his color is violent in hue and contrasting shades. The boldness and brutality of the brushwork express the artist's direct and emotional encounter with his subject matter. Like other members of the COBRA group, Appel was interested in the work of untrained artists. Here, the placement of one image above the other suggests the totems of primitive cultures. *Two Heads* is also reminiscent of Rouault and German Expressionists such as Kirchner and Nolde.

EXHIBITIONS:

New York, The Solomon R. Guggenheim Museum, *Younger European Painters: A Selection,* Dec. 3, 1953-May 2, 1954, no. 1, repr., traveled to Minneapolis, Walker Art Center, Aug. 8-Sept. 24; Portland (Ore.) Art Museum, Oct. 8-Nov. 14; San Francisco Museum of Art, Nov. 26, 1954-Jan. 23, 1955; Dallas Museum of Fine Arts, Feb. 1-27; Fayetteville, University of Arkansas, Mar. 7-Apr. 9; The Dayton Art Institute, Apr. 15-May 13; Andover, Mass., Addison Gallery of American Art, Phillips Academy, Oct. 1-31; Hanover, N.H., Carpenter Art Galleries, Dartmouth College, Nov. 5-Dec. 18; South Hadley, Mass., Dwight Art Memorial, Mount Holyoke College, Jan. 3-31, 1956; Middletown, Conn., Davison Art Center, Wesleyan University, Feb. 7-Mar. 31

London, Tate Gallery, *An exhibition of paintings from The Solomon R. Guggenheim Museum, New York,* Apr. 16-May 26, 1957, no. 1, traveled to The Hague, Gemeentemuseum, June 25-Sept. 1; Helsinki, Ateneumin Taidekokoelmat, Sept. 27-Oct. 20; Rome, Galleria Nazionale d'Arte Moderna, Dec. 5, 1957-Jan. 8, 1958; Cologne, Wallraf-Richartz-Museum, Jan. 26-Mar. 30, 1958; Paris, Musée des Arts Décoratifs, Apr. 23-June 1

New York, The Solomon R. Guggenheim Museum, *Inaugural Selection,* Oct. 21, 1959-June 19, 1960

Houston, Jones Hall Fine Arts Gallery, University of St. Thomas, *Persona Grata: An Exhibition of Masks from 1200 B.C. to the Present,* Nov. 3-Dec. 11, 1960, no. 214

New York, The Solomon R. Guggenheim Museum, *Van Gogh and Expressionism,* July 1-Sept. 13, 1964

REFERENCES:

J. Fitzsimmons, "New York: A Glittering Constellation," *Art Digest,* vol. 28, Dec. 1, 1953, p. 6, repr.

Handbook, 1959, p. 21, repr.

Pierre Alechinsky b. 1927

Pierre Alechinsky was born on October 19, 1927, in Brussels. From an early age Alechinsky was interested in graphic arts and in 1944 he entered the Ecole Nationale Supérieure d'Architecture et des Arts Décoratifs in Brussels, where he studied book illustration and typography. He also painted in a post-Cubist style and later in a manner reminiscent of Ensor. His paintings of monstrous women were shown in his first one-man exhibition at the Galerie Lou Cosyn in Brussels in 1947. The same year he became a member of the group *Jeune Peinture Belge.*

In 1948 expressionist artists including Appel, Jorn, Constant, Carl-Henning Pedersen and Corneille formed the COBRA group. Alechinsky joined COBRA in 1949 and participated in the first *Internationale tentoonstelling experimentele Kunst–COBRA* that year at the Stedelijk Museum in Amsterdam. He became a central figure in the group and organized its second international exhibition in Liège, Belgium, in 1951. Shortly thereafter COBRA disbanded.

Alechinsky moved to Paris in 1951 to study printmaking under a grant from the French government. He studied engraving with Stanley William Hayter at Atelier 17 in 1952. At about the same time he became fascinated by Japanese calligraphy and in 1955 he went to Tokyo and Kyoto. There he visited masters of the art and produced the award-winning film *Calligraphie japonaise.* In the 1960s Alechinsky traveled extensively in Europe, the United States and Mexico and participated in numerous international exhibitions. An Alechinsky retrospective organized by The Arts Club of Chicago toured the United States in 1965. In 1976 Alechinsky became the first recipient of the prestigious Andrew W. Mellon Prize for artists. The prize was accompanied by a major retrospective of his work in all media at the Museum of Art, Carnegie Institute, Pittsburgh, in 1977. The artist continues to paint and to make prints and book illustrations at his home in Bougival, France.

169 Vanish. 1959
(Disparaître)

67.1848

Oil on canvas, 78¾ x 110¼ in. (200 x 280 cm.)

Signed l.r.: *Alechinsky.* Not dated.

PROVENANCE:
from the artist
Galerie de France, Paris, 1960
Albert Loeb, New York, 1961
Jean Aberbach, Hamburg, 1961
Gift, Julian and Jean Aberbach, New York, 1967

The abstract and the concrete merge in Alechinsky's work. In *Vanish* he has focused on the appearance and disappearance of a female figure in the center of the canvas. This emergent shape and the background coalesce into a vigorously brushed surface which is distinguished by thickly impastoed white pigment and a network of predominantly blue lines. There are still traces of the allover patterning that characterizes the artist's watercolors and earlier canvases such as *Ant Hill* of 1954, which is also in the Guggenheim Museum collection. The fluidity and vitality evident in *Vanish* arise from Alechinsky's skill as a draftsman and his knowledge of Japanese calligraphy.

EXHIBITIONS:
Venice, XXX Biennale Internazionale d'Arte, *Belgian Pavilion,* June 18-Oct. 16, 1960, no. 17, repr.

Amsterdam, Stedelijk Museum, *Alechinsky + Reinhoud,* May 26-June 26, 1961, no. 23

Pittsburgh, Museum of Art, Carnegie Institute, *The 1961 Pittsburgh International Exhibition of Contemporary Painting and Sculpture,* Oct. 27, 1961-Jan. 7, 1962, no. 449

Pittsburgh, Museum of Art, Carnegie Institute, *Pierre Alechinsky,* Oct. 28, 1977-Jan. 8, 1978, no. 22, repr., traveled to Toronto, Art Gallery of Ontario, Mar. 10-Apr. 20

REFERENCES:
J. Grenier, "Pierre Alechinsky," *XXe siècle,* XXIIe année, June 1960, pp. 20, repr., 21

E. Jaguer, "Alechinsky ou la revanche des dragons," *Art International,* vol. VII, Jan. 25, 1963, pp. 63, 66

J. Putman, *Alechinsky,* Milan, 1967, pl. 61

Corneille b. 1922

Corneille was born Corneille Guillaume Beverloo on July 3, 1922, in Liège, Belgium, of Dutch parents. From 1940 to 1943 he studied drawing at the Rijksakademie van Beeldende Kunsten in Amsterdam. His first one-man show was held in 1946 at Het Beerenhuis in Groningen, The Netherlands. Corneille visited Hungary the following year, returning to The Netherlands in 1948 to co-found the *Nederlandse Experimentele Groep* (N.E.G.), which published the periodical *Reflex,* and the COBRA movement, which included Jorn, Appel, Constant, Christian Dotremont and Joseph Noiret. On his return from travels in North Africa Corneille participated in the 1949 N.E.G. and COBRA exhibitions at the Galerie Colette Allendy in Paris and the Stedelijk Museum in Amsterdam.

In 1950 the artist settled permanently in Paris and began exhibiting at the Salon de Mai. He studied etching with Stanley William Hayter in 1953 in Paris, and ceramics with Tullio Mazzotti in Albisola, Italy, during the summers of 1954 and 1955. Corneille received the Guggenheim International Award for The Netherlands in 1956, the year of his first one-man exhibition at the Stedelijk Museum, Amsterdam. In 1957 he participated in the Salon des Réalités Nouvelles in Paris. He traveled extensively during this period, visiting Africa, South America, The Netherlands Antilles and the United States.

In 1962 Corneille was given his first solo exhibition in New York at the Lefebre Gallery, where he has since shown frequently. During the next four summers he worked on gouaches in the Spanish coastal town of Cadaques. A Corneille retrospective was held at the Musée d'Antibes, France, in 1963. In 1968 he executed mosaics in Vela-Luka, Yugoslavia. Among his many one-man shows during the 1970s were those presented at Milan's Galleria d'Arte and the Museu de Arte of São Paulo in 1975, at Galerie Espace in Amsterdam in 1977 and at the Galleria C.M. in Rome and the Galerie Kände Malåra, Jönköping, Sweden, in 1978. Corneille now lives and works in Paris.

170 **Spell of the Island.** 1965
(Sortilège d'une île)

65.1781

Oil on canvas, 63½ x 51¼ in. (161.3 x 130.2 cm.)

Signed and dated l.c.: *Corneille '65*; inscribed on reverse: *"Sortilège / d'une île" / Corneille '65.*

PROVENANCE:

from the artist through Lefebre Gallery, New York, 1965

Spell of the Island was evidently inspired by the artist's summer sojourns along the Mediterranean coast. Brilliant reds, pinks, yellows, blues and greens are randomly arranged in mosaic patterns. Although the painting is entirely abstract, the protozoan shapes and organic colors and textures evoke associations with marine life and patches of vegetation. Corneille rejects formal rigidity and seeks spontaneity and the expression of joyous sensation.

EXHIBITIONS:

New York, Lefebre Gallery, *Corneille,* Oct. 12-Nov. 6, 1965, repr.

Amsterdam, Stedelijk Museum, *Corneille,* Oct. 21-Dec. 11, 1966, no. 72, repr., traveled to Städtische Kunsthalle Düsseldorf, Jan. 27-Mar. 5, 1967

Bogotá, Museo de Arte Moderno, *Color: 63 obras de arte por 56 artistas* (organized by The International Council of The Museum of Modern Art, New York), Feb. 24-Mar. 30, 1975, traveled to São Paulo, Museu de Arte, Apr. 18-May 18; Rio de Janeiro, Museu de Arte Moderno, June 12-July 20; Caracas, Museo de Bellas Artes, Aug. 3-Sept. 14; Mexico City, Museo de Arte Moderno, Oct. 2-Nov. 23

REFERENCES:

Handbook, 1970, pp. 78-79, repr.

F. T. Gribling, *Corneille,* Amsterdam, 1972, pl. 29

Antoni Tàpies b. 1923

Antoni Tàpies was born in Barcelona on December 13, 1923. His adolescence was disrupted by the Spanish Civil War and a serious illness of two-years duration. He was essentially self-taught as a painter; the few art classes he attended left little impression on him. Tàpies abandoned the study of law in 1946 to devote himself exclusively to art. Shortly after making this decision he began attending clandestine meetings of the *Blaus,* an iconoclastic group of Catalan artists and writers who produced the review *Dau al Set (Seven-faced Dice).*

Tàpies' work was exhibited for the first time in the controversial Saló d'Octubre of Barcelona in 1948, the year he met Miró. The influence of Miró, Klee, Ernst and Oriental philosophy is evident in his work of this period. His first one-man show was held at the Galeries Laietanes, Barcelona, in 1950. That same year the French government awarded Tàpies a scholarship which enabled him to spend a year in Paris, and he participated in the Carnegie International in Pittsburgh. He was given his first one-man show in New York in 1953 by Martha Jackson, who arranged for his work to be shown the following year in various parts of this country. Since then Tàpies has exhibited in major museums and galleries of the United States, Europe, Japan and South America.

In 1966 he and other Spanish intellectuals were fined and briefly imprisoned for attending an unauthorized student meeting in Barcelona; at this time he began his collection of writings *La practica de l'art.* In 1969 he and the poet Joan Brossa published their book *Frègoli;* a second collaborative effort, *Nocturn Matinal,* appeared the following year. Tàpies received the Rubens Prize of Siegen, Germany, in 1972. Among his recent important exhibitions were retrospectives at the Musée National d'Art Moderne in Paris in 1973 and at the Albright-Knox Art Gallery of Buffalo in 1977. He now lives in Barcelona.

171 **Great Painting.** 1958
(Gran pintura)

59.1551

Mixed media on canvas, 78½ x 103 in.
(199.3 x 261.6 cm.)

Not signed or dated.

PROVENANCE:
from the artist through Martha Jackson Gallery, New York, 1959

Tàpies' use of color and texture in *Great Painting* is characteristically Spanish: austere, somber, earthy. The massive wall-like plane, the emphasis on rough, encrusted surface and the integrity of the material itself extend beyond the realm of painting to suggest relief sculpture. The composition is a stable, almost static mass, symmetrically divided into large rectangular areas, enlivened by the scarred and pitted texture rather than by brushwork.

Since 1954 the artist has used clear latex as a binding medium with dry pigments, earth and marble particles. Like many of Tàpies' canvases, *Great Painting* brings to mind walls from the old quarters of his native city, Barcelona, which are eroded with age and chipped from human contact. Certain wedge-shaped markings suggest the cuneiform writing of Babylonia and Assyria. The ocher colors with gray stains and dark gouges are particularly evocative of architectural structures. Tàpies has made references to walls in interviews and writings such as *Communication on the Wall* of 1969. In fact, in his native Catalan tongue, the artist's surname means "walls."

EXHIBITIONS:
New York, Martha Jackson Gallery, *Antonio Tàpies,* Feb. 24-Mar. 21, 1959, no. 1
New York, The Solomon R. Guggenheim Museum, *Inaugural Selection,* Oct. 21, 1959-June 19, 1960
New York, The Solomon R. Guggenheim Museum, *Antoni Tàpies,* Mar. 22-May 13, 1962, repr.

REFERENCES:
J.-E. Cirlot, "La pintura de Antonio Tàpies," *Goya,* no. 34, Jan.-Feb. 1960, p. 234, repr.
Handbook, 1970, pp. 428-429, repr.
A. Cirici, *Tàpies: Witness of Silence,* New York, 1972, pl. 181
Buffalo, Albright-Knox Art Gallery, *Antoni Tàpies: Thirty-three Years of His Work,* exh. cat., 1977, pp. 12, 29, repr.
R. Penrose, *Tàpies,* New York, 1978, p. 86 and fig. 52

Eduardo Chillida b. 1924

Eduardo Chillida was born on January 10, 1924, in the Basque city of San Sebastián, Spain. After studying architecture from 1943 to 1947 at the University of Madrid, he began to concentrate on drawing and sculpture. He moved to Paris in 1948 and became close friends with Pablo Palazuelo, with whom he exhibited at the Salon de Mai of 1949. In 1950 Chillida lived in Villaines-sous-Bois, France, before moving the following year to Hernani, near San Sebastián, where he formed a friendship with José Cruz Iturbe.

Chillida's first one-man show was held at the Galería Clan in Madrid in 1954. The city of San Sebastián commissioned him to execute a monument to Alexander Fleming in 1955. In 1966 he was given the first of many one-man exhibitions at Galerie Maeght in Paris. He won the International Grand Prize for Sculpture at the Venice Biennale in 1958. This year he made his first visit to the United States, where he met James Johnson Sweeney, Mies van der Rohe and the composer Edgar Varèse. Chillida returned to San Sebastián in 1959. He was awarded the Kandinsky Prize by Nina Kandinsky in 1960. He traveled to Greece in 1963 and the following year he won the Sculpture Prize at the Carnegie International in Pittsburgh. He received two German museum awards in 1966: the prestigious Nordrhein-Westfalen Prize and the Wilhelm-Lehmbruck Prize. That same year the first Chillida retrospective in the United States took place at The Museum of Fine Arts in Houston. In 1968 Chillida met the philosopher Martin Heidegger, whose book, *Der Kunst und der Raum,* he illustrated.

Retrospectives of Chillida's work were held in 1969 at museums in Basel, Zürich and Munich. That same year he began a sculpture for the UNESCO Building in Paris and the following year executed a commission for the World Bank of Washington. In 1971 he was a visiting professor at the Carpenter Center in Cambridge, Massachusetts, and later in the year traveled to Barcelona on the occasion of his solo exhibition at the Sala Gaspar. Chillida and de Kooning shared the Andrew W. Mellon Prize, which was accompanied by a major show at the Museum of Art, Carnegie Institute, Pittsburgh, in 1979. Chillida works and lives in San Sebastián.

172 **From Within.** March 1953
(Desde dentro)

58.1504

Iron, 38¾ in. (98.4 cm.) high

Inscribed with insignia on top of hanging ring. Not dated.

PROVENANCE:

from the artist through Galerie Maeght, Paris, 1958

Pride in craftsmanship and in the wrought ironwork of the blacksmith are a part of the artist's Basque heritage. Since 1951 Chillida's sculpture has revealed the importance of the material. There is a vitality and tension in the bending and joining of iron elements in *From Within.* The curved and pointed shapes of iron bars constitute a silhouette which changes when seen from different angles. Skeletal forms are aligned in an open spatial organization around a central core. Thus, the demarcation of space is based on an essentially linear structure.

EXHIBITIONS:

Madrid, Galerie Clan, *Eduardo Chillida,* Apr. 19-30, 1954

Milan, Palazzo dell'Arte, *Decima Triennale: Spagna,* June 1954, pl. CI

Paris, Galerie Denise René, *Premier Salon de la sculpture abstraite,* Dec. 10, 1954-Jan. 15, 1955

Paris, Galerie Maeght, *Chillida,* Nov. 9-Dec. 9, 1956, no. 5

New York, The Solomon R. Guggenheim Museum, *Sculptures and Drawings from Seven Sculptors,* Feb. 12-Apr. 27, 1958

New York, The Solomon R. Guggenheim Museum, *Inaugural Selection,* Oct. 21, 1959-June 19, 1960

Houston, The Museum of Fine Arts, *Eduardo Chillida,* Oct. 4-Nov. 20, 1966, no. 4

Kunsthaus Zürich, *Eduardo Chillida,* Mar. 8-Apr. 13, 1969, no. 2, traveled to Amsterdam, Stedelijk Museum, Apr. 25-June 8

New York, The Solomon R. Guggenheim Museum, *Selected Sculpture and Works on Paper,* July 8-Sept. 14, 1969, p. 111, repr.

REFERENCES:

S. Geist, "Month in Review," *Arts,* vol. 32, Mar. 1958, p. 51, repr.

M. Netter, "Der baskische Bildhauer Eduardo Chillida," *Werk,* 49 Jg., Heft 6, June 1962, p. 215, repr.

P. Volboudt, *Chillida,* New York, 1967, pl. 8

Handbook, 1970, pp. 76-77, repr.

C. Esteban, *Chillida,* Paris, 1971, pp. 36, repr., 57, 201, no. 36

Hans Hartung b. 1904

Hans Heinrich Ernst Hartung was born in Leipzig on September 21, 1904. From 1924 to 1925 he studied philosophy at the University of Leipzig and art history at the Akademie der Schönen Künste. He continued his studies at the academies of Dresden and Munich. At the *Internationale Ausstellung* of 1926 in Dresden Hartung was introduced to the work of van Gogh, Munch, the French Impressionists, the Fauves and the Cubists. Later that year he settled in Paris. His first one-man exhibition was held at the Galerie Heinrich Kühl in Dresden in 1931. Hartung fled Germany the following year for the Balearic Islands. After a brief visit to Berlin in 1935 the artist left Germany forever, returning to France. In Paris he met Mondrian, Miró and Calder and began showing at the Salon des Surindépendants. He participated in an exhibition at the Galerie Pierre in 1936 with Arp, Kandinsky, Hélion and others. In 1937 he took part in an international show at the Jeu de Paume, where he was impressed by the sculpture of Julio Gonzalez, whose daughter he later married.

After serving in the French Foreign Legion during World War II, the French government decorated Hartung and granted him citizenship in 1945. That same year his work was included in group exhibitions at the Galerie Denise René and the Galerie Colette Allendy in Paris, and he participated in the Salon des Réalités Nouvelles. He met Soulages and Rothko in 1947, the year of his first one-man show in Paris at the Galerie Lydia Conti. The following year his work was shown at the Venice Biennale and in a circulating exhibition of French art in Germany. Throughout the 1950s and 1960s Hartung exhibited widely in Europe and the United States. He was awarded the International Grand Prize for Painting at the Venice Biennale of 1960. Traveling Hartung retrospectives opened in Switzerland in 1963, in France in 1969 and in Germany in 1974. In 1975 his photographs were published in *An Unnoticed World Seen by Hans Hartung,* and he was honored with a one-man show at The Metropolitan Museum of Art in New York. Hartung now lives in Paris and Antibes.

173 **T 56-6.** 1956

79.2525

Oil on canvas, 64 x 48½ in. (162.6 x 123 cm.)

Not signed or dated.

PROVENANCE:

from the artist through Kleemann Galleries, New York
Susan Morse Hilles, Branford, Connecticut, 1957-79
Gift, Susan Morse Hilles, 1979

Although Hartung was aware of German Expressionism and, later, Surrealism, his own work can be perceived as a European equivalent to American Abstract Expressionism. His facility in improvisation and freedom of expression as a painter give rise to a distinctive calligraphic abstraction. Vibrantly energetic sheaves of lines have a rhythmic, dynamic impact. In *T 56-6* the enlarged calligraphy of the draftsman is made explicit in a cluster of brushwork. Brilliant black strokes set off by a cool light-blue background impart a sense of movement, suggesting an outburst of activity. Hartung's painting captures the gesture with which it was painted.

EXHIBITIONS:

New York, Kleemann Galleries, *Hans Hartung: Paintings,* Mar. 11-Apr. 20, 1957, no. 23, repr.
New Haven, Yale University Art Gallery, *Two Modern Collectors: Susan Morse Hilles, Richard Brown Baker,* May 23-Sept. 1, 1963, no. 15, repr.

Pierre Soulages b. 1919

Pierre Soulages was born on December 24, 1919, in Rodez, France. In 1938 he visited Paris and he saw the work of Cézanne and Picasso for the first time. After his release from the army in 1941 Soulages studied at the Ecole des Beaux-Arts of Montpellier. During the German occupation he worked at a vineyard near Montpelier; he met Sonia Delaunay at this time.

In 1946 Soulages settled in Courbevoie, outside Paris, and began painting in earnest. The following year he exhibited for the first time at the Salon des Surindépendants in Paris. In 1948 the artist was invited to participate in the Salon des Réalités Nouvelles and in an exhibition of French abstract painting that toured Germany. His first one-man show was held at the Galerie Lydia Conti in Paris in 1949. That same year Soulages exhibited for the first time at the Salon de Mai and began executing stage designs. In 1953 he participated in the São Paulo Bienal, where he won a purchase prize, and in the exhibition *Younger European Painters,* which was presented at the Guggenheim Museum and circulated in the United States. From this time until 1966 he showed at the Kootz Gallery in New York.

One-man exhibitions of Soulages' work were held in London, New York and Chicago in 1955. While visiting the United States in 1957, he met Baziotes, de Kooning, Rothko and Robert Motherwell. This same year he received the Grand Prize at the Tokyo Biennial. In 1958 the artist visited the Far East, where he admired Oriental calligraphy and rock gardens. A Soulages retrospective was held at the Kestner-Gesellschaft in Hannover in 1960, followed by others in Essen, The Hague and Zürich the next year. He traveled to Mexico in 1961 and saw the Mayan temples of the Yucatán peninsula. During the 1960s and 1970s he was honored with retrospectives at major museums in Europe and the United States. He has received many prizes, among them the Guggenheim International Award for France in 1960 and the Grand Prize for Art of the City of Paris in 1975. The artist now lives in Paris.

174 **Painting.** November 20, 1956
(Peinture)

57.1469

Oil on canvas, 76¾ x 51¼ in. (195 x 130.2 cm.)

Signed and dated l.r.: *Soulages / 56*; on reverse: *SOULAGES / "20 Nov. 1956" / "Peinture."*

PROVENANCE:
from the artist, 1957

Soulages has divided his canvas into three horizontal registers and has articulated each with a repetition of broad, bold forms. These slab-like black shapes partake of an intense luminosity and a variety of red and brown nuances. Black has always been the basis of Soulages' palette, and he has continued to investigate its coloristic possibilities. The contrast of light and shade in his work suggests the warm darkness of Romanesque churches. In fact, Soulages has said that he decided to become a painter inside the church of Sainte-Foy in Conques-en-Rouergue near where he grew up in the south of France. The impressions of monumentality, stability, primitive force and clearly organized volumes characteristic of the Romanesque style as well as the mystery and sobriety of the dark church interiors are metaphorically transmitted in his mature style.

EXHIBITIONS:
New York, The Solomon R. Guggenheim Museum, *Inaugural Selection,* Oct. 21, 1959-June 19, 1960
Cambridge, The New Gallery, Hayden Library, Massachusetts Institute of Technology, *Soulages,* Jan. 10-30, 1962, no. 10
Houston, The Museum of Fine Arts, *Pierre Soulages,* Apr. 19-May 22, 1966
Paris, Musée National d'Art Moderne, *Soulages,* Mar. 22-May 21, 1967, no. 29
The Arts Club of Chicago, *The Calligraphic Statement,* Mar. 3-Apr. 11, 1970, no. 97

REFERENCES:
Handbook, 1970, pp. 424-425, repr.
J. J. Sweeney, *Soulages,* Greenwich, Conn., 1972, color pl. 47

Lucio Fontana 1899-1968

Lucio Fontana was born on February 19, 1899, in Rosario de Santa Fé, Argentina, of a Milanese father and an Argentinian mother. He lived in Milan from 1905 to 1922, when he went back to Argentina. In 1926 he participated in the Salon Nexus in Rosario de Santa Fé and the following year won a local monument competition. On returning to Italy in 1928 Fontana entered the Accademia di Belle Arti di Brera in Milan, which he attended for two years. His first one-man show opened in Milan in 1930 at the Galleria del Milione; in 1934 he joined a group of Italian abstract sculptors associated with this gallery. During these years Fontana executed several commissions for tombs. In 1935 he settled in Paris, where he joined the *Abstraction-Création* group and began working as a ceramicist. Two years later one-man exhibitions of Fontana's ceramics were held at the Galleria del Milione and the Galerie Jeanne Bucher-Myrbor in Paris. Around this time he met Miró, Brancusi and Tristan Tzara in Paris.

Fontana moved back to Argentina in 1940 and worked on sculptures for a monument to The Flag. He won First Prize for Sculpture in 1942 at the Salón Nacional de Bellas Artes de Buenos Aires. In 1946 Fontana cofounded the Academia de Altamira and with a group of his students published the *Manifiesto Blanco*. He resettled in Milan in 1947 and resumed his work in ceramics. In 1949 he created an *ambiente spaziale* (spatial environment) at the Galleria del Naviglio in Milan.

During the 1950s Fontana was given numerous one-man shows in Milan, and he worked on several projects with the architect Luciano Baldessari. He participated in the *Monochrome Malerei* exhibition at the Städtisches Museum in Leverkusen and a solo exhibition of his work took place at the Galerie Schmela in Düsseldorf in 1960. The following year the artist visited New York on the occasion of his one-man show at the Martha Jackson Gallery. He presented an *ambiente spaziale* at his retrospective at the Walker Art Center in Minneapolis in 1966. That same year Fontana produced costume and set designs for La Scala in Milan. A number of one-man exhibitions of his work were held in Europe in 1967. Fontana died on September 7, 1968, in Commabio, Italy.

175 **Spatial Concept, Expectations.** 1959
(Concetto spaziale, Attese)

77.2322

Water-based paint on canvas, 49⅝ x 98¾ in.
(126 x 250.9 cm.)

Signed on reverse: *l. fontana "concetto spaziale" "Attese."* Not dated.

PROVENANCE:

Estate of the artist, 1968-77
Gift, Mrs. Teresita Fontana, Milan, 1977

Fontana's canvas is painted a neutral olive green. With a knife he has cut four slits in it which reveal glimpses of black gauze backing and an evocative, mysterious space. Thus, he not only articulates the flat expanse but he opens up the space behind it. The artist attains a suspension and interaction between environmental and pictorial space. Beginning in 1948 Fontana wanted to make space the subject matter of the work as well as its locus. From that time he usually titled his works *Concetti spaziali (Spatial Concepts)*, and his search for imagery took many forms. The "holes" of 1949 to 1955 preceded the "cuts" of 1958 to 1968. The act of slashing, as opposed to puncturing, permitted the artist to retain the urgency of his gesture.

EXHIBITIONS:

Turin, Galleria Civica d'Arte Moderna, *Lucio Fontana*, Feb. 5-Mar. 28, 1970, no. 190, repr.

Paris, Musée d'Art Moderne de la Ville de Paris, *Lucio Fontana*, June 10-Sept. 6, 1970, no. 39

Milan, Palazzo Reale, *Lucio Fontana*, Apr. 19-June 21, 1972, no. 132, traveled to Brussels, Palais des Beaux-Arts

Kunsthaus Zürich, *Lucio Fontana: Concetti Spaziali*, Apr. 2-May 23, 1976, no. 84, color repr.

New York, The Solomon R. Guggenheim Museum, *Lucio Fontana, 1899-1968: A Retrospective*, Oct. 21-Dec. 8, 1977, no. 76, repr.

REFERENCE:

E. Crispolti and J. van der Marck, *Lucio Fontana*, Brussels, 1974, vol. I, p. 63, color repr. and vol. II, pp. 88-89, repr.

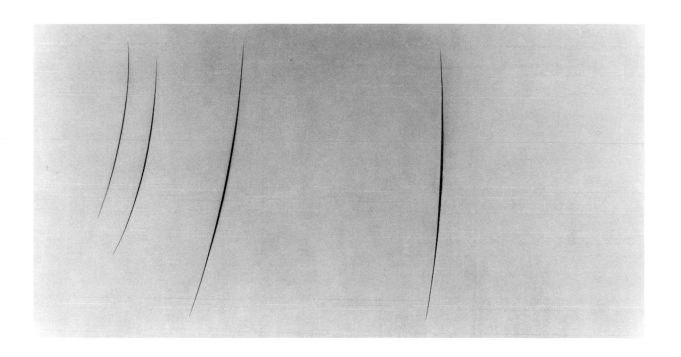

Alberto Burri b. 1915

Alberto Burri was born in Città di Castello, northern Umbria, on March 12, 1915. He received his medical degree from the University in Perugia in 1940 and practiced as a physician with the Italian Army in North Africa during World War II. In 1943 Burri was captured by the British, and the following year he was imprisoned by the Americans in Hereford, Texas. It was there that he began to paint.

Shortly after his repatriation, Burri moved to Rome. Although his earliest canvases were still lifes and landscapes, he soon started to paint abstract oils. His first one-man exhibition took place at the Galleria La Margherita in Rome in 1947. Burri visited Paris for the first time in 1949 and the following year he became a member of the *Origine* group in Rome. By 1949-50 he began to work with burlap; burlap and fabric collages continued to occupy him until 1960. Concurrent with these burlap *sacchi* (sacks) he experimented with *muffe* (molds) and *gobbi* (hunchbacks). His work was exhibited for the first time in the United States in a one-man show at the Frumkin Gallery in Chicago in 1953. In 1955 Burri began burning his media and the *combustione* resulted. Both the *legni* (wood pieces) and *ferri* (iron pieces) employ aspects of the *combustione* process.

An important Burri exhibition was held at the Carnegie Institute in Pittsburgh in 1957 and subsequently circulated in the United States. He was awarded the UNESCO Prize at the São Paulo Bienal of 1959 and was honored with a one-man exhibition at the Venice Biennale the following year. In 1965 he won the Grand Prize at the São Paulo Bienal. Burri's use of unconventional and common materials continued into the sixties and seventies with the *plastiche* (plastics); the white plastics; the *cretti* (cracks) and the works in cellotex. He has designed decor for ballets at La Scala in Milan (1963) and the opera in Rome (1972) and for other performances. A retrospective which traveled in the United States in 1977-78 to museums including the Guggenheim was his first major show in this country in more than a decade. Burri currently resides in Città di Castello.

176 **Composition.** 1953
(Composizione)

53.1364

Oil, gold paint and glue on burlap and canvas, 33 ⅞ x 39½ in. (86 x 100.4 cm.)

Signed u.r.: *Burri*; on reverse: *Burri*. Not dated.

PROVENANCE:
from the artist, 1953

When Burri began to use sacking as a collage element in 1949-50, he had already worked with single color paintings and with shaped projections from his canvases. During the 1950s he effectively exploited the natural texture of burlap, with its varied horizontals and verticals in the weave, in the *sacchi* by juxtaposing different shades and patterns and making prominent stitches. This *Composition* consists of more than a dozen patches glued and sewn together, decorated with touches of gold paint and torn to expose a violent red. The burlap itself provokes associations of poverty and humility. The materiality of the medium and emphasis on surface texture are among the characteristics of *art informel,* predominant in Europe during the fifties.

EXHIBITIONS:
New York, The Solomon R. Guggenheim Museum, *Younger European Painters: A Selection,* Dec. 3, 1953-May 2, 1954, no. 5, repr., traveled to Minneapolis, Walker Art Center, Aug. 8-Sept. 24; Portland (Ore.) Art Museum, Oct. 8-Nov. 14, 1954; San Francisco Museum of Art, Nov. 26, 1954-Jan. 23, 1955; Dallas Museum of Fine Arts, Feb. 1-27; Fayetteville, University of Arkansas, Mar. 7-Apr. 9; The Dayton Art Institute, Apr. 15-May 13; Andover, Mass., Addison Gallery of American Art, Phillips Academy, Oct. 1-31; Hanover, N. H., Carpenter Art Galleries, Dartmouth College, Nov. 5-Dec. 18; South Hadley, Mass., Dwight Art Memorial, Mount Holyoke College, Jan. 3-31, 1956; Middletown, Conn., Davison Art Center, Wesleyan University, Feb. 7-Mar. 31

Ann Arbor, Museum of Art, University of Michigan, *Images at Mid-Century,* Apr. 13-June 12, 1960

Hartford, Wadsworth Atheneum, *Salute to Italy: 100 Years of Italian Art 1861-1961,* Apr. 21-May 28, 1961, repr.

New York, Martha Jackson Gallery, *International 4: Collages and Constructions,* Apr. 6-May 1, 1965

New York, The Solomon R. Guggenheim Museum, *Alberto Burrri: A Retrospective View 1948-1978,* June 20-Aug. 27, 1978, not in cat.

REFERENCES:
J. J. Sweeney, *Burri,* Rome, 1955, pl. 15

C. Brandi, *Burri,* 1963, pl. 20

Handbook, 1970, pp. 52-53, repr.

Yves Klein 1928-1962

Yves Klein was born on April 28, 1928, in Nice. From 1944 to 1946 he studied at the Ecole Nationale de la Marine Marchande and the Ecole Nationale des Langues Orientales and began practicing judo. At this time he became friends with Claude Pascal and Arman Fernandez and started to paint. Klein composed his first "Symphonie monoton" in 1947. During the years 1948 to 1952 he traveled to Italy, Great Britain, Spain and Japan. In 1955 Klein settled permanently in Paris, where he was given a one-man show at the Club des Solitaires. His monochrome paintings were shown at the Galerie Colette Allendy in Paris in 1956.

The artist entered his blue period in 1957; this year a double exhibition of his work was held at the Galerie Iris Clert and the Gallery Colette Allendy in Paris. In 1958 he began using nude models as "living paintbrushes." Also in that year he undertook a project for the decoration of the entrance hall of the new opera house in Gelsenkirchen, Germany. The first manifesto of the group *Nouveaux Réalistes* was written in 1960 by Pierre Restany and signed by Klein, Arman, Daniel Spoerri, Jean Tinguely and others. In 1961 Klein was given a retrospective at the Museum Haus Lange in Krefeld, and his first one-man show in the United States at the Leo Castelli Gallery in New York. He and the architect Claude Parent collaborated that year on the design for fountains of water and fire, *Les Fontaines de Varsovie*, for the Palais de Chaillot in Paris. In 1962 Klein executed a plaster cast of Arman and took part in the exhibition *Antagonismes 2: l'objet* at the Musée des Arts Décoratifs of Paris. Shortly before his death he appeared in the film *Mondo Cane*. Klein died suddenly on June 6, 1962, at age thirty-four, in Paris.

177 **Blue Sponge.** 1959
(*L'Eponge bleue*)

64.1752

Stone, metal and painted coral, 39 in. (99 cm.) high

Not signed or dated.

PROVENANCE:
from the artist through Galerie Iris Clert, Paris
Mr. and Mrs. Andrew P. Fuller, New York, 1959-64
Gift, Mrs. Andrew P. Fuller, 1964

In his preoccupation with monochromatic paintings (the first of which he executed in 1955), Klein is linked with Burri and Fontana and, historically, with Malevich. After his first experiments with monochromes in orange, yellow and red, the artist concentrated from 1957 on a particular deep, electric shade of cobalt which he named "International Klein Blue." This color was an essence that symbolized infinite space and the immaterial, evoking sky and the void. By 1958 he was producing sponge reliefs and individual sponges on natural stone pedestals: the latter number more than two hundred examples. In these sculptures coral impregnated with blue paint has the appearance of an eerie cobalt sponge. Klein was obsessed with blue as a means of communication and an embodiment of energy.

EXHIBITIONS:
Paris, Galerie Iris Clert, *Yves Klein: bas-reliefs dans une forêt d'éponges,* June 15-30, 1959
New York, The Jewish Museum, *Yves Klein,* Jan. 25-Mar. 12, 1967, repr.
New York, The Solomon R. Guggenheim Museum, *Selected Sculpture and Works on Paper,* July 8-Sept. 14, 1969, p. 133, repr.

REFERENCES:
P. Wember, *Yves Klein,* Cologne, 1969, p. 92, repr., no. SE160
Handbook, 1970, pp. 242, color repr., 243

Etienne-Martin b. 1913

Etienne Martin was born in Loriol, in Provence, on February 4, 1913. In 1929 he entered the Ecole des Beaux-Arts in Lyon to study sculpture. He was awarded the Prix de Paris by the Ecole in 1933, which permitted him to travel to the capital the following year. In Paris Etienne-Martin worked with Charles Malfray at the Académie Ranson. In the mid-1930s he participated in the artists' group *Témoignage,* which included Marcel Michaud, François Stahly, Jean Le Moal and Alfred Manessier. Before the outbreak of World War II Etienne-Martin moved to Dieulefit, Drôme, but shortly thereafter he entered the army and was taken prisoner. After his release the artist returned in 1943 to Dieulefit; there he met the writer Henri-Pierre Roché, with whom he collaborated. Other friends during the 1940s were the architect Paul Herbé and Wols.

In 1947 Etienne-Martin moved to Paris and met Brancusi, Dubuffet and Michaux. His first one-man show was held in 1960 at the Galerie Breteau in Paris, where he exhibited again in 1962, 1963 and 1965. He taught at the Ecole Américaine at Fontainebleau in 1960. Retrospectives of Etienne-Martin's work took place in 1963 at the Kunsthalle Bern and the Stedelijk Museum in Amsterdam, in 1964 at the Stedelijk van Abbemuseum in Eindhoven and in 1965 at the Palais des Beaux-Arts in Brussels. His first solo exhibition in the United States was held at the Lefebre Gallery in New York in 1965. The following year Etienne-Martin was awarded the International Grand Prize for Sculpture at the Venice Biennale. The Musée d'Art et d'Industrie of Saint-Etienne honored him with a retrospective in 1966. He was studio master at the Ecole Nationale Supérieure des Beaux-Arts in Paris in 1968. In 1970 a show of Etienne-Martin's work took place at the Galerie Michel Couturier in Paris on the occasion of the publication of a monograph on the artist by Michel Ragon. In 1972 he was given a one-man show at the Musée Rodin in Paris. Etienne-Martin now lives in Paris.

178 **Anemone.** 1955
(Anémone)

57.1486

Elm wood, 43½ x 49½ x 30 in. (110.5 x 125.7 x 76.2 cm.)

Not signed or dated.

PROVENANCE:
from the artist, 1957

Etienne-Martin began his sculpture by selecting a massive tree root which he perceived in part as a found object. Proceeding from what nature created, the artist carved out the apertures and smoothed the wood. The title, *Anemone,* is suggested by the organic shapes implicit in the material and the curved forms surrounding the central void. Etienne-Martin has demonstrated a preference for wood carving although he has also had many bronzes cast. *Anemone* dates from the same time he began work on the labyrinthian *Dwellings,* a series of large sculptures that resemble man's architectural environment.

EXHIBITIONS:
New York, The Solomon R. Guggenheim Museum, *Sculptures and Drawings from Seven Sculptors,* Feb. 12-Apr. 27, 1958

New York, The Solomon R. Guggenheim Museum, *Inaugural Selection,* Oct. 21, 1959-Apr. 4, 1960

New York, The Solomon R. Guggenheim Museum, *Selected Sculpture and Works on Paper,* July 8-Sept. 14, 1969, p. 137, repr.

Portland (Ore.) Art Museum, *Masterworks in Wood: The Twentieth Century,* Sept. 17-Oct. 19, 1975, no. 21, repr.

REFERENCES:
S. Geist, "Month in Review," *Arts,* vol. 32, Mar. 1958, pp. 51-52, repr.

M. Ragon, "Etienne-Martin," *Cimaise,* 7e année, July 1960, pp. 52, 54, repr.

Handbook, 1970, pp. 110-111, repr.

H. H. Arnason, *History of Modern Art,* rev. ed., New York, 1977, p. 598, fig. 1054

Jean Ipoustéguy b. 1920

Jean-Robert Ipoustéguy was born on January 6, 1920, in Dun-sur-Meuse, France. In 1938 he moved to Paris and studied in the atelier of the artist Robert Lesbounit. Ipoustéguy primarily painted and designed tapestries and stained-glass windows in the 1940s. In 1949 he moved to Choisy-le-roi, near Paris, and from that time devoted himself exclusively to sculpture, working in bronze. His sculpture was first exhibited in 1956 at the Salon de Mai, Paris. In 1962 the Galerie Claude Bernard, Paris, gave Ipoustéguy his first one-man show. In 1964 he was awarded a prize from the Bright Foundation at the Venice Biennale; his first one-man exhibition in the United States took place at the Albert Loeb Gallery in New York.

In the summer of 1967 Ipoustéguy began to work for the most part in Carrara marble, a medium he has continued to use to the present. The following year the city of Darmstadt awarded him its art prize, and the Galerie Claude Bernard gave him another one-man exhibition. An Ipoustéguy retrospective was mounted by the Kunsthalle in Darmstadt in 1969. The Kunsthalle Basel presented a one-man exhibition of his work in 1970, as did the Artel Galerie, Geneva, in 1974. In 1973-74 he lived in Berlin as a guest of the Deutsche Akademische Austauschdienst (German Academic Exchange Service). Ipoustéguy was given an important one-man show at the Nationalgalerie Berlin in 1974. The artist continues to exhibit at the Galerie Claude Bernard in Paris and he lives and works in Choisy-le-roi.

179 Lenin. 1967
(*Lénine*)

68.1872

Marble and metal, 23 in. (58.4 cm.) high

Signed and dated on left shoulder: *Ipoustéguy 67.*

PROVENANCE:

from the artist through Galerie Claude Bernard, Paris, 1968

In a work like *Lenin* Ipoustéguy exhibits his probing concern with famous historical figures and he characteristically refers to the art of the past: specifically Renaissance and Mannerist sculpture. The face emerging from the stone recalls Michelangelo's figures being freed from blocks of marble. Ipoustéguy has a predilection for working in marble and for representing the human body. He achieves a strange effect of flesh and bone that proceeds from Surrealist imagery. Through the erosion of facial features and the use of ball bearings for misplaced and unmatched eyes, he shatters reality.

EXHIBITIONS:

Paris, Galerie Claude Bernard, *Ipoustéguy: marbres,* Nov.-Dec. 1968, repr.

New York, The Solomon R. Guggenheim Museum, *Selected Sculpture and Works on Paper,* July 8-Sept. 14, 1969, p. 130, repr.

REFERENCES:

D. Miller, "Ipoustéguy: The Art of Astonishment," *Art International,* vol. XIV, Feb. 20, 1970, p. 45, repr.

Handbook, 1970, pp. 164, repr., 165

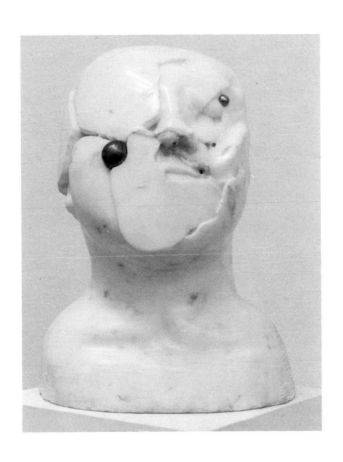

Victor Vasarely b. 1908

Victor Vasarely was born on April 9, 1908, in Pécs, Hungary. He began to study medicine at the University of Budapest in 1925. In 1927 he enrolled at the Poldini-Volkmann Academy of Painting in Budapest. Vasarely entered the Mühely (known as the Bauhaus of Budapest) in 1929 and studied there under Alexander Bortnyik. At this time he was introduced to Constructivism, Cubism and Suprematism. In 1930 Vasarely moved to Paris and for the next ten years supported himself as a graphic artist. In 1944 he ceased commercial work and started to exhibit at the Galerie Denise René, Paris.

Vasarely's early painting falls into the Belle-Isle (1947), Gordes-Crystal (1948), Denfert (1951) and Kinetic (1955) periods. He published his *Manifeste jaune (Yellow Manifesto)* in 1955. In the mid-fifties he started to make silk-screen prints and during the early sixties began colored wood reliefs and metal sculptures. In 1965 he won the Grand Prize at the São Paulo Bienal and was named Chevalier de l'Ordre des Arts et Lettres by the French government. In 1967 Vasarely received the Carnegie International Painting Prize. The official inauguration of Vasarely's own museum at Gordes Château, Vaucluse, France, was held in 1970, the year the artist was named Chevalier de la Légion d'Honneur by the French government. The Sidney Janis and Denise René galleries in New York presented an important double exhibition of Vasarely's work in 1972. Since that time the artist has participated in many group shows and has been given numerous one-man exhibitions in Europe and the United States. Vasarely lives and works in Paris and Gordes.

180 **Reytey.** 1968

73.2042

Tempera on canvas, 63 x 63 in. (160 x 160 cm.)

Signed l.c.: *Vasarely*; signed and dated on reverse: *Vasarely / "REYTÉY" / 160 x 160 / 1968.*

PROVENANCE:

from the artist
Galerie Chalette, New York, 1970-73

Like Albers, Herbin, Max Bill and Soto, Vasarely has investigated perceptual phenomena and the optical effects of color. Paintings such as *Reytey* consist of uniform, geometric patterns arranged with mechanical precision in a square format. The organization of the painted surface into color scales gives the illusion of sharp recession into depth. Here the artist proceeds from the outer black band through eight gradations of gray. The alignment of the next seven color gradations shifts and moves inward from violet to dark purple, then changes again to five blue zones, concluding with a dark blue square slightly to the lower right of center. Vasarely intentionally avoids painterliness and any trace of subjectivity and freedom of handling. *Reytey* (which means "secret" in Hungarian) belongs to his Vonal series. He painted three smaller versions with the same title after executing the Guggenheim's canvas.*

* correspondence with the author, Apr. 1979

EXHIBITION:

New York, Galerie Chalette, *Vasarely,* Apr. 25-May 30, 1970

Jesús Soto b. 1923

Jesús Rafael Soto was born on June 6, 1923, in Ciudad Bolívar, Venezuela. After working as a commercial artist, he attended the Escuela de Artes Plásticas in Caracas from 1942 to 1947. He saw the work of Braque and Picasso in reproduction and in 1943 began exhibiting at the Salón Oficial Anual de Arte Venezolano in Caracas. Soto served as director of the Escuela de Artes Plásticas in Maracaibo, Venezuela, from 1947 to 1950. His first one-man show was held in 1949 at the Taller Libre de Arte in Caracas.

Soto settled in Paris in 1950 and first exhibited at the Salon des Réalités Nouvelles the following year. During this period he developed an interest in the work of Mondrian and Malevich. The Galerie Denise René in Paris gave Soto a one-man exhibition in 1956. Two years later he participated in the *Exposition Internationale* in Brussels and executed a sculpture for the Escuela de Arquitectura in Caracas. The Museo de Bellas Artes of Caracas awarded him the National Prize for Painting in 1960. In 1965 Soto was given his first one-man show in the United States at the Kootz Gallery in New York. He took part in Expo 67 in Montreal in 1967 and in 1968 began a commission for two walls and a sculpture for the University at Rennes in France. That same year an important Soto retrospective was held at the Stedelijk Museum in Amsterdam, followed by another at the Musée d'Art Moderne de la Ville de Paris in 1969. The artist made an environment for the UNESCO Building in Paris in 1970 and was given a large retrospective at the Museo de Arte Moderno in Bogotá in 1972. In 1973 the Museo de Arte Moderno Jesús Soto, designed by Carlos Raul Villanueva, was inaugurated in Ciudad Bolívar, and Soto collaborated on a kinetic environment for the new Renault factory in Paris. The Solomon R. Guggenheim Museum presented an exhibition of his work in 1974-75. Soto lives and works in Paris.

181 Cube with Ambiguous Space. 1974
(Cubo a espacio ambiguo)

78.2520

Painted plexiglass, 88½ x 88½ x 88½ in.
(225 x 225 x 225 cm.)

Not signed or dated.

PROVENANCE:
Gift of the artist, 1978

Cube with Ambiguous Space is a huge transparent box made from six identical sections of plexiglass. Each side has an open square center surrounded by concentric squares of black and blue vertical lines. Thus, the two-dimensional aspect of each surface bears a strong resemblance to Albers' *Homage to the Square*. However, Soto's interest in the modulation of light and shadow and manipulation of the third dimension bring to mind the work of Moholy-Nagy. The ideas Soto articulates in the Guggenheim structure were first set forth in 1955 in his *Little Villaneuva Box*, where the vertical lines on three layers of plexiglass shift and halate as the viewer moves.

Soto's transparent construction as well as the superposition of linear patterns and squares allow for the spectator's visual participation, whereas he becomes physically involved in the artists' coeval *Penetrables* by actually entering them.

Another *Cube with Ambiguous Space* dating from 1969 is in the Museo de Arte Moderno Jesús Soto in Ciudad Bolívar, Venezuela.

EXHIBITION:
New York, The Solomon R. Guggenheim Museum, *Soto: A Retrospective Exhibition*, Nov. 8, 1974-Jan. 26, 1975, no. 61, color repr., traveled to Washington, D. C., The Hirshhorn Museum and Sculpture Garden, Smithsonian Institution, Sept. 26-Nov. 9

Pol Bury b. 1922

Pol Bury was born on April 26, 1922, in Haine-Saint-Pierre, Belgium. In 1938 he studied briefly at the Académie des Beaux-Arts of Mons. While living in La Louvière in 1939, he met the poets Achille Chavée and André Lorent. Bury took part in the *Exposition Internationale du Surréalisme* of 1945 in Brussels, where he became affiliated with the group *Jeune Peinture* two years later. In 1949 he met Alechinsky and began his two-year association with the COBRA group. His first mobiles were presented at the Galerie Apollo in Brussels in 1953. Around this time Bury and André Balthazar founded the Académie de Montbliart, which later issued the *Daily-Bûl*. He participated in the exhibition *Le Mouvement* at the Galerie Denise René in Paris in 1955. Around 1957 Bury constructed his first motorized mobiles. His work was included in the *Kinetische Kunst* show at the Zürich Kunstgewerbemuseum in 1960. In 1961 the artist published *La Boule et le trou (The Ball and the Hole)* and was given a one-man show at the Galerie Smith in Brussels. That same year he moved to Fontenay-aux-Roses, near Paris.

Bury's first one-man exhibition in Paris was mounted at the Galerie Iris Clert in 1962. He executed stage designs for the ballet at the Palais des Beaux-Arts of Charleroi in 1964. That same year the artist traveled to New York on the occasion of his one-man show at the Lefebre Gallery and wrote his essay "Time Dilates." Throughout the 1960s Bury showed internationally in numerous group and one-man exhibitions. In 1967 he illustrated Stendhal's *Piccola guida all'uso di un viaggiatore in Italia* and participated in the show *The 1960s* at The Museum of Modern Art in New York. The following year he received a commission for a fountain at the University of Iowa. The Galerie Maeght in Paris hosted a one-man show of Bury's work in 1969.

A Bury retrospective was organized by the University of California at Berkeley and The Solomon R. Guggenheim Museum in 1970. During the early 1970s he executed monumental sculpture projects and began working in film. He was given a retrospective at the Galerie Maeght in Barcelona in 1975. Bury lives in Paris.

182 **The Staircase.** 1965
(*L'Escalier*)

65.1765

Wood with motor, 78⅝ x 27 x 16¼ in.
(200 x 68.6 x 41.3 cm.)

Not signed or dated.

PROVENANCE:

from the artist through Lefebre Gallery, New
York, 1965

Around 1953 Agam, Jean Tinguely, Soto and Bury were
independently investigating problems of movement.
Bury's sculptures move with a mystifying and often
almost imperceptible slowness, punctuated by creak-
ing noises of wood on wood or the sound of metal on
metal. He conceals the motors, pulleys or magnets
which activate his work. Not only the threshhold between mobility and immobility but, as Peter Selz has
pointed out, the paradox of "levity vs. gravity, movement vs. stability—the juxtaposition of these opposites
is what strikes terror in the spectator—the terror of
the unexpected." (Berkeley, University Art Museum,
1970, p. 6)

On the eight successively slanting planes of *The Staircase* Bury has positioned twenty-three wooden balls.
Slowly they creep down the steep inclines only to roll
back up again. By denying the viewer's expectation
that they will fall, the balls seem to defy the law of
gravity.

EXHIBITIONS:

New York, The Solomon R. Guggenheim Museum, *Selected
Sculpture and Works on Paper,* July 8-Sept. 11, 1969, p. 99,
repr.

Berkeley, University Art Museum, University of California,
Pol Bury, Apr. 28-May 31, 1970, no. 13, repr., traveled to
St. Paul, Minn., The College of St. Catherine and Minne-
apolis, Walker Art Center, Aug. 2-Sept. 10; Iowa City,
Museum of Art, University of Iowa, Sept. 20-Oct. 31; The
Arts Club of Chicago, Nov. 24, 1970-Jan. 2, 1971; Houston,
Institute for the Arts, Rice University, Jan. 25-Mar. 7; New
York, The Solomon R. Guggenheim Museum, Apr. 15-
June 6

REFERENCES:

S. W. Taylor, "Pol Bury: Clinamen in Art," *Studio International,* vol. 169, June 1965, p. 236, repr.

A. Balthazar, *Pol Bury,* Milan, 1967, repr.

D. Ashton, *Pol Bury,* Paris, 1970, p. 38, no. 9, repr.

E. Ionesco and A. Balthazar, *Pol Bury,* Brussels, 1976 [pp.
4-5], repr.

H. H. Arnason, *History of Modern Art,* rev. ed., New York,
1977, p. 666, fig. 1197

Richard Hamilton b. 1922

Richard Hamilton was born on February 24, 1922, in London. His schooling took place entirely in London. While working in advertising in 1936, he attended classes at Westminster Technical College and St. Martin's School of Art. From 1938 to 1940 and again in 1946 Hamilton studied painting at the Royal Academy Schools. After his expulsion he served in the army until 1948, when he entered the Slade School of Fine Art. He devised and designed the 1951 exhibition *Growth and Form* at the Institute of Contemporary Art (I.C.A.) in London.

In 1952 Hamilton began teaching at the Central School of Arts and Crafts in London and joined the *Independent Group* at I.C.A. with Lawrence Alloway, John McHale, Eduardo Paolozzi and others. From 1953 to 1966 he taught at King's College, University of Durham, which was to become the University of Newcastle-upon-Tyne. The show *Man, Machine and Motion* was organized by Hamilton and presented at the Hatton Gallery, Newcastle-upon-Tyne, and I.C.A. in 1955. He collaborated with McHale and John Voelcker on an environment for the *This is Tomorrow* exhibition of 1956 at the Whitechapel Art Gallery in London.

In 1960 Hamilton received the William and Noma Copley Foundation award for painting and produced his typographic reproduction of Duchamp's *Green Box*. His 1963 visit to the United States familiarized him with the work of the American Pop artists. He continued his homage to Duchamp, reconstructing the *Large Glass* in 1965-66 and organizing the show *The Almost Complete Works of Marcel Duchamp* at the Tate Gallery in London the following year. In 1967 Hamilton's graphics were exhibited at the Galerie Ricke in Kassel and his paintings at the Alexandre Iolas Gallery in New York. He was given one-man shows in 1969 at the Robert Fraser Gallery in London, the Galerie Hans Neuendorf, Hamburg, and Studio Marconi in Milan. One-man exhibitions of his work were presented by the National Gallery of Canada, Ottawa, in 1970, the Stedelijk Museum in Amsterdam in 1971 and The Solomon R. Guggenheim Museum in 1973. Hamilton lives near London.

183 **The Solomon R. Guggenheim (Black); (Black and White); (Spectrum).** 1965-66

67.1859.1-3

Fiberglas and cellulose, three reliefs, each 48 x 48 x 7½ in. (122 x 122 x 19 cm.)

Not signed or dated.

PROVENANCE:
from the artist through Robert Fraser Gallery, London, 1967

These three reliefs belong to a series of six Hamilton made in fiberglas from the same mould in 1965-66. A color postcard of Frank Lloyd Wright's Guggenheim Museum was the catalyst which led the artist to study photographs as well as the architect's plans for the building and then to make his own elevations, sections and numerous preparatory sketches and prints. Each relief has the same single, large spiral form seen in false perspective but painted a different color. Consequently, each has a different appearance. The *Black and White* version accentuates the projecting spiral bands and contrasting recessions. The *Black* relief merges with reflections of the surrounding environment: its slick, glossy finish dissolves its three-dimensional form. In the last example the colors move

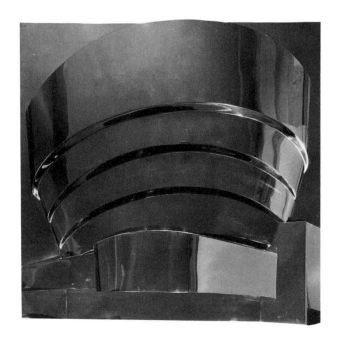

386

through the spectrum from red to yellow and blue to violet, vertically superimposed on the curved horizontals. Hamilton said "Instead of *being* the rainbow, the Guggenheim is seen at the bottom of the rainbow." (Russell, p. 118) His other reliefs in the series are Gold, Metalflake and Neapolitan ice cream colors.

EXHIBITIONS:

London, Robert Fraser Gallery, *Guggenheim Reliefs and Studies,* Oct. 18-Nov. 14, 1966

New York, Alexandre Iolas Gallery, *Richard Hamilton: Paintings 1964-1967,* May 3-27, 1967

Kassel, Museum Fridericianum, *4. Documenta Internationale Ausstellung,* June 27-Oct. 6, 1968, nos. 6-8

Milan, Studio Marconi, *Richard Hamilton: Dipinti e disegni 1957-1968,* Nov. 1968

London, Tate Gallery, *Richard Hamilton,* Mar. 12-Apr. 19, 1970, nos. 109, repr., 111, repr., 114, repr., traveled to Eindhoven, Stedelijk van Abbemuseum, May 15-June 28; Kunsthalle Bern, July 25-Aug. 30

New York, The Solomon R. Guggenheim Museum, *Richard Hamilton,* Sept. 14-Nov. 4, 1973, nos. 85, repr., 87, 90, repr., traveled to Cincinnati, The Contemporary Arts Center, Jan. 7-Feb. 14, 1974; Munich, Städtische Galerie im Lenbachhaus, Mar. 15-Apr. 15; Kunsthalle Tübingen, May 10-June 30; Berlin, Nationalgalerie, July 16-Aug. 26

REFERENCES:

Black:

J. Burr, "Sermons of Sorrow," *Apollo,* vol. LXXXIV, Oct. 1966, p. 333

G. Baro, "Hamilton's Guggenheim," *Art and Artists,* vol. I, Nov. 1966, p. 31, repr.

E. Lucie-Smith, "Pragmatists and Theoreticians," *Studio International,* vol. 172, Dec. 1966, pp. 314-315, repr.

Black and White:

J. Burr, "Sermons of Sorrow," *Apollo,* vol. LXXXIV, Oct. 1966, p. 333

"On Exhibitions," *Studio International,* vol. 172, Oct. 1966, p. 205, repr.

G. Baro, "Hamilton's Guggenheim," *Art and Artists,* vol. I, Nov. 1966, p. 28, repr.

Spectrum:

J. Burr, "Sermons of Sorrow," *Apollo,* vol. LXXXIV, Oct. 1966, p. 333

G. Baro, "Hamilton's Guggenheim," *Art and Artists,* vol. I, Nov. 1966, p. 31

J. Russell, "Richard Hamilton," *Art in America,* vol. 58, Mar. 1970, p. 118, color repr.

José Luis Cuevas b. 1933

José Luis Cuevas was born on February 26, 1933, in Mexico City. He attended "La Esmeralda" school of painting and sculpture in Mexico City for one term at the age of ten and studied engraving with Lola Cueto at Mexico City College in 1948 but is otherwise self-taught as an artist. In 1947, when he was only fourteen years old, Cuevas rented an empty loft and exhibited his work there. He was given his first one-man show at the Prisse Gallery, Mexico City, in 1953. Subsequently Cuevas exhibited widely in the United States, Latin America and Europe; in 1959 he won the First International Prize for Drawing at the São Paulo Bienal for his Funeral of a Dictator series.

Since the 1950s Cuevas has been preoccupied with morbid and grotesque aspects of human experience. However, his graphic style, which features fine line and delicate washes of color, is often in marked contrast to the violent, nightmarish character of the figures and situations he depicts. In addition to drawings in ink and watercolor, Cuevas is known for series of lithographs and engravings and has illustrated a number of books. His autobiography, Cuevas por Cuevas, was published in 1965. He has had many exhibitions at museums, including the Museo de Arte Moderno in Mexico City in 1972, the Musée d'Art Moderne de la Ville de Paris in 1976 and the Museum of Modern Art of Latin America in Washington, D.C., in 1978. Since the mid-1970s Cuevas has lived in Paris.

184 **The Printmaker Désandré Working on a Self-Portrait.** 1965
(El grabador Désandré trabajando en un autoretrato)

65.1774

Ink and watercolor on paper, 18¼ x 22¾ in. (46.2 x 57.8 cm.)

Signed l.r.: *Cuevas*; inscribed l.r.: *El grabador Désandré / trabajando en un autoretrato*; u.c.: *Dé Sandré*; c.r.: *Aprile / Charenton*; on reverse: *José Luis Cuevas / "The printmaker Désandré Working in one Self-portrait."*

PROVENANCE:
from the artist through Grace Borgenicht Gallery, New York, 1965

Cuevas' frequent references to earlier artists (particularly Old Masters) and the recurrent theme of self-portraiture are brought together in *The Printmaker Désandré Working on a Self-Portrait*. Other drawings from the mid-sixties represent *The Decameron with Self-Portrait in the Manner of Brueghel, The Artist Gavarin, Cuevas with Rembrandt Model* and *Rembrandt, Duchamp and Model in the Asylum of Charenton*. In the Guggenheim watercolor Cuevas has chosen to portray a little known French nineteenth-century painter, Jules-Marie Desandre, whose work was readily accessible through lithographs.* At the time of its execution he was working on lithographs for the *Cuevas-Charenton* portfolio which included literary figures and artists among the inmates at Charenton. In fact, he has included that name in our watercolor. Amidst undecipherable handwriting, heads peer out from the background. Cuevas has always demonstrated a predilection for drawing. Here he combines acuteness of line with gray, tan and brown washes of color.

*correspondence with the author, July 1979

EXHIBITIONS:
New York, Grace Borgenicht Gallery, *Recent Drawings by José Luis Cuevas,* May 18-June 5, 1965

Ithaca, N.Y., Andrew Dickson White Museum of Art, Cornell University, *The Emergent Decade: Latin American Painters and Painting in the 1960's,* Oct. 8-Nov. 8, 1965, color repr., traveled to Dallas Museum of Fine Arts, Dec. 18, 1965-Jan. 18, 1966; Ottawa, National Gallery of Canada, Apr. 1-May 1; New York, The Solomon R. Guggenheim Museum (organizer), May 20-June 19; Champaign-Urbana, Krannert Art Museum, University of Illinois, Sept. 16-Oct. 9; Lincoln, Mass., De Cordova Museum, Nov. 6-Dec. 4; Sarasota, John and Mable Ringling Museum of Art, Apr. 9-May 7, 1967

Wilmington, Delaware Art Center, *Contemporary Latin American Artists,* Mar. 9-Apr. 7, 1968

New York, Art Gallery, Center for Inter-American Relations, *Latin American Paintings From the Collection of The Solomon R. Guggenheim Museum,* July 2-Sept. 14, 1969

REFERENCE:
Handbook, 1970, pp. 84-85, repr.

Horst Antes b. 1936

Horst Antes was born on October 28, 1936, in Heppenheim, Germany. From 1957 to 1959 he attended the Staatliche Akademie der bildenden Künste, Karlsruhe. Antes' first one-man show was held at the Galerie der Spiegel in Cologne in 1960.

In 1960 Antes' painting began to reflect the formulations of his mature style: torsoless figures shown in profile with large heads and staring, almond-shaped eyes reminiscent of ancient Egyptian sculpture. From 1962 to 1963 Antes lived in Florence and Rome. In 1965 he returned to Karlsruhe and began to teach at the Akademie in that city. The artist was awarded the UNESCO Prize for Painting at the 1966 Venice Biennale, and in 1967 the Lefebre Gallery presented his first one-man show in New York. Antes was a guest professor at the Hochschule für bildende Künste, Berlin, in 1968. In 1971 he took a leave of absence from the Akademie in Karlsruhe to work exclusively on his painting. In the same year a retrospective of his work was held at the Staatliche Kunsthalle Baden-Baden. Antes has participated in many group shows and been given numerous one-man exhibitions in Germany, London and New York since that time. The artist now lives in Tuscany and in Wolfartsweler, near Karlsruhe, where he continues to teach at the Akademie.

185 **Large Black Figure.** 1968
(Grosse schwarze Figur)

69.1880

Aquatec, charcoal and masking tape on canvas, 59¼ x 47⅜ in. (150.5 x 120.3 cm.)

Signed l.r.: *Antes*; inscribed on reverse: *grosse Schwarze / Figur / Aquatec / 1968 / Antes.*

PROVENANCE:
from the artist through Lefebre Gallery, New York, 1969

Since 1960 the persistent theme of Antes' oeuvre has been a mythical, trunkless man. Sometimes he depicts the figure with arms, sometimes he shows only the head and, on occasion, he presents personages imprisoned behind bars. Here, the black silhouette overpowers the cramped surrounding space. In the areas of the head, legs and especially the feet, pentimenti are evident: in fact, the painting appears unfinished. The flat, precisely outlined black figure casts a colored shadow whose variegated stripes suggest a cerebral response to his environment. Antes was well aware of Surrealist imagery and primitive art. His fantastic figures are expressive of the anxiety and anonymity of modern man and manifest the spirit of tragicomic postwar German literature.

EXHIBITIONS:
New York, Lefebre Gallery, *Horst Antes,* Mar. 4-25, 1969, no. 21, repr.

São Paulo, X Bienal, *German Pavilion,* Sept.-Dec. 1969, no. 25

Staatliche Kunsthalle Baden-Baden, *Antes: Bilder 1965-1971,* July 30-Sept. 26, 1971, no. 36, color repr., traveled to Kunsthalle Bern, Oct. 16-Nov. 21; Kunsthalle Bremen, Dec. 5, 1971-Jan. 30, 1972; Frankfurter Kunstverein, Feb. 11-Mar. 26

The Arts Club of Chicago, *Horst Antes: Paintings,* Nov. 15-Dec. 27, 1976, no. 12, color repr.

REFERENCE:
Handbook, 1970, pp. 20-21, repr.

Alexander Calder 1898-1976

Alexander Calder was born on July 22, 1898, in Lawnton, Pennsylvania, into a family of artists. In 1919 he received an engineering degree from Stevens Institute of Technology in Hoboken, New Jersey. Calder attended the Art Students League in New York from 1923 to 1926, studying briefly with Thomas Hart Benton and John Sloan among others. As a free-lance artist for the *National Police Gazette* in 1925 he spent two weeks sketching at the circus; his fascination with the subject dates from this time.

Calder's earliest sculptures were animals and wire and wood figures made in 1926. His first exhibition of paintings took place in 1926 at The Artist's Gallery in New York. Later this year Calder went to Paris and attended the Académie de la Grande Chaumière. In Paris he met Stanley William Hayter, exhibited at the 1926 Salon des Indépendants and in 1927 began giving performances of his miniature circus. The first show of his wire animals and caricature portraits was held at the Weyhe Gallery, New York, in 1928. The same year he met Miró, who became his lifelong friend. Subsequently Calder divided his time between France and the United States. In 1929 the Galerie Billiet gave him his first one-man show in Paris. He met Léger, Frederick Kiesler and van Doesburg and visited Mondrian's studio in 1930. Calder began to experiment with abstract sculpture at this time and in 1931-32 introduced moving parts into his work. These moving sculptures were called mobiles; the stationary constructions were to be named stabiles. He exhibited with the *Abstraction-Création* group in Paris in 1933. In 1943 The Museum of Modern Art in New York gave him a major one-man exhibition.

During the 1950s Calder traveled widely and executed Towers (wall mobiles) and Gongs (sound mobiles). He won First Prize for Sculpture at the 1952 Venice Biennale. Late in the decade the artist worked extensively with gouache; from this period he executed numerous major public commissions. In 1964-65 the Guggenheim Museum presented an important Calder retrospective. He began the Totems and the Animobiles, variations on the standing mobile, in 1966 and 1971 respectively. A major Calder exhibition was held at the Whitney Museum of American Art in New York in 1976. Calder died in New York on November 11, 1976.

186 Romulus and Remus. 1928
(Romulus et Remus)

65.1738

Wire and wood, 31 x 112 x 30 in. (78.7 x 284.5 x 76.2 cm.)

Signed in wire on tail: *Calder*. Not dated.

PROVENANCE:

from the artist through Perls Galleries, New York, 1965

Calder's earliest artistic efforts were humorous line drawings made when he was an illustrator for the *National Police Gazette*. Subsequently, in 1926, he turned to wood carving, constructing animated toys and figures for his miniature circus and creating large figures out of wire. *Romulus and Remus* and *Spring* (cat. no. 187) are essentially line drawings in space in which the medium is bent wire rather than ink. Despite their large size, they retain all the freshness and spontaneity of the rapidly executed drawings as well as the delightful humor present in all Calder's work. The use of the material itself is witty: wooden doorstops represent nipples and genitals. The artist treats a mythological subject with inventiveness and irreverence.

EXHIBITIONS:

New York, The Waldorf-Astoria, *12th Annual Exhibition of The Society of Independent Artists*, Mar. 9-Apr. 1, 1928, no. 139, repr.

Paris, Grand Palais, Société des Artistes Indépendants, *40e Exposition*, Jan. 18-Feb. 28, 1929, no. 699

New York, The Solomon R. Guggenheim Museum, *Alexander Calder: A Retrospective Exhibition*, Nov. 6, 1964-Jan. 31, 1965, no. 52, repr., traveled to St. Louis, The Washington University Gallery of Art, Feb. 21-Mar. 26; The Art Gallery of Toronto, Apr. 30-May 30; Paris, Musée National d'Art Moderne, July 1-Oct. 15

New York, The Solomon R. Guggenheim Museum, *Selected Sculpture and Works on Paper*, July 8-Sept. 14, 1969, p. 100, repr.

New York, Whitney Museum of American Art, *Calder's Universe*, Oct. 14, 1976-Feb. 6, 1977, p. 238, repr.

REFERENCES:

J. J. Sweeney, *Alexander Calder*, New York, 1951, p. 22

H. H. Arnason, *Calder*, Princeton, N. J., 1966, pp. 26, 28, 30-31, repr.

A. Calder and J. Davidson, *Calder: An Autobiography with Pictures*, New York, 1966, pp. 87, 88-89, repr.

Handbook, 1970, pp. 54, repr., 55

H. H. Arnason, *History of Modern Art*, rev. ed., New York, 1977, p. 405, fig. 650

M. C. Hayes, *Three Alexander Calders: A Family Memoir*, Middlebury, Conn., 1977, pp. 216, 218, 220

187 Spring. 1928
(Printemps)

65.1739

Wire and wood, 94½ in. (240 cm.) high

Signed in wire on right hip: *Calder.* Not dated.

PROVENANCE:
Gift of the artist, 1965

Like *Romulus and Remus* (cat. no. 186), *Spring* is one
of Calder's first wire sculptures. After exhibiting both
pieces in New York in 1928 and Paris in 1929, he packed
them away and did not retrieve them until thirty-five
years later when he and Thomas M. Messer were pre-
paring works to be shown in the retrospective at the
Guggenheim Museum in 1964-65. The female figure of
Spring measures over seven feet in height. A single piece
of wire gives the summarizing contour of her arm and
shoulder and the distinctive stance of her legs and hips;
complex twisted wire details contrast with the long,
sweeping outlines of the figure. Around 1930 Calder's
wire sculpture evolved into abstract constructions
which, by 1931-32, contained moving parts.

EXHIBITIONS:
New York, The Waldorf-Astoria, *12th Annual Exhibition
of the Society of Independent Artists,* Mar. 9-Apr. 1, 1928,
no. 138, repr.

Paris, Grand Palais, Société des Artistes Indépendants, *40e
Exposition,* Jan. 18-Feb. 28, 1929, no. 700

New York, The Solomon R. Guggenheim Museum, *Alexander Calder: A Retrospective Exhibition,* Nov. 6, 1964-Jan.
31, 1965, no. 73, repr., traveled to Milwaukee Art Center,
Feb. 25-Mar. 28; Des Moines Art Center, Apr. 28-May 30;
Paris, Musée National d'Art Moderne, July 1-Oct. 15

New York, The Solomon R. Guggenheim Museum, *Selected
Sculpture and Works on Paper,* July 8-Sept. 14, 1969, p. 99,
repr.

REFERENCES:
H. H. Arnason, *Calder,* Princeton, N. J., 1966, pp. 26, 28,
29, repr.

A. Calder and J. Davidson, *Calder: An Autobiography with
Pictures,* New York, 1966, p. 87

Handbook, 1970, p. 56, repr.

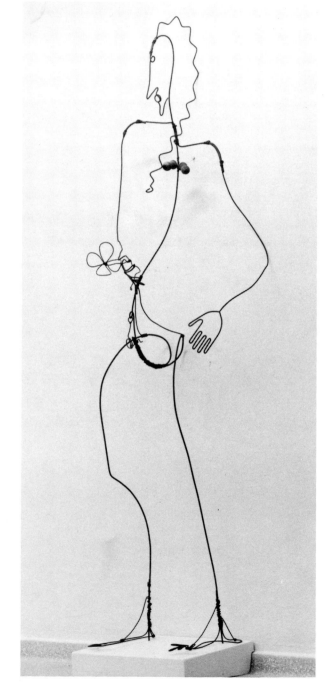

188 Constellation. 1943

54.1393

Wood and metal rods, 22 x 44½ in. (55.9 x 113 cm.)

Not signed or dated.

PROVENANCE:

from the artist
Mary Reynolds, Paris and Chicago, ca. 1946-53
Collection Mary Reynolds, Gift of her brother, 1954

Constellations are a special variety of stabiles dating
from the time of World War II and constructed from
pieces of wood and thin metal rods. The stabiles originated in the early 1930s (the same period as the
mobiles) and were named by Arp. It is no coincidence
that Arp had created Constellations in the 1930s (cat.
no. 128), as had Miró, another of Calder's friends,
around 1940-41.

Some of Calder's Constellations were meant for horizontal placement, while others (such as the Guggenheim example) were designed as wall pieces. The
wooden elements contrast in color, shape and texture
with the spiky black rods: their configuration fixes
precise points in space.

EXHIBITIONS:

New York, The Solomon R. Guggenheim Museum,
Inaugural Selection, Oct. 21, 1959-June 19, 1960

New York, The Solomon R. Guggenheim Museum, *Alexan-
der Calder: A Retrospective Exhibition,* Nov. 6, 1964-Jan.
31, 1965, no. 203, color repr., traveled to Milwaukee Art
Center, Feb. 25-Mar. 28; Des Moines Art Center, Apr. 28-
May 30; Paris, Musée National d'Art Moderne, July 1-
Oct. 15

Berlin, Akademie der Kunst, *Alexander Calder,* May 21-July
16, 1967, no. 68, repr.

New York, The Solomon R. Guggenheim Museum, *Selected
Sculpture and Works on Paper,* July 8-Sept. 14, 1969, p. 106,
repr.

Chicago, Museum of Contemporary Art, *Alexander Calder,*
Oct. 26-Dec. 8, 1974

Munich, Haus der Kunst, *Calder,* May 10-July 13, 1975,
no. 57, repr., traveled to Kunsthaus Zürich, Aug. 16-Nov. 2

REFERENCES:

H. H. Arnason, *Calder,* Princeton, N. J., 1966, p. 56, repr.

Handbook, 1970, p. 62, repr.

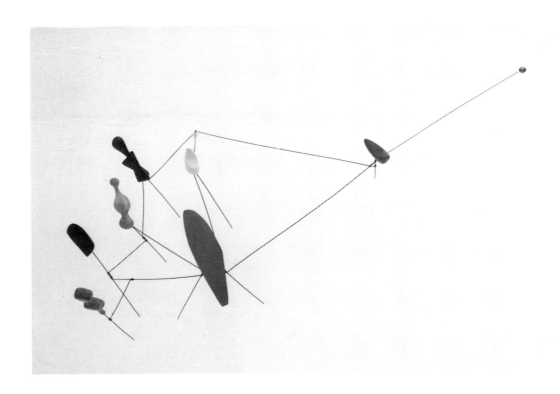

Calder

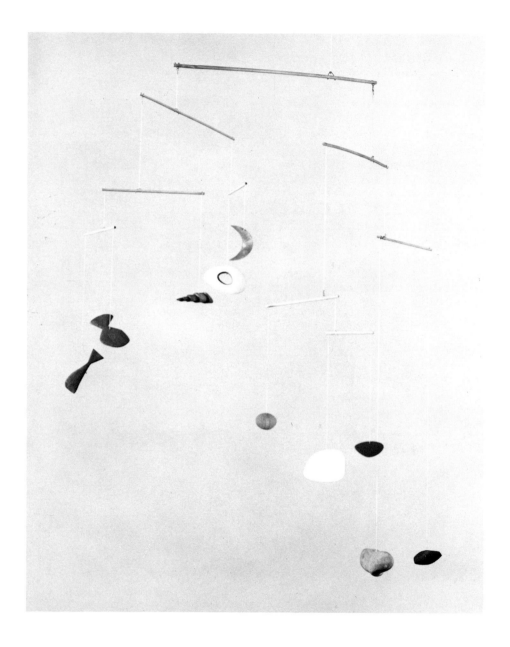

189 Mobile. ca. 1943-46

54.1390

Wood, metal and cord, 67 x 65 in. (170.2 x 165.1 cm.)

Not signed or dated.

PROVENANCE:

Gift of the artist
Mary Reynolds, Paris and Chicago, ca. 1946-53
Collection Mary Reynolds, Gift of her brother, 1954

Calder's first mobiles date from the early 1930s, when he lived in Paris. His friend Duchamp arrived at the term to describe the diverse types of Calder's moving sculptures, of which the hanging mobile is most familiar. In this example simple wooden shapes—most of them painted—are suspended from wooden dowels. Responding to air currents, the mobile's ever-shifting profile moves spontaneously and unpredictably, different elements traveling in different directions at varying rates of speed.

In *Calder: An Autobiography with Pictures,* the artist related that "there were two mobiles of the epoch of the constellations—the war period—made of bits of hardwood, carved, painted, and hanging on strings at the end of dowel sticks. Carré had previously deleted these from what he wanted to show, so I gave them to Mary Reynolds, who was back in Paris. And she always refers to them, ever since, as the 'Pas Nobles Mobiles' (the undignified mobiles). These now belong to the Guggenheim museum." (p. 189)

EXHIBITIONS:

New York, The Solomon R. Guggenheim Museum, *Inaugural Selection,* Oct. 21, 1959-June 19, 1960

The Cleveland Museum of Art, *Paths of Abstract Art,* Oct. 4-Nov. 13, 1960, no. 111, repr.

New York, The Solomon R. Guggenheim Museum, *Alexander Calder: A Retrospective Exhibition,* Nov. 6, 1964-Jan. 31, 1965, no. 146, traveled to St. Louis, The Washington University Gallery of Art, Feb. 21-Mar. 26; The Art Gallery of Toronto, Apr. 30- May 30; Paris, Musée National d'Art Moderne, July 1-Oct. 15

New York, The Solomon R. Guggenheim Museum, *Selected Sculpture and Works on Paper,* July 8-Sept. 14, 1969, p. 104, repr.

Munich, Haus der Kunst, *Calder,* May 10-July 13, 1975, no. 26, repr., traveled to Kunsthaus Zürich, Aug. 16-Nov. 2

REFERENCES:

H. H. Arnason, *Calder,* Princeton, N. J., 1966, p. 48, repr.

A. Calder and J. Davidson, *Calder: An Autobiography with Pictures,* New York, 1966, p. 189

Handbook, 1970, pp. 60-61, repr.

Calder

190 Red Lily Pads. 1956
(Nénuphars rouges)

65.1737

Painted sheet metal, metal rods and wire, 42 x 201 x
109 in. (106.7 x 510.6 x 276.9 cm.)

Signed and dated on largest lily pad: *CA/56.*

PROVENANCE:

from the artist through Perls Galleries, New York, 1965

Red Lily Pads is at once an abstract composition of
red-painted discs, rods and wires, and a giant emblem
of leaves floating on water. With the complex distri-
bution of weight, Calder maintains a continually
changing equilibrium. The large scale of this mobile
activates the Guggenheim's interior space, and the
suspension of abstract shapes exemplifies mobility
and freedom.

In the 1940s Jean-Paul Sartre wrote about Calder's
work: "A mobile does not suggest anything: it captures genuine living movements and shapes them.
Mobiles have no meaning, make you think of nothing but themselves. They are, that is all; they are
absolutes. There is more of the unpredictable about
them than in any other human creation. . . . In short,
although mobiles do not seek to imitate anything . . .
they are nevertheless at once lyrical inventions, technical combinations of an almost mathematical quality
and sensitive symbols of Nature." (J. Lipman, *Calder's Universe,* New York, 1976, p. 261)

EXHIBITIONS:

New York, The Solomon R. Guggenheim Museum, *Alexander Calder: A Retrospective Exhibition,* Nov. 6, 1964-Jan. 31,
1965, no. 160, repr., traveled to St. Louis, The Washington
University Gallery of Art, Feb. 21-Mar. 26; The Art Gallery
of Toronto, Apr. 30-May 30

New York, The Solomon R. Guggenheim Museum, *Selected
Sculpture and Works on Paper,* July 8-Sept. 14, 1969, p. 109,
color repr.

Moscow, Sokolniki Park, *USA-Two Hundred Years* (organized by United States Information Agency), Nov. 11-Dec.
13, 1976

REFERENCES:

H. H. Arnason, *Calder,* Princeton, N. J., 1966, pp. 81, 135,
color repr.

Handbook, 1970, p. 63, color repr.

Stuart Davis 1894-1964

Stuart Davis was born December 7, 1894, in Philadelphia and moved with his family to East Orange, New Jersey, in 1901. Through his parents he had early contact with Robert Henri, John Sloan, William Glackens and other realist artists. In 1909 Davis left high school to become an artist and enrolled at the Henri School in New York, studying there until 1912. He showed with the *Independents* in New York in 1910 and in 1913 exhibited watercolors at the Armory Show, where he was impressed by the modern Europeans including Cézanne, van Gogh, Matisse and Picasso. That same year he began to work as an illustrator for *The Masses*. In 1915 Davis spent the first of many summers until 1934 in Gloucester, Massachusetts; the area provided the motifs for a number of important paintings.

Davis' first one-man show took place at the Sheridan Square Gallery in New York in 1917. He experimented with non-imitative color and multiple images derived from Cubism. In the 1920s he exhibited at the Whitney Studio Club and in 1927 was given his first show at Edith Halpert's The Downtown Gallery, where he continued to exhibit until 1962. In 1928 Davis went to live in Paris for a year. After returning to New York, Davis taught at the Art Students League in 1931-32 and joined the Public Works of Art Project in 1933. The following year he was elected president of the Artists' Union; he edited its magazine *Art Front* in 1935-36. From 1935 Davis executed several murals for the WPA Federal Art Project. He became a charter member of the American Artists' Congress in 1936 and subsequently served as its national secretary and chairman. From 1940 to 1950 the artist taught at the New School for Social Research, New York.

Davis was an important influence on younger artists including Gorky and de Kooning; he was, as well, a precursor of Pop Art. He was honored with many one-man museum shows during his lifetime. Davis died in New York on June 24, 1964. The National Collection of Fine Arts, Washington, D.C., organized a memorial exhibition of his work in 1965, and The Brooklyn Museum presented a major Davis retrospective in 1978.

191 **Cliché.** 1955

55.1428

Oil on canvas, 56¼ x 42 in. (142.8 x 106.6 cm.)

Signed u.l.: *Stuart Davis*. Not dated.

PROVENANCE:
from the artist through The Downtown Gallery, New York, 1955

The black calligraphic line seen against the brilliant red-orange painted surface of *Cliché* brings to mind Davis' use of line in his drawings of the 1930s. Yet the boldness and essentiality are characteristic of his late work. The disposition of forms in *Cliché* corresponds closely with that in a coeval painting, *Ready to Wear* (Collection The Art Institute of Chicago). While the red, blue, black and white shapes of *Ready to Wear* explore spatial relationships, the red-orange of *Cliché* emphasizes the flatness of the picture plane. The letters "XRD" are a reference to Davis' art theories. From his study of the artist's writings, John R. Lane* has determined that "RD" stands for "ratio differentiation," and "X" probably refers to "external relations" or the orders of patterns concerning perspective, color and the relative size and position of shapes. Davis stressed the importance of the width and color as well as the length of a line.

He favored catchy, witty titles. "Cliché" means not only a trite phrase but also, in French, a photo or instantaneous impression. In 1955 Davis executed a gouache study for *Cliché* as well as a lithograph with the same title.

* correspondence with the author, Mar. 1978

EXHIBITIONS:
New York, The Downtown Gallery, *30th Annual Exhibition*, Oct. 4-29, 1955, no. 1

New York, The Solomon R. Guggenheim Museum, *Selection VI*, Jan. 25-May 1, 1956

New York, The Downtown Gallery, *Stuart Davis: Exhibition of Recent Paintings 1954-56*, Nov. 6-Dec. 1, 1956, no. 9

London, Tate Gallery, *An exhibition of paintings from The Solomon R. Guggenheim Museum, New York*, Apr. 16-May 26, 1957, no. 12, traveled to The Hague, Gemeentemuseum, June 25-Sept. 1; Helsinki, Ateneumin Taidekokoelmat, Sept. 27-Oct. 20; Rome, Galleria Nazionale d'Arte Moderna, Dec. 5, 1957-Jan. 8, 1958; Cologne, Wallraf-Richartz-Museum, Jan. 26-Mar. 30; Paris, Musée des Arts Décoratifs, Apr. 23-June 1

New York, The Solomon R. Guggenheim Museum, *Inaugural Selection*, Oct. 21, 1959-June 1, 1960.

Washington, D. C., National Collection of Fine Arts, *Stuart Davis Memorial Exhibition*, May 28-July 5, 1965, no. 99, repr., traveled to The Art Institute of Chicago, July 30-Aug. 29; New York, Whitney Museum of American Art, Sept. 14-Oct. 17; The Art Galleries, University of California at Los Angeles, Oct. 31-Nov. 28

Paris, Musée d'Art Moderne de la Ville de Paris, *Stuart Davis: 1894-1964,* Feb. 15-Mar. 14, 1966, no. 36, repr., traveled to Berlin, Amerika Haus, Apr. 22-May 21; London, Chancery Building, June 7-24

New York, Lawrence Rubin Gallery, *Stuart Davis: Major Drawings on Canvas and Paper from 1928 to 1964,* Jan. 30-Mar. 1, 1971, no. 9

New York, The Solomon R. Guggenheim Museum, *Acquisition Priorities: Aspects of Postwar Painting in America,* Oct. 14, 1976-Jan. 16, 1977, no. 10, repr.

REFERENCES:

Art News, vol. 54, Jan. 1956, p. 5 and cover repr.

J. Lucas, "The Fine Art Jive of Stuart Davis," *Art News,* vol. 31, Sept. 1957, p. 37

E. C. Goossen, *Stuart Davis,* New York, 1959, pl. 68

Handbook, 1959, p. 43, repr.

D. Kelder, ed., *Stuart Davis,* New York, 1971, pl. 42

Josef Albers 1888-1976

Josef Albers was born March 19, 1888, in Bottrop, Germany. From 1905 to 1908 he studied to become a teacher in Büren and then taught in Westphalian primary schools from 1908 to 1913. After attending the Königliche Kunstschule in Berlin from 1913 to 1915, he was certified as an art teacher. Albers studied art in Essen and Munich before entering the Bauhaus in Weimar in 1920. There he initially concentrated on glass painting and in 1929, as a *Bauhausgeselle* (journeyman), he reorganized the glass workshop. In 1923 he began to teach the *Vorkurs,* a basic design course. When the Bauhaus moved to Dessau in 1925, he became a *Bauhausmeister* (professor). In addition to working in glass and metal, he designed furniture and typography.

After the Bauhaus was forced to close in 1933, Albers emigrated to the United States. That same year he became head of the art department at the newly established, experimental Black Mountain College in Black Mountain, North Carolina. Albers continued to teach at Black Mountain until 1949. In 1935 he took the first of many trips to Mexico, and in 1936 was given his first one-man show in New York at J. B. Neumann's New Art Circle. He became a United States citizen in 1939. In 1949 Albers began his Homage to the Square series.

He lectured and taught at various colleges and universities throughout the United States and from 1950 to 1958 served as head of the design department at Yale University. In addition to painting, printmaking and executing murals and architectural commissions, Albers published poetry, articles and books on art. Thus, as a theoretician and teacher, he was an important influence on generations of young artists. A major Albers exhibition, organized by The Museum of Modern Art, New York, traveled throughout South America, Mexico and the United States from 1965 to 1967, and a retrospective of his work was held at The Metropolitan Museum of Art, New York, in 1971. Albers lived and worked in New Haven until his death there on March 25, 1976.

192 **b and p.** 1937

48.1172 X264

Oil on Masonite, 23⅞ x 23¾ in. (60.6 x 60.2 cm.)

Signed and dated l.r.: *A 37;* inscribed on reverse: *"b and p" / (B + P) / Albers '37.*

PROVENANCE:

J. B. Neumann, New York, by 1945
Karl Nierendorf, New York, by 1946
Estate of Karl Nierendorf, 1948

Josef Albers began to work in oil paint after his arrival in the United States in 1933. Strictly limiting his colors to blue and white, the artist allows the Masonite support to function coloristically to create a wider range of hue and texture.

The paired images found in the Treble Clef series of 1932 to 1935 reappear in *b and p,* where the shapes are not identical but stand in inverted relationship to each other. The essentially linear structure of the letters in our painting would become more schematic and simplified, and the rectangular border would be developed as a controlling design element in Albers' subsequent work of the 1940s. In its parallel construction around two light foci *b and p* anticipates the Variants.

EXHIBITIONS:

Minneapolis, University Gallery, University of Minnesota, *Josef Albers,* Jan. 7-28, 1938, traveled to Northfield, Minn., Carleton College; St. Paul, Minn., The St. Paul Gallery and School of Art

New York, New Art Circle, *Josef Albers,* Jan. 2-17, 1945

New Haven, Yale University Art Gallery, *Josef Albers: Paintings, Prints, Projects,* Apr. 25-June 18, 1956, no. 17

New York, The Solomon R. Guggenheim Museum, *Inaugural Selection,* Oct. 21, 1959-June 19, 1960

Washington, D.C., The Washington Gallery of Modern Art, *Josef Albers: The American Years,* Oct. 30-Dec. 31, 1965, no. 14, traveled to New Orleans, Isaac Delgado Museum of Art, Jan. 23-Feb. 27, 1966; San Francisco Museum of Art, June 2-26; Santa Barbara, The Art Galleries, University of California, July 8-Sept. 7; Waltham, Mass., Rose Art Museum, Brandeis University, Sept. 23-Oct. 29

Princeton, N. J., The Art Museum, Princeton University, *Josef Albers: Paintings and Graphics, 1917-1970,* Jan. 5-26, 1971, no. 3

Dallas Museum of Fine Arts, *Geometric Abstraction: 1926-1942,* Oct. 7-Nov. 19, 1972, no. 3, repr.

Münster, Westfälisches Landesmuseum für Kunst und Kulturgeschichte, *Abstraction-Création, 1931-1936,* Apr. 2-June 4, 1978, no. 1, repr., traveled to Paris, Musée d'Art Moderne de la Ville de Paris, June 16-Sept. 17

REFERENCES:

I. Finkelstein, *The Life and Art of Josef Albers,* Ph.D. dissertation, Institute of Fine Arts, New York University, 1967, pp. 123-125 and fig. 97

E. Gomringer, *Josef Albers: His work as contribution to visual articulation in the twentieth century,* New York, 1968, p. 70, color repr.

Handbook, 1970, pp. 12-13, repr.

M. Rowell, "On Albers' Color," *Artforum,* vol. X, Jan. 1972, p. 36, repr.

Rudenstine, *Collection Catalogue,* 1976, no. 1, repr.

Albers

93 Homage to the Square: Apparition. 1959

61.1590

Oil on Masonite, 48 x 48 in. (121.9 x 121.9 cm.)

Signed and dated l.r.: *A 59*; inscribed on reverse: *Homage to the Square / "Apparition" / Albers 1959.*

PROVENANCE:

from the artist
Sidney Janis Gallery, New York, 1961

Albers began his series of paintings exploring the possibilities of color interactions within the format of single-centered squares in 1949. *Homage to the Square: Apparition* dates from 1959 and exemplifies an arrangement of four nested squares: one of four formats evolved by the artist. While Malevich, Mondrian and *De Stijl* painters had employed the square format, Albers chose this simplest of geometric shapes and divided it into three or four concentric squares. Depending upon the hues juxtaposed, the colors can be seen as advancing or receding.

With a palette knife he applied unmixed oil colors to a well-primed white ground on Masonite panel. He painted each precisely measured square up to its very edge, where the next one began. Albers avoided complementary colors and, after early Homages, shunned strong color contrasts and favored yellows and grays. The sharpness of contour separating squares is dependent upon the degree of contrast between adjacent hues. In *Apparition* the subdued hues of green, blue and gray permit the central yellow square to come forward like sunlight shining through a window. Albers' lifelong preoccupation with the interaction of color and light culminated in the infinite variations of Homage to the Square.

EXHIBITIONS:

New York, The Solomon R. Guggenheim Museum, *American Abstract Expressionists and Imagists*, Oct. 13-Dec. 31, 1961, no. 1

Princeton, N. J., The Art Museum, Princeton University, *Josef Albers: Paintings and Graphics, 1917-1970*, Jan. 5-26, 1971, no. 16, repr.

New York, The Solomon R. Guggenheim Museum, *Acquisition Priorities: Aspects of Postwar Painting in America*, Oct. 15, 1976-Jan. 16, 1977, no. 8, repr.

REFERENCES:

E. Gomringer, *Josef Albers: His work as contribution to visual articulation in the twentieth century*, New York, 1968, p. 151, repr.

Handbook, 1970, pp. 14-15, color repr.

H. H. Arnason, *History of Modern Art*, rev. ed., New York, 1977, p. 321 and color pl. 138

Hans Hofmann 1880-1966

Hans Hofmann was born March 21, 1880, in Weissenburg, Bavaria. He was raised in Munich, where in 1898 he began to study at various art schools. The patronage of Philip Freudenberg, a Berlin art collector, enabled Hofmann to live in Paris from 1904 to 1914. In Paris he attended the Académie de la Grande Chaumière, where Matisse was also a student; he met Picasso, Braque and other Cubists and was a friend of Robert Delaunay, who stimulated his interest in color. In 1909 Hofmann exhibited with the *Secession* in Berlin, and in 1910 was given his first one-man show at Paul Cassirer's gallery in Berlin. During this period he painted in a Cubist style.

At the outbreak of World War I Hofmann was in Munich; he remained there and in 1915 opened an art school which became highly successful. Hofmann taught at the University of California at Berkeley during the summer of 1930. He returned to teach in California in 1931, and his first exhibition in the United States took place that summer at the California Palace of the Legion of Honor, San Francisco. In 1932 he closed his Munich school and decided to settle in the United States. His first school in New York opened in 1933 and was succeeded in 1934 by the Hans Hofmann School of Fine Arts; in 1935 he established a summer school in Provincetown, Massachusetts.

After an extended period devoted to drawing, Hofmann returned to painting in 1935, combining Cubist structure, vivid color and emphatic gesture. He became a United States citizen in 1941. Completely abstract works date from the 1940s. His first one-man show in New York took place at Peggy Guggenheim's gallery, Art of This Century, in 1944. Hofmann was an important influence upon younger artists. In 1958 the artist closed his schools to devote himself full-time to painting. Among Hofmann's major museum exhibitions were retrospectives at The Museum of Modern Art, New York, in 1963 and the Hirshhorn Museum and Sculpture Garden, Washington, D.C., and The Museum of Fine Arts, Houston, 1976-77. Hans Hofmann died in New York on February 17, 1966.

194 The Gate. 1959-60

62.1620

Oil on canvas, 75⅛ x 48½ in. (190.7 x 123.2 cm.)

Signed and dated l.r.: *hans hofmann 60*; inscribed on reverse: *1959 / the gate / hans / hofmann / 75-48.*

PROVENANCE:

from the artist through Samuel M. Kootz Gallery, New York, 1962

It is most likely that Hofmann painted *The Gate* in 1959, as indicated by the inscription on the reverse of the canvas. Related in style to works such as *Equipoise,* 1958, and *Elysium,* 1960, the title suggests a stable, architectural image as do the titles *Cathedral,* 1959, *City Horizon,* 1959, and *The Golden Wall,* 1961. Hofmann retained the easel painting format and often worked with rectangular areas of color which are lined up precisely with the edges of the canvas and reinforce its rectangular shape.

The Gate is distinguished by vivid, radiant colors and a sense of the weight and density of paint. Against a background of freely-brushed green pigment (a hue Hofmann favored), he has laid on oblong slabs of fully saturated color. The central red rectangle and the large yellow one above it come forward from the picture plane. These floating rectangles, which began to appear in Hofmann's paintings around 1954-55, allow him to create complex spatial relationships between colors and shapes. The rectangular planes of color are placed on the canvas so as to produce a rhythm and tension between force and counterforce equivalent to that found in nature.

EXHIBITIONS:

Venice, XXX Biennale Internazionale d'Arte, *United States Pavilion,* June-Oct. 1960, no. 26

New York, The Museum of Modern Art, *Hans Hofmann,* Sept. 11-Nov. 28, 1963, no. 18, repr.

New York, Marlborough-Gerson Gallery, *The New York Painter, A Century of Teaching: Morse to Hofmann, Benefit Exhibition for the New York University Art Collection,* Sept. 27-Oct. 14, 1967, repr.

New York, The Solomon R. Guggenheim Museum, *Acquisition Priorities: Aspects of Postwar Painting in America,* Oct. 14, 1976-Jan. 16, 1977, no. 7, repr.

New York, Blum-Helman Gallery, *Hans Hofmann,* Nov. 3-Dec. 3, 1977

REFERENCES:

C. Greenberg, *Hofmann,* Paris, 1961, p. 31, color repr.

D. Ashton, " 'Summer Night Bliss,' A New Painting by

Hans Hofmann," *The Baltimore Museum of Art News,* vol. XXV, spring 1962, pp. 6, repr., 7

S. Hunter, *Hans Hofmann,* New York, 1963, no. 110, repr.

Handbook, 1970, pp. 162-163, repr.

H. H. Arnason, *History of Modern Art,* rev. ed., New York, 1977, color pl. 203

Ilya Bolotowsky 1907-1981

Ilya Bolotowsky was born July 1, 1907, in St. Petersburg, Russia. He attended the College of St. Joseph in Constantinople from 1921 to 1923 and emigrated with his family to the United States in September 1923. From 1924 to 1930 Bolotowsky studied at the National Academy of Design in New York where he worked in academic and Impressionist figurative styles. Bolotowsky became an American citizen in 1929. In 1930 his first one-man show took place at the G.R.D. Studios, New York.

Bolotowsky traveled in Europe in 1932 but was not inspired to paint in an abstract mode until 1933, when he saw Mondrian's work for the first time in the Gallatin Collection and a Miró show at the Pierre Matisse Gallery in New York. In 1935, with Gottlieb, Rothko and others, Bolotowsky formed *The Ten*, a group of artists sympathetic to expressionism and abstraction. In the late thirties and early forties Bolotowsky executed a number of murals under the WPA Federal Art Project. During this period he exhibited regularly with the *American Abstract Artists*, of which he was a founding member in 1936, and at the Museum of Non-Objective Painting in New York. At this time his work was characterized by biomorphic as well as geometric shapes. In the mid-1940s the influence of Mondrian's Neo-Plasticism became more pronounced in his painting.

From 1946 to 1948 Bolotowsky was acting head of the art department at Black Mountain College, Black Mountain, North Carolina; he subsequently taught at the University of Wyoming and at various universities throughout the United States. From 1961 he made three-dimensional painted columns. Bolotowsky wrote several plays and produced a number of experimental films. In 1974 a major retrospective of his work originated at The Solomon R. Guggenheim Museum and traveled to the National Collection of Fine Arts, Washington, D.C. Bolotowsky died in New York on November 22, 1981.

195 Blue Plane. 1963

64.1724

Oil on canvas, two panels, total 69½ x 86½ in. (176.5 x 219.7 cm.)

Signed and dated l.r.: *Ilya Bolotowsky / 63.*

PROVENANCE:
from the artist, 1964

In *Blue Plane* Bolotowsky combines two panels to form a single unified composition. Working within the Neo-Plastic idiom, the artist limits himself to the right angle and rectangular areas of dark blue, black and white. In contrast to Mondrian's paintings, where the white picture plane is articulated with a few black lines and small rectangular areas in red, yellow or blue, here Bolotowsky makes the color zones significantly larger in relation to the white ones. Moreover, he uses black for architectonic, planar surfaces. At the upper right Bolotowsky juxtaposes three different whites, thereby creating subtle contrasts of closely related tonalities. The placement of elements is careful and deliberate, although Bolotowsky does not use a predetermined system of proportion. The balance and tension between the horizontal and vertical elements and their relation to the edges of the canvas are essential to the achievement of the desired equilibrium.

EXHIBITION:
New York, The Solomon R. Guggenheim Museum, *Ilya Bolotowsky*, Sept. 20-Nov. 11, 1974, no. 37, repr., traveled to Washington, D.C., The National Collection of Fine Arts, Dec. 21, 1974-Feb. 17, 1975

REFERENCE:
Handbook, 1970, pp. 40-41, repr.

Richard Lindner 1901-1978

Richard Lindner was born in Hamburg on November 11, 1901. His childhood was spent in Nuremburg, where he studied music. He later studied art at the Akademie der bildenden Künste in Munich. During this early period he was interested in Dada and the published works of Duchamp and Picabia. Lindner spent a year in Berlin in 1928 and then returned to Munich to become art director of the publishing firm Knorr und Hirth.

In 1933, the day after the Nazis came to power, Lindner fled Germany. He settled in Paris where he was able to work from time to time as a graphic artist. In 1939 he was interned by the French for five months; after a turbulent period, during which he served briefly in the French Army and fled to Free France, he managed to escape to the United States in 1941. Living in New York, he became well-known as an illustrator for *Vogue, Harper's Bazaar* and *Fortune*. He received his United States citizenship in 1948. In 1952 Lindner abandoned illustrating and began to teach painting and drawing at Pratt Institute, Brooklyn. Saul Steinberg and Hedda Sterne were among his friends.

Lindner's first one-man exhibition was held in 1954 at the Betty Parsons Gallery, New York, where his work was shown until the latter part of the decade. In 1965 he resigned from Pratt and devoted himself full-time to painting. He was elected to the National Institute of Arts and Letters in 1972. A Lindner retrospective traveled to the Städtische Kunsthalle Düsseldorf and to the Musée National d'Art Moderne, Paris, in 1974. In 1977 the artist was given an important one-man show at the Museum of Contemporary Art in Chicago. On April 16, 1978, Lindner died at his home in New York.

196 The Secret. 1960

77.2397

Oil on canvas, 50 x 40 in. (127 x 101.6 cm.)

Signed and dated l.l.: *R. Lindner 1960.*

PROVENANCE:

from the artist through Cordier & Ekstrom, New York
Myron Orlofsky, White Plains, New York, 1962-72
M. Knoedler and Co., Inc., New York, 1972
Fischer Fine Art, Ltd., London, 1973
Joachim Jean Aberbach, New York, 1973-77
Gift, Joachim Jean Aberbach, 1977

Lindner differentiates one portion of the canvas from another by means of flat, smoothly finished color areas. The figure of a boy seen in profile occupies the lower right; his hand holds a string which leads to the girl. Confined to a hoop-like circle, she bears a strong resemblance to a china doll. The color wheel on the surface is also like a toy friction metal sparkler that Lindner owned—and is similar to the distinctive object in his painting *The Target* from the previous year (Collection Mr. and Mrs. Joseph R. Shapiro, Oak Park, Illinois). The detached spectator at the upper right attracts our attention and reminds us of the theatricality of the figure arrangement contrived by the artist. Through the compartmentalization of pictorial space and the isolation of the figures, Lindner emphasizes the secret lives of people.

A reproduction of our painting appeared with the following statement by the artist:

"I can not talk about painting.
I have now even doubts that there is such a thing as art in general. More and more I believe in the secret behaviour of human beings. Maybe all of us are creative if we listen to the secret of our inner voice." (New York, The Museum of Modern Art, 1963, p. 60)

EXHIBITIONS:

New York, The Museum of Modern Art, *Americans 1963,* May 20-Aug. 18, 1963, repr., traveled to Ottawa, National Gallery of Canada, Nov. 8-Dec. 1; Artists' Guild of St. Louis, Dec. 18, 1963-Jan. 15, 1964; The Toledo Museum of Art, Feb. 3-Mar. 2; Sarasota, John and Mable Ringling Museum of Art, Mar. 18-Apr. 15; Colorado Springs Fine Arts Center, May 1-29; San Francisco Museum of Art, June 16-Aug. 9; Seattle Art Museum, Sept. 9-Oct. 11; Detroit Institute of Arts, Nov. 1-29

Städtisches Museum Leverkusen, *Richard Lindner,* Oct. 11-Nov. 24, 1968, no. 53, repr., traveled to Kestner-Gesellschaft Hannover, Dec. 6, 1968-Jan. 19, 1969; Staatliche Kunsthalle Baden-Baden, Jan.-Mar. 9; Berlin, Haus am Waldsee, Apr. 17-May 18

Berkeley, University Art Museum, University of California, *Lindner*, June 17-July 27, 1969, no. 34, repr., traveled to Minneapolis, Walker Art Center, Aug. 11-30

Sarasota, John and Mable Ringling Musuem of Art, *After Surrealism: Metaphors and Similes*, Nov. 17-Dec. 10, 1972

London, Fischer Fine Art Ltd., *Universe of Art III*, June-July 1973, no. 35, repr.

Paris, Musée National d'Art Moderne, *Richard Lindner*, Jan. 5-Mar. 3, 1974, no. 18, color repr., traveled to Rotterdam, Museum Boymans-van Beuningen, Mar. 16-May 12; Kunsthalle Düsseldorf, June 13-July 28; Kunsthaus Zürich, Aug. 7-Sept. 29

Chicago, Museum of Contemporary Art, *Richard Lindner: A Retrospective Exhibition*, May 7-July 3, 1977

St. Paul de Vence, France, Fondation Maeght, *Richard Lindner*, May 12-June 30, 1979, no. 13, repr.

REFERENCES:
S. Tillim, *Lindner*, Chicago, 1961, pl. 18
D. Ashton, *Richard Lindner*, New York, 1969, pp. 42, 43, color repr., 44

Joseph Cornell 1903-1972

Joseph Cornell was born on December 24, 1903, in Nyack, New York. From 1917 to 1921 he attended Phillips Academy in Andover, Massachusetts. He was an ardent collector of memorabilia and, while working as a woolen-goods salesman in New York for the next ten years, he developed a passion for ballet, literature and the opera.

In the early thirties Cornell met Surrealist writers and artists at the Julien Levy Gallery in New York and saw Ernst's collage-novel *La Femme 100 têtes*. Cornell's early constructions of found objects were first exhibited in *Surrealism,* presented at the Wadsworth Atheneum in Hartford and subsequently at Julien Levy's in 1932. From 1934 to 1940 Cornell supported himself by working at the Traphagen studio in New York. During these years he became familiar with Duchamp's Readymades and Schwitters' box constructions. Cornell was included in the 1936 exhibition *Fantastic Art, Dada, Surrealism* at The Museum of Modern Art, New York. Always interested in film and cinematic techniques, he made a number of movies, including *Rose Hobart* of 1931, and wrote two film scenarios. One of these, *Monsieur Phot* of 1933, was published in 1936 in Levy's book *Surrealism.*

Cornell's first one-man exhibition took place at the Julien Levy Gallery in 1939: included was an array of objects, a number of them in shadow boxes. During the forties and fifties he made Medici boxes, boxes devoted to stage and screen personalities, Aviary constructions, Observatories, Night Skies, Winter Night Skies and Hotel boxes. In the early 1960s Cornell stopped making new boxes and began to reconstruct old ones and to work intensively in collage. Major Cornell retrospectives were held in 1967 at the Pasadena Art Museum and The Solomon R. Guggenheim Museum, New York. In 1971 The Metropolitan Museum of Art in New York mounted an exhibition of his collages. Cornell died on December 29, 1972, at his home in Flushing, New York.

197 Space Object Box: "Little Bear, etc." motif.
Mid-1950s-early 1960s

68.1878

Construction and collage, 11 x 17½ x 5¼ in. (28 x 44.5 x 13.3 cm.)

Signed on reverse: *Joseph Cornell*. Not dated.

PROVENANCE:
from the artist, 1968

Within the confines of this small box Cornell has assembled two metal rods with a ring, a cork ball, a toy block, pieces of driftwood and a map fragment of Ursa Minor (Little Bear). The representation of the Northern Sky with Little Dipper in *Space Object Box* came from a book on astronomy that belonged to the artist.* Always fascinated with astronomy, he often referred to constellations and stars in his work. Cornell has extended the coordinate lines of this star map across the back wall of the box, thus incorporating the ball and ring into the celestial system. The ball positioned on the rods implies the movement of the sun across the sky, and the ring suggests the orbits of planets around the sun.

Cornell's artistic production is comprised of constructions, collages and films rather than paintings or sculptures. He combined objects and fragments he found and collected. Seen through the glass of *Space Object Box*, they are transformed into a world of their own. By isolating and juxtaposing disparate objects, Cornell formulated new relationships of space and time.

* conversation with Lynda Roscoe Hartigan, Oct. 1979

EXHIBITIONS:
New York, The Solomon R. Guggenheim Museum, *Joseph Cornell,* May 4-June 25, 1967

New York, The Solomon R. Guggenheim Museum, *Selected Sculpture and Works on Paper,* July 8-Sept. 14, 1969, p. 114, repr.

REFERENCES:
Handbook, 1970, pp. 80-81, repr.

D. Waldman, *Joseph Cornell,* New York, 1977, pp. 28, 119 and pl. 95

Arshile Gorky 1904-1948

Arshile Gorky was born Vosdanik Adoian in the village of Khorkom, province of Van, Armenia, on April 15, 1904. The Adoians became refugees from the Turkish invasion; Gorky himself left Van in 1915 and arrived in the United States around March 1, 1920. He stayed with relatives in Watertown, Massachusetts, and with his father who had settled in Providence, Rhode Island. By 1922 he lived in Watertown and taught at the New School of Design in Boston. In 1925 he moved to New York and changed his name to Arshile Gorky. He entered the Grand Central School of Art in New York as a student but soon became an instructor of drawing; from 1926 to 1931 he was a member of the faculty. Throughout the 1920s Gorky's painting was influenced by Cézanne, Braque and, above all, Picasso.

In 1930 Gorky's work was included in a group show at The Museum of Modern Art in New York. During the thirties he associated closely with Stuart Davis, John Graham and de Kooning; he shared a studio with de Kooning late in the decade. Gorky's first one-man show took place at the Mellon Galleries in Philadelphia in 1931. From 1935 to 1937 he worked under the WPA Federal Art Project on murals for the Newark Airport. His involvement with the WPA continued into 1941. Gorky's first one-man show in New York was held at the Boyer Galleries in 1938. The San Francisco Museum of Art exhibited his work in 1941.

In the 1940s he was profoundly affected by the work of European Surrealists, particularly Miró, André Masson and Matta. By 1944 he met André Breton and became friends with other Surrealist emigrés in this country. Gorky's first exhibition at the Julien Levy Gallery in New York took place in 1945. From 1942 to 1948 he worked for part of each year in the countryside of Connecticut or Virginia. A succession of personal tragedies, including a fire in his studio which destroyed much of his work, a serious operation and an automobile accident, preceded Gorky's death by suicide on July 21, 1948, in Sherman, Connecticut.

198 Untitled. 1943

77.2332

Wax crayon and pencil on paper, 20 x 26¾ in. (50.8 x 67.9 cm.)

Signed and dated l.l.: *A. Gorky / 43.*

PROVENANCE:

from the artist
Mina Boehm Metzger, New York, ca. 1943
Rook McCulloch, Old Lyme, Connecticut, by 1975
Gift, Rook McCulloch, 1977

In the 1940s Gorky executed hundreds of drawings in mixed media which were not specifically related to oil paintings. He worked from nature at his in-laws' farm in Hamilton, Virginia, during the summers of 1943, 1944 and 1946. Gorky investigated and inventively incorporated myriad natural forms in his work: leaves, petals, seed pods, stalks, plants, fields, rocks and water. The genesis or transmutation of biomorphic forms and the intensification of imagery originated, at least in part, from the artist's concentration on details of visual experience.

This untitled crayon and pencil drawing dated 1943 is distinguished by a very dark and heavily worked background, which is contrasted with brilliant color at the upper and lower right and an openness at the center of the composition. Pencil lines accentuate contours of rounded, flower-like forms and spiky details. In comparison, the wash drawing from about 1946 (cat. no. 199) is more evenly and thinly worked. Contours are defined not by repeated lines but with a single stroke. Gorky has rubbed on isolated areas of green, red, orange and black crayon. His interpretation of nature is both lyrical and associative; his forms are delicate, fluid and incisive.

EXHIBITIONS:

New York, Whitney Museum of American Art, *Arshile Gorky Memorial Exhibition,* Jan. 5-Feb. 18, 1951, no. 72, traveled to Minneapolis, Walker Art Center, Mar. 4-Apr. 22; San Francisco Museum of Art, May 9-July 9

Princeton, N. J., The Art Museum, Princeton University, *Arshile Gorky: A Loan Exhibition of Paintings and Drawings,* Oct. 6-26, 1952

Venice, XXXI Biennale Internazionale d'Arte, *Italian Pavilion: Arshile Gorky,* June 16-Oct. 7, 1962, no. 34

New York, The Museum of Modern Art, *Arshile Gorky: Paintings, Drawings, Studies,* Dec. 19, 1962-Feb. 12, 1963, no. 52, repr., traveled to Washington, D.C., Gallery of Modern Art, Mar. 12-Apr. 14

New York, M. Knoedler and Co., Inc., *Gorky Drawings,* Nov. 25-Dec. 27, 1969, no. 66

Austin, University Art Museum, University of Texas, *Arshile Gorky: Drawings to Paintings,* Oct. 12-Nov. 23, 1975, traveled to San Francisco Museum of Art, Dec. 4, 1975-Jan. 12, 1976; Purchase, Roy R. Neuberger Museum, The State University of New York at Purchase, Feb. 10-Mar. 14; Utica, N. Y., Munson-Williams-Proctor Institute, Apr. 4-May 9

REFERENCE:
J. Levy, *Arshile Gorky,* New York, 1966, pl. 109

Gorky

199 Untitled. ca. 1946

76.2276

Ink, watercolor, pencil and wax crayon on paper,
18¾ x 24⅛ in. (47.5 x 61.2 cm.)

Not signed or dated.

PROVENANCE:

from the artist
Mina Boehm Metzger, New York, ca. 1946
Rook McCulloch, Old Lyme, Connecticut, by 1975
Gift, Rook McCulloch, 1976

EXHIBITIONS:

New York, M. Knoedler and Co., Inc., *Gorky Drawings*,
Nov. 25-Dec. 27, 1969, no. 13a

Austin, University Art Museum, University of Texas, *Arshile
Gorky: Drawings to Paintings*, Oct. 12-Nov. 13, 1975, traveled to San Francisco Museum of Art, Dec. 4, 1975-Jan. 12,
1976; Purchase, Roy R. Neuberger Museum, The State University of New York at Purchase, Feb. 10-Mar. 14; Utica,
N. Y., Munson-Williams-Proctor Institute, Apr. 4-May 9

New York, Washburn Gallery, *Arshile Gorky: In Memory*,
Nov. 4-28, 1978, no. 12, repr.

Willem de Kooning b. 1904

Willem de Kooning was born April 24, 1904, in Rotterdam. From 1916 to 1925 he studied at night at the Academie voor Beeldende Kunsten en Technische Wetenschappen, Rotterdam, while apprenticing to a commercial art and decorating firm and later working for an art director. In 1924 he visited museums in Belgium and studied further in Brussels and Antwerp. De Kooning came to the United States in 1926 and settled briefly in Hoboken, New Jersey. He worked as a house painter before moving to New York in 1927, where he met John Graham, Stuart Davis and Gorky. He worked at commercial art and various odd jobs until 1935-36, when he was employed in the mural and easel divisions of the WPA Federal Art Project. Thereafter he painted full-time. In the late 1930s his abstract as well as figurative work was primarily influenced by the Cubism and Surrealism of Picasso and also of Gorky, with whom he shared a studio.

In 1938 de Kooning started his first series of Women, which would become a major recurrent theme. During the 1940s he participated in group shows with other artists who would form the New York School of Abstract Expressionism. De Kooning's first one-man show, which took place at the Egan Gallery in New York in 1948, included a number of the allover black-and-white abstractions he had initiated in 1946 and established his reputation as a major artist. The Women of the early 1950s were followed by abstract urban landscapes, Parkways, rural landscapes and, in the 1960s, a new group of Women.

In 1968 de Kooning visited The Netherlands for the first time since 1926 for the opening of his major retrospective at the Stedelijk Museum in Amsterdam. In Rome in 1969 de Kooning executed his first sculptures —figures modeled in clay and later cast in bronze—and in 1970-71 he began a series of life-size figures. In 1974 the Walker Art Center in Minneapolis organized a show of de Kooning's drawings and sculpture that traveled throughout the United States, and in 1978 The Solomon R. Guggenheim Museum mounted an important exhibition of his recent work. In 1979 de Kooning and Chillida received the Andrew W. Mellon Prize, which was accompanied by an exhibition at the Museum of Art, Carnegie Institute, in Pittsburgh. De Kooning lives in The Springs, East Hampton, Long Island, where he settled in 1963.

200 **Composition.** 1955

55.1419

Oil, enamel and charcoal on canvas, 79⅛ x 69⅛ in. (201 x 175.6 cm.)

Signed l.r.: *de Kooning.* Not dated.

PROVENANCE:

from the artist through Martha Jackson Gallery, New York, 1955

Throughout his career de Kooning has worked in both abstract and figurative modes. His abstractions of the late 1940s culminated in pictures like *Asheville,* 1949 (The Phillips Collection, Washington, D.C.) and *Excavation,* 1950 (Collection The Art Institute of Chicago). At approximately the same time de Kooning began a series of paintings of women that occupied him for several years and is probably best exemplified by *Woman I,* 1950-52 (Collection The Museum of Modern Art, New York). By early 1955 the figure gradually dissolved into an abstraction which retained compositional elements of the paintings of women. Completed by March 1955, *Composition* belongs to the period of transition from figure to landscape to abstraction. As early as 1953 the artist perceptively commented on his work that "the landscape is in the Woman and there is Woman in the landscapes." (New York, The Museum of Modern Art, 1968, p. 100)

While related to "urban landscapes" such as *Police Gazette* of 1954-55 and *Gotham News* of 1955-56, the Guggenheim *Composition* contains suggestions of female anatomy displaced and ambiguously rearranged on the picture plane. De Kooning does not focus solely on the two basic red forms but on the spaces between these shapes as well. Any resulting opposition between surface areas has been resolved through the use of color, the heavily-brushed painted surface and the heroic function of line.

EXHIBITIONS:

New York, Martha Jackson Gallery, *Recent Oils by Willem de Kooning,* Nov. 9-Dec. 3, 1955, no. 1

Houston, The Museum of Fine Arts, *New York and Paris Painting of the Fifties,* Jan. 16-Feb. 8, 1959

New York, The Solomon R. Guggenheim Museum, *Inaugural Selection,* Oct. 21, 1959-June 19, 1960

London, USIS Gallery, American Embassy, *Vanguard American Painting,* Feb. 28-Mar. 30, 1962, no. 17, repr., traveled to Darmstadt, Hessisches Landesmuseum, Apr. 14-May 13

Amsterdam, Stedelijk Museum, *The Dutch Contribution to the International Development of Art Since 1945,* June 29-Sept. 17, 1962, no. 52, traveled to Montreal, Museum of

Fine Arts, Oct. 5-Nov. 4; Ottawa, National Gallery of Canada, Nov. 15-Dec. 31; Buffalo, Albright-Knox Art Gallery, Jan. 15-Feb. 17, 1963

Amsterdam, Stedelijk Museum, *Willem de Kooning,* Sept. 19-Nov. 17, 1968, no. 68, repr., traveled to London, Tate Gallery, Dec. 5, 1968-Jan. 26, 1969; New York, The Museum of Modern Art, Mar. 6-Apr. 27

New York, The Solomon R. Guggenheim Museum, *Acquisition Priorities: Aspects of Postwar Painting in America,* Oct. 15, 1976-Jan. 16, 1977, no. 22, repr.

REFERENCES:

D. Ashton, "Arts," *Arts & Architecture,* vol. 72, Dec. 1955, p. 34

T. B. Hess, *Willem de Kooning,* New York, 1959, pl. 139

Handbook, 1970, pp. 252-253, color repr.

H. Rosenberg, *De Kooning,* New York, 1973, pl. 118

H. H. Arnason, *History of Modern Art,* rev. ed., New York, 1977, p. 522 and color pl. 205

Jackson Pollock 1912-1956

Paul Jackson Pollock was born January 28, 1912, in Cody, Wyoming. He grew up in Arizona and California and in 1928 began to study painting at the Manual Arts High School in Los Angeles. In the autumn of 1930 Pollock came to New York and studied under Thomas Hart Benton at the Art Students League. Benton encouraged him throughout the succeeding decade. By the early 1930s he knew and admired the murals of José Clemente Orozco and Diego Rivera. Much of Pollock's time was spent in New York, where he settled permanently in 1935 and worked on the WPA Federal Art Project from 1935 to 1942. In 1936 he worked in David Alfaro Siqueiros' experimental workshop in New York.

Pollock's first one-man show was held at Peggy Guggenheim's Art of This Century gallery in New York in 1943. Mrs. Guggenheim gave him a contract which lasted through 1947, permitting him to devote all his time to painting. Prior to 1947 Pollock's depiction of mythical or totemic figures as archetypes of the human subconscious reflected the influence of Surrealism. 1947 marks the beginning of his mature style: the large unprimed canvases covered with multicolored skeins of dripped paint, at once evoking the meanderings of the subconscious mind and emphasizing the primacy of paint and the force of spontaneous gesture. By 1951 Pollock's paintings, while remaining dynamically fluid, were limited to black and white and became more sparse and austere.

From the autumn of 1945, when Lee Krasner and Pollock were married, they lived in The Springs, East Hampton. Pollock participated in the Venice Biennale in 1950. His work was widely known and exhibited, but the artist never traveled outside the United States. He was killed in an automobile accident August 11, 1956, in The Springs.

201 Ocean Greyness. 1953

54.1408

Oil on canvas, 57¾ x 90⅛ in. (146.7 x 229 cm.)

Signed and dated l.r.: *53 Jackson Pollock.*

PROVENANCE:
from the artist through Sidney Janis Gallery, New York, 1954

Ocean Greyness belongs to Pollock's late work: thus, it postdates his development of poured and dripped paint (1947 to 1950) which culminated in monumental examples. Pollock's innovative and now famous technique involved working from all sides around the canvas placed directly on the floor. He created an allover composition that did not focus on a single point and seemed to defy the limits of the canvas. Not only the freedom of spontaneous gesture in dripping and flinging paint but also the energetic movements of the artist's body were manifestations of the creative act of painting.

In *Ocean Greyness* the complexity of linear patterning is augmented by densely worked shapes articulated with a brush. This awareness of concrete forms, the emergent imagery of eyes, reverts to his earlier work. Pollock's explicit reference to the ocean recalls his seascapes from the late 1930s, has specifically Jungian connotations and reappears in such coeval pictures as *The Deep* (Collection Musée National d'Art Moderne, Paris), *Sleeping Effort* (Collection Washington University, St. Louis) and *Greyed Rainbow* (Collection The Art Institute of Chicago). In *Ocean Greyness* the surface pulsates with rhythmic energy. The turbulence is emotional rather than merely oceanic.

EXHIBITIONS:
East Hampton, N. Y., Guild Hall, *17 East Hampton Artists,* July 25-Aug. 15, 1953, no. 44

New York, Sidney Janis Gallery, *Jackson Pollock,* Feb. 1-27, 1954

New York, The Solomon R. Guggenheim Museum, *Younger American Painters: A Selection,* May 12-Sept. 26, 1954, no. 41, repr. (withdrawn Sept. 8: see following exhibition), traveled to Portland (Ore.) Art Museum, Sept. 2-Oct. 9, 1955; Seattle, Henry Gallery, University of Washington, Oct. 16-Nov. 13; San Francisco Museum of Art, Nov. 15, 1955-Jan. 22, 1956; Los Angeles County Museum of Art, Feb. 1-29; Fayetteville, University of Arkansas, Mar. 9-Apr. 10; New Orleans, Isaac Delgado Museum of Art, Apr. 15-May 20

The Art Institute of Chicago, *61st American Exhibition: Painting and Sculpture,* Oct. 21-Dec. 5, 1954, no. 121

New York, The Museum of Modern Art, *Jackson Pollock,* Dec. 19, 1956-Feb. 3, 1957, no. 35

London, Tate Gallery, *An exhibition of paintings from The Solomon R. Guggenheim Museum, New York,* Apr. 16-May 26, 1957, no. 65, repr., traveled to The Hague, Gemeentemuseum, June 25-Sept. 1; Helsinki, Ateneumin Taidkokoelmat, Sept. 27-Oct. 20; Rome, Galleria Nazionale d'Arte Moderna, Dec. 5, 1957-Jan. 8, 1958

New York, The Solomon R. Guggenheim Museum, *Inaugural Selection,* Oct. 21, 1959-June 19, 1960

Seattle, World's Fair, *Art Since 1950: American and International,* Apr. 21-Oct. 21, 1962, no. 53, repr., traveled to Waltham, Mass., The Poses Institute of Fine Arts, Brandeis University, Nov. 21-Dec. 23

Adelaide, National Gallery of South Australia, *The Adelaide Festival of Arts 1964: Contemporary American Paintings,* Mar. 7-Apr. 5, 1964, no. 41

New York, The Museum of Modern Art, *Jackson Pollock,* June 4-Sept. 15, 1967, no. 77

New York, The Solomon R. Guggenheim Museum, *Acquisition Priorities: Aspects of Postwar Painting in America,* Oct. 15, 1976-Jan. 16, 1977, no. 35, repr.

REFERENCES:

J. Fitzsimmons, "Art," *Arts & Architecture,* vol. 71, Mar. 1954, pp. 7, 30, repr.

F. O'Hara, *Jackson Pollock,* New York, 1959, pl. 70

W. Rubin, "Notes on Masson and Pollock," *Arts,* vol. 34, Nov. 1959, p. 43, repr.

B. Robertson, *Jackson Pollock,* New York, 1960, p. 139 and pl. 162

Handbook, 1970, pp. 380-381, repr.

B. H. Friedman, *Jackson Pollock: Energy Made Visible,* New York, 1972, pp. 190, 206-207

J. Wolfe, "Jungian Aspects of Jackson Pollock's Imagery," *Artforum,* vol. XI, Nov. 1972, pp. 72-73

F. V. O'Connor and E. V. Thaw, *Jackson Pollock: A Catalogue Raisonné of Paintings, Drawings and Other Works,* New Haven and London, 1978, vol. II, pp. 204-205, repr., no. 369

D. Ashton, "Jackson Pollock's Arabesque," *Arts Magazine,* vol. 53, Mar. 1979, p. 143, repr.

William Baziotes 1912-1963

William Baziotes was born to parents of Greek origin on June 11, 1912, in Pittsburgh. He grew up in Reading, Pennsylvania, where he worked at the Case Glass company from 1931 to 1933, antiquing glass and running errands. At this time he took evening sketch classes and met the poet Byron Vazakas, who became his life-long friend. Vazakas introduced Baziotes to the work of Baudelaire and the Symbolist poets. In 1931 Baziotes saw the Matisse exhibition at The Museum of Modern Art in New York and in 1933 he moved to this city to study painting. From 1933 to 1936 Baziotes attended the National Academy of Design.

In 1936 he was included in his first group exhibition at the Municipal Art Gallery, New York, and was employed by the WPA Federal Art Project as an art teacher at the Queens Museum. Baziotes worked in the easel division of the WPA from 1938 to 1941. He was one of the first American artists to meet the Surrealist emigrés in New York in the late thirties and early forties. By 1940 Baziotes knew Matta, Jimmy Ernst and Gordon Onslow-Ford. He began to experiment with Surrealist automatism at this time. In 1941 Matta introduced Baziotes to Robert Motherwell, with whom he formed a close friendship. André Masson invited Baziotes to participate with Motherwell, Hare and others in the 1942 exhibition *First Papers of Surrealism* at the Whitelaw Reid Mansion in New York. In 1943 he took part in two group shows at Peggy Guggenheim's Art of This Century, New York, where his first one-man exhibition was held the following year. With Motherwell, Rothko and Hare, Baziotes founded The Subjects of the Artist school in New York in 1948. Over the next decade Baziotes held a number of teaching positions: at the Brooklyn Museum Art School and at New York University from 1949 to 1952; at the People's Art Center, The Museum of Modern Art, from 1950 to 1952; and at Hunter College from 1952 to 1962. Baziotes died in New York on June 6, 1963. A memorial exhibition of his work was presented at The Solomon R. Guggenheim Museum in 1965.

202 Dusk. 1958

59.1544

Oil on canvas, 60⅜ x 48¼ in. (153.3 x 122.5 cm.)

Signed l.r.: *Baziotes*; signed and dated on reverse: *"DUSK" / W. Baziotes / 1958.*

PROVENANCE:

from the artist through Samuel M. Kootz Gallery, New York, 1959

Baziotes knew Matta, Gorky and other Surrealists, and although his work is associated with Abstract Expressionism, his imagery had its source in Surrealism. In *Dusk* the large form at the left undoubtedly derives from an archetypal animal shape (perhaps a proto-horse). It was Baziotes' custom to begin his paintings with a few areas of color or several lines and one color. He worked slowly and applied layers of nuanced hues to achieve softly glowing translucent color. The painting was developed intuitively and becomes suggestive of a feeling or mood.

The Guggenheim canvas is not his first called *Dusk* (another was exhibited in 1954); it should be seen within the context of other pictures about twilight, night and sleep from the 1950s and, more specifically, it can be viewed in relation to *Dawn,* 1962 (Collection Mr. and Mrs. William C. Janss, Sun Valley, Idaho). Our painting was completed before October 23, 1958, when it went to the Samuel M. Kootz Gallery.*

* Archives of American Art, Baziotes Papers, Roll 347, Frame 384

EXHIBITIONS:

Pittsburgh, Museum of Art, Carnegie Institute, *The 1958 Pittsburgh Bicentennial International Exhibition of Contemporary Painting and Sculpture,* Dec. 5, 1958-Feb. 8, 1959, no. 34

New York, Sidney Janis Gallery, *New Paintings by Baziotes,* Mar. 13-Apr. 8, 1961

The Minneapolis Institute of Arts, *Four Centuries of American Art,* Nov. 27, 1963-Jan. 19, 1964

New York, The Solomon R. Guggenheim Museum, *William Baziotes: A Memorial Exhibition,* Feb. 5-Mar. 21, 1965, no. 38, traveled to Cincinnati Art Museum, Apr. 9-May 2; The Reading (Pa.) Public Museum and Art Gallery, May 23-June 27; The Santa Barbara Museum of Art, July 13-Aug. 22; Milwaukee Art Center, Sept. 9-Oct. 10; Waltham, Mass., Rose Art Center, Brandeis University, Nov. 1-30; Utica, N. Y., Munson-Williams-Proctor Institute, Dec. 11, 1965-Jan. 11, 1966; The Columbus Gallery of Fine Arts, Jan. 27-Feb. 28; Washington, D.C., The Corcoran Gallery of Art, Mar. 15-Apr. 15; The Minneapolis Institute of Arts, May

15-June 15; Dallas Museum of Fine Arts, July 4-Aug. 4; Akron Art Institute, Oct. 10-Nov. 14

New York, Marlborough Gallery, *William Baziotes: Late Work 1946-1962,* Feb.-Mar. 1971, no. 19

New York, The Solomon R. Guggenheim Museum, *Acquisition Priorities: Aspects of Postwar Painting in America,* Oct. 14, 1976-Jan. 16, 1977, no. 29, repr.

Newport Beach, Cal., Newport Harbor Art Museum, *William Baziotes: A Retrospective Exhibition,* Mar. 24-June 4, 1978, no. 31, repr., traveled to University of Maryland Art Gallery, Aug. 24-Oct. 7; Ithaca, N. Y., Herbert F. Johnson Museum of Art, Cornell University, Oct. 25-Dec. 10

REFERENCES:

Handbook, 1970, pp. 36-37, repr.

H. H. Arnason, *History of Modern Art,* rev. ed., New York, 1977, color pl. 209

M. B. Hadler, *The Art of William Baziotes,* Ph.D. dissertation, Columbia University, 1977, pp. 204, 228, 229, 289, fig. 158

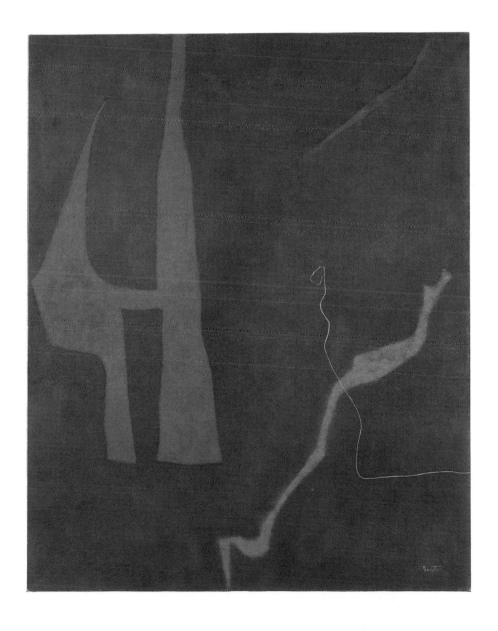

Baziotes

203 Aquatic. 1961

63.1630

Oil on canvas, 66 x 78⅛ in. (167.6 x 198.4 cm.)

Signed l.r.: *Baziotes*; signed and dated on reverse: *"AQUATIC"* / *W. Baziotes 1961.*

PROVENANCE:
Collective Anonymous Gift, 1963

While *Aquatic* contains three elements similar to those in *Dusk* (cat. no. 202), they are dispersed over the canvas so that they appear as distinctly separate entities. In his late work Baziotes simplified his compositions, suspended forms in an expansive space and created a more freely painted surface suggesting an aquatic environment. The theme of water emerged in the work of several other American painters including Gottlieb, Rothko and Theodoros Stamos in the 1940s and was developed further by Baziotes in the late 1950s and early 1960s. As in Baziotes' *Serpentine* of 1961 (Collection Mr. and Mrs. Gilbert H. Kinney, Washington, D.C.), the undulating shape at the bottom of *Aquatic* conjures up the image of a marine form, perhaps an eel (a species known to have fascinated the artist).* The floating, light-colored shapes refer not only to the specific forms that may have inspired them but also evoke a mood. The artist wrote: "I want my paintings to take effect slowly, to haunt, to obsess." (*It is,* no. 4, autumn 1959, p. 11)

* Hadler, *Arts Magazine,* p. 104

EXHIBITIONS:
The Dallas Museum for Contemporary Arts, *1961,* Apr. 3-May 13, 1962, no. 4

Venice, XXXII Biennale Internazionale d'Arte, *Today's Art in Museums: The Solomon R. Guggenheim Museum,* June 20-Oct. 18, 1964, no. 3

New York, The Solomon R. Guggenheim Museum, *William Baziotes: A Memorial Exhibition,* Feb. 5-Mar. 21, 1965, no. 40, repr., traveled to Cincinnati Art Museum, Apr. 9-May 2; The Reading (Pa.) Public Museum and Art Gallery, May 23-June 27; The Santa Barbara Museum of Art, July 13-Aug. 22; Milwaukee Art Center, Sept. 9-Oct. 10; Waltham, Mass., Rose Art Center, Brandeis University, Nov. 1-30; Utica, N.Y., Munson-Williams-Proctor Institute, Dec. 11, 1965-Jan 11, 1966; The Columbus Gallery of Fine Arts, Jan. 27-Feb. 28; Washington, D.C., The Corcoran Gallery of Art, Mar. 15-Apr. 15; The Minneapolis Institute of Arts, May 15-June 15; Dallas Museum of Fine Arts, July 4-Aug. 4; Akron Art Institute, Oct. 10-Nov. 14

New York, Marlborough Gallery, *William Baziotes: Late Work 1946-1962,* Feb.-Mar. 1971, no. 23

New York, The Solomon R. Guggenheim Museum, *Acquisition Priorities: Aspects of Postwar Painting in America,* Oct. 14, 1976-Jan. 16, 1977, no. 30, repr.

REFERENCES:
Handbook, 1970, pp. 38-39, repr.

M. Hadler, "William Baziotes: A Contemporary Poet-Painter," *Arts Magazine,* vol. 51, June 1977, pp. 102, repr., 104

M. B. Hadler, *The Art of William Baziotes,* Ph.D. dissertation, Columbia University, 1977, pp. 243, 290, fig. 94

Mark Rothko 1903-1970

Marcus Rothkowitz was born in Dvinsk, Russia, on September 25, 1903. In 1913 he left Russia and settled with the rest of his family in Portland, Oregon. Rothko attended Yale University in New Haven on a scholarship from 1921 to 1923. This year he left Yale without receiving a degree and moved to New York. In 1925 he studied under Max Weber at the Art Students League. He participated in his first group exhibition at the Opportunity Galleries in New York in 1928. During the early 1930s Rothko became close friends with Milton Avery and Gottlieb. His first one-man show took place at the Museum of Art in Portland in 1933.

Rothko's first one-man exhibition in New York was held at the Contemporary Arts Gallery in 1933. In 1935 he was a founding member of *The Ten*, a group of artists sympathetic to abstraction and expressionism. He executed easel paintings for the WPA Federal Art Project from 1936 to 1937. By 1936 Rothko knew Barnett Newman. In the early forties he worked closely with Gottlieb, developing a painting style with mythological content, simple flat shapes and imagery inspired by primitive art. By mid-decade his work incorporated Surrealist techniques and images. Peggy Guggenheim gave Rothko a one-man show at Art of This Century in New York in 1945.

In 1947 and 1949 Rothko taught at the California School of Fine Arts, San Francisco, where Clyfford Still was a fellow instructor. Together with Baziotes, Hare and Robert Motherwell, Rothko founded the short-lived The Subjects of the Artist school in New York in 1948. The late forties to early fifties saw the emergence of Rothko's mature style in which frontal, luminous rectangles seem to hover on the canvas surface. In 1958 the artist began his first commission, monumental paintings for the Four Seasons Restaurant in New York. The Museum of Modern Art, New York, gave Rothko an important one-man exhibition in 1961. He completed murals for Harvard University in 1962 and in 1964 accepted a mural commission for a chapel in Houston. Rothko took his own life in his New York studio on February 25, 1970. A year later the Rothko Chapel in Houston was dedicated. A major retrospective of his work was held at The Solomon R. Guggenheim Museum in 1978-79.

204 Violet, Black, Orange, Yellow on White and Red. 1949

78.2461

Oil on canvas, 81½ x 66 in. (207 x 167.6 cm.)

Signed and dated on reverse: *Mark Rothko 1949.*

PROVENANCE:

Estate of the artist
Gift, Elaine and Werner Dannheisser and The Dannheisser Foundation, 1978

With paintings like *Violet, Black, Orange, Yellow on White and Red,* Rothko established the horizontal and vertical structure of his mature work. He has united color with space, light and form. In his multiform paintings of a year or two earlier, he brought loosely organized color areas forward onto the picture plane. Tension resulted from colors pushing forward and pulling back on the surface. In 1949-50 Rothko succeeded in maintaining all color forms on a single plane. His luminous colors radiate from the canvas.

In the Guggenheim painting the greater weight of the violet rectangle at the top is counteracted by the adjacent vertical red bars and balanced by the juxtaposition of orange and yellow below. Black interrupts the color rectangles, and the surrounding white paint frees the composition so it appears to float. Over the next two decades Rothko would refine and simplify the pictorial organization arrived at here. The intensity and warmth of the colors in the Guggenheim painting would be developed to express a wide range of mood and emotion.

EXHIBITIONS:
New York, Betty Parsons Gallery, *Mark Rothko,* Jan. 3-21, 1950
Kunsthaus Zürich, *Mark Rothko,* Mar. 21-May 9, 1971, no. 14, color repr., traveled to Berlin, Neue Nationalgalerie, May 26-July 19; Städtische Kunsthalle Düsseldorf, Aug. 24-Oct. 3; Rotterdam, Museum Boymans-van Beuningen, Nov. 20, 1971-Jan. 2, 1972; London, Hayward Gallery, Feb. 2-Mar. 12; Paris, Musée National d'Art Moderne, Mar. 23-May 8
New York, The Solomon R. Guggenheim Museum, *Mark Rothko, 1903-1970: A Retrospective,* Oct. 26, 1978-Jan. 21, 1979, no. 90, color repr., traveled to Houston, The Museum of Fine Arts, Feb. 15-Apr. 8; Minneapolis, Walker Art Center, Apr. 25-June 10; Los Angeles County Museum of Art, July 3-Sept. 26

REFERENCE:
L. Seldes, *The Legacy of Mark Rothko,* New York, 1978, pp. 247, 248, 320

Adolph Gottlieb 1903-1974

Adolph Gottlieb was born March 14, 1903, in New York. He studied at the Art Students League with John Sloan and Robert Henri in 1920. During a two-year period in Europe from 1921 to 1923 he attended the Académie de la Grande Chaumière, Paris, and other studio schools and traveled to Berlin and Munich. Returning to New York in 1923, Gottlieb subsequently finished high school and studied at Parsons School of Design, the Art Students League, where his friendship with Barnett Newman developed, Cooper Union and the Educational Alliance Art School. In 1930 his first one-man show took place at the Dudensing Gallery in New York. His close friendship with Milton Avery and Rothko began in the early thirties. From 1935 to 1940 he exhibited with *The Ten,* a group of artists devoted to expressionist and abstract painting. In 1936 Gottlieb worked in the easel division of the WPA Federal Art Project; the next year he moved to the desert near Tucson, Arizona. He returned to New York in 1939 and spent the summers from 1939 to 1946 in Gloucester, Massachusetts.

By 1941 Gottlieb had painted his first pictographs—compositions divided into irregular grids, each compartment of which is filled with archetypal, mythic and symbolic images. Continuing to express universal themes, in 1951 he began imaginary landscapes in which the field is divided into two horizontal zones: sky, with a number of shapes floating above the horizon, and landscape or sea below. These elements were simplified in the Burst paintings of 1957 to the early 1970s. Here, on large color fields, a disc characteristically hovers above an explosive, calligraphic mass.

Associated with the New York School, Gottlieb exhibited extensively from the 1940s until his death. He was given one-man shows at The Jewish Museum, New York, in 1957, and at the Walker Art Center, Minneapolis, in 1963; the latter exhibition was presented later that same year at the São Paulo Bienal. In 1968 a retrospective of his work was organized jointly by The Solomon R. Guggenheim Museum and the Whitney Museum of American Art, New York. He spent summers in Provincetown, Massachusetts, from 1946 until 1960, when he moved to East Hampton, Long Island. Gottlieb died in New York on March 4, 1974.

205 W. 1954

54.1401

Oil with sand on canvas, 72 x 36 in. (182.9 x 91.5 cm.)

Signed l.r.: *Adolph Gottlieb.* Not dated.

PROVENANCE:
from the artist through Samuel M. Kootz Gallery, New York, 1954

Paintings such as *W* from 1954 demonstrate the evolution from the grid of Gottlieb's pictographs to the isolation of forms which would dominate his later work. The thick gray lines, which provide structure, reach to the edges of the canvas and are, in turn, superimposed with two large, white emblematic images. Gottlieb frequently paints lighter values over darker ones; thus, as here, he minimizes illusionistic space. Moreover, the pink background areas come forward close to the picture plane where the white signs are located. The title derives from the black calligraphic shape in the center that resembles a "w." Gottlieb had titled earlier paintings *E* and *I* and continued to use letters in *Blue at Noon* of 1955 (Collection Walker Art Center, Minneapolis) and *Blue at Night* of 1957 (Collection The Virginia Museum of Fine Arts, Richmond).

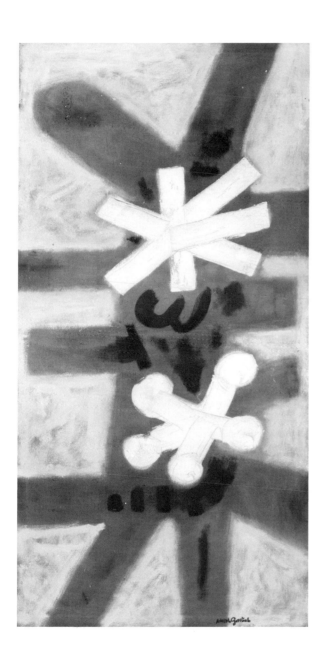

EXHIBITIONS:

New York, The Solomon R. Guggenheim Museum, *Younger American Painters: A Selection,* May 12-Sept. 26, 1954, no. 20, repr., traveled to Portland (Ore.) Art Museum, Sept. 2-Oct. 9, 1955; Seattle, Henry Gallery, University of Washington, Oct. 16-Nov. 13; San Francisco Museum of Art, Nov. 15, 1955-Jan. 22, 1956; Los Angeles County Museum of Art, Feb. 1-29; Fayetteville, University of Arkansas, Mar. 9-Apr. 10; New Orleans, Isaac Delgado Museum of Art, Apr. 15-May 20

London, Tate Gallery, *An exhibition of paintings from The Solomon R. Guggenheim Museum, New York,* Apr. 16-May 26, 1957, no. 24, traveled to The Hague, Gemeentemuseum, June 25-Sept. 1; Helsinki, Ateneumin Taidekokoelmat, Sept. 27-Oct. 20; Rome, Galleria Nazionale d'Arte Moderna, Dec. 5, 1957-Jan. 8, 1958; Cologne, Wallraf-Richartz-Museum, Jan. 26-Mar. 30; Paris, Musée des Arts Décoratifs, Apr. 23-June 1

New York, The Solomon R. Guggenheim Museum, *Inaugural Selection,* Oct. 21, 1959-June 19, 1960

Minneapolis, Walker Art Center, *Adolph Gottlieb,* Apr. 28-June 9, 1963, no. 9, repr., traveled to São Paulo, VII Bienal, Sept.-Dec.; New York, Marlborough-Gerson Gallery, Feb. 18-Mar. 3, 1964

Venice, XXXII Biennale Internazionale d'Arte, *Today's Art in Museums: The Solomon R. Guggenheim Museum,* June 20-Oct. 18, 1964, no. 8

New York, The Solomon R. Guggenheim Museum, *Acquisition Priorities: Aspects of Postwar Painting in America,* Oct. 14, 1976-Jan. 16, 1977, no. 16, repr.

REFERENCES:

Handbook, 1970, pp. 142-143, repr.

H. Rand, "Adolph Gottlieb in Context," *Arts Magazine,* vol. 51, Feb. 1977, pp. 125, repr., 126

206 Mist. 1961

78.2401

Oil on canvas, 72 x 48 in. (182.9 x 121.9 cm.)

Signed and dated on reverse: *Adolph Gottlieb /
#6122 "MIST" / 72" x 48" / 1961.*

PROVENANCE:

from the artist through Sidney Janis Gallery, New York
Susan Morse Hilles, Branford, Connecticut, 1962-78
Gift, Susan Morse Hilles, 1978

Gottlieb's distinctive color harmonies, forcefulness of
imagery and strong verticality of composition, already
evident in *W* (cat. no. 205), are simplified and intensified in *Mist.* As its title implies, the palette consists of
delicate nuances ranging from white and pale gray to
blackish gray. A white circular form is diffused into a
surrounding aura; it hovers over a vigorously painted,
dynamic black shape. This division of the canvas into
upper and lower segments remains constant in Gottlieb's Burst paintings (the earliest of which dates from
1957). He was interested in exploring the infinite and
peculiar variations on the relationship between top
and bottom elements of his compositions. Through
the reduction of means, his images acquire a com-
manding presence.

EXHIBITIONS:

New York, Sidney Janis Gallery, *Sixteen Recent Paintings
by Adolph Gottlieb,* Oct. 1-27, 1962, no. 1, repr.

New Haven, Yale University Art Gallery, *Two Modern
Collectors: Susan Morse Hilles, Richard Brown Baker,* May
23-Sept. 1, 1963, no. 14, repr.

New York, Whitney Museum of American Art, *Adolph
Gottlieb,* Feb. 14-Mar. 31, 1968, no. 84, repr.

New York, The Solomon R. Guggenheim Museum, *Acquisition Priorities: Aspects of Postwar Painting in America,*
Oct. 14, 1976-Jan. 16, 1977, no. 17, color repr.

Franz Kline 1910-1962

Franz Josef Kline was born on May 23, 1910, in Wilkes-Barre, Pennsylvania. While enrolled at Boston University he took art classes at the Boston Art Students League from 1931 to 1935. In 1935 Kline went to London and attended Heatherley's Art School from 1936 to 1938. He settled permanently in New York in 1939. Kline was fortunate to have the financial support and friendship of two patrons, Dr. Theodore J. Edlich, Jr. and I. David Orr, who commissioned numerous portraits and bought many other works from him. During the late 1930s and 1940s, Kline painted cityscapes and landscapes of the coal-mining district where he was raised as well as commissioned murals and portraits. In this period he received awards in several National Academy of Design Annuals.

In 1943 Kline met de Kooning at Marca-Relli's studio and within the next few years also met Pollock. Kline's interest in Japanese art began at this time. His mature abstract style, characterized by bold gestural strokes of fast-drying black and white enamel, developed about 1949-50. His first one-man exhibition was held at the Egan Gallery in New York in 1950. Soon after, he was recognized as a major figure in the emerging Abstract Expressionist New York School. Although Kline was best-known for his black and white paintings, he also worked extensively in color from the mid-1950s to the end of his life.

Kline spent a month in Europe in 1960 and traveled mostly in Italy. In the decade before his death, he was included in major international exhibitions, for example the 1956 and 1960 Venice Biennales and the 1957 São Paulo Bienal, and won a number of important prizes. Kline died on May 13, 1962, in New York. The Gallery of Modern Art in Washington, D.C., organized a memorial exhibition of his work that same year. In 1963-64 The International Council of The Museum of Modern Art circulated a Kline retrospective in Europe and in 1968 the Whitney Museum of American Art in New York organized a retrospective which traveled in the United States.

207 Painting No. 7. 1952

54.1403

Oil on canvas, 57½ x 81¾ in. (146 x 207.6 cm.)

Signed and dated on reverse: *Franz Kline / No 7 1952.*

PROVENANCE:
from the artist through Egan Gallery, New York, 1954

The artist has selected an essentially horizontal format where the verticals on the left reinforce the impenetrable block-like shape at the right. He used housepainters' brushes in varying widths and commercially prepared house paints. Although some canvases may look spontaneous, Kline's paintings were not done at one time but evolved gradually as he repainted, shifted and changed edges. Working on several canvases at a time, he allowed the paint to dry and kept the black and white areas separate.

It is significant that the artist arrived at his mature style with its broad directional strokes around 1949-50, after enlarging one of his sketches with a Bell-Opticon projector. The change of scale had wide ramifications. In working out the compositions of his paintings, he usually made sketches on pages of a telephone book or, less often, on newspaper. However, no studies for *Painting No. 7* have come to light.

Kline did not consider his paintings as black figures on white ground but as a conflict between the white and black that resolved itself into a final unity. During the late forties and early fifties, a number of painters including Pollock, Barnett Newman, de Kooning, Robert Motherwell and Kline experimented with restricting their palettes to black and white. For Kline the reduction of color was a way of concentrating on the essentials: this is evident in the stability and inevitability of the forms in *Painting No. 7.*

EXHIBITIONS:
New York, The Solomon R. Guggenheim Museum, *Younger American Painters: A Selection*, May 12-Sept. 26, 1954, no. 27, repr., traveled to Portland (Ore.) Art Museum, Sept. 2-Oct. 9, 1955; Seattle, Henry Gallery, University of Washington, Oct. 16-Nov. 13; San Francisco Museum of Art, Nov. 15, 1955-Jan. 22, 1956; Los Angeles County Museum of Art, Feb. 1-29; Fayetteville, University of Arkansas, Mar. 9-Apr. 10; New Orleans, Isaac Delgado Museum of Art, Apr. 15-May 20

London, Tate Gallery, *An exhibition of paintings from The Solomon R. Guggenheim Museum, New York,* Apr. 16-May 26, 1957, no. 37, traveled to The Hague, Gemeentemuseum, June 25-Sept. 1; Helsinki, Ateneumin Taidekokoelmat, Sept. 27- Oct. 20; Rome, Galleria Nazionale d'Arte Moderna, Dec. 5, 1957-Jan. 8, 1958; Cologne, Wallraf-Richartz-

Museum, Jan. 26-Mar. 30; Paris, Musée des Arts Décoratifs, Apr. 23-June 1

New York, The Solomon R. Guggenheim Museum, *Inaugural Selection,* Oct. 21, 1959-June 19, 1960

New York, The Solomon R. Guggenheim Museum, *Van Gogh and Expressionism,* July 1-Sept. 13, 1964

New York, The Solomon R. Guggenheim Museum, *Acquisition Priorities: Aspects of Postwar Painting in America,* Oct. 14, 1976-Jan. 16, 1977, no. 28, repr.

REFERENCES:

E. de Kooning, "Subject: What, how or who?," *Art News,* vol. 54, Apr. 1955, p. 28, repr.

Handbook, 1970, pp. 248-249, repr.

H. F. Gaugh, "Franz Kline's Romantic Abstraction," *Artforum,* vol. XIII, summer 1975, pp. 31, repr., 34

James Brooks b. 1906

James Brooks was born on October 18, 1906, in St. Louis. He attended Southern Methodist University in Dallas from 1923 to 1925, majoring in art, and studied at the Dallas Art Institute in 1925-26. When he moved to New York in 1926, Brooks supported himself as a commercial letterer and studied at the Art Students League at night. During this early period he knew Bradley Walker Tomlin and worked in a social realist style. From 1936 to 1942 Brooks painted murals for the WPA Federal Art Project in New York. Through the Project he met Pollock and Guston.

In 1945, after military service as a combat artist, Brooks turned to abstraction. He studied in New York with Wallace Harrison in 1946-47 and taught drawing at Columbia University from 1946 to 1948 and lettering at Pratt Institute, Brooklyn, from 1948 to 1959. Brooks was given his first one-man exhibition at the Peridot Gallery in New York in 1950. From 1955 to 1960 he was Visiting Critic of Advanced Painting at Yale University. The artist has received a number of important prizes, including the First Painting Prize and Logan Medal from The Art Institute of Chicago in 1957 and a Ford Foundation Purchase Award in 1962. Brooks was Artist in Residence at the American Academy in Rome in 1963, the year the Whitney Museum of American Art in New York presented a retrospective of his work, which subsequently circulated in the United States.

Brooks has continued to teach in the 1960s and 1970s at various institutions, among them Queens College, New York, and the University of Pennsylvania, Philadelphia. He was the recipient of a John Simon Guggenheim Foundation Fellowship in 1969 and was elected to the National Institute of Arts and Letters in 1973. The Dallas Museum of Fine Arts organized a retrospective of his work in 1972. Since 1946 Brooks has lived in New York and East Hampton, Long Island.

208 Dolamen. 1958

59.1546

Oil with sand on canvas, 66 x 28⅛ in. (167.6 x 71.4 cm.)

Signed l.l.: *J. Brooks*; signed and dated on reverse: *"DOLAMEN 1958" / James Brooks / [66] x 28.*

PROVENANCE:
from the artist through Stable Gallery, New York, 1959

Brooks is known to experiment with the medium and to exploit accidents that occur in the process of painting. In *Dolamen* he contrasts black with white, applying the latter over the former, and adds accents of pale blue and a bold red horizontal over the black at the bottom. The strong color and jagged, weighty shapes make the canvas look larger than it is.

Since 1954 the artist has assigned titles to his pictures in alphabetical sequence based on the order in which he completes them. Thus, *Acanda* was painted first and *Dolamen* fourth in 1958. To the initial letter Brooks randomly added syllables, often "inventing a word or using a seldom used, unfamiliar one with the intention of not leading the spectator to expect a certain feeling from the work. . . . Now I feel there is a vague connection to dolmen and the prehistoric" in the Guggenheim painting.*

* correspondence with the author, Feb. 1979

EXHIBITIONS:
New York, Stable Gallery, *James Brooks*, Feb. 2-21, 1959
New York, The Solomon R. Guggenheim Museum, *Inaugural Selection,* Oct. 21, 1959-June 19, 1960
New York, Finch College Museum of Art, *James Brooks,* Apr. 30-June 8, 1975, no. 6

REFERENCE:
Handbook, 1959, p. 29, repr.

Philip Guston 1913-1980

Philip Guston was born June 27, 1913, in Montreal. In 1919 his family moved to Los Angeles, where Guston attended Manual Arts High School and became friends with his schoolmate Pollock. In 1930 he entered the Otis Art Institute, Los Angeles, on a scholarship but left after several months and continued to study drawing and painting on his own. During this period Guston was deeply impressed by the works of Giorgio de Chirico. In 1934 he traveled in Mexico and studied the murals of José Clemente Orozco and Diego Rivera. He moved to New York in 1936, working from this time through 1940 in the mural division of the WPA Federal Art Project. From 1941 to 1945 he taught at the State University of Iowa, Iowa City. His first one-man show in New York took place at the Midtown Galleries in 1945. Guston was Artist in Residence at Washington University, St. Louis, from 1945 to 1947 and traveled in Europe in 1948-49 on a John Simon Guggenheim Foundation Fellowship, a Prix de Rome and a grant from the American Academy of Arts and Letters.

In the 1940s Guston was recognized as a leading figurative painter of political and social themes. However, by 1950 he had eliminated representational elements from his work. His abstractions of the early 1950s feature centralized areas of overlapping brushstrokes in luminous color; their Impressionistic qualities yielded to an increasingly sober mood in the canvases of the 1960s. In the late 1960s Guston returned to figuration, and his recent paintings are characterized by satirical, cartoon-like imagery and social comment.

Guston taught at New York University, Pratt Institute, Brooklyn, Yale Summer School, Norfolk, Connecticut, Columbia University and other schools. His major exhibitions include retrospectives at The Solomon R. Guggenheim Museum in 1962, The Poses Institute of Fine Arts, Brandeis University, Waltham, Massachusetts, in 1966, a one-man show at The Jewish Museum, New York, in 1966, and a drawings retrospective at The Metropolitan Museum of Art, New York, in 1973. From 1947 to 1967 Guston divided his time between Woodstock, New York, and New York City. He lived year-round in Woodstock from 1967 until his death on June 7, 1980.

209 **Duo.** 1961

64.1683

Oil on canvas, 72⅛ x 68 in. (183.1 x 172.6 cm.)

Signed l.l.: *Philip Guston.* Not dated.

PROVENANCE:

from the artist through Sidney Janis Gallery, New York, 1964

Like many of Guston's paintings from the early sixties, *Duo* is dominated by two black shapes situated in a multitude of subtly differentiated grays. Touches of blue, red, yellow and pink are woven through the gray brushstrokes so as to create an atmosphere surrounding the major rectangular shapes. By leaving the periphery of the canvas bare, Guston has focused upon the center where he has built up layers of pigment.

By the late 1950s Guston was attempting to solve the formal problem of using black as an actual color and handling it so that it would not recede into the background but maintain its place on the picture plane. Likewise, in his drawings of the same period he did away with illusionistic space and brought all elements forward to the surface plane. In *Duo* the brushstrokes themselves assume a crucial role in bringing cohesiveness to the painted surface. The underlying structure of the picture recalls Piero della Francesca's architectonic compositions, which Guston admired and wrote about. In canvases like this one Guston investigates the distinctions between form and non-form.

EXHIBITIONS:

New York, The Solomon R. Guggenheim Museum, *American Abstract Expressionists and Imagists,* Oct. 13-Dec. 31, 1961, no. 23, repr.

New York, The Solomon R. Guggenheim Museum, *Philip Guston,* May 3-July 1, 1962, no. 91, color repr., traveled to Amsterdam, Stedelijk Museum, Sept. 21-Oct. 15; London, Whitechapel Art Gallery, Jan. 1-Feb. 15, 1963; Brussels, Palais des Beaux-Arts, Mar. 1-31; Los Angeles County Museum of Art, May 21-June 30

Venice, XXXII Biennale Internazionale d'Arte, *Today's Art in Museums: The Solomon R. Guggenheim Museum,* June 20-Oct. 18, 1964, no. 9

Waltham, Mass., The Poses Institute of Fine Arts, Brandeis University, *Philip Guston,* Feb. 27-Mar. 27, 1966, no. 22

New York, The Solomon R. Guggenheim Museum, *Acquisition Priorities: Aspects of Postwar Painting in America,* Oct. 14, 1976-Jan. 16, 1977, no. 36, repr.

REFERENCES:

D. Ashton, "Art," *Arts & Architecture,* vol. 78, Dec. 1961, p. 5, repr.

S. Hunter, "Philip Guston," *Art International,* vol. VI, May 1962, p. 67, color repr.

M. Kozloff, "Modern art and the virtues of decadence," *Studio International,* vol. 174, Nov. 1967, p. 197, repr.

H. H. Arnason, *History of Modern Art,* New York, 1968, pl. 209

Handbook, 1970, pp. 154-155, repr.

Jack Tworkov 1900-1982

Jack Tworkov was born August 15, 1900, in Biala, Poland. In 1913 he emigrated to the United States and settled in New York, where he majored in English at Columbia University from 1920 to 1923. He also studied at the National Academy of Design from 1923 to 1925 and at the Art Students League in 1925-26. In 1923 Tworkov spent the first of many summers in Provincetown, Massachusetts. He became a United States citizen in 1928.

In 1934 Tworkov worked in the Treasury Department's Public Works of Art Project, and from 1935 to 1941 he was employed in the easel division of the WPA Federal Art Project. He was given his first one-man show at the A.C.A. Gallery in New York in 1940. From 1942 to 1945 Tworkov stopped painting and worked in the war industry as a tool designer. Whereas his still lifes, figures and landscapes of the 1920s and 1930s reflected an interest in Cézanne, Tworkov began to experiment with abstraction when he resumed painting in 1945. From 1948 to 1953 his studio adjoined de Kooning's; the two artists' close association was a factor in the development in the 1950s of Tworkov's mature Abstract Expressionist style. From the 1960s Tworkov often limited his palette to monochromatic grays and subdued pastels, and his paintings of the 1970s became more tightly organized and geometric.

Tworkov taught at colleges and universities throughout the country, including Black Mountain College, Black Mountain, North Carolina, Pratt Institute, Brooklyn, and Yale University, New Haven, where he served as chairman of the art department from 1963 to 1969. In 1964 the Whitney Museum of American Art, New York, organized a retrospective of his work which traveled across the United States. Tworkov lived and worked in New York and Provincetown. He died in Provincetown on September 4, 1982.

210 Diptych II. 1972

72.2021

Oil on canvas, two panels, each 76 x 76 in. (193.1 x 193.1 cm.)

Not signed or dated.

PROVENANCE:
from the artist through French and Company, New York, 1972
Purchased with the aid of funds from the National Endowment for the Arts in Washington, D.C., a Federal Agency; matching funds donated by Mrs. Leo Simon, New York

Since 1965 Tworkov has based his paintings on carefully worked out geometric structure, whereas in his previous Abstract Expressionist work he was primarily concerned with unconscious, spontaneous gesture. *Diptych II* combines a systematic, diagrammatic composition with a gestural, brushed surface. The suppression of color to gray tones underscores the artist's ongoing interest in drawing and more specifically relates the canvas to charcoal drawings he did as early as 1956.

Two separate but adjoining square panels contain rectilinear and diagonal repeated patterns. Intersecting diagonal lines reinforce the rhythmic effect of painterly brushwork. The countless individual strokes that constitute the allover surface embody the intuitive quality always evident in Tworkov's work but now more strictly controlled than before.

EXHIBITION:
New York, The Solomon R. Guggenheim Museum, *Acquisition Priorities: Aspects of Postwar Painting in America*, Oct. 15, 1976-Jan. 16, 1977, no. 14, repr.

REFERENCE:
K. L. Gula, "The Indian Summer of Jack Tworkov," *Art in America*, vol. 61, Sept. 1973, p. 64, repr.

Alfred Jensen 1903-1981

Alfred Julio Jensen was born on December 11, 1903, in Guatemala City, Guatemala. Following his mother's death in 1910, he was sent to live with relatives in Horsholm, Denmark. In 1923 Jensen settled briefly in Guatemala and in 1924 moved to southern California, where he received a scholarship to study painting at the San Diego School of Fine Arts. He journeyed to Munich in 1926 and met Carl Holty and Vaclav Vytlacil. They encouraged Jensen to enroll in Hans Hofmann's painting school; there he met Saidie A. May, an American student and patron of the arts. With her support Jensen was able to continue his education at the Académie Scandinave in Paris in 1929. During the 1930s he traveled extensively with Mrs. May and he advised her on the formation of her collection of modern art until her death in 1951. In 1938 he met André Masson and was encouraged by the painting and writing of Herbin to undertake an intensive study of many years duration of Goethe's color theories.

Jensen settled in New York in 1951. In 1952 his first one-man show took place at the John Heller Gallery, New York. This same year he met Rothko, with whom he formed a close friendship. During the 1950s Jensen was included in a number of group shows and in 1955 he was given a one-man exhibition at the Tanager Gallery, New York. He taught at the Maryland Institute, Baltimore, during the summer of 1958. In 1959 Henry Luce III commissioned a mural from Jensen for the Time-Life building in Paris. An exhibition of Jensen's work was held in 1961 at The Solomon R. Guggenheim Museum. In 1964 Jensen was honored with one-man shows at the Stedelijk Museum, Amsterdam, and the Kunsthalle Basel. He traveled to Guatemala and Mexico in 1968. In 1978 the Albright-Knox Art Gallery, Buffalo, organized a show of his paintings executed between 1957 and 1977. The artist lived and worked in Glen Ridge, New Jersey, until his death on April 4, 1981.

211 Uaxactun. 1964

72.2018

Oil on canvas, 50¼ x 50¼ in. (127.7 x 127.7 cm.)

Signed and dated on reverse: *Title: "Uaxactun." / Size 50¼" x 50¼" / Painted by Alfred Jensen / in 1964.*

PROVENANCE:
from the artist through The Pace Gallery, New York, 1972

Uaxactun, like much of Jensen's work, is concerned with arithmetic properties of squared numbers. The twenty-eight squares of the perimeter stand in what the artist calls a reciprocal relationship to the total number of squares in the painting. While his source is the mathematician Pythagoras, he associates the numerical relationships with the astronomical theories of Central American cultures. Jensen has explained: "Concretely rendered my art is composed by color and form (numbers) structured in the terms of the pyramid builders' concepts. These expressions are represented in my pictures as time-cycles, the count of the orbits of the planets and the sun shown in their universal settings against their background of fixed stars. My travel moments observed from an airplane, when I saw a landscape from many sides at once, are similar in structure to planetary time counts, experienced last winter in the various landscapes of Central America. There I visited amongst the pyramids of Guatemala, Yucatan and Mexico." (New York, Cordier & Ekstrom, 1970)

The composition of *Uaxactun* resembles a Mayan stepped pyramid as seen from above, and the title refers to a well-known site in northeastern Guatemala where there is an early astronomical observatory.

EXHIBITIONS:
New York, Cordier & Ekstrom, *Alfred Jensen: The Aperspective Structure of a Square,* Mar. 11-Apr. 4, 1970, color repr.

New York, Whitney Museum of American Art, *The Structure of Color,* Feb. 25-Apr. 18, 1971

New York, The Pace Gallery, *Alfred Jensen: Paintings 1964-1972,* May 6-June 7, 1972

New York, The Solomon R. Guggenheim Museum, *Acquisition Priorities: Aspects of Postwar Painting in America,* Oct. 15, 1976-Jan. 16, 1977, no. 18, repr.

Richard Pousette-Dart b. 1916

Richard Pousette-Dart was born on June 8, 1916, in St. Paul, Minnesota. His father was a painter and writer, his mother a poet. In 1936 he briefly attended Bard College in Annandale-on-Hudson, New York. That same year Pousette-Dart moved to New York, where he worked as a secretary and bookkeeper and painted at night for several years. By 1940 he left his job to paint full-time. His first one-man exhibition took place at the Artists Gallery in New York in 1941.

With a number of the artists who became known as the Abstract Expressionists, Pousette-Dart participated in the exhibition *Abstract Painting and Sculpture in America* at The Museum of Modern Art in New York in 1944. At this time his work featured heavy impasto and totemic imagery. He was given one-man exhibitions at the Betty Parsons Gallery, New York, in 1948. Pousette-Dart moved from Manhattan to Sloatsburg, New York, in 1950. The artist experimented with a variety of media, including collage, photography, watercolor and wire and metal sculpture. In 1951 Pousette-Dart received a John Simon Guggenheim Foundation Fellowship. Throughout the fifties Pousette-Dart showed extensively in both one-man and group exhibitions. He was included in *II. Documenta* in Kassel, Germany, in 1959, and in 1963 the Whitney Museum of American Art, New York, held a major Pousette-Dart retrospective.

His allover abstractions of the 1960s were Impressionist or Pointillist in feeling; their configurations often resembled exploding celestial bodies. In Pousette-Dart's more recent paintings small shapes form an allover pattern, or a large centralized image, often circular or elliptical, predominates. A second important retrospective of his work was presented at the Whitney Museum in 1974. The artist continues to paint at his home in Suffern, New York.

212 Blue Scroll. 1958

77.2337

Oil and gold paint on canvas, 48 x 36 in.
(122 x 91.3 cm.)

Signed and dated on reverse: *R. Pousette-Dart / 58.*

PROVENANCE:

from the artist through Betty Parsons Gallery, New York
Mr. and Mrs. Frederic E. Ossorio, Greenwich, Connecticut, 1959-77
Gift, Mr. and Mrs. Frederic E. Ossorio, 1977

Pousette-Dart's work of the 1940s contained biomorphic forms and symbols not unlike those found in the painting of Gottlieb, Pollock and Rothko. In canvases like *Blue Scroll* specific shapes have dissolved into an allover color pattern, although traces of them can still be discerned. Small touches of paint, carefully applied in layer after layer, form a radiant, encrusted surface. The central gold and blue rectangle is set off from and reinforced by a rather unusual painted gold frame. Through the rhythmic patterning and luminosity of his canvas, Pousette-Dart evokes a contemplative, spiritual realm.

EXHIBITIONS:
New York, Betty Parsons Gallery, *Richard Pousette-Dart,* Mar. 30-Apr. 18, 1959
New York, Andrew Crispo Gallery, *20th Century American Masters,* Oct. 1977

Lee Krasner b. 1908

Lee Krasner was born Lenore Krassner on October 27, 1908, in Brooklyn, of Russian parents. She studied in New York at the Women's Art School of Cooper Union from 1926 to 1929 and at the Art Students League in the summer of 1928. Krasner was deeply affected by the works of Picasso and Matisse she saw at The Museum of Modern Art which opened in New York in 1929. She attended the National Academy of Design from 1929 to 1931 and during the early thirties participated in various New Deal art projects.

After studying at the Hans Hofmann School of Fine Arts from 1937 to 1940, Krasner exhibited for the first time in 1940 with the *American Abstract Artists* at the American Fine Arts Galleries in New York. In 1941 she was invited by John Graham to take part in the *American and French Painting* exhibition at the McMillen Gallery, New York. One of her co-exhibitors was Jackson Pollock, whom she married in 1945. Together with Gorky, Gottlieb, Hofmann, Pousette-Dart, Rothko and Pollock, Krasner participated in the 1945 show *Challenge to the Critic* at Gallery 67 in New York. Shortly after their marriage they moved to The Springs, East Hampton, where Krasner began her Little Images series of paintings, which she continued until the end of the decade.

Krasner's first solo exhibition was held at the Betty Parsons Gallery in New York in 1951. From 1953 to 1955 she explored the medium of collage. In 1954 she was included in a show of women artists at the Hampton Gallery and Workshop in Amagansett, New York. Krasner traveled to Europe in the summer of 1956. A one-woman show of her work took place at the Martha Jackson Gallery in 1958, and the following year she completed two mosaic murals for the Uris building at 2 Broadway in New York. In 1960 and 1962 the Howard Wise Gallery, New York, gave her one-woman shows. A major Krasner retrospective opened in 1965 at the Whitechapel Art Gallery in London. In 1973 the Whitney Museum of American Art in New York showed her *Large Paintings* and in 1975 The Corcoran Gallery of Art in Washington, D.C., exhibited her collages and works on paper dating from 1933 to 1974. Krasner now lives and works in New York and The Springs.

213 **Past Continuous.** 1976

77.2334.1-3

Collage on canvas, three panels, 72 x 48 in. (183 x 122 cm.); 72 x 72 in. (183 x 183 cm.); 72 x 60 in. (183 x 152.4 cm.)

Signed and dated center panel l.c.: *Lee Krasner '76.*

PROVENANCE:

from the artist through The Pace Gallery, New York, 1977
Purchased with the aid of funds from the National Endowment for the Arts in Washington, D.C., a Federal Agency; matching funds donated by anonymous donors

Past Continuous is one of several large-scale collages Krasner executed in the mid-1970s. In them the artist has used old charcoal drawings, packed away for decades, which she had made as a student at Hans Hofmann's school in the late 1930s. She radically altered the Cubist space of her early work by cutting and reassembling fragments of the old drawings to develop completely new compositions and a new style. In 1975 Krasner was eager to return to collage, a medium she had not worked in for twenty years.

In *Past Continuous* Krasner combines figurative passages, Cubist segments, bare canvas and bold red and black areas and disposes them in basically rectangular sections over three separate panels. In confronting her early work the artist introduces an element of time. She returns to the past and uses it to create a new present. Significantly, Krasner's titles for this group of pictures are grammatical tenses and moods of verbs, many specifically referring to the past, present and future.

EXHIBITION:
New York, The Pace Gallery, *Lee Krasner: eleven ways to use the words to see,* Feb. 19-Mar. 19, 1977, color repr.

REFERENCES:
B. Rose, "Lee Krasner and the Origins of Abstract Expressionism," *Arts Magazine,* vol. 51, Feb. 1977, pp. 99, repr., 100

D. Kuspit, "Lee Krasner at Pace," *Art in America,* vol. 65, Nov. 1977, p. 136

Conrad Marca-Relli b. 1913

Corrado Marca-Relli was born on June 5, 1913, in Boston. His childhood was spent in Europe and Boston, until the family settled in New York in 1926. In 1930 Marca-Relli enrolled at Cooper Union for one year of study. By 1931 he had his own studio and supported himself by teaching and drawing for newspapers and magazines. From 1935 to 1938 Marca-Relli worked in the easel and mural divisions of the WPA Federal Art Project. Through the Project he became acquainted with artists such as de Kooning and Kline, who introduced him to the work of Picasso, Matisse and Miró. Marca-Relli first exhibited in 1941 at the Contemporary Arts Gallery in New York. His career was interrupted by military service from 1941 to 1945. In 1946 he returned to New York, and the following year the Niveau Gallery, New York, gave the artist his first one-man show. Marca-Relli spent a year in 1948-49 in Rome and Paris. Upon his return to New York he became a founding member of *The Club*, an informal group of Abstract Expressionists. He studied ancient and Renaissance art and architecture in Rome in 1951-52.

Marca-Relli visited Mexico in the summer of 1953; while there he ran out of paint and began to experiment with collage. This same year the artist moved to East Hampton, New York, where he associated with de Kooning and Pollock. He was Visiting Critic at Yale University in 1954-55. In 1956 Marca-Relli participated in the Venice Biennale and in 1958 he taught at the University of California at Berkeley. From 1960 to 1967 he made annual trips to Europe. The Whitney Museum of American Art, New York, gave him a retrospective in 1967. Marca-Relli moved to Ibiza, Spain, in 1973, and was elected a member of the American Academy and Institute of Arts and Letters in 1976. The artist now lives and works in Ibiza and Florida.

214 **Warrior.** 1956

57.1458

Oil and collage on canvas, 85 x 50 in. (215.9 x 127 cm.)

Signed l.r.: *Marca-Relli*; inscribed on stretcher: *(THE WARRIOR) MARCA-RELLI / L-4-56.* Not dated.

PROVENANCE:

from the artist through Stable Gallery, New York, 1957

Since 1953 Marca-Relli has used collage to create essentially pictorial effects of color, texture and depth. In *Warrior* he has arranged many abstract, cut-out canvas shapes on a large canvas; he has emphasized these interlocking forms with touches of oil paint. The focus on a central form which resembles a figure in this picture and in *Ajax* (Private Collection), both dating from 1956, points to their evolution from single figure compositions of the preceding years. Marca-Relli elaborated upon the complexity of figure relationships and movement in a large, strongly horizontal picture of the same year, *The Battle* (Collection The Metropolitan Museum of Art, New York).

Neutral colors, stability of forms and, above all, his use of collage bring to mind contemporary works by Burri. The collage technique has played a crucial role in twentieth-century art from Picasso and Braque to Motherwell and Rauschenberg: Marca-Relli is well aware of this tradition.

EXHIBITIONS:

New York, Stable Gallery, *Marca-Relli*, Nov. 5-Dec. 1, 1956

Worcester Art Museum, *Some Younger Names in American Painting*, Feb. 6-Mar. 16, 1958

Ann Arbor, Museum of Art, University of Michigan, *Images at Mid-Century*, Apr. 13-June 12, 1960

Venice, XXXII Biennale Internazionale d'Arte, *Today's Art in Museums: The Solomon R. Guggenheim Museum*, June 20-Oct. 18, 1964, no. 12

New York, Whitney Museum of American Art, *Marca-Relli*, Oct. 4-Nov. 12, 1967, no. 15, repr., traveled to Waltham, Mass., Rose Art Museum, Brandeis University, Dec. 3, 1967-Jan. 28, 1968

REFERENCES:

Handbook, 1959, p. 116, repr.

P. Tyler, *Marca-Relli,* Paris, 1960, repr.

H. H. Arnason, *Marca-Relli,* New York, 1963, pl. 32

447

David Hare b. 1917

David Hare was born on March 10, 1917, in New York. From 1936 to 1937 he studied biology and chemistry at Bard College in Annandale-on-Hudson, New York. In the late thirties he began to experiment with color photography, which the Walker Galleries in New York exhibited in 1939. Hare opened a commercial photography studio in New York in 1940, and in the same year the Julien Levy Gallery, New York, gave him a solo exhibition. During the early forties Hare came into contact with a number of the Surrealist emigrés in New York and in 1942 he started to make sculpture. From 1942 to 1944 Hare founded and edited the Surrealist magazine *VVV* with André Breton, Duchamp and Max Ernst. Peggy Guggenheim presented one-man shows of Hare's work in her Art of This Century gallery from 1944 to 1946. In 1948 he was a founding member, together with Robert Motherwell, Baziotes and Rothko, of The Subjects of the Artist school in New York and he became friendly with Jean-Paul Sartre. This same year he moved to Paris where he met Balthus, Brauner, Giacometti and Picasso. He returned to New York in 1953 but spent the next two summers in Paris.

Hare was included in the 1951 and 1957 São Paulo Bienals, and in 1958 he received a sculpture commission for the Uris building at 750 Third Avenue, New York. Hare began to concentrate on painting in the sixties. From the mid-sixties into the seventies Hare held various teaching positions. He was included in The Museum of Modern Art's 1968 *Dada, Surrealism and Their Heritage* exhibition. The following year he received an honorary doctorate from the Maryland Institute of Art, Baltimore. In the late sixties the artist began his Cronus series, which he has continued to pursue to the present. These works, consisting of drawings, paintings and sculpture, were the subject of a one-man exhibition at The Solomon R. Guggenheim Museum in 1977. Hare lives and works in New York.

215 Cronus Mad. 1968

77.2323

Acrylic and collage on Masonite, 64¾ x 48 in. (164.5 x 122 cm.)

Signed l.r.: *Hare*; signed and dated on reverse: *Cronus Mad / 48 x 65 / Hare / 1968*.

PROVENANCE:

from the artist
Gift, Hamilton Gallery of Contemporary Art, New York, 1977

Known primarily for his sculpture, Hare has also worked extensively in painting, drawing and collage. In the late 1960s he initiated the Cronus series, which to date includes approximately 250 works. He uses the myth of Cronus from Hesiod, "as a symbol, as a jumping off place. *Cronus* was part man, part earth, part time. I use him as a symbol of growth through time .... *Cronus* grows and loves, and eats what he loves. Becomes old and mad and wise and dead and alive again." (statement by the artist, New York, Alessandra Gallery, 1976)

Here Cronus appears in dog-like guise; his penetrating gaze suggests many levels of awareness. Similar images of *Cronus Mad*, all affixed with black tape, occur in a larger coeval collage on canvas (Collection John Goodwin, New Mexico) and a sculpture executed in bronze, plexiglass and steel in 1975 (Collection of the artist).

EXHIBITION:
New York, Alessandra Gallery, *David Hare*, May 8-June 8, 1976, color repr.

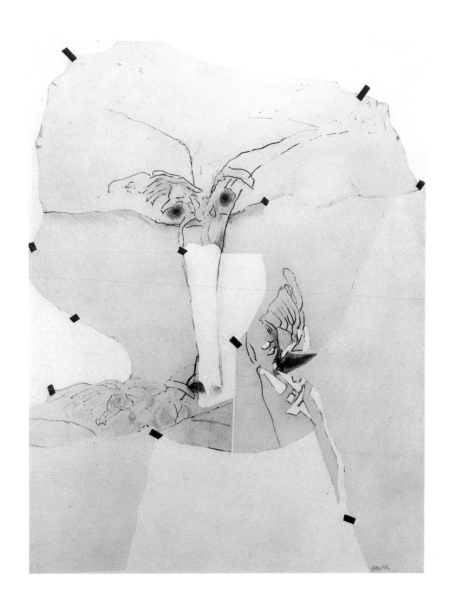

Alexander Liberman b. 1912

Alexander Liberman was born in Kiev, Russia, in 1912. The family moved to St. Petersburg in 1913 and to Moscow in 1917. In 1921 his father smuggled him out of Russia and placed him in school in London. In 1924 he joined his parents in Paris, where he attended the Ecole des Roches, took drawing classes and learned to forge metal. By the late twenties Liberman's mother had introduced him to Chagall, Larionov, Léger and Alexandra Exter. In Paris he studied painting with André Lhote in 1931 and briefly attended the Ecole Spéciale d'Architecture and the Ecole des Beaux-Arts in 1932. Liberman was art director of the magazine *Vu* from 1932 until 1936, when he decided to devote himself entirely to painting, writing and film making.

World War II forced Liberman to flee France; he arrived in New York in 1941 and that same year began to work at *Vogue* magazine. In 1945 he resumed painting, which he had abandoned during the war. The following year he became a United States citizen. In 1947 Liberman began to make annual trips to Europe. Around this time his paintings became increasingly abstract and he started to photograph School of Paris artists. In 1954 he participated in his first exhibition, *Younger American Painters,* at the Guggenheim Museum. Shortly thereafter Liberman began to investigate the realm of accident and chance. In St. Maxime, France, in 1959, he learned to weld and made his first welded sculpture.

Liberman's first one-man show took place in 1960 at the Betty Parsons Gallery in New York. This same year a book of his photographs, *The Artist in His Studio,* was published. Around 1963 he moved from hard-edge geometric abstractions to freer, more gestural paintings. Since 1962 he has been Editorial Director of all Condé Nast publications. The Jewish Museum, New York, presented an important one-man show of his sculpture in 1966, and in 1970 a major Liberman retrospective was held at The Corcoran Gallery of Art, Washington, D.C. Liberman lives and works in New York and Warren, Connecticut.

216 Sixteen Ways. 1951

77.2335

Oil and enamel on Masonite, 50 x 123 in.
(127 x 312.4 cm.)

Not signed or dated.

PROVENANCE:

Gift of the artist
Francine and Cleve Gray, Cornwall Bridge, Connecticut, 1957-77
Gift, Francine and Cleve Gray, 1977

As early as 1950 Liberman employed industrial materials such as enamel sprayed on Masonite. Around this time he limited himself to investigating the formal and philosophical possibilities of the circle: its essentiality and mystical purity liberated him from Cubism.

Sixteen Ways consists of four rectangular panels, each containing a circle placed above center. From left to right the circles are yellow, red, blue and black on a gleaming white background: the panels can, however, be rearranged. The size of the rectangles and circles is determined by mathematical relationships. With the simplicity and precision of his circle paintings, Liberman is an early precursor of Hard-Edge Abstraction. *Sixteen Ways* also foretells his own cylindrical sculpture.

EXHIBITIONS:

Washington, D.C., The Corcoran Gallery of Art, *Alexander Liberman: Painting and Sculpture 1950-1970,* Apr. 19-May 31, 1970, no. 6, repr.

New York, André Emmerich Gallery, *Alexander Liberman: The Circle Paintings 1950-1964,* Oct. 5-23, 1974, color repr.

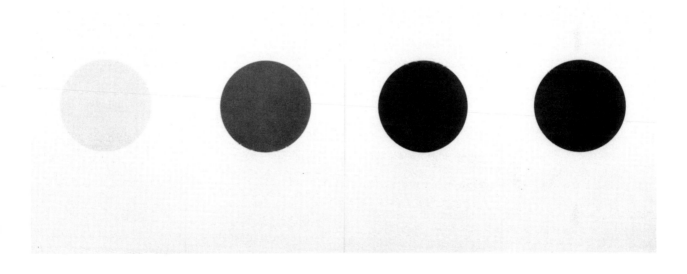

Attilio Salemme 1911-1955

Attilio Salemme was born on October 18, 1911, in Brookline, Massachusetts. After completing junior high school in 1926, he began to work at odd jobs to support his family. In his spare time Salemme studied the ancient art collections in the Museum of Fine Arts in Boston. In 1927 he enlisted in the Marine Corps and was sent to Haiti for six months. He resumed working in Boston after his discharge the following year.

In 1930 the family moved to New York, and for the next five years Salemme took various jobs including work as a laborer on early WPA projects. During this period he attended high school at night and planned to become a chemist; he also taught chemistry in the Adult Education Division of the WPA. From 1938 Salemme became increasingly interested in art. In 1942 he worked part-time as a frame-maker at the Museum of Non-Objective Painting in New York; here he was introduced to modern art, met artists and was included in his first group exhibition. Salemme's mature style began to emerge in 1943. His first one-man show took place in 1945 at Howard Putzel's Gallery 67 in New York. In 1947 he received an award at The Art Institute of Chicago Annual and a commission for a large painting for an ocean liner. In 1948 the Passedoit Gallery in New York gave Salemme a one-man show, and his work was included in the Whitney Annual in New York.

The artist was represented in the Venice Biennale in 1950 and was given a number of one-man shows in the early fifties. Salemme died suddenly on January 24, 1955, in New York. In 1959 the Institute of Contemporary Art in Boston presented a retrospective of his work which circulated in the United States, and in 1978 the National Collection of Fine Arts, Washington, D.C., organized a Salemme show which traveled to The Solomon R. Guggenheim Museum.

217 Lunar Voyage. 1954

72.2012

Oil on canvas, 24 x 36 in. (61 x 91.5 cm.)

Signed and dated l.r.: *Attilio Salemme / '54.*

PROVENANCE:
Estate of the artist through Catherine Viviano Gallery, New York
Denis E. Paddock, New York, 1960-72
Gift, Denis E. Paddock, 1972

Salemme's paintings are reminiscent of Giorgio de Chirico, Klee and of Kandinsky's late work. Angular, linear forms inhabit a stage-like space; their simplified, geometric shapes and unmodulated color areas augment a sense of spatial isolation. The artist stated that "people are the subject of my painting; what they are doing is usually indicated by the titles." (Washington, D.C., National Collection of Fine Arts, 1978, p. 10) *Lunar Voyage* is, of course, purely imaginary since it was painted before the era of space exploration. However, scientists and writers had long speculated about spacemen and space vehicles.

EXHIBITIONS:
Urbana, College of Fine and Applied Art, University of Illinois, *Contemporary American Painting and Sculpture,* Feb. 27-Apr. 3, 1955, pl. 79
New York, Duveen-Graham, *Attilio Salemme 1911-1955,* May 2-31, 1955, no. 32
New York, Catherine Viviano Gallery, *Attilio Salemme: Paintings 1946-1955,* May 3-28, 1960, no. 16
Washington, D.C., National Collection of Fine Arts, Smithsonian Institution, *Attilio Salemme: Inhabitant of a Dream,* Mar. 3-May 7, 1978, no. 44, repr., traveled to New York, The Solomon R. Guggenheim Museum, June 23-Aug. 6

REFERENCE:
Boston, Institute of Contemporary Art, *Attilio Salemme,* 1958, n.p.

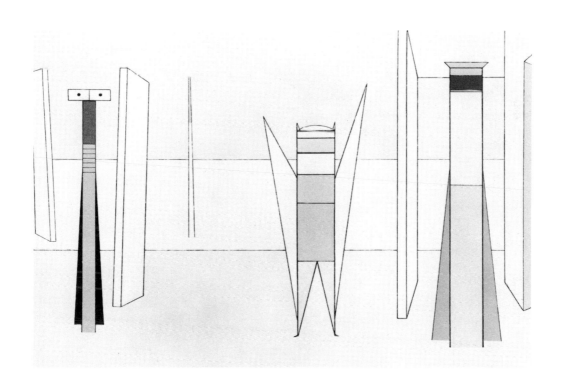

Jimmy Ernst 1920-1984

Jimmy Ernst was born Ulrich Ernst on June 24, 1920, in Brühl, near Cologne. During his youth he studied printing techniques and typography at the Kunstgewerbeschule in Altona, Germany, and became a printer's apprentice in Cologne. As the son of the art critic Louise Strauss and the Surrealist artist Max Ernst, he knew Giacometti, Tanguy, Man Ray, Paul Eluard, André Breton and Bertolt Brecht, all of whom he visited in Paris.

He came to the United States in 1938 and began painting, although he had no formal artistic training. Ernst's first one-man show was held at the Norlyst Gallery in New York in 1941. In the 1940s his circle of friends included Baziotes, Matta and Gordon Onslow-Ford. He was given solo exhibitions at the Laurel Gallery in New York in 1948 and 1950. During the early 1950s he began teaching at Pratt Institute in Brooklyn and at Brooklyn College. One-man shows of his work were presented annually by the Grace Borgenicht Gallery in New York from 1952 to 1976.

Ernst was a visiting artist at the University of Colorado in 1954. In 1956 he was included in the *Younger American Painters* show at the Guggenheim Museum and participated in the Whitney Annual as well as the Venice Biennale. The Museum of Fine Arts in Houston mounted a Jimmy Ernst show in 1956. Ernst received a Creative Arts Award from Brandeis University in Waltham, Massachusetts, in 1957, and the following year he executed a mural commission for the Continental Bank Building in Lincoln, Nebraska. He visited the Soviet Union on a cultural exchange program in 1961 and moved to New Canaan, Connecticut, after his return to the United States. One-man exhibitions of his work were presented by the Kölnischer Kunstverein and the Detroit Institute of Arts in 1963, the Städtisches Kunsthaus of Bielefeld in 1964, The Arts Club of Chicago in 1969 and the Galerie Lucie Weill in Paris in 1972. Ernst lived and worked in East Hampton, New York, until his death on February 6, 1984.

218 **A Triptych.** 1971

72.1989.1-3

Oil on canvas, three panels, each 50 x 60 in.
(127 x 152.4 cm.)

Signed and dated right panel l.r.: *Jimmy Ernst 71.*

PROVENANCE:
from the artist through Grace Borgenicht Gallery, New York, 1972

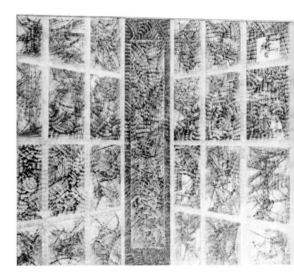

Jimmy Ernst structures his composition with three vertical divisions which do not coincide with the three panels of the triptych format. A network of white painted lines intersects the segmented patterning and seems alternately to advance and recede. The red, orange, yellow, green and blue abstract shapes within the white lines give the effect of stained-glass windows. This *Triptych* displays the skillfulness and delicacy of execution associated with all of Ernst's work as well as the bright, colorful palette encountered in his paintings of the 1970s.

EXHIBITION:
New York, Grace Borgenicht Gallery, *Jimmy Ernst,* Jan. 29-Feb. 24, 1972

REFERENCE:
A. Mikotajuk, "In the Galleries," *Arts Magazine,* vol. 46, Mar. 1972, p. 66

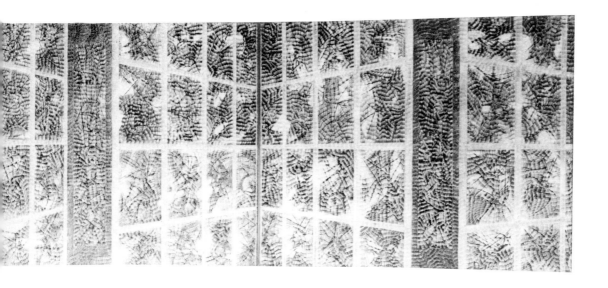

Kenzo Okada 1902-1982

Kenzo Okada was born on September 28, 1902, in Yokohama, Japan. In 1922 he enrolled in the Tokyo Fine Arts University and in 1924 moved to Paris. In Paris Okada studied with Tsugouhara Foujita and was influenced by French painting. His work was exhibited at the Salon d'Automne, Paris, from 1924 to 1927. Okada returned to Japan in 1927. Two years later his first one-man show took place at the Michido Gallery in Tokyo, where he continued to exhibit until 1935. In 1936 the *Nikakai Group* of contemporary Japanese artists awarded Okada a prize; in 1938 he joined this group and began to show with them. The artist taught in Tokyo at the School of Fine Arts, Nippon University, from 1940 to 1942, the Musachino Art Institute in 1947 and 1950 and Tama Fine Arts College from 1949 to 1950. He was given solo exhibitions at the Hokuso Gallery, Tokyo, in 1948 and 1950.

Okada moved to New York in 1950, and his first one-man show in the United States was held in this city at the Betty Parsons Gallery in 1953. In 1955 he was included in the São Paulo Bienal and the Pittsburgh International and he was given a one-man exhibition at The Corcoran Gallery of Art in Washington, D.C. Okada participated in the 1958 Venice Biennale. In 1960 he became a United States citizen and moved to Rensselaerville, New York. The Betty Parsons Gallery, New York, gave him a one-man show in 1964, and the following year Okada was honored with a retrospective at the Albright-Knox Art Gallery in Buffalo. During the seventies he showed regularly at the Betty Parsons Gallery. In 1979 The Phillips Collection, Washington, D.C., included him in their exhibition *Three Pioneers of Abstract Painting in 20th Century Japan*. The artist divided his time between New York and Tokyo before his death on July 25, 1982.

219 **Solstice.** March 1954

54.1407

Oil on canvas, 57¼ x 70⅝ in. (145.5 x 179.4 cm.)

Signed l.r.: *Kenzo Okada*. Not dated.

PROVENANCE:

from the artist, 1954

Only after Okada came to the United States in 1950 did his work become abstract. In paintings like *Solstice* the formal and poetic features of traditional Japanese painting merge with the conventions of Abstract Expressionism. Here he maintains a tenuous balance between the flat plane, characteristic of twentieth-century art, and the shifting forms located in a shallow space, recalling the tilted perspective of Oriental landscapes. Responsive to nature, Okada frequently draws upon landscape elements in his work. His title for our picture suggests seasons and planets. The smooth, flat abstract shapes and the muted palette of white, black, subdued grays and soft blues project a mood of calm and serenity.

EXHIBITIONS:

New York, The Solomon R. Guggenheim Museum, *Younger American Painters: A Selection,* May 12-Sept. 8, 1954, no. 40, repr., traveled to Portland (Ore.) Art Museum, Sept. 2-Oct. 9, 1955; Seattle, Henry Gallery, University of Washington, Oct. 16-Nov. 13; San Francisco Museum of Art, Nov. 15, 1955-Jan. 22, 1956; Los Angeles County Museum of Art, Feb. 1-29; Fayetteville, University of Arkansas, Mar. 9-Apr. 10; New Orleans, Isaac Delgado Museum of Art, Apr. 15-May 20

The Art Institute of Chicago, *61st American Exhibition: Paintings and Sculpture,* Oct. 21-Dec. 5, 1954, no. 109

London, Tate Gallery, *An exhibition of paintings from The Solomon R. Guggenheim Museum, New York,* Apr. 16-May 26, 1957, no. 57, traveled to The Hague, Gemeentemuseum, June 25-Sept. 1; Helsinki, Ateneumin Taidekokoelmat, Sept. 27-Oct. 20; Rome, Galleria Nazionale d'Arte Moderna, Dec. 5, 1957-Jan. 8, 1958; Cologne, Wallraf-Richartz-Museum, Jan. 26-Mar. 30; Paris, Musée des Arts Décoratifs, Apr. 23-June 1

Ann Arbor, Museum of Art, University of Michigan, *Images at Mid-Century,* Apr. 13-June 12, 1960, repr.

Washington, D.C., The Phillips Collection, *Okada, Shinoda, and Tsutaka: Three Pioneers of Abstract Painting in 20th Century Japan,* Apr. 14-May 24, 1979, p. 15, color repr.

REFERENCES:

Art Institute of Chicago Quarterly, vol. XLVIII, Nov. 15, 1954, p. 78, repr.

Art News, vol. 53, Dec. 1954, p. 62, repr.

Handbook, 1959, p. 140, repr.

Sam Francis b. 1923

Samuel Lewis Francis was born in San Mateo, California, on June 25, 1923. From 1941 to 1943 he studied psychology and medicine at the University of California at Berkeley. He began to paint in 1944 while hospitalized during his Air Corps service. Shortly thereafter Francis studied under David Park at the California School of Fine Arts in San Francisco. His first abstract work dates from 1947. From 1948 to 1950 he completed his studies at Berkeley, receiving a B.A. and an M.A. in art. In 1950 Francis settled in Paris, where he briefly attended the Académie Fernand Léger and became friends with Canadian painter Jean-Paul Riopelle and young American artists. His first one-man show took place at the Galerie du Dragon in Paris in 1952. In 1956 he began a mural for the Kunsthalle Basel (completed 1958) and was given his first one-man exhibition in New York at the Martha Jackson Gallery.

In 1957 and 1958 the artist traveled around the world twice, stopping in New York, Mexico, Thailand and India and staying for an extended period in Japan. While in Tokyo Francis painted a mural for the Sogestsu School of the sculptor and flower arranger Sofu Teshigahara. The Japanese particularly admired the relationship between Francis' abstraction and their *haboku* (flung ink painting). He was included in The Museum of Modern Art's *The New American Painting* exhibition which circulated in Europe in 1958-59. Francis participated in the *II. Documenta*, Kassel, Germany, and the São Paulo Bienal in 1959. This same year he executed a mural for the Chase Manhattan Bank at Fifty-fifth Street and Park Avenue in New York.

Francis made his first lithographs in Zürich in 1960 and became increasingly interested in printmaking; he worked at the Tamarind Lithography Workshop in Los Angeles in 1963. The following year in Kyoto he made his first sculptures. Francis built a studio in Santa Monica in 1965. He experimented with skywriting in color in 1966 and with colored light projections two years later. A major Francis retrospective was presented at the Albright-Knox Art Gallery in Buffalo in 1972; this exhibition traveled in the United States into the following year. Francis lives in Santa Monica and sojourns frequently in Japan.

220 Shining Back. 1958

59.1560

Oil on canvas, 79½ x 53 in. (202 x 134.6 cm.)

Not signed or dated.

PROVENANCE:

from the artist through Martha Jackson Gallery, New York, 1959

Shining Back was painted in 1958, soon after Francis' extensive travels and visit to the Orient. Vibrant color-shapes occupy the lateral portions of the canvas and are separated by the central white interstice. Throughout, drips and splatters of blue, purple, green and red paint animate the surface. They are evidence of a new openness and freedom of gesture in Francis' work. Canvases done earlier in the 1950s (such as *Red and Black* of 1954 in the Guggenheim Museum collection) exhibit a tighter allover pattern and cellular structural organization. In *Shining Back* the emphasis is on a gestural mode of painting and floating, falling forms.

EXHIBITIONS:

Washington, D.C., The Phillips Gallery, *Paintings by Sam Francis*, Oct. 19-Nov. 20, 1958

New York, Martha Jackson Gallery, *Sam Francis,* Nov. 25-Dec. 20, 1958

San Francisco Museum of Art, *Paintings by Sam Francis, Wally Hedrick and Manuel Neri,* Feb. 3-22, 1959, traveled to Pasadena Art Museum, Mar. 3-Apr. 10; Seattle Art Museum, Apr. 24-May 17

Ann Arbor, Museum of Art, University of Michigan, *Images at Mid-Century,* Apr. 13-June 12, 1960

Venice, XXXII Biennale Internazionale d'Arte, *Today's Art in Museums: The Solomon R. Guggenheim Museum,* June 20-Oct. 18, 1964, no. 7, repr.

New York, Robert Elkon Gallery, *Sam Francis: "The Fifties,"* Dec. 11, 1974-Jan. 16, 1975

New York, The Solomon R. Guggenheim Museum, *Acquisition Priorities: Aspects of Postwar Painting in America,* Oct. 15, 1976-Jan. 16, 1977, no. 42, repr.

REFERENCES:

Handbook, 1970, pp. 122-123, repr.

P. Selz, *Sam Francis,* New York, 1974, p. 169, pl. 94

H. H. Arnason, *History of Modern Art,* rev. ed., New York, 1977, p. 679, fig. 1223

I. Sandler, *The New York School: The Painters and Sculptors of the Fifties,* New York, 1978, p. 87, fig. 54

Joan Mitchell b. 1926

Joan Mitchell was born on February 12, 1926, in Chicago. She attended Smith College in Northampton, Massachusetts, from 1942 to 1944 and received her B.F.A. from The Art Institute of Chicago in 1947. Her earliest works were figurative. Mitchell lived in Europe in 1948-49 on a fellowship awarded by The Art Institute of Chicago. She returned to the United States in 1950 and attended Columbia University, New York, and earned an M.F.A. from The Art Institute of Chicago. Her landscapes of this period were influenced by Cézanne, van Gogh and Matisse. Mitchell's work was first exhibited in 1950 in a one-woman show in St. Paul, Minnesota.

Living in New York in the early 1950s, Mitchell participated in meetings of *The Club* and became friendly with Abstract Expressionists such as de Kooning, Guston and Kline. In 1951 she participated in the *Ninth Street Show* and the Whitney Annual. The New Gallery gave Mitchell her first one-woman show in New York in 1951.

In 1955 Mitchell went to Paris and began to divide her time between France and New York. From then until the early sixties her work was presented in several solo exhibitions at the Stable Gallery in New York and in group shows including the 1958 Venice Biennale and the 1959 São Paulo Bienal. In 1966 she executed the Seine series; these were followed by the Sunflower paintings. Mitchell bought a house and studio in Vétheuil, France, in 1969. The Everson Museum of Art in Syracuse, New York, presented a major Mitchell exhibition in 1972. The following year she received the Brandeis Creative Arts Award Medal and in 1974 she was honored with a one-woman show at the Whitney Museum of American Art, New York. Mitchell still lives and works in Vétheuil.

221 **Place for Puppies.** 1976

79.2515

Oil on canvas, two panels, total 63¾ x 102½ in. (161.9 x 260.4 cm.)

Not signed or dated.

PROVENANCE:
from the artist through Xavier Fourcade, Inc., New York
Gift, Elizabeth and Jonathan Greenburg, New York, 1979

Mitchell has said: "Music, poems, landscape and dogs make me want to paint." (New York, Whitney Museum of American Art, *Joan Mitchell*, 1974, p. 7) Many of her canvases transmit the feeling of landscape, often the remembrance of landscape. She lives in France at Vétheuil, where Monet painted from 1878 to 1881. Indeed, the predominance of blue and green in Mitchell's palette and her practice of juxtaposing two or three large canvases recall Monet's work.

Mitchell has employed a diptych format in *Place for Puppies*. The loosely articulated strokes of paint are green-blue, purple and a range of tan earth colors. The brushwork retains the vigor of the artist's gesture and the surface is animated as well with impasto, drips and other properties of oil paint. From the profusion of brushstrokes a patterning and coherence emerge.

EXHIBITION:
New York, Xavier Fourcade, Inc., *Joan Mitchell-New Paintings,* Nov. 23-Dec. 31, 1976, not in cat.

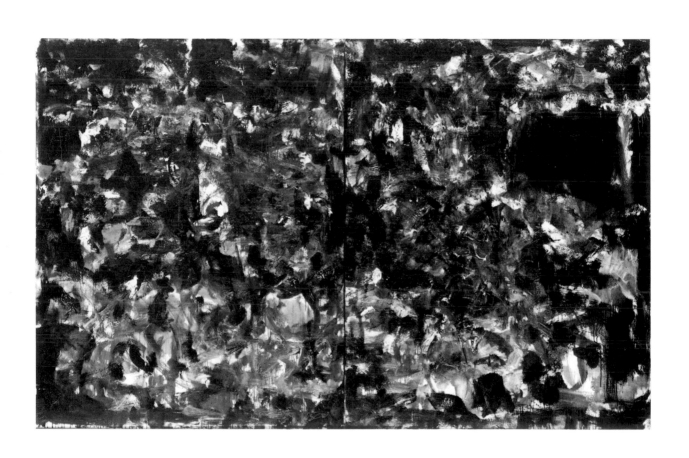

Richard Diebenkorn b. 1922

Richard Clifford Diebenkorn was born on April 22, 1922, in Portland, Oregon. The family moved to San Francisco in 1924. Diebenkorn studied at Stanford University in Palo Alto from 1940 to 1943; he transferred to the University of California at Berkeley and graduated in 1943. In 1946, after military service, he enrolled at the California School of Fine Arts, San Francisco, where David Park, Elmer Bischoff and Hassel Smith were teachers. This year Diebenkorn moved to Woodstock, New York, where he knew Guston and Bradley Walker Tomlin. He met Kline at this time.

In 1947 Diebenkorn returned to California, taught drawing at the California School of Fine Arts and saw the work of Clyfford Still. His first one-man exhibition was at the California Palace of the Legion of Honor, San Francisco, in 1948, the year he met Rothko and was introduced to de Kooning's work. In 1950-51 he enrolled in the M.F.A. program at the University of New Mexico at Albuquerque and began his Albuquerque paintings. Deeply moved by the Matisse exhibition in Los Angeles in 1952, Diebenkorn was inspired this same year to begin the vibrantly colored Urbana paintings in Illinois. In 1953, while teaching at the California College of Arts and Crafts, Oakland, Diebenkorn began his Berkeley paintings. From 1955 to the mid-sixties the artist painted in a figurative manner. He participated in the 1955 São Paulo Bienal and was given a retrospective in 1960 at the Pasadena Art Museum. In 1964-65 Diebenkorn traveled to the Soviet Union and saw the Matisses in the Shchukin and Hermitage collections.

By 1967 he had moved to the Ocean Park section of Santa Monica and started to paint the large, abstract Ocean Park canvases, a series he is still developing. Diebenkorn was included in the 1968 Venice Biennale and was given a one-man show in 1969 at the Los Angeles County Museum of Art. In 1975 the San Francisco Museum of Art presented a large exhibition of his Ocean Park paintings, and in 1976 the Albright-Knox Art Gallery, Buffalo, organized a major Diebenkorn retrospective which traveled in the United States into 1977. He was given a one-man show at the 1978 Venice Biennale. Diebenkorn still lives and works in Santa Monica.

222 Ocean Park No. 96. 1977

77.2307

Oil on canvas, 93⅛ x 85⅛ in. (236.3 x 216.1 cm.)

Signed and dated on reverse: *R. DIEBENKORN/ OCEAN PARK #96—1977.*

PROVENANCE:

from the artist through M. Knoedler and Co., Inc., New York, 1977
Purchased with the aid of funds from the National Endowment for the Arts in Washington, D.C., a Federal Agency; matching funds donated by Mr. and Mrs. Stuart M. Speiser and Louis and Bessie Adler Foundation, Inc., Seymour M. Klein, President

Ocean Park No. 96 is one of a series of large, totally abstract paintings that was initiated in 1967 and is still in progress. Ocean Park is the name of a section of Santa Monica where the artist's studio is located. The light-filled colors suggest sky, sea, sand and earth. In fact, Diebenkorn has stated that temperamentally he has always been a landscape painter.

In *Ocean Park No. 96* the composition is governed by a reiteration of rectangles formed by the intersection of horizontal and vertical lines which occurs primarily at the upper right and left corners. Diagonal accents cut across color areas. Diebenkorn has partially painted over certain lines to suggest continuity rather than explicit partitioning. His Ocean Park pictures are either square or, as here, vertical in format. The subtle differentiation in width and length of color zones and the spatial implications of structure dominate the series.

EXHIBITIONS:

New York, M. Knoedler and Co., Inc., *Recent Paintings by Richard Diebenkorn,* May 7-June 2, 1977

Venice, XXXVIII Biennale Internazionale d'Arte, *United States Pavilion: Richard Diebenkorn,* July 2-Oct. 1978, no. 14, color repr.

Jan Müller 1922-1958

Jan Müller was born on December 27, 1922, in Hamburg. In 1933 his family fled the Nazis to Prague, and later to Bex-les-Bains, Switzerland; there he experienced the first of several attacks of rheumatic fever. He visited Paris in 1938 and two years later was apprehended and interned in a camp near Lyon. Shortly after the fall of Paris Müller was released, at which time he moved to Ornaisons, near Narbonne. Following an unsuccessful attempt to escape to the United States from Marseille, he was able to cross the border into Spain in 1941 and proceed via Portugal to New York.

Müller supported himself with a variety of jobs. He began to paint and study art in New York in 1945: first at the Art Students League for six months, then at the Hans Hofmann School of Fine Arts, which he attended for five years. In 1951 he participated in a show at the gallery 813 Broadway in New York with Miles Forst, John Grillo, Lester Johnson, Wolf Kahn and Felix Pasilis. His first solo exhibition was held in 1953 at the cooperative Hansa Gallery in New York, which he founded with Allan Kaprow and Stankiewicz, among others. Müller exhibited regularly at the Hansa Gallery from this time. During the 1950s he spent several summers in Provincetown, Massachusetts, where he was given one-man shows at The Sun Gallery in 1955 and 1956.

Although his health deteriorated throughout the decade, Müller continued to paint. In 1957 he became a United States citizen. That same year his work appeared in group shows at the Whitney Museum of American Art, The Jewish Museum and The Museum of Modern Art in New York and at The Art Institute of Chicago. Müller died on January 29, 1958, at age thirty-six, in New York. A retrospective of his work was organized by The Solomon R. Guggenheim Museum in 1962.

223 Jacob's Ladder. January 1958

62.1609

Oil on canvas, 83½ x 115 in. (212.1 x 292.1 cm.)

Not signed or dated.

PROVENANCE:
Estate of the artist, 1962

In his figurative work Müller drew upon mythology, the Bible, Shakespeare and often Goethe for his subject matter. The theme of Jacob's Ladder comes from Genesis. In this picture the single ladder in Jacob's dream has been replaced by many. Presumably the green reclining figure in the lower right corner is Jacob, although his pose brings to mind scenes of Christ's Deposition.

The freely-brushed paint, the vivid palette of black, gray, white, blue, red and green, the expressive angular forms and the red and green mask-like faces belong to a German Expressionist tradition. According to the artist's widow, this canvas, which was begun not long before Müller's death and remains unfinished, is concerned with Hell and Conformity, the reverse theme of Jacob's Ladder.*

* New York, The Solomon R. Guggenheim Museum, 1962 [p. 3]

EXHIBITIONS:
New York, The Solomon R. Guggenheim Museum, *Jan Müller, 1922-1958*, Jan. 11-Feb. 25, 1962, repr., traveled to Boston, Institute of Contemporary Art, Mar. 16-Apr. 22

Venice, XXXI Biennale Internazionale d'Arte, *United States Pavilion,* June 16-Oct. 7, 1962, no. 38

New York, The Solomon R. Guggenheim Museum, *Van Gogh and Expressionism,* July 1-Sept. 13, 1964

San Francisco Museum of Art, *Colorists 1950-1965,* Oct. 15-Nov. 21, 1965, repr.

REFERENCES:
M. Sawin, "Jan Müller: 1922-1958," *Arts,* vol. 33, Feb. 1959, pp. 41, repr., 44

J. S[chuyler], "Five star shows this winter," *Art News,* vol. 60, Feb. 1962, p. 44, repr.

"Fifty-six Painters and Sculptors," *Art in America,* vol. 52, Aug. 1964, pp. 28-29, repr.

B. Rose, *American Art Since 1900,* New York, 1967, p. 236, repr., 237

I. Sandler, *The New York School: The Painters and Sculptors of the Fifties,* New York, 1978, p. 124, fig. 86

Isamu Noguchi b. 1904

Isamu Noguchi was born on November 17, 1904, in Los Angeles. His Japanese father was a poet and his mother an American writer. In 1906 the family moved to Japan. He was sent to Indiana for schooling in 1918, and in 1922 he apprenticed to the sculptor Gutzon Borglum in Connecticut. For the next two years he was a premedical student at Columbia University and took sculpture classes at the Leonardo da Vinci School in New York. Noguchi decided to become an artist and left Columbia in 1925. A John Simon Guggenheim Foundation Fellowship in 1927 enabled him to go to Paris, where he worked as Brancusi's studio assistant. In Paris he became friendly with Calder, Jules Pascin and Stuart Davis. Noguchi returned to New York in 1928 and the following year showed abstract sculpture in his first one-man show at the Eugene Schoen Gallery.

In 1930 Noguchi traveled in Europe and the Orient, studying calligraphy in China and pottery in Japan. In New York during the early thirties he associated with Gorky, Chaim Gross, John Graham and Moses and Raphael Soyer and introduced social content into his work. He began to design playgrounds, furniture and theater decor, executing the first of numerous sets for Martha Graham. Noguchi spent six months in 1941-42 in a Japanese-American relocation camp. In 1949 he was given a one-man show at the Egan Gallery, New York. In Japan in 1950-51 he designed gardens, bridges and monuments and developed his paper lanterns (akari). He showed at the Stable Gallery in New York in 1954 and 1959.

In 1961 Noguchi moved to Long Island City. Noguchi's first one-man exhibition in Paris was held at the Galerie Claude Bernard in 1964. The Whitney Museum of American Art, New York, honored him with a major retrospective in 1968. Throughout the seventies Noguchi has continued to make large outdoor sculpture and fountains. A comprehensive show of his sculpture, theater sets and environmental works took place in 1978 at the Walker Art Center in Minneapolis. Noguchi lives in New York and spends part of each year in Japan.

224 The Cry. 1959

66.1812

Balsa wood on steel base, 84 x 30 x 18 in. (213.4 x 76.2 x 45.7 cm.)

Not signed or dated.

PROVENANCE:
from the artist through Daniel Cordier and Michel Warren, Inc., New York
Mary Sisler, New York, 1961
Cordier & Ekstrom, New York, by 1966

In the late 1950s, while continuing to work in cast-iron and carve in marble, Noguchi explored the possibilities inherent in lightweight materials. He sought to convey a sense of lightness and weightlessness in aluminum pieces such as *Lunar* and in balsa wood sculptures such as *The Cry*, both in the Guggenheim Museum collection. Noguchi had occasionally employed balsa, one of the lightest woods, since the 1940s. In *The Cry* he presents abstract shapes in asymmetrical alignment: biomorphic forms seem to float effortlessly in space. Not only does the lateral element appear precariously suspended but it is attached so it can move very slightly, responding to air currents and vibrations.

As Noguchi's interest in mass and gravity evolved, he decided to have several wood pieces cast in bronze in 1962. Bronze versions of *The Cry* are in the Albright-Knox Art Gallery in Buffalo, the San Francisco Museum of Modern Art and four other collections.

EXHIBITIONS:
New York, Daniel Cordier and Michel Warren, Inc., *Isamu Noguchi: Weightlessness,* May 16-June 17, 1961
New York, Whitney Museum of American Art, *Isamu Noguchi,* Apr. 17-June 16, 1968, no. 33, repr.
New York, The Solomon R. Guggenheim Museum, *Selected Sculpture and Works on Paper,* July 8-Sept. 14, 1969, p. 144, repr.
New York, The Metropolitan Museum of Art, *New York Painting and Sculpture: 1940-1970,* Oct. 18, 1969-Feb. 1, 1970, no. 275, repr.
The Portland (Ore.) Art Museum, *Masterworks in Wood: The Twentieth Century,* Sept. 17-Oct. 19, 1975, no. 39, repr.
Minneapolis, Walker Art Center, *Noguchi's Imaginary Landscapes,* Apr. 23-June 18, 1978

REFERENCES:
I. Noguchi, *Isamu Noguchi: A Sculptor's World,* New York and Evanston, Ill., 1968, pl. 94
Handbook, 1970, pp. 348, repr., 349

467

Louise Nevelson b. 1899

Louise Berliawsky was born on September 23, 1899, in Kiev, Russia. By 1905 her family had emigrated to the United States and settled in Rockland, Maine. In 1920 Louise Berliawsky married Charles Nevelson and moved to New York. At this time she studied visual and performing arts, including dramatics with Frederick Kiesler. Nevelson enrolled at the Art Students League in 1928 and also studied with Hilla Rebay. During this period she was introduced to the work of Duchamp and Picasso. In 1931, while traveling in Europe, she briefly attended Hofmann's school in Munich. Nevelson returned to New York in 1932 and assisted Diego Rivera on murals he was executing under the WPA Federal Art Project. Shortly thereafter, in the early thirties, she turned to sculpture. Between 1933 and 1936 Nevelson's work was included in numerous group exhibitions in New York, and in 1937 she joined the WPA as a teacher for the Educational Alliance School of Art.

Nevelson's first one-woman show took place in 1941 at the Nierendorf Gallery in New York. In 1943 she began her Farm assemblages, in which pieces of wood and found objects were incorporated. She studied etching with Stanley William Hayter at his Atelier 17 in New York in 1947 and in 1949-50 worked in marble and terra-cotta and executed her totemic *Game Figures*. Nevelson showed in 1953 and 1955 at the Grand Central Moderns Gallery in New York. In 1957 she made her first reliefs in shadow boxes as well as her first wall. Two years later Nevelson participated in her first important museum exhibition, *Sixteen Americans* at The Museum of Modern Art in New York, and the Martha Jackson Gallery gave her a one-woman show. She was included in the Venice Biennale in 1962.

Nevelson was elected President of National Artists Equity in 1965 and the following year she became Vice-President of the International Association of Artists. Her first major museum retrospective took place in 1967 at the Whitney Museum of American Art in New York. Princeton University commissioned Nevelson to create a monumental outdoor steel sculpture in 1969, the same year The Museum of Fine Arts, Houston, gave her a solo exhibition. Other Nevelson shows took place in 1970 at the Whitney Museum and in 1973 at the Walker Art Center in Minneapolis. Nevelson lives and works in New York.

225 Luminous Zag: Night. 1971

77.2325

Painted wood, 105 boxes, total 120 x 193 x 10¾ in. (304.8 x 490.3 x 27.3 cm.); each 16⅝ x 12⅝ x 10¾ in. (42.2 x 32 x 27.3 cm.)

Not signed or dated.

PROVENANCE:

from the artist through The Pace Gallery, New York
Gift, Sidney Singer, 1977

Nevelson has worked almost exclusively in wood and has chosen to paint her sculpture, thus obscuring the grain, color and other inherent qualities of the material. The majority of her work is painted black, although many sculptures are completely white or gold. In large wall pieces such as *Luminous Zag: Night,* black paint unifies the large number of components and contributes an element of regularity to the multiplicity of shapes within the total composition. Nevelson's construction is seven boxes high and fifteen across; it reaches a height of ten feet and extends to sixteen feet in width. Within individual boxes she has variously arranged horizontal zigzag elements, columns and balusters. *Luminous Zag: Night* has a strongly horizontal emphasis punctuated with occasional verticals. It is closely related to *Luminous Zag* (Collection The Pace Gallery, New York), a smaller coeval sculpture which also displays indented zigzag patterns. Working with her own formal vocabulary, Nevelson attains consistency through modular organization and the use of uniform color.

EXHIBITIONS:

Milan, Studio Marconi, *Louise Nevelson,* May-June 1973, no. 26, traveled to Stockholm, Moderna Museet, Sept. 8-Oct. 14; Aalborg, Denmark, Nordjyllandes Kunstmuseum, Nov. 3-Dec. 9; Brussels, Palais des Beaux-Arts, Jan. 8-Feb. 3, 1974; Paris, Centre National d'Art Contemporain, Apr. 9-May 13; Berlin, Nationalgalerie, June 5-July 1

Mountainville, N. Y., Storm King Art Center, *Sculpture: A Study in Materials,* May 17-Oct. 30, 1978, repr.

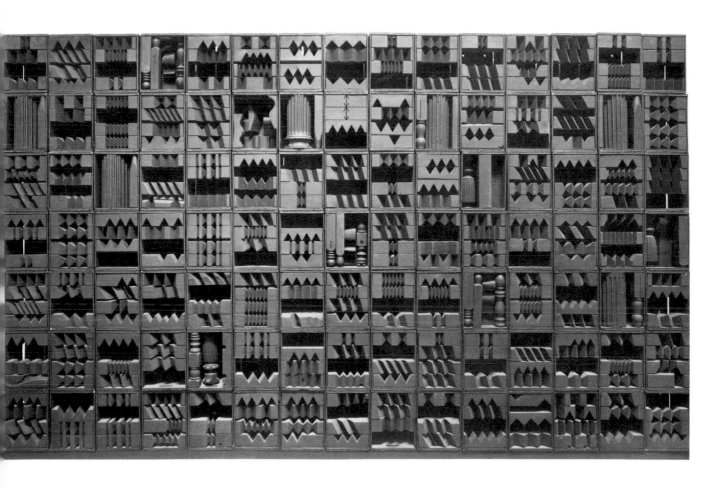

David Smith 1906-1965

David Roland Smith was born on March 9, 1906, in Decatur, Indiana. During high school he took a correspondence course with the Cleveland Art School. In 1924 Smith studied at Ohio University, Athens. He worked as an automobile welder and riveter in the summer of 1925. He then attended Notre Dame University for two weeks before moving to Washington, D.C. In 1926 Smith moved to New York, where he studied at the Art Students League with Richard Lahey and John Sloan and privately with Jan Matulka. In 1929 Smith met John Graham who later introduced him to the welded steel sculpture of Picasso and Julio Gonzalez. This year he bought a farm in Bolton Landing near Lake George in upstate New York.

Gorky, de Kooning, Pollock, Jean Xceron, Stuart Davis and Edgar Levy were his friends throughout the thirties. In the Virgin Islands in 1931-32 Smith made his first sculpture from pieces of coral. He began making completely metal sculpture in 1933 and in 1934 he set up a studio at the Terminal Iron Works in Brooklyn. From 1935 Smith committed himself primarily to sculpture. In 1935-36 he visited France, Greece, England and Russia. Upon his return to New York Smith began the *Medals for Dishonor,* anti-war medallions. In 1937 he made sculpture for the WPA Federal Art Project. Smith's first one-man show of drawings and welded steel sculpture was held at Marion Willard's East River Gallery in New York in 1938.

In 1940 he settled permanently in Bolton Landing. From 1942 to 1944 Smith worked as a locomotive welder in Schenectady. A one-man show of his work took place at the Walker Art Center, Minneapolis, in 1941. Smith taught at Sarah Lawrence College, Bronxville, New York, from 1948 to 1950, at Bennington College, Bennington, Vermont, and other schools during the fifties. About 1951 he met Noland. The Museum of Modern Art, New York, presented a Smith retrospective in 1957 and organized a major traveling exhibition of his work in 1961. In 1962, at the invitation of the Italian government, Smith went to Voltri, near Genoa, and executed twenty-seven sculptures for the Spoleto festival. In 1963 he began his Cubi series of monumental, geometric steel sculptures. David Smith died on May 23, 1965, in an automobile accident near Bennington. The Guggenheim Museum organized an exhibition of his work in 1969.

226 Cubi XXVII. March 1965

67.1862

Stainless steel, 111⅜ x 87¾ x 34 in.
(282.9 x 222.9 x 86.4 cm.)

Signed and dated on lowest horizontal beam: *David Smith Mar 3 1965 / CUBI XXVII.*

PROVENANCE:

Estate of the artist through Marlborough-Gerson Gallery, New York, 1967

Smith's Cubi series consists of twenty-eight sculptures of that title, all constructed in stainless steel. *Cubi XXVII* is the penultimate work of the theme which began in 1963 and ended with the artist's death in May 1965. Like *Cubi XXIV,* which is dated December 8, 1964, and *Cubi XXVIII,* the Guggenheim variant assumes the appearance of a monumental gate. The geometric forms achieve an asymmetrical balance and greater stability than in many preceding Cubi, where shapes are placed precariously, one on top of another. For these sculptures Smith chose burnished, reflective surfaces which respond to the changing colors and light of their surroundings. The reflective properties deny the solidity and weight implied by the massive forms. The frontality of the composition emphasizes how the sculpture should be seen and relates it to the two-dimensionality of painting and drawing. Smith made sprayed pencil drawings for many of the Cubi, including the present example.

EXHIBITIONS:

Los Angeles County Museum of Art, *David Smith: A Memorial Exhibition,* Nov. 3, 1965-Jan. 30, 1966, no. 11, repr.

New York, The Solomon R. Guggenheim Museum, *Guggenheim International Exhibition, 1967: Sculpture from Twenty Nations,* Oct. 20, 1967-Feb. 4, 1968, p. 41, repr., traveled to Toronto, Art Gallery of Ontario, Feb. 24-Mar. 27; Ottawa, National Gallery of Canada, Apr. 26-June 9; Montreal Museum of Fine Arts, June 20-Aug. 18

New York, The Solomon R. Guggenheim Museum, *David Smith,* Mar. 29-May 11, 1969, no. 97, color repr., traveled to Dallas Museum of Fine Arts, June 25-Sept. 1; Washington, D.C., The Corcoran Gallery of Art, Oct. 18-Dec. 7

Mountainville, N. Y., Storm King Art Center, *David Smith,* May 12-Oct. 31, 1976

REFERENCES:

J. H. Cone and M. Paul, "The Sculpture of David Smith: A Handlist," *David Smith, 1906-1965: A Retrospective Exhibition,* Cambridge, Mass., 1966, p. 82, no. 543

C. W. Millard, "David Smith," *The Hudson Review,* vol. XXII, summer 1969, pp. 272-273, repr.

Handbook, 1970, pp. 416-417, repr.

R. E. Krauss, *Terminal Iron Works: The Sculpture of David Smith,* Cambridge, Mass., and London, 1971, p. 178 and pl. 142

R. E. Krauss, *The Sculpture of David Smith: A Catalogue Raisonné,* New York, 1977 (photo reprint of Ph.D. dissertation, Harvard University, 1969) p. 121, no. 675, repr.

George Rickey b. 1907

George Rickey was born on June 6, 1907, in South Bend, Indiana. When he was five his family moved to Helensburgh, Scotland. In 1926 Rickey entered Balliol College of Oxford University, graduating in 1929 with a degree in modern history. At the same time he studied drawing and painting at Oxford's Ruskin School of Drawing and Fine Art. After graduation Rickey moved to Paris, where he studied painting at the Académie André Lhote and with Léger and Amédée Ozenfant at the Académie Moderne. In the following years Rickey traveled between Europe and the United States, painting and teaching history and art at numerous schools. In 1939 he made the first of several trips to Mexico. Rickey continued to paint during his service in the United States Army Air Corps from 1942 to 1945: the mechanical training he received at that time led him to experiment with metal sculpture. He built his first mobiles in an Army machine shop in 1945. Rickey did graduate work in art history at the Institute of Fine Arts, New York University, in 1945-46. Study at the Institute of Design in Chicago in 1948 and exposure to David Smith's sculpture further stimulated his interest in constructed work. In 1949 he made mobiles of cut glass and the following year he began making kinetic sculptures influenced by the work of his friend Calder.

From 1951 to 1954 he taught at Indiana University in Bloomington, Indiana, where David Smith joined the faculty in 1954. The following year the first New York showing of Rickey's sculpture was held at the Kraushaar Gallery. His first one-man exhibition in Europe took place at Amerika Haus, Hamburg, in 1957. The artist traveled extensively in Europe that year and again in 1961. In 1960 the John Simon Guggenheim Foundation awarded Rickey a fellowship which was renewed in 1961. Among the important group exhibitions in which Rickey has participated are *Bewogen-Beweging*, at the Stedelijk Museum, Amsterdam, 1961, and *Kinetische Kunst* at the Haus am Waldsee, West Berlin, 1968. His book *Constructivism: Origins and Evolution* was published in 1967. Rickey was visiting artist, Berliner Künstlerprogramm, West Berlin, in 1968 and 1971. He has received many important sculpture commissions, including one for the Neue Nationalgalerie, Bonn, executed in 1969. A retrospective of Rickey's sculpture, organized by the Art Museum of the University of California at Los Angeles, toured the United States in 1971-72. Since 1960 Rickey has lived and worked in East Chatham, New York.

227 **Two Open Rectangles Excentric VI, Square Section.** 1976-77

78.2518

Stainless steel, 144 x 36 in. (366 x 91.4 cm.); each rectangle, 96 x 16⅜ x 1⅞ in. (244 x 41.6 x 4.8 cm.)

Not signed or dated.

PROVENANCE:

from the artist, 1978
Purchased with the aid of funds from the National Endowment for the Arts in Washington, D.C., a Federal Agency; matching funds donated by Evelyn Sharp and anonymous donors

Rickey is concerned primarily with movement in his sculpture. Proceeding from Calder's innovations with moving sculptures and mobiles, he employs bearings, weights and other technical devices to prevent the parts from colliding. Activated by the wind, his large outdoor sculpture slowly tips, swings in wide arcs and, on occasion, twists violently but always moves in synchronized patterns. Although it reacts to random movements of air, precision and order govern his work.

The way Rickey has polished the stainless-steel surface of *Two Open Rectangles Excentric VI* is reminiscent of David Smith's work (see cat. no. 226). At rare moments when the Guggenheim piece is at rest, it presents a decidedly frontal, two-dimensional, frame-like appearance. However, the two open rectangles are usually turning to the side or moving back into depth. It is constructed with the bearings on the face of the elements, whence the term "excentric." The earliest variation of *Two Open Rectangles* dates from the fall of 1974. Our sculpture is number two in an edition of three: the other two examples are at Middlebury College in Vermont and the Peoria Airport in Illinois.

EXHIBITION:

New York, The Solomon R. Guggenheim Museum, *George Rickey*, Sept. 7-Oct. 14, 1979

Robert Rauschenberg b. 1925

Milton Rauschenberg, who was to become known as Bob in the 1940s, was born on October 22, 1925, in Port Arthur, Texas. He studied briefly at the University of Texas in 1942 before serving in the Navy from 1942 to 1945. Under the G.I. Bill he attended the Kansas City Art Institute from 1947 until early 1948, when he went to Paris and enrolled at the Académie Julian. In the fall of 1948 he returned to the United States to study with Albers at Black Mountain College, Black Mountain, North Carolina. At Black Mountain he met John Cage and Merce Cunningham. In 1949 Rauschenberg moved to New York and studied at the Art Students League with Morris Kantor and Vaclav Vytlacil until 1952.

Rauschenberg experimented with photographic blueprints between 1949 and 1951. His first one-man show took place at Betty Parsons Gallery, New York, in 1951, and he produced all-black and all-white paintings in 1951-52. In 1952 the artist began his travels to Italy, France, Spain and North Africa. He exhibited small objects and boxes in Rome and Florence before returning to New York in the spring of 1953. That same year he began a series of all-red paintings and made his gesture of erasing a de Kooning drawing. In this period Rauschenberg started to design sets and costumes for Cunningham's dance company and for Paul Taylor.

From 1955 to 1959 Rauschenberg worked on "combines"—constructions, classifiable neither as painting nor sculpture, in which he incorporated objects (a stuffed goat, a bed, tires). During these years he worked closely with Jasper Johns who, like himself, was influenced by Duchamp. In 1961 Rauschenberg made his first lithograph; he has subsequently incorporated the silk-screen process in many canvases and experimented with various printmaking techniques. In the mid-1960s he created his own dances and performances. Throughout the 1960s and 1970s he has continued to explore new techniques and materials. In 1966 he co-founded E.A.T. (Experiments in Art and Technology), to promote cooperation between artists and engineers, and in 1970 established Change Inc., a foundation that provides financial aid to artists. In 1976-77 a major Rauschenberg retrospective organized by The National Collection of Fine Arts, Washington, D.C., traveled in the United States. Rauschenberg lives in New York and Captiva, an island off the Florida coast.

228 Red Painting. 1953

63.1688

Oil, cloth and newsprint on canvas with wood, 79 x 33⅛ in. (200.6 x 84.1 cm.)

Not signed or dated.

PROVENANCE:

from the artist
Walter K. Gutman, New York, 1955-63
Gift, Walter K. Gutman, 1963

In *Red Painting* Rauchenberg has built up a layered, patched surface from overlapping pieces of newspaper and cloth covered with several different shades of red paint, through which areas of black and white underpainting are partially visible. Like his white paintings and black paintings of 1951-52, Rauschenberg's series of red paintings reflects his direct exposure to European artists who were similarly concerned with single color pictures, materiality and surface qualities. For example, in March 1953 Rauschenberg twice visited the studio of Burri, who was then working with burlap and other unconventional materials (see cat. no. 176).

The artist's experimental use of unusual art materials, already evident in this *Red Painting,* would be developed even further in subsequent "combine paintings" in which he incorporated not only paper and fabric but glass, metal and wood. By 1954-55 he was attaching actual objects to two-dimensional wood or canvas supports. Like Jasper Johns, Rauschenberg played a vital role in the 1950s as a link between the painterliness and emotional content of Abstract Expressionism and the use and alteration of banal subjects that were to characterize Pop Art in the 1960s.

EXHIBITIONS:

New York, The Jewish Museum, *Robert Rauschenberg,* Mar. 30-Apr. 30, 1963, no. 6

New York, The Solomon R. Guggenheim Museum, *Acquisition Priorities: Aspects of Postwar Painting in America,* Oct. 15, 1976-Jan. 16, 1977, no. 47, repr.

REFERENCES:

A. Forge, *Rauschenberg,* New York, 1969, p. 174, color repr.

Handbook, 1970, pp. 382-383, repr.

R. Krauss, "Rauschenberg and the Materialized Image," *Artforum,* vol. XIII, Dec. 1974, p. 37, color repr.

Jim Dine b. 1935

Jim Dine was born June 16, 1935, in Cincinnati, Ohio. He studied at night at the Cincinnati Art Academy during his senior year of high school and then attended the University of Cincinnati, the School of the Museum of Fine Arts, Boston, and Ohio University, Athens, from which he received his B.F.A. in 1957. Dine moved to New York in 1959 and soon became a pioneer creator of Happenings together with Allan Kaprow, Claes Oldenburg and Robert Whitman. He exhibited at the Judson Gallery, New York, in 1958 and 1959, and his first one-man show took place at the Reuben Gallery, New York, in 1960.

Dine is closely associated with the development of Pop Art in the early 1960s. Frequently he affixed everyday objects, such as tools, rope, shoes, neckties and other articles of clothing and even a bathroom sink, to his canvases. Characteristically, these objects were Dine's personal possessions. This autobiographical content was evident in Dine's early Crash series of 1959-60 and appeared as well in subsequent recurrent themes and images such as the Palettes, Hearts and bathrobe Self-Portraits. Dine has also made a number of three-dimensional works and environments, and is well-known for his drawings and prints. He has written and illustrated several books of poetry.

In 1965 Dine was a guest lecturer at Yale University, New Haven, and Artist in Residence at Oberlin College, Oberlin, Ohio. He was Visiting Artist at Cornell University, Ithaca, New York, in 1967. From 1967 to 1971 he and his family lived in London. Dine has been given one-man shows in museums in Europe and the United States. In 1970 the Whitney Museum of American Art, New York, organized a major retrospective of his work, and in 1978 The Museum of Modern Art, New York, presented a retrospective of his etchings. After returning to the United States in 1970, Dine lives in New York and Putney, Vermont.

229 Pearls. 1961

63.1681

Oil and collage on canvas, 70 x 60 in.
(177.7 x 152.3 cm.)

Inscribed l.c.: *PEARLS*. Not signed or dated.

PROVENANCE:

from the artist through Martha Jackson Gallery, New York
Leon A. Mnuchin, New York, 1962
Gift, Leon A. Mnuchin, 1963

Pearls is one of several paintings Dine executed in 1961 in which he presents a single object with its written equivalent. An over life-size necklace, attached to and projecting from the top of the painterly pink field, is both contrasted with and paralleled by the word *"pearls"* spelled out at the bottom edge. Made from halves of rubber balls and painted a metallic gray, the simulated necklace is immediately perceived as an object. The collage element is united with the open expanse of the support, as is the unfinished transcription of the word *"pearls."*

Dine's collage-paintings implicitly raise and incorporate questions about the relation between art and life, illusion and reality. Whereas his presentation of simple, everyday objects links him with such Pop artists as Warhol and Lichtenstein, the painterly quality of Dine's brushwork underscores not only his roots in Abstract Expressionism but also strong affinities with Rauschenberg and Jasper Johns.

EXHIBITION:

New York, Martha Jackson Gallery, *Jim Dine,* Jan. 9-Feb. 3, 1962

REFERENCES:

J. Gordon, *Jim Dine,* exh. cat., New York, 1970, no. 27
Handbook, 1970, pp. 96, repr., 97

PEARLS

Andy Warhol b. 1928

Andrew Warhola was born August 6, 1928, in Pittsburgh. He received his B.F.A. from the Carnegie Institute of Technology, Pittsburgh, in 1949. This year he came to New York, where he soon became successful as a commercial artist and illustrator. During the 1950s Warhol's drawings were published in *Glamour* and other magazines and displayed in department stores, and he became known for his illustrations of I. Miller shoes. In 1952 the Hugo Gallery in New York presented a show of Warhol's illustrations for Truman Capote's writings. He traveled in Europe and Asia in 1956.

By the early 1960s Warhol began to paint comic-strip characters and images derived from advertisements; this work was characterized by repetition of banal subjects such as Coke bottles and soup cans as well as celebrities. Warhol's new painting was exhibited for the first time in 1962: initially at the Ferus Gallery in Los Angeles, then in a one-man show at the Stable Gallery in New York. By 1963 he had substituted a silk-screen process for hand painting. Working with assistants, he produced series of disasters, flowers, cows, portraits as well as three-dimensional facsimile Brillo boxes and cartons of other well-known household products.

From the mid-1960s at The Factory, his New York studio, Warhol concentrated on making films which were marked by repetition and an emphasis on boredom. In the early 1970s he began to paint again and produced monumental portraits of Mao Tse-tung, commissioned portraits and the Hammer and Sickle series. Warhol has returned to gestural brushwork in these recent works. He has also become interested in writing: his autobiography, *The Philosophy of Andy Warhol (From A to B and Back Again)*, was published in 1975, and The Factory publishes *Interview* magazine. A major retrospective of Warhol's work organized by the Pasadena Art Museum in 1970 traveled in the United States and abroad. Warhol lives in New York.

230 Orange Disaster. 1963

75.2118

Acrylic and silk-screen enamel on canvas, 106 x 81½ in. (269.2 x 207 cm.)

Not signed or dated.

PROVENANCE:
from the artist through Stable Gallery, New York
Harry N. Abrams Family Collection, New York, 1963-74
Gift, Harry N. Abrams Family Collection, 1974

Orange Disaster is one of several paintings featuring multiple images of an electric chair that Warhol executed in the same format but different colors (for example, *Lavender Disaster* of 1964). The artist employed the same photograph as a single image in a series of Little Electric Chairs in 1965 and in the Big Electric Chairs of 1967. Moreover, *Orange Disaster* is related to a number of other death or disaster themes of the period, all based on news photographs: car crashes, suicides, race riots, hospital images.

Warhol used a photomechanical silk-screen process, whereby the artist is significantly removed from the act of painting. In *Orange Disaster* one image is replicated fifteen times, but each frame in the sequence varies somewhat because of irregularities in the application of paint. The choice of such an emotionally charged subject as the electric chair is in marked contrast to the anonymity, detachment and mechanical repetition of Warhol's method. In general, serial imagery and the single color scheme reinforce the banality of Warhol's subjects. It is ironic that the selection of images directly from the mass media and popular culture should become the mark of individuality in his art.

EXHIBITIONS:
Boston, Institute of Contemporary Art, *Andy Warhol*, Oct. 1-Nov. 6, 1966, no. 19

New York, The Metropolitan Museum of Art, *New York Painting and Sculpture: 1940-1970*, Oct. 18, 1969-Feb. 1, 1970, no. 407, repr.

Pasadena Art Museum, *Andy Warhol*, May 12-June 21, 1970, traveled to New York, Whitney Museum of American Art, May 1-June 20, 1971

New York, The Solomon R. Guggenheim Museum, *Acquisition Priorities: Aspects of Postwar Painting in America*, Oct. 15, 1976-Jan. 16, 1977, no. 50, repr.

Kunsthaus Zürich, *Andy Warhol*, May 26-July 30, 1978, no. 81, repr., traveled to Humelbaek, Denmark, Louisiana Museum, Oct. 6-Nov. 26

REFERENCES:

Art News, vol. 69, May 1970, p. 5 and cover repr.

R. Crone, *Andy Warhol,* New York, 1970, no. 333, p. 195, repr.

Roy Lichtenstein b. 1923

Roy Lichtenstein was born on October 27, 1923, in New York. During the summer of 1939 he studied with Reginald Marsh at the Art Students League and in 1940 he entered the School of Fine Arts at Ohio State University, in Columbus, where Hoyt L. Sherman was his teacher. After military service from 1943 to January 1946 Lichtenstein returned to Ohio State, receiving his B.F.A. in 1946 and M.F.A. in 1949. He remained at Ohio State as an instructor from 1949 to 1951. In 1951 his first one-man show took place in New York at the Carlebach Gallery. That same year Lichtenstein moved to Cleveland, where he continued to paint while supporting himself as an engineering draftsman until 1957. Subsequently, he taught at the State University of New York, Oswego (1957 to 1960), and at Douglass College, Rutgers University, New Brunswick, New Jersey (1960 to 1963). In 1963 he moved to New York and began to paint full-time.

Lichtenstein progressed from depicting Americana subjects of the Old West to an Abstract Expressionist mode in the late 1950s. While teaching at Rutgers he met artists who were significant in the development of Happenings, including Allan Kaprow, Claes Oldenburg, Dine, Lucas Samaras, Segal and Robert Whitman. At this time he was a seminal figure in the Pop Art movement. In 1961 he used Ben Day dots for the first time and began to paint comic-strip subjects, isolated household objects and images from advertisements. Subsequently he produced stylized landscapes (1964-65), parodies of Abstract Expressionist brushstrokes (1965-66), Pop versions of paintings by modern masters such as Cézanne, Mondrian, Monet and Picasso and compositions based on Art Deco motifs and WPA murals (1966 to 1970). In the 1970s he has painted mirrors and entablatures in a more abstract style. Lichtenstein has also made sculpture in polychrome ceramics as well as in brass and aluminum and has produced numerous silk-screen prints. From 1962 he has shown regularly at the Leo Castelli Gallery in New York, and in 1966 participated in the Venice Biennale. Major exhibitions of his work were organized by the Pasadena Art Museum in 1967 and The Solomon R. Guggenheim Museum in 1969. Since 1970 Lichtenstein has lived in Southampton, Long Island.

231 Preparedness. 1968

69.1885.1-3

Magna on canvas, three panels, each 120 x 72 in. (304.8 x 183 cm.)

Signed and dated on reverse of third panel: *Roy Lichtenstein / 1968.*

PROVENANCE:

from the artist through Leo Castelli Gallery, New York, 1969

As Roy Lichtenstein has said, *Preparedness* is "a muralesque painting about our military-industrial complex." The artist deliberately chose the title for its "call-to-arms quality" and fully intended direct social comment (Waldman, pp. 26-27). Painted late in 1968 at the height of the Vietnam War, *Preparedness* shows, at the left, factories and smokestacks, a prerequisite for mobilization of the military. In the central panel a row of helmeted soldiers dominates under a display of girders and gears and a hand holding a hammer, while, in the right panel, a soldier and an airplane window complete the composition. The three large panels are united by strong diagonals and geometric compositional elements, by the use of primary colors and by the technique of Ben Day dots which uniformly articulate the canvases.

Lichtenstein wanted to make a statement about heroic compositions with strong overtones of the 1930s. Beginning in 1966 the artist explored the stylistic possibilities in reinterpreting the motifs of the 1930s as seen from the vantage point of the late 1960s, an interest perhaps best exemplified by Lichtenstein's sculpture.

A painting, *Study for Preparedness* (Ludwig Collection, Wallraf-Richartz-Museum, Cologne) is remarkably similar to the Guggenheim's final version in all respects but size. There is also a colored drawing of the same composition in a New York private collection.

EXHIBITIONS:

New York, The Solomon R. Guggenheim Museum, *Roy Lichtenstein,* Sept. 19-Nov. 9, 1969, no. 55, color repr.

Houston, Contemporary Arts Museum, *Roy Lichtenstein,* June 21-Aug. 20, 1972, no. 5, color repr.

New York, The Solomon R. Guggenheim Museum, *Acquisition Priorities: Aspects of Postwar Painting in America,* Oct. 15, 1976-Jan. 16, 1977, no. 45, repr.

Albany, The New York State Museum, *New York: The State of Art,* Oct. 8-Nov. 27, 1977, no. 532, color repr.

Boston, Institute of Contemporary Art, *Lichtenstein: The Modern Work, 1965-1970,* Nov. 8-Dec. 31, 1978, repr.

REFERENCES:

N. Calas, "Roy Lichtenstein: Insight through Irony," *Arts Magazine,* vol. 44, Sept.-Oct. 1969, p. 33, color repr.

Handbook, 1970, pp. 272-273, repr.

D. Waldman, *Roy Lichtenstein*, New York, 1971, pp. 26-27 and no. 174, color repr.

John Chamberlain b. 1927

John Angus Chamberlain was born on April 16, 1927, in Rochester, Indiana. He grew up in Chicago and attended The Art Institute of Chicago from 1950 to 1952. At that time he began making flat, welded sculpture influenced by the work of David Smith. For a year in 1955-56 Chamberlain studied and taught sculpture at Black Mountain College in Black Mountain, North Carolina, where his friends were, for the most part, poets, among them Charles Olson, Robert Creeley and Robert Duncan. By 1957 he began to include scrap metal from cars in his work and from 1959 he concentrated on sculpture built entirely of crushed automobile parts welded together. Chamberlain's first major one-man show was held at the Martha Jackson Gallery in New York in 1960.

Chamberlain's work was widely acclaimed in the early 1960s. His sculpture was included in *The Art of Assemblage* at The Museum of Modern Art, New York, in 1961, and the same year he participated in the São Paulo Bienal. From 1962 Chamberlain showed frequently at the Leo Castelli Gallery in New York, and in 1964 his work was exhibited at the Venice Biennale. While he continued to make sculpture from auto parts, Chamberlain also experimented with other media. From 1963 to 1965 he made geometric paintings with sprayed automobile paint. In 1966 he began a series of sculptures of rolled, folded and tied urethane foam. These were followed in 1970 by sculptures of melted or crushed metal and heat-crumpled plexiglass. Chamberlain has also worked in photography and video and has made several short films. A major retrospective of Chamberlain's work was presented at The Solomon R. Guggenheim Museum in 1971.

In the early 1970s Chamberlain began once more to make large pieces from automobile parts. Until the mid-seventies the artist assembled these auto sculptures on the ranch of collector Stanley Marsh in Amarillo. These Texas pieces were shown in the sculpture garden at the Dag Hammerskjold Plaza in New York in 1973 and at the Houston Museum of Contemporary Art in 1975. The artist now lives and works in New York and Essex, Connecticut.

232 Dolores James. 1962

70.1925

Welded and painted steel, 76 x 97 x 39 in. (193 x 246.4 x 99.1 cm.)

Not signed or dated.

PROVENANCE:

from the artist through Leo Castelli Gallery, New York, 1970

Chamberlain assembles old automobile parts which he fits together and welds. Each component has its own properties of form and color. While the parts may be manipulated by the artist, their essential characteristics are preserved. For example, fenders and bumpers have associations with particular models of cars and trucks and certain colors—such as the greens in *Dolores James*—were prevalent only in the late 1950s. The auto parts, found in the junkyard, show signs of age and abuse and have been forced together violently. Moreover, crushed cars inevitably bear connotations of disaster.

In wall pieces like *Dolores James*, these parts constitute planes projecting from and seen in relation to the wall. Chamberlain remembered that he worked at the sculpture over a period of time in 1962 but never felt it was complete. One night he threw a sledgehammer at it: "all the pieces went chink, chink, chink" and shifted slightly into place. (Tuchman, p. 39)

EXHIBITIONS:

New York, Leo Castelli Warehouse, *John Chamberlain: Recent Sculpture*, Feb. 1-22, 1969

New York, The Metropolitan Museum of Art, *New York Painting and Sculpture: 1940-1970*, Oct. 18, 1969-Feb. 8, 1970, no. 26, repr.

New York, The Solomon R. Guggenheim Museum, *John Chamberlain: A Retrospective Exhibition*, Dec. 22, 1971-Feb. 20, 1972, no. 47, color repr.

REFERENCES:

E. C. Baker, "The Secret Life of John Chamberlain," *Art News,* vol. 68, Apr. 1969, p. 51, repr.

E. Wasserman, "Review: New York," *Artforum*, vol. VII, Apr. 1969, pp. 72-73, repr.

P. Tuchman, "An Interview with John Chamberlain," *Artforum*, vol. X, Feb. 1972, p. 39

J. Wilmerding, *American Art,* New York, 1978, pp. 211-212, pl. 265

Richard Stankiewicz 1922-1983

Richard Peter Stankiewicz was born on October 18, 1922, in Philadelphia. He grew up in Detroit and attended public schools there. From 1941 to 1947 Stankiewicz served in the Navy in Alaska and Hawaii as a radio-telegrapher and technician. He remained in Hawaii to paint for several months after his discharge. In 1948 he moved to New York to study at the Hans Hofmann School of Fine Arts, where he became friends with Jean Follett. Stankiewicz studied in Paris with Léger and Ossip Zadkine under the G.I. Bill from 1950 to 1951. Shortly after his return to New York in the winter of 1951-52, the artist began experimenting with junk excavated from the courtyard of his loft building, incorporating this material into his sculpture. Not long thereafter he taught himself how to weld.

In 1952 Stankiewicz was an organizer of the Hansa Gallery in New York, where he had his first one-man show the following year. He held various offices in this cooperative gallery until his resignation in 1958. In 1955 he was chosen by Thomas B. Hess for a group show organized at the Stable Gallery in New York. His work was included in the Whitney Annual in 1956 and the Carnegie International in Pittsburgh and the Venice Biennale in 1958. In 1961 he participated in *The Art of Assemblage* at The Museum of Modern Art in New York. That same year the sculptor moved to western Massachusetts. He was given one-man shows regularly at Zabriskie Gallery in New York from 1972. From 1967 he taught at the State University of New York at Albany. Stankiewicz died in Worthington, Massachusetts, on March 27, 1983.

233 **Untitled.** 1975

76.2268

Mild steel, 70 x 36 x 37 in. (177.8 x 91.4 x 94 cm.)

Not signed or dated.

PROVENANCE:

from the artist through Zabriskie Gallery, New York, 1976
Purchased with the aid of funds from the National Endowment for the Arts in Washington, D.C., a Federal Agency; matching funds donated by anonymous donors

In the early 1950s Stankiewicz was one of the first American artists to incorporate pieces of junk into his sculpture: a procedure followed somewhat later by Rauschenberg and Chamberlain. His work has evolved from assemblages with Surrealist overtones to an investigation of the formal properties of cylinders and cubes. For the Guggenheim sculpture Stankiewicz made steel drums which he then welded together into a precarious consolidation of forms. He prefers the industrial aspect of rusty steel to the polished surfaces sometimes found in the work of Smith and Rickey (for example, cat. nos. 226 and 227). While this sculpture by Stankiewicz has compositional affinities with Brancusi's *The Sorceress* (cat. no. 91), it shows respect for the qualities inherent in steel and the welding technique. The artist presents a dynamic, essentially unstable arrangement of volumes held in equilibrium.

EXHIBITION:
New York, Zabriskie Gallery, *Richard Stankiewicz,* Mar. 15-Apr. 19, 1975

George Segal b. 1924

George Segal was born on November 26, 1924, in New York. In 1940 his family moved to South Brunswick, New Jersey. In 1941 Segal enrolled at the Cooper Union School of Art and Architecture in New York, but returned to work on his parents' chicken farm in New Jersey in 1942. While working, he studied part-time at Rutgers University, North Brunswick, for the next four years. In 1947-48 he attended the Pratt Institute of Design, Brooklyn, and in 1948 he took classes at New York University with Baziotes and Tony Smith.

Segal visited New York often; he frequented *The Club* and also met Allan Kaprow who introduced him to Hofmann. From 1949 to 1958 he operated his own chicken farm in South Brunswick to support himself while painting in a figurative mode. These early works were included in the artist's first one-man show at the Hansa Gallery, New York, in 1956. From 1958 until 1964 he taught English and art. Segal exhibited at Hansa until it closed in 1959 and he formed a close friendship with Müller, who was also a member of the gallery. In 1958 he executed his first sculpture and placed it in front of a painting; in 1961 he made his first plaster-cast figure and put it in a setting of real furniture. During this formative period Segal participated in Kaprow's Happenings.

From 1960 to 1964 Segal exhibited at Richard Bellamy's Green Gallery, New York. In 1963 he earned his M.F.A. from Rutgers. The Museum of Contemporary Art, Chicago, gave him an important one-man show in 1968. In 1968-69 he taught sculpture at Princeton University and in 1970 he received an honorary doctorate from Rutgers. Segal visited the Soviet Union on a cultural exchange program in 1976. In 1978 the Walker Art Center in Minneapolis honored him with a major retrospective which traveled in the United States into 1979. The artist lives and works on his farm in South Brunswick.

234 Picasso's Chair. 1973

76.2279

Plaster, wood, cloth, rubber and string, 78 x 60 x 32 in. (198.1 x 152.4 x 81.3 cm.)

Not signed or dated.

PROVENANCE:
from the artist through Sidney Janis Gallery, New York
Dr. Milton D. Ratner, New York and Nokomis, Florida, 1974-76
Gift, Dr. Milton D. Ratner, 1976

Although Segal's subjects usually come from familiar, banal, particularly American surroundings, he has turned to a Picasso etching as the source of *Picasso's Chair*. As he recalls: "I was attracted to an etching as a blueprint from which I could build a genuine cubist sculpture. I cut out a piece of plywood and that was the wall, except it was standing in pure space. I added one element on top of and in front of the back plane, another element in front of that, another element in front of that; it also had a broken plane that went backwards. . . . Picasso's cubist, surrealistic drawing is a vicious, cutting metaphor for a beautiful, neo-classical Greek maiden. I omitted the surrealistic parts." (Minneapolis, Walker Art Center, 1978, p. 49) Segal used a real chair with arms and he has transformed the maiden into a life-size white plaster sculpture which contemplates the assemblage at the right.

While Picasso's 1933 etching, *Model and Surrealist Figure* from the Vollard Suite, is not an integral part of the sculpture, Segal agrees* that it can be exhibited in conjunction with his piece. The artist's fondness for art history, explicit in *Picasso's Chair*, was manifested six years earlier in *Portrait: Plaster Figure of Sidney Janis with Mondrian's "Composition," 1933, on an Easel*, where Segal's sculpture reaches out to touch another work of art.

* conversation with Dana Cranmer, Feb. 1977

EXHIBITIONS:
New York, Sidney Janis Gallery, *New Sculpture by George Segal*, Oct. 1-26, 1974
New York, Whitney Museum of American Art, *Art about Art*, July 19-Sept. 24, 1978, p. 116, repr.
Minneapolis, Walker Art Center, *George Segal: Sculptures*, Oct. 29, 1978-Jan. 7, 1979, no. 31, repr., traveled to San Francisco Museum of Modern Art, Feb. 18-Apr. 1; New York, Whitney Museum of American Art, May 16-July 8

REFERENCES:

J. van der Marck, *George Segal*, New York, 1975, p. 68
and pl. 142

C. Geelhaar, "Marriage Between Matter and Spirit: Interview with George Segal," *Pantheon*, Jg. XXXIV, July 1976,
pp. 231, repr., 233, 235

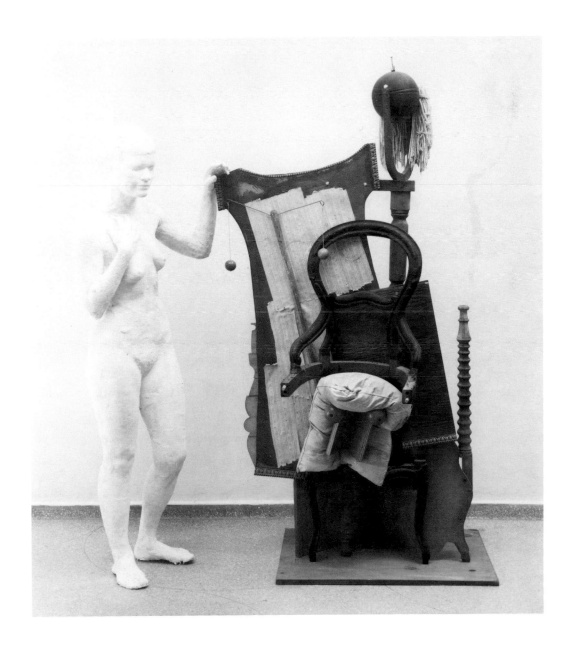

Paul Feeley 1910-1966

Paul Feeley was born on July 27, 1910, in Des Moines, Iowa. In 1922 the family moved to Palo Alto, California. Feeley's first one-man show of drawings took place in 1927 at the Palo Alto Public Library. From 1928 to 1929 he studied with Hobart B. Jacobs in Palo Alto and from 1930 to 1931 he attended Menlo College in Menlo Park, California. In 1931 Feeley decided to become an artist and moved to New York, where he took figure painting with George Bridgeman and Thomas Hart Benton at the Art Students League. He supported himself by painting portraits and murals and working for a decorating firm. In 1935 Feeley began teaching at the Cooper Union Art School, where he remained until 1939. In this same year he opened a commercial studio and designed store windows, displays for the New York World's Fair and stage sets.

From 1939 to 1943 Feeley taught painting at Bennington College, Bennington, Vermont. He served in the United States Marine Corps from 1943 to 1946 and saw action in the Pacific Theater. After the war he returned to Bennington; he was to continue teaching there until his death. In 1951 he began to invite advanced artists, among them David Smith, Pollock, Gottlieb and Hofmann, to show at Bennington. Feeley's work was included in *Emerging Talent* at the Kootz Gallery, New York, in 1954, and the following year his first one-man show of large oils took place at the Tibor de Nagy Gallery, New York. In 1956-57 he toured southern Spain and lived briefly in Malaga. The Betty Parsons Gallery, New York, gave him a solo exhibition in 1969. Feeley traveled in Europe in 1961 and visited England and Ireland on the occasion of his show at the Kasmin Gallery, London, in 1964. In 1965 he began to make painted wood sculpture which was exhibited in a one-man show at the Betty Parsons Gallery in the same year. Feeley traveled again in 1966 to the Mediterranean, sojourning in Italy and Spain, where he became ill. He died on June 10, 1966, in New York. Two years later The Solomon R. Guggenheim Museum presented a memorial exhibition of his work.

235 Formal Haut. 1965

66.1832

Acrylic on canvas, 60 x 60 in. (152.4 x 152.4 cm.)

Signed and dated on stretcher: *"FORMAL HAUT" PAUL FEELEY 1965.*

PROVENANCE:
Estate of the artist
Betty Parsons Gallery, New York, 1966

In *Formal Haut* there is an economy and clarity in the smoothly painted, spare forms on the bare canvas. The modular character of the shapes, their symmetrical arrangement on a square canvas and the rhythmic play of convex and concave contours are particularly striking. This picture bears a close relationship to *Alnium* of 1964 (Collection Philip Johnson, New Canaan, Connecticut) in its colors as well as its pictorial elements. In his painting around 1964-65 Feeley frequently used the baluster motif and jack shape and he enlarged the latter in a seven and a half foot gold-leaf sculpture, *Jack*. Several of Feeley's titles from these years are derived from the names of stars: Fomalhaut is a first magnitude star in the Southern Sky in September. By adapting the name, Feeley appears not only to refer to the star but to play upon the word "formal" as well.

EXHIBITIONS:
New York, Betty Parsons Gallery, *Paul Feeley,* Nov. 1-26, 1966
New York, The Solomon R. Guggenheim Museum, *Paul Feeley (1910-1966): A Memorial Exhibition,* Apr. 11-May 26, 1968, repr.

REFERENCE:
Handbook, 1970, pp. 114-115, color repr.

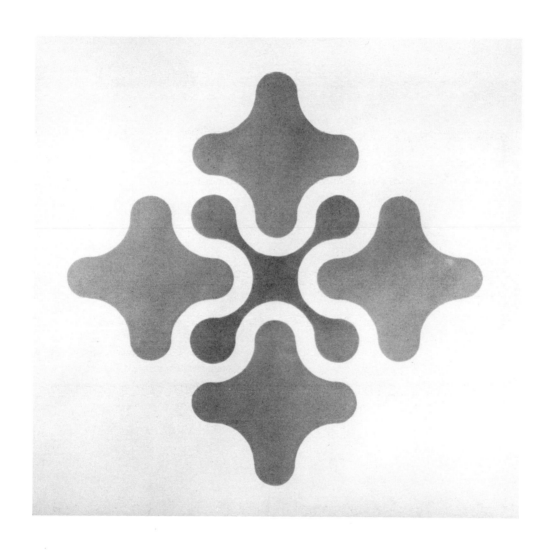

Helen Frankenthaler b. 1928

Helen Frankenthaler was born on December 12, 1928, in New York. She studied painting with Tamayo at the Dalton School, New York, before attending Bennington College, Vermont, from 1946 to 1949. At Bennington she studied with Feeley and during non-resident terms in New York she worked for the magazine *Art Outlook*, attended the Art Students League and studied with Wallace Harrison. She briefly attended graduate school at Columbia University, studying with Meyer Schapiro. By the spring of 1950 she had met the critic Clement Greenberg and many of the Abstract Expressionists; that summer she studied with Hofmann in Provincetown, Massachusetts.

Frankenthaler's first one-woman show took place at the Tibor de Nagy Gallery in New York in 1951. That same year she was deeply moved by Pollock's exhibition at Betty Parsons Gallery. In 1952, staining thinned pigment into unprimed canvas, Frankenthaler executed *Mountains and Sea*—a painting which influenced Louis and Noland. She continued to explore stain techniques in her subsequent mature work: large-scale, lyrical color abstractions that often suggest organic and landscape elements. Frankenthaler was married to Robert Motherwell from 1958 to 1971. She spent summers from 1961 to 1969 in Provincetown. Since 1960 she has executed lithographs, aquatints and woodcuts. She began to work in ceramics in 1964 and made her first sculpture in 1972. Frankenthaler has taught at various schools including New York University and the School of Art and Architecture, Yale University. She was honored with retrospectives at The Jewish Museum, New York, in 1960, the Whitney Museum of American Art, New York, in 1969, and The Corcoran Gallery of Art, Washington, D.C., in 1975. Her ceramic tiles were shown at The Solomon R. Guggenheim Museum in 1975. The artist lives in New York.

236 Canal. 1963

76.2225

Acrylic on canvas, 81 x 57½ in. (205.7 x 146 cm.)

Inscribed on stretcher, not by the artist: *"SOUTHWESTER" 1963 / Helen Frankenthaler.*

PROVENANCE:

Gift of the artist
Clement Greenberg, New York, ca. 1964-76
Acquavella Gallery, New York, 1976
Purchased with the aid of funds from the National Endowment for the Arts in Washington, D.C., a Federal Agency; matching funds donated by Evelyn Sharp, New York

Frankenthaler painted *The Bay, Low Tide, Blue Tide, Blue Causeway, Canal* and other water-inspired canvases in 1963, when she divided her time between New York City and Provincetown in the summer. In *Canal* several large, irregular areas of color interlock and, in places, flow together. Vibrant blue and gold forms that merge into more muted green and brown tones almost fill the surface. The artist has cropped the picture so that small areas of bare unsized canvas remain only at the bottom and right edges. Frankenthaler's tendency toward the creation of an allover color field differs from her practice around 1960, when she centered smaller abstract images on expanses of raw canvas. This development coincides with the artist's change from oil-base paint to the acrylic colors she began to use in 1962. In adapting her stain techniques to the new medium, Frankenthaler creates shapes in semitransparent, atmospheric tones and in brilliant, dense color with distinct and strong edges. She allows for accident and intuition while controlling the interplay of form, color and space.

EXHIBITIONS:

New York, Whitney Museum of American Art, *Helen Frankenthaler*, Feb. 20-Apr. 6, 1969, no. 25, repr., traveled to London, Whitechapel Art Gallery, May 6-June 22; Hannover, Orangerie Herrenhausen, Aug. 20-Sept. 20; Berlin, Kongresshalle, Oct. 1-21

New York, The Solomon R. Guggenheim Museum, *Acquisition Priorities: Aspects of Postwar Painting in America*, Oct. 15, 1976-Jan. 16, 1977, no. 49, color repr.

REFERENCE:

B. Rose, *Frankenthaler*, New York, 1972, p. 92 and pl. 32

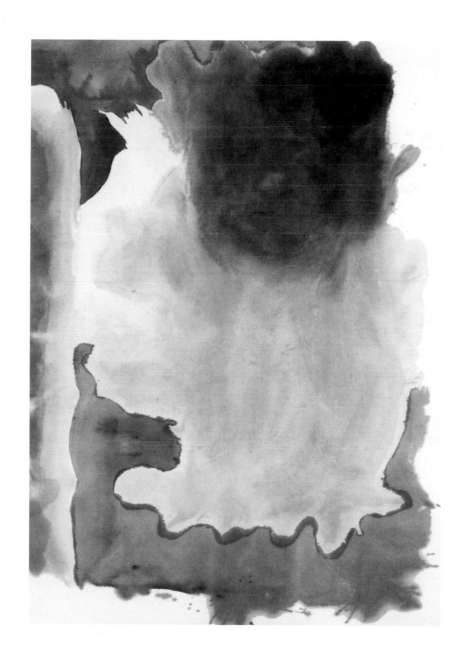

Morris Louis 1912-1962

Morris Louis Bernstein was born on November 28, 1912, in Baltimore. From 1929 to 1933 he studied at the Maryland Institute of Fine and Applied Arts on a scholarship but left shortly before completing the program. He worked at various odd jobs to support himself while painting and in 1935 served as President of the Baltimore Artists' Association. From 1936 to 1940 Louis lived in New York, where he worked in the easel division of the WPA Federal Art Project. During this period he knew David Alfaro Siqueiros, Gorky and Tworkov and he dropped his last name.

He returned to Baltimore in 1940 and taught privately. In 1948 he started to use Magna acrylic paints. In 1952 Louis moved to Washington, D.C. There he taught at the Washington Workshop Center of the Arts and met fellow instructor Noland, who became a close friend. Louis' first one-man show took place at the Workshop Center Art Gallery in 1953.

In 1953 he and Noland visited Frankenthaler's New York studio: there they saw and were greatly impressed by her stain painting *Mountains and Sea* of 1952. Upon their return to Washington, Louis and Noland together experimented with various techniques of paint application. In 1954 Louis produced his mature Veil paintings, which were characterized by overlapping, superimposed layers of transparent color poured and stained into sized or unsized canvas. Louis' first one-man show in New York was held at the Martha Jackson Gallery in 1957. He destroyed many of the paintings in this show but resumed work on the Veils in 1958-59. These were followed by Florals and Columns (1960), Unfurleds (1960-61)—where rivulets of more opaque, intense color flow from both sides of large white fields—and Stripe paintings (late 1961-62). Louis died in Washington, D.C., on September 7, 1962. A memorial exhibition of his work was held at The Solomon R. Guggenheim Museum in 1963. Major Louis exhibitions were also organized by the Museum of Fine Arts, Boston, in 1967, and the National Collection of Fine Arts, Washington, D.C., in 1976.

237 Saraband. 1959

64.1685

Acrylic resin on canvas, 101⅛ x 149 in. (257 x 378.5 cm.)

Signed and dated l.l.: *M. Louis 59.*

PROVENANCE:
from the artist through French & Company, Inc., New York
William Rubin, New York, 1960-ca. 1962
Exchanged with the artist
Estate of the artist
André Emmerich Gallery, Inc., New York, 1964

Louis' large painting, *Saraband,* demonstrates his innovative manner of pouring thinned acrylic paint on unprimed cotton duck canvas. Here, successive washes of bright colors were followed by a final dark layer. That the support has absorbed the colors is evident in the stained, translucent surface. Like Frankenthaler, Louis expanded upon Pollock's stylistic and technical breakthrough.

Louis' first Veil paintings date from 1954; he returned to them in 1958-59. These canvases are often hung so that the paint touches the bottom edge and the white margin is at the top. *Saraband,* however, was not hung this way during the artist's lifetime,* and the position of his signature confirms how he meant it to be seen. In *Saraband* and other paintings of the series, veils of color extend almost to the perimeters and fill the great expanse of canvas. Louis has superceded the traditional figure-ground relationship and eliminated painterly gesture and drawing per se. He has united color, form, texture and movement in a totally abstract, rhythmic pictorial surface.

* According to William Rubin in *Morris Louis: The Veil Cycle,* exh. cat., Minneapolis, 1977, p. 29 and in conversation with the author, June 1979

EXHIBITIONS:
New York, French & Company, Inc., *New Paintings by Morris Louis,* Mar. 23-Apr. 16, 1960, no. 17

New York, The Solomon R. Guggenheim Museum, *Morris Louis, 1912-1962: Memorial Exhibition,* Sept. 25-Oct. 27, 1963, no. 10, repr.

Los Angeles County Museum of Art, *Morris Louis 1912-1962,* Feb. 15-Mar. 26, 1967, no. 28, color repr., traveled to Boston, Museum of Fine Arts, Apr. 13-May 24; City Art Museum of Saint Louis, June 16-Aug. 6

New York, The Metropolitan Museum of Art, *New York Painting and Sculpture: 1940-1970,* Oct. 18, 1969-Feb. 8, 1970, no. 240, repr.

New York, The Solomon R. Guggenheim Museum, *Acquisition Priorities: Aspects of Postwar Painting in America,* Oct. 15, 1976-Jan. 16, 1977, no. 31, repr.

Albany, The New York State Museum, *New York: The State of Art,* Oct. 8-Nov. 28, 1977, no. 533, color repr.

REFERENCES:
R. Rosenblum, "Morris Louis at the Guggenheim Museum," *Art International,* vol. 7, Dec. 1963, pp. 24, 25, repr.

M. Fried, *Morris Louis,* New York, 1970, pp. 28, 30 and color pl. 10

Handbook, 1970, pp. 278-279, color repr.

D. U. Headley, "Documentation: The Veil Paintings," *Morris Louis: The Veil Cycle,* exh. cat., Minneapolis, 1977, pp. 29, 36 fn., 38, 39, 41

D. U. Headley, "In Addition to the Veils," *Art in America,* vol. 66, Jan. 1978, pp. 90-91, repr.

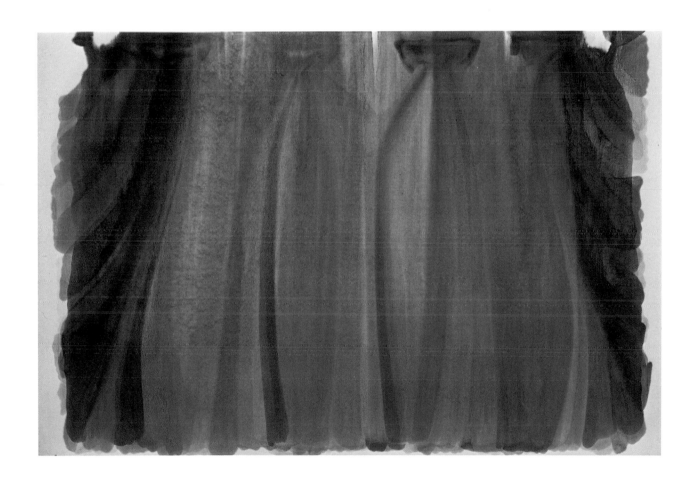

238 **I-68.** 1962

68.1846

Acrylic resin on canvas, 83¾ x 42 in. (212.7 x 106.7 cm.)

Not signed or dated.

PROVENANCE:
Estate of the artist
André Emmerich Gallery, Inc., New York, 1968

Louis' Stripe paintings, which were preceded by the
Unfurleds, were executed during the last year and a
half of his life. In these canvases, parallel vertical
bands of varying widths and contrasting colors are
placed side by side. Unlike the Veils (cat. no. 237),
much of the canvas remains bare in the Stripes. Louis
isolates individual colors and plays upon their chromatic relationships. *I-68* features two groups of stripes
in bold, intense shades of red, green, orange, yellow
and brown. The strict separation of color zones into
either diagonal, horizontal or vertical stripes recalls
somewhat Noland's earlier canvases of concentric
circles and at the same time it foreshadows his later
horizontal band paintings. In contrast to Noland's pictures (for example cat. no. 239), Louis' canvases are
usually cut so that the stripes do not extend from one
edge to the other but are anchored on only one side.

EXHIBITIONS:
Los Angeles County Museum of Art, *Morris Louis 1912-
1962,* Feb. 15-Mar. 26, 1967, no. 46, color repr., traveled to
Boston, Museum of Fine Arts, Apr. 13-May 24; City Art
Museum of Saint Louis, June 16-Aug. 6

Worcester Art Museum, *The Direct Image in Contemporary
American Painting,* Oct. 16-Nov. 30, 1969, no. 4, repr.

New York, The Solomon R. Guggenheim Museum, *Acquisition Priorities: Aspects of Postwar Painting in America,*
Oct. 15, 1976-Jan. 16, 1977, no. 32, repr.

REFERENCES:
M. Fried, "The Achievement of Morris Louis," *Artforum,*
vol. V, Feb. 1967, p. 38, repr.

M. Fried, *Morris Louis,* New York, 1970, color pl. 166

Handbook, 1970, pp. 280-281, repr.

B. Rose, "Quality in Louis," *Artforum,* vol. X, Oct. 1971,
p. 62, repr.

D. Wall, "The Striped Paintings of Gene Davis and Morris
Louis," *Arts Magazine,* vol. 51, Dec. 1976, p. 111

Kenneth Noland b. 1924

Kenneth Noland was born April 10, 1924, in Asheville, North Carolina. After serving in the Air Force, he attended Black Mountain College, Black Mountain, North Carolina, from 1946 to 1948 on the G.I. Bill. There he studied for the most part with Bolotowsky and also for one semester with Albers. Noland went to Paris and studied with Ossip Zadkine in 1948-49. His first one-man show, of work primarily influenced by Klee, took place at the Galerie Raymond Creuze, Paris, in 1949.

In 1949 Noland settled in Washington, D.C., where he taught at the Institute of Contemporary Arts from 1949 to 1951 and at Catholic University from 1951 to about 1960. His friendships with Clement Greenberg and David Smith date from about 1950. While teaching at the Washington Workshop Center of the Arts in 1952 he met fellow instructor Morris Louis, who became his close friend and collaborator. In 1953 Noland and Louis saw Frankenthaler's stain painting *Mountains and Sea*, 1952, at her New York studio. After returning to Washington, Noland and Louis experimented together with pouring and staining techniques. From 1953-54 Noland used Magna acrylics; he explored various styles and techniques, ranging from Abstract Expressionist impasto to staining with thin washes. In 1957 his first one-man show in New York was held at the Tibor de Nagy Gallery.

Noland's first mature canvases featuring concentric circles date from 1958, and gradually his work became more geometric and hard-edged. The circles were followed in the 1960s by lozenge, diamond and rounded-off square and chevron motifs, diamond and attenuated diamond-shaped canvases and horizontal stripe paintings. Influenced by his friend Anthony Caro, Noland began to make sculpture in 1966. His plaid paintings date from the early 1970s, and since 1973 he has worked with irregularly shaped canvases. An important one-man show of his work took place at The Jewish Museum, New York, in 1963, and a major Noland retrospective was held at The Solomon R. Guggenheim Museum in 1977 and traveled in the United States. From 1963 to 1979 Noland lived at the Robert Frost farm in South Shaftsbury, Vermont. He now lives in South Salem, New York.

239 April Tune. 1969

69.1915

Acrylic on canvas, 65¾ x 124⅛ in. (167 x 315.3 cm.)

Signed and dated on reverse: *APRIL TUNE / 1969 / Kenneth Noland / 65¾" x 10'4"*.

PROVENANCE:
from the artist through Lawrence Rubin Gallery, New York, 1969

Around 1967 Noland adopted a horizontal format which he articulated with continuous bands of color of varying widths at top and bottom. In *April Tune* a large area of ocher is framed above and below by relatively thin stripes of pink, blue and lavender as well as green and maroon at the very bottom edge. By keeping the value difference at a minimum, Noland allows the hues to relate to each other and elicit an allover harmony. His procedure involved stapling a length of canvas to the floor, painting the color field and, with the use of tape, adding stripes. He then cropped the canvases and had them stretched to determine the exact proportion of marginal color bands and color field.

EXHIBITIONS:
New York, The Solomon R. Guggenheim Museum, *Acquisition Priorities: Aspects of Postwar Painting in America*, Oct. 14, 1976-Jan. 16, 1977, no. 46, repr.

New York, The Solomon R. Guggenheim Museum, *Kenneth Noland: A Retrospective*, Apr. 15-June 19, 1977, no. 94, repr., traveled to Washington, D. C., The Corcoran Gallery of Art, Sept. 29-Nov. 27; The Toledo Museum of Art, Jan. 22-Mar. 5, 1978; The Denver Art Museum, Mar. 23-May 7

REFERENCES:
W. D. Bannard, "Notes on American Painting of the Sixties," *Artforum*, vol. XIII, Jan. 1970, p. 44, repr.

Handbook, 1970, pp. 352-353, repr.

K. Moffett, *Kenneth Noland*, New York, 1977, color pl. 190

Gene Davis b. 1920

Gene Davis was born on August 22, 1920, in Washington, D.C. He studied at the University of Maryland at College Park from 1938 to 1940 and at Wilson Teacher's College in Washington, D.C., in 1941. Davis then worked as a reporter and writer, serving as a White House correspondent from 1942 to 1952. He had no formal artistic training but began to paint in his spare time in 1949. His early works reflect the influence of Klee, Barnett Newman and Gorky. In 1951 Davis met and became friends with Noland. The Dupont Theater Art Gallery, Washington, D.C., gave Davis his first one-man show in 1952. In 1953 Noland organized a one-man show of Davis' paintings for Catholic University in Washington.

Davis began to paint in an Abstract Expressionist mode in 1954. The following year he was given a one-man exhibition at American University in Washington. He began his vertical stripe canvases in 1958; these paintings were exhibited for the first time in a group show at the Jefferson Place Gallery, Washington, in 1960. Davis' work was shown for the first time in New York in 1963 in a group exhibition at the Poindexter Gallery. The following year his first major museum exhibition took place at The Corcoran Gallery of Art in Washington. Davis has been identified as one of the Washington Color Painters from the mid-sixties. In 1965 he won the Bronze Medal at the Corcoran Biennial. Since 1967 he has taught at the Corcoran School of Art; he has held a number of other teaching positions as well. He began to paint full-time in 1968; this year The Jewish Museum in New York and the San Francisco Museum of Art gave Davis important shows. In 1969 he received a mural commission for the South Mall Project for the New York State Capitol in Albany. Throughout the seventies Davis has continued to develop his stripe paintings. He received a John Simon Guggenheim Foundation Fellowship in 1974. Davis executed commissions for the Kennedy Center and The Corcoran Gallery in 1974 and 1975 respectively. The artist lives and works in Washington, D.C.

240 **Wheelbarrow.** 1971

72.1993

Acrylic on canvas, 118 x 217 in. (299.7 x 551.2 cm.)

Not signed or dated.

PROVENANCE:
Anonymous Gift, 1972

Gene Davis regards stripes as his subject matter: since the late 1950s he has limited himself almost exclusively to painting and drawing them. The stripes range from hard-edge broad bands to freehand thin pinstripes; his pictures vary from exceptionally small "micro-paintings" to mural-scale canvases. In *Wheelbarrow* as in many other works, the vertical alignment extends from the top edge to the bottom, the variety of colors is wide and the interval between colors is crucial. Davis intuitively places the stripes and selects their width and color, normally working with one hue at a time. When seen from a distance, the colors blend together and take on a softness not suggested by their clarity when viewed at close proximity.

EXHIBITION:
New York, Fischbach Gallery, *Gene Davis: Recent Paintings,* Nov. 20-Dec. 20, 1971

REFERENCE:
D. Wall, ed., *Gene Davis*, New York, 1975, pp. 168, color repr., 215, repr.

Voy Fangor b. 1922

Wojciech Bonawentura Fangor was born on November 15, 1922, in Warsaw. He studied painting with Felicjan Kowarski at the underground Akademia Sztuk Pięknych in Warsaw from 1942 to 1945 and received the equivalent of an M.A. in 1946. Fangor's first one-man show was held at the Galeria Teatr Zydowski in Warsaw in 1949. He began teaching at the Akademia in 1954.

In 1958 the artist exhibited environmental work for the first time at the Galeria Teatr Zydowski. The architect Stan Zamescznik and he collaborated on an environment for a show of contemporary Polish painting at the Stedelijk Museum in Amsterdam in 1959. Fangor's first solo exhibition in the United States was held at the Gres Gallery in Washington, D.C., in 1961. That same year he took part in *Fifteen Polish Painters* at The Museum of Modern Art in New York and moved to Vienna.

Fangor visited the United States for the first time in 1962 and later that year moved to Paris, where he exhibited at the Galerie Lambert in 1964. In 1964 he was awarded a Ford Foundation Fellowship which enabled him to spend a year in West Berlin. In 1965 he taught at the Bath Academy of Art in Corsham, Wiltshire, England, and participated in *The Responsive Eye* at The Museum of Modern Art in New York. Fangor settled in Madison, New Jersey, in 1966, and began teaching there at Fairleigh Dickinson University. His first one-man exhibition in New York took place at the Galerie Chalette in 1967. He was given a one-man show at The Solomon R. Guggenheim Museum in 1970. In 1971 he became a United States citizen and changed his first name. In 1978 Fangor moved to New York, where he lives now.

241 New Jersey 5. June 1965

65.1783

Oil on canvas, 55⅞ x 55⅞ in. (142 x 142 cm.)

Signed and dated on reverse: *FANGOR / NJ 5 1965.*

PROVENANCE:
from the artist
Gift, Mary M. Peer, Short Hills, New Jersey, in memory of Alfred J. Peer, 1965

Fangor's primary concern is color, which he applies in flat, uniform areas and manipulates to achieve optical effects. He prefers oil paint to acrylics because of the high color density it provides and because it does not dry quickly. He blends the colors where they meet at an edge.* Thus, in the Guggenheim's painting the transitional zone between the central red circle and the surrounding dark blue one has been blurred so the two colors merge. In a similar fashion, the bright blue halo emanating from the outer circle continues the pulsating effect of color into the surrounding area. Circumferences formed by the juxtaposition of colors expand, contract and dissolve the forms.

* Margit Rowell, *Fangor*, exh. cat., New York, 1971, pp. 12-13

EXHIBITIONS:
Madison, N. J., Fairleigh Dickinson University, *International Artists' Seminar 1965: Optical Art*, July 31-Aug. 31, 1965, traveled to New York, Riverside Museum, Sept. 26-Nov. 7, 1965

New York, Galerie Chalette, *Fangor*, Mar. 3-May 1967

New York, The Solomon R. Guggenheim Museum, *Fangor*, Dec. 18, 1970-Feb. 7, 1971, no. 1, color repr., traveled to Fort Worth Art Center Museum, Apr. 4-May 9; Berkeley, University Art Museum, University of California, July 6-Aug. 22

REFERENCE:
Handbook, 1970, pp. 112-113, repr.

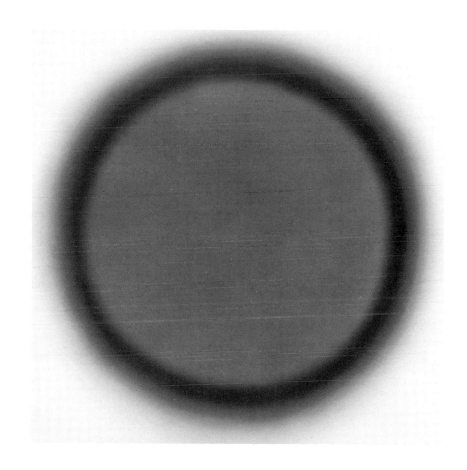

Ellsworth Kelly b. 1923

Ellsworth Kelly was born on May 31, 1923, in New-burgh, New York. He studied at Pratt Institute, Brooklyn, in 1941-42. After military service in a camouflage unit in Europe from 1943 to 1945 he attended the School of the Museum of Fine Arts, Boston, from 1946 to 1948. In 1948 Kelly went to France and enrolled at the Ecole des Beaux-Arts in Paris under the G.I. Bill. In France he studied Romanesque art and architecture and Byzantine art; here he was introduced to Surrealism and Neo-Plasticism, which led him to experiment with automatic drawing and geometric abstraction. In 1950 Kelly met Arp and that same year began to make chance collages and wood reliefs. He met other artists in Paris including Brancusi, Vantongerloo, Picabia and Sophie Täuber-Arp. Kelly taught at the American School in Paris in 1950-51. His first one-man show took place at the Galerie Arnaud, Paris, in 1951. In 1951-52 he worked in Sanary in the south of France.

Kelly returned to the United States in 1954; he moved to Coenties Slip in lower Manhattan, where his neighbors were Martin, Robert Indiana and Jack Younger-man, who had been a close friend in Paris. His first one-man show in New York was held at the Betty Parsons Gallery in 1956. Since the early 1950s Kelly has alternated between basic hard-edged elements and curved shapes. He uses brilliant, unmodulated colors as well as black and white and variations of gray in single-canvas formats and compositions of two or more panels. In addition to his abstract work Kelly has made many contour drawings of plants. He has also worked extensively in sculpture, collage and various print mediums. Kelly has executed a number of important public commissions, including a mural for UNESCO in Paris in 1969. Among his extensive exhibitions in the United States and abroad are important one-man shows at the Albright-Knox Art Gallery, Buffalo, 1972, The Museum of Modern Art, New York, 1973 and The Metropolitan Museum of Art, New York, 1979. Kelly lives in Chatham, New York.

242 **Blue, Green, Yellow, Orange, Red.** 1966

67.1833

Acrylic on canvas, five panels, each 60 x 48 in. (152.3 x 121.9 cm.)

Signed on reverse of first panel: *E.K.* Not dated.

PROVENANCE:
from the artist through Sidney Janis Gallery, New York, 1967

As early as 1952-53 Kelly made innovative paintings by juxtaposing a series of individual, vertical panels that are identical in size but different in color. However, when he returned to this format in 1966, his selection of colors became more systematic: for example, in this painting the primary colors, blue, yellow and red, alternate from left to right with the complementaries, green and orange. By increasing the scale of unmodulated expanses of bright, highly

saturated hues and eliminating any trace of brush-work, Kelly makes color area synonymous with the shape of the canvas. Each of the five horizontally aligned panels is distinguished by its color, while it functions simultaneously as an integral unit within the whole.

Although the title encourages the viewer to read the painting from left to right, it is not necessary to see them in a particular order and the colors may be visually grouped and regrouped in several ways. Furthermore, the large scale forces the viewer to remain at a distance to see the work in its entirety. An intensification and vibration of color occurs where one panel adjoins the next; yet the five different color values are remarkably balanced and hold the same flat plane. Kelly is generally considered reductive in his concentration on pure shape, line and color. However, his exploration of these basic elements is decidedly sensuous rather than austere.

EXHIBITIONS:

New York, The Solomon R. Guggenheim Museum, *Systemic Painting,* Sept. 21-Nov. 27, 1966, color repr.

New York, Sidney Janis Gallery, *Ellsworth Kelly,* Mar. 1-25, 1967, no. 2

New York, The Solomon R. Guggenheim Museum, *Acquisition Priorities: Aspects of Postwar Painting in America,* Oct. 15, 1976-Jan. 16, 1977, no. 43, repr.

REFERENCES:

R. Pincus-Witten, " 'Systemic Painting': A well-chosen view is presented by Lawrence Alloway," *Artforum,* vol. V, Nov. 1966, p. 43

Handbook, 1970, pp. 216-217, repr.

J. Coplans, *Ellsworth Kelly,* New York, 1971, color pl. 178

H. H. Arnason, *History of Modern Art,* rev. ed., New York, 1977, color pl. 276

Agnes Martin b. 1912

Agnes Martin was born March 22, 1912, in Maklin, Saskatchewan, Canada, and grew up in Vancouver, British Columbia. She came to the United States in 1932 and lived in Washington and Oregon until 1940. Martin studied at Western Washington State College, Bellingham, the University of New Mexico, Albuquerque, and received her B.S. and M.A. from Teachers College, Columbia University. She taught at public schools in Washington, Delaware and New Mexico during the late 1930s and the 1940s, at the University of New Mexico in the late 1940s and at Eastern Oregon College, La Grande, in 1952-53. She became a United States citizen in 1950.

Martin lived and taught periodically in New York in the 1940s and early 1950s. In 1957 she settled on Coenties Slip in lower Manhattan, where her friends and neighbors included Kelly, Jack Youngerman and Robert Indiana. In 1958 her first one-woman show took place at Section Eleven of the Betty Parsons Gallery, New York. By the late 1950s Martin's landscape and figurative watercolors, Surrealistic oils and three-dimensional sculptural objects were supplanted by her highly simplified abstractions. These mature works, distinguished by square formats, grids or lines drawn on canvas and monochromatic color with subtle variations in hue, have been an important influence on younger artists.

After Martin left New York and moved to Cuba, New Mexico, in 1967, she did not paint for seven years. However, in 1974 she completed a group of new paintings and since 1975 has exhibited regularly. In a number of these recent works, Martin has replaced neutral tones with brighter color. In 1973 an exhibition of work dating from 1957 to 1967 was organized by the Institute of Contemporary Art, University of Pennsylvania, Philadelphia, and traveled to the Pasadena Art Museum. Martin currently lives in Cuba, New Mexico.

243 Untitled No. 14. 1977

77.2336

India ink, graphite and gesso on canvas, 72 x 72 in. (182.7 x 182.7 cm.)

Signed and dated on reverse: *a. martin / 1977.*

PROVENANCE:

from the artist through The Pace Gallery, New York
Gift, Mr. and Mrs. Werner Dannheisser,
New York, 1977

Untitled No. 14 confirms Martin's continuing commitment to infinite variations of a horizontal and vertical grid system. Here, as in *White Flower* of 1960 (Collection The Solomon R. Guggenheim Museum), she limits herself to neutral tones and works in a six-foot-square format. In comparison with the earlier painting, the lightly penciled linear organization of *Untitled No. 14* has been significantly enlarged and simplified, and the grid extends to the edges of the canvas. The monochromatic pale gray surface is very thinly brushed so that the texture of the white canvas remains visible, and there are subtle, atmospheric changes in light and tone. Through this meditative, infinite grayness, Martin gives intense meaning to slight modulations. Nothing sensuous detracts from the cool, detached, even remote presence of the whole.

Robert Morris b. 1931

Robert Morris was born on February 9, 1931, in Kansas City, Missouri. He studied engineering at the University of Kansas City and attended the Kansas City Art Institute from 1948 to 1950 and the California School of Fine Arts, San Francisco, in 1950-51. After military service he studied at Reed College in Portland, Oregon, from 1953 to 1955. In 1955 Morris settled in San Francisco, where he painted and did theater improvisation. In 1957 his first one-man show of paintings was held at the Dilexi Gallery, San Francisco.

By 1961 Morris had moved to New York and had begun to concentrate on sculpture. He studied art history at Hunter College, New York, from 1961 to 1966 and received an M.A. in 1966; he has taught at Hunter since 1962. His first one-man exhibition in New York took place at the Green Gallery in 1963. At this time Morris made neo-Dada objects in lead, rope and mixed media. In the mid-1960s, however, he emerged as a leading Minimalist and worked with geometric structures and impersonal industrial materials. During this period he became increasingly concerned with the relationship of sculpture to the surrounding space. Morris also collaborated as a dancer and choreographer with Yvonne Rainer and other avant-garde performers.

In the late 1960s he turned to soft materials such as felt and dirt; his emphasis on process led him to create Earthworks and environmental proposals. During the 1970s Morris has experimented with a variety of forms including mazes, theatrical tableaux and sound installations as well as large-scale sculptures. His essays on art, published regularly since 1966, continue to influence younger artists. A major Morris exhibition was organized jointly by the Detroit Institute of Arts and The Corcoran Gallery of Art, Washington, D.C., in 1969-70. One-man shows of his work have been presented at the Whitney Museum of American Art, New York, in 1970 and at the Stedelijk Museum, Amsterdam, in 1977. Morris lives in New York.

244 Untitled. 1967

67.1865

Steel, nine units, total 36 x 180 x 180 in. (91.4 x 457.3 x 457.3 cm.), each 36 x 36 x 36 in. (91.4 x 91.4 x 91.4 cm.)

Not signed or dated.

PROVENANCE:

from the artist through Leo Castelli Gallery, New York Purchase Award, Guggenheim International Exhibition, 1967

In this sculpture Morris uses identical units to create a "field situation." The rational, mathematical structure of the work is based on the number three: there are three rows of three units each, and each unit is separated from those adjacent to it by aisles three feet in width. Moreover, each unit occupies a spatial cube measuring three feet on a side and is constructed with three sheets of steel, each three feet square. These gray steel modular components, which demonstrate Morris' preference for neutral yet resistant surfaces, were made by an industrial fabricator to the artist's specifications. The size of the upright elements is significant, since Morris has deliberately avoided any clear relationship to the scale of the human body or of architecture.

The work cannot be visually or physically understood as a whole unless the viewer moves through and around it. This process involves time, an element Morris consistently seeks to introduce into his work.

EXHIBITIONS:
New York, The Solomon R. Guggenheim Museum, *Guggenheim International Exhibition, 1967: Sculpture from Twenty Nations,* Oct. 20, 1967-Feb. 4, 1968, p. 115, repr., traveled to Toronto, The Art Gallery of Ontario, Feb. 24-Mar. 27; Ottawa, National Gallery of Canada, Apr. 26-June 9; Montreal Museum of Fine Arts, June 20-Aug. 18

New York, The Solomon R. Guggenheim Museum, *Selected Sculpture and Works on Paper,* July 8-Sept. 14, 1969, p. 143, repr.

The Denver Art Museum, *American Report: The 1960s,* Oct. 24-Dec. 7, 1969

REFERENCES:
Handbook, 1970, pp. 340-341, repr.

H. H. Arnason, *History of Modern Art,* rev. ed., New York, 1977, p. 655 and fig. 1183

Carl Andre b. 1935

Carl Andre was born in Quincy, Massachusetts, on September 16, 1935. From 1951 to 1953 he attended Phillips Academy in Andover, Massachusetts, where he studied art with Patrick Morgan. After a brief enrollment in Kenyon College in Gambier, Ohio, Andre earned enough money working at Boston Gear Works to travel to England and France in 1954. The following year he joined United States Army Intelligence in North Carolina. In 1957 he settled in New York and worked as an editorial assistant for a publishing house. Shortly thereafter he began executing wood sculptures influenced by Brancusi and by the black paintings of his friend Frank Stella. In addition to his work as a sculptor Andre has written several volumes of poetry and in 1959 completed a short novel. From 1960 to 1964 he was a freight brakeman and conductor for the Pennsylvania Railroad in New Jersey.

Andre's first one-man show was held in 1965 at the Tibor de Nagy Gallery in New York. Together with Flavin, Sol LeWitt, Donald Judd and others he participated in *Primary Structures*, an exhibition of Minimalist sculpture at The Jewish Museum in New York in 1966. In 1967 solo exhibitions of Andre's work took place at the Dwan Gallery in New York and Los Angeles and at the Galerie Konrad Fischer in Düsseldorf. Andre retrospectives were presented by the Guggenheim Museum in New York in 1970 and the Kunsthalle Bern in 1975. Andre prepared installations for the Portland Center for the Visual Arts in Oregon and the Minneapolis College of Art and Design in 1973 and 1976 respectively. In 1977 he executed *Stone Field Sculpture* in Hartford. An Andre retrospective organized by the Laguna Gloria Art Museum in Austin, Texas, began touring the United States and Canada in 1978. Andre now lives and works in New York.

245 Trabum. 1977

78.2519

Douglas fir, nine sections, total 36 x 36 x 36 in. (91.4 x 91.4 x 91.4 cm.); each 12 x 12 x 36 in. (30.5 x 30.5 x 91.4 cm.)

Not signed or dated.

PROVENANCE:

from the artist through Sperone Westwater Fischer, Inc., New York, 1978
Purchased with the aid of funds from the National Endowment for the Arts in Washington, D.C., a Federal Agency; matching funds donated by Mr. and Mrs. Donald Jonas

Andre's sculpture, a closed, block-like cubic form, was made from timber in 1977. However, as early as 1960 he conceived the Element Series (of which this is an example), where each component measures twelve by twelve by thirty-six inches. *Trabum* consists of modular units: nine pieces of wood of identical dimensions stacked in alternating layers, lying at right angles to one another, of three pieces each. The title refers to the genitive plural case of the Latin word *trabs*, which means beam, log or timber.*

Like other Minimal sculptors, Andre prefers standard commercial units and materials. Here the emphasis on cut wood and the rough honesty of the material is reminiscent of Brancusi, whose work clearly influenced Andre.

* D. Bourdon, *Carl Andre,* exh. cat., Austin, 1978, p. 68

EXHIBITIONS:

New York, Sperone Westwater Fischer, Inc., *Group Show,* Oct. 18-Nov. 12, 1977

Austin, Laguna Gloria Art Museum, *Carl Andre: Sculpture 1959-1977,* Jan. 7-Feb. 19, 1978, no. 16, repr., traveled to Cincinnati, Contemporary Arts Center, Mar. 2-Apr. 16; Buffalo, Albright-Knox Art Gallery, July 8-Aug. 20; The Art Institute of Chicago, Dec. 9, 1978-Jan. 14, 1979; La Jolla Museum of Contemporary Art, Feb. 2-Mar. 18; Berkeley, University Art Museum, University of California, May 9-June 24; Dallas Museum of Fine Arts, July 18-Sept. 3; Montreal, Musée d'Art Contemporaine, Oct. 15-Nov. 23; Boston, Institute of Contemporary Art, Jan. 7-Feb. 17, 1980

REFERENCE:

R. H. Fuchs, *Carl Andre Wood,* Eindhoven, 1978, no. 76, repr.

Walter De Maria b. 1935

Walter Joseph De Maria was born on October 1, 1935, in Albany, California, near San Francisco. In 1957 he graduated from the University of California at Berkeley, where he earned his M.F.A. in painting two years later. De Maria and his friend, the avant-garde composer La Monte Young, participated in Happenings and theatrical productions in the San Francisco area.

In 1960 De Maria moved to New York; here he wrote essays on art, which were published in 1963 in Young's *An Anthology,* and took part in Happenings and multimedia presentations. In 1961 he made his first wooden box sculptures. De Maria and Robert Whitman opened the 9 Great Jones Street gallery in New York in 1963; the same year De Maria's first one-man show of sculpture was presented there. This year he worked as drummer for The Velvet Underground rock group. He continued to work in wood, began his "invisible drawings" and composed music. With the support of collector Robert C. Scull, De Maria started making pieces in metal in 1965. In 1966 he was given a one-man show at Cordier & Ekstrom, New York, and participated in *Primary Structures* at The Jewish Museum, New York.

De Maria emerged as a leader of the Earthworks movement in 1968 when he filled the Galerie Heiner Friedrich in Munich with dirt. This year he also made his *The Mile Long Drawing in the Desert* in the Mojave Desert for *Walls in the Desert,* a project, originally conceived in 1962, which is to consist of two parallel mile-long walls. In 1968 he also participated in *4. Documenta* in Kassel, Germany. A major exhibition of De Maria's sculpture was held at the Kunstmuseum Basel in 1972. Earthworks and serial geometric sculpture continue to occupy De Maria in the seventies: his *Three Continent Project* was completed in 1972 and the *Lightning Field* in Arizona was finished in 1974. In 1977 De Maria recreated his *Earth Room* at the Heiner Friedrich Gallery in New York. The artist lives and works in New York.

246 Cross. 1965-66

73.2033

Aluminum, 4 x 42 x 22 in. (10.2 x 106.7 x 55.9 cm.)

Not signed or dated.

PROVENANCE:
from the artist through Cordier & Ekstrom, New York
William Copley, New York, 1966-73
Galerie Heiner Friedrich, Cologne, 1973

De Maria realized the possibility of presenting these three sculptures as a group only after he completed the third piece, *Star,* in 1972. The three sculptures remain autonomous, but when presented together their meanings are intensified and expanded to many levels. The cross, star and swastika are ancient symbolic shapes. However, each has acquired a specific and universally accepted meaning: the Christian cross, Jewish star and Nazi swastika stand for political-religious ideologies. Unlike De Maria's related works *Circle, Square* and *Triangle* of 1972, here the symbolic associations take precedence over the geometric forms. With the introduction of balls, De Maria emphasizes the reflective properties of polished aluminum and the interior space of each piece. There is the possibility that the ball could move, but it does not. It arrests the viewer's attention at a certain point within the smooth channel of each sculpture, momentarily diverting him from its overwhelming symbolic meaning.

EXHIBITIONS:
New York, Cordier & Ekstrom, *Walter De Maria, Sculptures and Drawings,* Nov. 8-Dec. 3, 1966
Kunstmuseum Basel, *Walter De Maria: Skulpturen,* Oct. 28, 1972-Jan. 7, 1973, no. 1, repr.

REFERENCES:
D. Adrian, "Walter De Maria: Word and Thing," *Artforum,* vol. V, Jan. 1967, p. 29, repr.
D. Bourdon, "Walter De Maria: The Singular Experience," *Art International,* vol. 12, Dec. 1968, pp. 41, repr., 43

246 Museum Piece. 1966

73.2034

Aluminum, 4 x 36 x 36 in. (10.2 x 91.5 x 91.5 cm.)

Not signed or dated.

PROVENANCE:

from the artist probably through Noah Goldowsky
Gallery, New York
Samuel J. Wagstaff, Jr., Detroit and New York,
by 1969-73
Galerie Heiner Friedrich, Cologne, 1973

EXHIBITIONS:

New York, Cordier & Ekstrom, *Walter De Maria, Sculptures and Drawings,* Nov. 8-Dec. 3, 1966

Los Angeles County Museum of Art, *American Sculpture of the Sixties,* Apr. 28-June 25, 1967, no. 38, repr., traveled to Philadelphia Museum of Art, Sept. 15-Oct. 29

New York, Noah Goldowsky Gallery, *Three Sculptors: Mark di Suvero, Walter De Maria, Richard Serra,* Feb. 17-Mar. 15, 1968

Detroit Institute of Arts, *Other Ideas,* Sept. 10-Oct. 19, 1969

New York, The Solomon R. Guggenheim Museum, *Guggenheim International Exhibition, 1971,* Feb. 12-Apr. 11, 1971, repr.

Kunstmuseum Basel, *Walter De Maria: Skulpturen,* Oct. 28, 1972-Jan. 7, 1973, no. 4

REFERENCE:

P. Restany, "Notes de voyage," *Domus,* no. 498, May 1971, p. 48, repr.

246 Star. 1972

73.2035

Aluminum, 4 x 44 x 50 in. (10.2 x 111.8 x 127 cm.)

Not signed or dated.

PROVENANCE:

Galerie Heiner Friedrich, Cologne, 1973

EXHIBITION:

Kunstmuseum Basel, *Walter De Maria: Skulpturen,* Oct. 28, 1972-Jan. 7, 1973, no. 9

Eva Hesse 1936-1970

Eva Hesse was born in Hamburg on January 11, 1936. Her family fled the Nazis and arrived in New York in 1939. She became a United States citizen in 1945. Hesse entered Pratt Institute in Brooklyn in 1952 but left the following year and enrolled at the Art Students League. She studied at Cooper Union from 1954 to 1957. At this time Hesse painted in an Abstract Expressionist style. After winning a scholarship to Yale-Norfolk Summer Art School in 1957, she was accepted by Yale University's School of Art and Architecture, where she studied painting with Albers. In 1959 Hesse received her B.F.A. from Yale and returned to New York.

In New York she met Claes Oldenburg and Sol LeWitt among other artists. She was included in a watercolor exhibition at The Brooklyn Museum and in *Drawings: Three Young Americans* at the John Heller Gallery in New York in 1961. This same year Hesse married the sculptor Tom Doyle. She spent the summer of 1962 in Woodstock, New York, and there made her first sculpture. Hesse's first one-woman show of drawings took place at the Allan Stone Gallery in New York in 1963. In 1964 she went to Kettwig-am-Ruhr, Germany, and while in Europe traveled in Italy, France and Switzerland. Hesse's first one-woman show of sculpture was held at the Kunstverein für die Rheinlande und Westfalen, Düsseldorf, in 1965. She returned to New York in 1965, the year of her last paintings. Among Hesse's friends were Keith Sonnier, Mel Bochner, Richard Serra, Robert Smithson, Andre, Morris and the critic Lucy Lippard. She was included in *Abstract Inflationism and Stuffed Expressionism* at the Graham Gallery in New York in 1966. The artist began making sculpture with latex in 1967 and first used fiberglas in 1968. In the same year she was given an important solo exhibition at the Fischbach Gallery in New York. She became seriously ill this year. From 1968 to 1970 Hesse taught at the School of Visual Arts, New York, and participated in several exhibitions of Minimal and Post-Minimal sculpture. Hesse died in New York on May 29, 1970. A memorial exhibition of her sculpture was held at the Guggenheim Museum in 1972.

247 Expanded Expansion. 1969

75.2138

Fiberglas and rubberized cheesecloth, three units of three, five and seven poles each, 122 x 60 in. (310 x 152.4 cm.); 122 x 120 in. (310 x 304.8 cm.); 122 x 180 in. (310 x 457.2 cm.)

Not signed or dated.

PROVENANCE:
Estate of the artist
Gift, Family of Eva Hesse, 1975

Expanded Expansion, which was finished by February 8, 1969, was made by spreading cheesecloth on plastic and then brushing on a layer of rubber. Fiberglas poles were laid down on the cheesecloth and fiberglas was applied over the rubber on each pole and, finally, resin was applied to both sides.*

The piece consists of flexible modular elements which can be compressed or extended laterally. Like Hesse's *Vinculum I,* 1969 (Collection Mr. and Mrs. Victor W. Ganz, New York) and *Accretion,* 1968 (Collection Rijksmuseum Kröller-Müller, Otterlo) it leans against a wall. She had intended to "make more sections so they could be extended to a length in which they really would be environmental but illness prevented that." (the artist quoted in Nemser, 1975, pp. 217-218) In discussing her frequent use of repetition, Hesse explained that "it's not just an esthetic choice. If something is absurd, it's much more greatly exaggerated, absurd, if it's repeated." (p. 211)

*Lippard, p. 151

EXHIBITIONS:
New York, Whitney Museum of American Art, *Anti-Illusion: Procedures / Materials,* May 19-July 6, 1969, repr.

New York, The Solomon R. Guggenheim Museum, *Eva Hesse: A Memorial Exhibition,* Dec. 7, 1972-Feb. 11, 1973, no. 42, repr., traveled to Buffalo, Albright-Knox Art Gallery, Mar. 8-Apr. 22; Chicago, Museum of Contemporary Art, May 19-July 8; Pasadena Art Museum, Sept. 18-Nov. 11; Berkeley, University Art Museum, University of California, Dec. 12, 1973-Feb. 3, 1974

REFERENCES:
C. Nemser, "An Interview with Eva Hesse," *Artforum,* vol. VIII, May 1970, pp. 61, repr., 63

R. Pincus-Witten, "Eva Hesse: Post-Minimalism into Sublime," *Artforum,* vol. X, Nov. 1971, pp. 39, repr., 42

C. Nemser, *Art Talk: Conversations with 12 Women Artists,* New York, 1975, pp. 202, 211, 217, 218, 228, repr.

L. Lippard, *Eva Hesse,* New York, 1976, pp. 150-151, repr., 155, 232, no. 95

London, Whitechapel Art Gallery, *Eva Hesse: Sculpture,* 1979, n.p., repr.

Dan Flavin b. 1933

Daniel Nicholas Flavin was born in Jamaica, New York, on April 1, 1933. He studied for the priesthood for a time. During military service Flavin studied art through the University of Maryland Extension Program in Korea. Upon his return to New York in 1956 he briefly attended the Hans Hofmann School of Fine Arts and studied art history at the New School for Social Research. In 1959 he took drawing and painting classes at Columbia University; this year he began to make assemblages and collages in addition to painting. Flavin's early paintings reflect the influence of Abstract Expressionism. His first one-man show of constructions and watercolors was held at the Judson Gallery in New York in 1961.

In the summer of 1961, while working as a guard at The American Museum of Natural History, New York, Flavin started to make sketches for sculptures in which electric lights were incorporated. Late in that year he made his first light sculptures; he called these "icons." In 1963 he began to work with colored fluorescent tubes. His sculpture was shown in a one-man exhibition, *some light,* at the Kaymar Gallery in New York in 1964. In 1967 Flavin was a guest instructor of design at the University of North Carolina in Greensboro. By 1968 he had developed his sculpture into room-size environments of light: this year he outlined an entire gallery in ultraviolet light at 4. *Documenta* in Kassel, Germany. A retrospective of Flavin's work was organized by the National Gallery of Canada in Ottawa in 1969; the exhibition traveled to The Jewish Museum in New York in 1970. Among Flavin's numerous exhibitions in Europe were one-man shows in Cologne in 1974 and Basel in 1975. He has executed many commissions, including the lighting of several tracks at Grand Central Station in New York in 1976. Dan Flavin now lives and works in Garrison-on-Hudson and Bridgehampton, New York.

248 Untitled (to Ward Jackson, an old friend and colleague who, during the Fall of 1957 when I finally returned to New York from Washington and joined him to work together in this museum, kindly communicated). 1971

72.1985

A system of two alternating modular units in fluorescent light, sixteen white bulbs, each 24 in. (61 cm.); four pink bulbs, four yellow bulbs, four green bulbs, four blue bulbs, each 96 in. (243.8 cm.)

Not signed or dated.

PROVENANCE:
from the artist through John Weber Gallery, New York
Partial Gift of the artist in honor of Ward Jackson, 1972

The sixth *Guggenheim International Exhibition* in 1971 provided Flavin with the opportunity to transform Frank Lloyd Wright's architecture with pink, green, blue, yellow and white lights. The artist chose the sixth ramp of the museum for his installation and made several preparatory drawings. Multicolored light united an entire ramp of nine bays; most important, the flow of color joined each bay with those adjacent to it. The alternately blue and green lights on the rear wall mixed with the warm yellow, pink and white lights at the front of the web partitions which separate the space into bays. Not only did the lights flood the surfaces with their own colors but they also combined to form secondary colors. Flavin's work both depends upon and enhances architectural space.

As the title indicates, Flavin's familiarity with this institution dates from the late 1950s, when he worked here briefly before Wright's building was completed. This installation is the third work he has dedicated to his friend and fellow artist Ward Jackson, who is on the Guggenheim staff.

EXHIBITIONS:
New York, The Solomon R. Guggenheim Museum, *Guggenheim International Exhibition, 1971,* Feb. 12-Apr. 11, 1971
New York, The Solomon R. Guggenheim Museum, *Museum Collection: Recent American Art,* May 11-Sept. 7, 1975

REFERENCES:
J. Monte, "Looking at the Guggenheim International," *Artforum,* vol. IX, Mar. 1971, pp. 28, color repr., 29
P. Restany, "Notes de voyage," *Domus,* no. 498, May 1971, p. 48, repr.
Kunsthalle Köln, *Dan Flavin: Drei Installationen in fluoreszierendem Licht,* 1973, pp. 44-45, repr.

Larry Bell b. 1939

Larry Bell was born on December 6, 1939, in Chicago. In 1957 he settled in Los Angeles, where he attended the Chouinard Art Institute for two years and supported himself with a variety of jobs. In the early 1960s Bell was among the first of the West Coast artists to execute shaped canvases. He traveled in Mexico in 1962; this year his first one-man show was held at the Ferus Gallery in Los Angeles, where he exhibited again in 1963 and 1965. In 1963 Bell won the William and Noma Copley Foundation award. He showed for the first time in New York in 1964 in *Seven New Artists* at the Sidney Janis Gallery. The Pace Gallery in New York gave Bell one-man shows regularly from 1965 to 1973. In 1967 his work was exhibited at the Galerie Ileana Sonnabend in Paris and the Stedelijk Museum in Amsterdam. From 1969 to 1970 the artist taught at the University of California at Irvine and in 1970 at the California State College in Hayward. He received a John Simon Guggenheim Foundation Fellowship in 1969.

After a visit to North Africa in 1970 Bell taught at the University of California at Berkeley and the University of South Florida in Tampa. Around this time he began making large tempered-glass panels which stand at right angles to one another on the floor. From 1973 to 1974 he traveled to Australia and Southeast Asia. A solo exhibition of Bell's work was organized in 1974 by Marlborough Galleria d'Arte in Rome. That same year he formed the *Don Quijote Collective* with Newton Harrison, Bob Irwin, Joshua Young, the architect Frank Geary and the life scientist Ed Wirtz: the group collaborated on the design of a new city. Bell exhibitions were held in 1975 at the Fort Worth Art Museum, in 1976 at the Santa Barbara Museum of Art and in 1977 at the Hayden Gallery of the Massachusetts Institute of Technology in Cambridge. Bell now lives and works in Ranchos de Taos, New Mexico.

249 Untitled. 1969

77.2318

Glass and stainless steel, 20 x 20 x 20 in. (50.8 x 50.8 x 50.8 cm.) on plexiglass base, 40⅝ x 20¼ x 20¼ in. (103.1 x 51.4 x 51.4 cm.)

Not signed or dated.

PROVENANCE:
from the artist through The Pace Gallery, New York
Gift, American Arts Foundation, 1977

This sculpture is one of approximately twenty glass boxes comprising Bell's "terminal series," which marks the end of his involvement with the form of the cube. The Guggenheim work is particularly austere, lacking the conspicuous gradations of color and degrees of reflectiveness found in other examples from the series. Bell achieved the subtle coloration by depositing vaporized metal onto the glass surface within a vacuum chamber housed in his studio in Venice, California.

The box defines a volume of space outlined by the strips of stainless steel along its edges. However, as the viewer circles the piece the sense of volume is dissipated by the shifting and overlapping of its grayish planes and the intrusion of the environment through them. The plexiglass base, originally conceived in glass,* allows light to penetrate from all sides, further dematerializing the form. The refinement and precision of the object's construction contrast with the visual disorientation produced by its qualities of transparency and reflectiveness.

*correspondence with Lucy Flint, June 1979

EXHIBITIONS:
The Art Institute of Chicago, *69th American Exhibition,* Jan. 17-Feb. 22, 1970, no. 36

New York, The Pace Gallery, *Larry Bell: The 1969 Terminal Series of Boxes,* Jan. 8-Feb. 2, 1972

Rome, Marlborough Galleria d'Arte, *Larry Bell,* June-July 1974, no. 2, traveled to Venice, Galleria del Cavallino, Jan. 14-Feb. 5, 1975

Richard Estes b. 1936

Richard William Estes was born in Kewanee, Illinois, on May 14, 1936. He grew up in Sheffield and Evanston. From 1952 to 1956 Estes studied at The Art Institute of Chicago and admired the works of El Greco, Degas and Seurat. In 1956 he supported himself by doing paste-ups and mechanicals for various publishing and advertising firms. Estes moved to New York in 1959 and continued to take jobs as a graphic artist. In 1962 he lived and painted in Spain. For the next few years Estes did free-lance assignments and was employed by a magazine publisher in New York. In 1966 he began to devote himself full-time to painting. He painted in a highly realistic style, often from his own photographs and charcoal or watercolor sketches.

Estes' first one-man show was held at the Allan Stone Gallery in New York in 1968. The following year he was included in the Milwaukee Art Center's traveling exhibition *Directions 2: Aspects of a New Realism*, and he was recognized as a major Photo-Realist painter. Estes participated in the 1970 Annual at the Whitney Museum of American Art, New York, and in the 1971 *Biennial Exhibition of Contemporary American Painting* at the Corcoran Gallery of Art, Washington, D.C. In 1972 his work was shown at the Venice Biennale and at *Documenta 5*, in Kassel, Germany. The Museum of Contemporary Art in Chicago presented a one-man show of Estes' work in 1974. In 1978 the Museum of Fine Arts, Boston, organized an important Estes exhibition which traveled in the United States into 1979. The artist lives and works in New York and Northeast Harbor, Maine.

250 **The Solomon R. Guggenheim Museum.** Summer 1979

79.2552

Oil on canvas, 31⅛ x 55⅛ in. (79 x 140 cm.)

Signed and dated c.l.: *R / Este*[s]; *79 RWE.*

PROVENANCE:
commissioned from the artist, 1979
Purchased with the aid of funds from the National Endowment for the Arts in Washington, D.C., a Federal Agency; matching funds donated by Mr. and Mrs. Barrie M. Damson

As Richard Estes began to formulate his ideas for a painting of the Guggenheim Museum early in 1979, he took dozens of color photographs from various exterior and interior points of view. By May the quality of light on the facade was significantly different from that during the winter months. Especially on clear spring days just before sunset, the trees in Central Park cast distinct shadows on the building. From the rolls of film he shot in May, Estes selected three views upon which he based the composition. Comparison of the canvas with the site at Fifth Avenue and 88th Street reveals various differences—primarily adjustments in size, scale and color.

It is the artist's usual practice to edit his photographs extensively and to combine several views of a scene into a composite. After he establishes the composition, he works slowly to achieve the desired clarity of light and the proper relationship between elements. *The Solomon R. Guggenheim Museum* is exceptional in Estes' work: it is the only time he set out to paint a specific, well-known building.*

* conversation with the author, Oct. 1979

INDEX